III	IV	V	VI	VII	He 4.003 0.1785g/l	$n = 1$
	5 B 10.82 2.53	6 C 12.01 3.514(dia)	7 N 14.01 1.251g/l	8 O 16.00 1.429g/l	9 F 19.00 1.69g/l	10 Ne 20.18 0.900g/l	2
	13 Al 26.98 2.70	14 Si 28.09 2.33	15 P 30.98 2.20 (red)	16 S 32.07 2.07(rh)	17 Cl 35.46 3.220g/l	18 Ar 39.94 1.783g/l	3
9 Cu 63.54 8.96	30 Zn 65.38 7.1	31 Ga 69.72 5.93	32 Ge 72.60 5.323	33 As 74.91 5.73	34 Se 78.96 4.79	35 Br 79.92 3.12	36 Kr 83.80 3.68g/l	4
7 Ag 107.9 10.49	48 Cd 112.4 8.65	49 In 114.9 7.28	50 Sn 118.7 7.3 (met)	51 Sb 121.8 6.62	52 Te 127.6 6.25	53 I 126.9 4.94	54 Xe 131.3 5.85g/l	5
9 Au 197.0 19.3	80 Hg 200.6 13.6	81 Tl 204.4 11.86	82 Pb 207.2 11.34	83 Bi 209.0 9.78	84 Po 210 9.32	85 At 210	86 Rn 222 9.73g/l	6

7

5 Tb 158.9 8.234	66 Dy 162.5 8.540	67 Ho 164.9 8.781	68 Er 167.3 9.045	69 Tm 168.9 9.314	70 Yb 173.0 6.972	71 Lu 175.0 9.835	$n = 6$
7	98	99	100	101	102	103	7
		More Transuranium Elements					

SOLID STATE PHYSICS

FOR ENGINEERING AND MATERIALS SCIENCE

SOLID STATE PHYSICS

FOR ENGINEERING
AND MATERIALS SCIENCE

JOHN P. McKELVEY

Department of Physics
The Pennsylvania State University

KRIEGER PUBLISHING COMPANY

MALABAR, FLORIDA

1993

Original Edition 1993

Printed and Published by
KRIEGER PUBLISHING COMPANY
KRIEGER DRIVE
MALABAR, FLORIDA 32950

Copyright © 1993 by Krieger Publishing Company

FROM A DECLARATION OF PRINCIPLES JOINTLY ADOPTED BY A COMMITTEE OF THE AMERICAN BAR ASSOCIATION AND A COMMITTEE OF PUBLISHERS:

This publication is designed to provide accurate and authoritative information in regard to the subject matter covered. It is sold with the understanding that the publisher is not engaged in rendering legal, accounting, or other professional service. If legal advice or other expert assistance is required, the services of a competent professional person should be sought.

Library of Congress Cataloging-In-Publication Data
McKelvey, John Philip.
  Solid state physics for engineering and materials science / John
P. McKelvey.
    p.   cm.
  ISBN 0-89464-436-X (alk. paper)
  1. Solid state physics. 2. Semiconductors--Junctions. 3. Quantum
wells. I. Title.
QC176.M38 1993
530.4'1--dc20   93-4226
                                                   CIP

10   9   8   7   6   5   4   3   2

CONTENTS

PREFACE

This text owes much in choice of topics and basic philosophy of presentation to the author's earlier book, *Solid State and Semiconductor Physics*, first published in 1966. Many of its illustrations, derivations, and discussions will be familiar to those who have used the older text. This familiarity is not unintentional, for the old book has been in print for over 25 years, and has been used extensively, and successfully, as a text. It is getting out of date, however, and needs to be replaced by a more modern work, one specifically designed--as the other was not--for the use of students in applied science, electrical engineering, materials science, engineering physics, and other applied areas of endeavor.

The present book, however, is more than merely a revision of an earlier work. It is a different book, rewritten from beginning to end, with a somewhat different choice of topics, and treatments of many subjects that differ markedly from those employed in the earlier work. There is, of course, the danger of tinkering a good book into one not so good. This is a problem that the author has tried hard to avoid, and trusts that he has successfuly circumvented. Nearly 350 problems are included; other solid-state texts may have more, but not to the author's knowledge.

This book is a presentation of a limited number of *basic* subject areas in solid state physics, areas that are of central importance to persons interested in electronic materials, semiconductor devices, and integrated circuits. It is about solid-state physics, however, not device technology, integrated circuit fabrication, or materials preparation and characterization. Examples related to the basic principles of all these applications are discussed, but the focus is to learn the basic science needed to go on into any of these fields and learn their details with real comprehension. This book is therefore *not* an encyclopedia; you will not find a discussion of every imaginable electronic device, or how to prepare and characterize every known semiconductor. You will find a discussion of the basic physics needed to pursue these topics, carried to a depth often considerably greater than one finds in more wide-ranging texts. Chapters dedicated to basic quantum mechanics and statistical physics are included. More than the usual space is devoted to these subjects, abstract as they are, for they are absolutely required for any understanding of solid-state applications beyond the most superficial. You have to learn to live with the abstraction of these subjects, however, and the treatment given here is designed to enable the student to come to terms with it with as painlessly as possible. Lattice vibrations, crystal symmetry, X-ray crystallography, thermal properties, free electron theory, and the one-electron quantum theory of periodic potentials are covered in some depth. Also, in-depth chapters on semiconductor materials and devices are included. That's enough for one book. Dielectrics and magnetic materials are not covered, nor is there much information about superconductivity, though a brief descriptive survey is given in the final chapter. The detailed coverage of some advanced topics in the physics of semiconductor materials and devices that was included in the older book is out-of-date, and has been dropped. What remains is what you need to know to pursue further studies in any of these areas with confidence. The old Gaussian units have mostly been discarded in favor of MKS, though the author has felt free to use centimeters, millimeters, Ångstroms and microns when they're most convenient. It's silly to express the volume of a device 0.1mm in extent in cubic meters. Many users seemed to value the earlier text for its selectivity. They may find this book even more to their liking. Those who demand a treatment based on a superficial glance at every solid-state device and into every corner of materials technology, will find many such treatments already available.

The text is directed toward students at the senior or first-year graduate level. Familiarity with calculus, differential equations and matrix algebra is presumed, though more advanced mathematical topics are explained as needed in the text. The reader is also assumed to have a good understanding of elementary physics and chemistry. There is enough material in this book for a two-semester course, and probably too much for a one-semester survey. The chapters are designed, however, to be as self-contained as possible; that is why some of them are so long. They are more detailed than necessary in a survey course, but there is no need to cover more sophisticated and complicated sections in detail. What one wishes to omit is a matter for the individual instructor's interests to determine. The following sections can be omitted in a shorter survey course; 2.5; 3.8–3.11; 4.8, 4.13 beyond orthogonality; 6.6–6.9; 7.4, 7.5; 8.5, 8.6; 9.6, 9.7, much of 9.8, 9.9; and 10.5–10.10.

This book was typeset in its entirety by the author, and all the graphics are his work also. Therefore, he is responsible for any typographical errors that may be found. The work was done on an Apple MacIntosh SE/20, and an Apple Laserwriter IINT, both of which have worked flawlessly for nearly four years. As software, Microsoft Word 4.0 has been augmented with Claris McDraw II (Version 1.1), and an excellent mathematical typesetting program, Mathtype 2.0, by Design Sciences, Inc. This strategy has allowed the inclusion of many intermediate mathematical expressions to aid in the presentation of complicated algebraic developments, and to allow the student to follow them with less than the usual trauma. There are a few inconsistencies in subscript/superscript sizes, designed to aid readability, which the author hopes will not bother critical readers.

Many of the ideas for this book, and some of the approaches to basic topics were developed during a very rewarding visiting year (1987-88) spent in the Physics Department of Virginia Polytechnic Institute and State University, Blacksburg, VA. A. L. Ritter and T. K. Lee will find the extensive use of dispersion relations familiar, as well as some of the problems that I have assigned, and I am indebted to them for these ideas. Helpful discussions with Richard Zahlen and Paul Zweifel are also acknowledged. I have also had helpful advice and interaction with P. H. Cutler and R.M. Herman at Penn State, for which I am very grateful. Finally I should like to thank Mr. R. E. Krieger and Ms. Marie Bowles of Krieger Publishing Company for their support, patience, and suggestions during the preparation of this manuscript.

John P. McKelvey

University Park, PA
May, 1993.

CHAPTER 1

MATERIALS PROPERTIES AND CRYSTAL LATTICES

1.1 INTRODUCTION.

The development of materials has played a crucial role in the growth of our present technological society. This book, while addressed primarily to students of engineering and materials science, is not about materials as such, but about the basic physics that determines what properties materials will have. Though its contents should be of interest to anyone concerned with materials, its main focus will be on electronic materials--the materials that go into integrated circuits and other solid-state devices. In view of this, a brief treatment of some elementary solid-state devices is also included.

The technology of electronic materials really began with Thomas A. Edison's quest for a practical incandescent lamp. This quest resolved itself into a search for a satisfactory filament material--one that would operate at a high temperature for a long time without burning out, and without consuming too much electrical energy. Edison finally developed a reasonably successful carbon-filament high-vacuum incandescent lamp in 1878. These bulbs, however, were fragile. Moreover, they darkened rapidly as a result of the deposition of carbon on the glass envelope, and suffered from premature burnout. Tungsten was known to be a potentially superior filament material in view of its low vapor pressure at high temperatures, but turned out to be almost impossible to form into wires and filaments. It took over 20 years to develop the technology of refining and forming tungsten, but at last the problems were overcome, and much better incandescent lamps--the kind we use today--were developed.

The development of tungsten filaments, and the related art of sealing electrodes into evacuated glass envelopes soon gave birth to high-vacuum diode rectifiers, and finally, in 1906, led to de Forest's invention of the vacuum triode, a device which could be used as an amplifier or oscillator, and which soon brought forth the branch of technology we now know as *electronics*. Edison himself had been (in 1886) the first to observe the curious unidirectional currents that could be made to flow in the apparently empty space between a hot filament and a cathode sealed in a high vacuum. Indeed, had he exhibited the slightest interest in the origin of this effect, he might well have become the discoverer of the electron. Unfortunately, however, he was obsessed with the development of incandescent lighting, and the electron was not identified until 1897 by J. J. Thomson, a Cambridge physics professor. Thomson was awarded the 1906 Nobel Prize in physics for the discovery of the electron.

By 1947, a large communications and consumer electronics industry had been spawned by the technology of vacuum-tube electronics. Radio transmitters and receivers, television sets, disc and tape recording and playback equipment, and radar and other defense systems all utilized vacuum tubes, despite inherent problems related to size, filament power dissipation, fragility, and limited service life. These problems stimulated scientific research in such subjecs as electron physics, gas discharges, thermionic emission from metals and oxide-coated cathodes, secondary electron emission, photoemission, etc. During the first half of the 20th Century, the behavior of electrons in metals and other crystals also began to be studied in a systematic way, and by about 1940 a discipline called solid-state physics had achieved legitimacy as a subfield of modern physics.

The earliest application of solid-state electronics was in crystal detectors of radiofrequency signals in early radio receivers. These devices were simply rectifiers consisting of a fine metallic point--usually referred to as a "cat whisker"--in contact with a crystalline semiconductor such as galena, i.e., lead sulfide. The cat whisker had to be positioned carefully in the vicinity of a "hot spot" on the crystal to make the device work properly. Actually, nobody understood exactly how these devices operated, but they were nevertheless in fairly widespread use in simple receivers (known as "crystal sets") during the first two decades of this century. During World War II, semiconductors came to be better understood, and point contact rectifiers, now using crystals of germanium and silicon, were designed for use at microwave frequencies as radar detectors.

It soon became apparent that it should be possible to utilize electron currents in semiconductor crystals to do all the useful tasks that could be accomplished by vacuum tubes. Soon after World War II, physicists began an intense study of the properties of these materials with the objective of fabricating a solid-state triode. This objective was realized with the invention of the transistor by Shockley, Bardeen and Brattain, at Bell Laboratories in December 1947. The invention of this device was a direct outgrowth of fundamental research in semiconductor physics.

Since then, the growth of electronics has been associated almost exclusively with the development of solid-state materials, solid-state devices, and integrated circuits fabricated from solid-state elements. If you wish to pursue the study of electronics, electronic materials, electron devices, or for that matter materials science in general, you must therefore begin by learning the fundamentals of solid-state physics. You will also have to learn the elements of *quantum mechanics*, because the laws of classical physics are inadequate to describe the behavior of matter on the atomic scale. In this book, that subject is presented as an integral part of the text, and you will learn it as you go along. In fact, the road begins at this point.

1.2 SOLIDS, LIQUIDS, AND GASES

Most of the materials we encounter in everyday life can be classified as solids, liquids, or gases. In gases, the molecules are relatively far apart, and the forces between them are not strong enough to bind the atoms or molecules tightly to each other. There are therefore comparatively few molecules per unit volume, and the density of the substance is relatively low. A gram mole of an ideal gas, for example, occupies a volume of 22.4 liters at 0°C and one atmosphere pressure. In gases, the positive kinetic energy of the molecules is greater than their mutual potential energy of interaction, which will be negative if the intermolecular forces are attractive, as they ordinarily are. This means that the system has net kinetic energy, and that if it is unconfined, the molecules will escape to infinity. The situation is like that of a rocket given an initial upward velocity greater than the escape velocity associated with the earth's gravitational field at the launch site. Such an object has more positive kinetic energy than negative gravitational potential energy, and it will escape to infinity rather than falling back to the earth's surface. In a gas, the molecular velocities, on the average, are greater than the "escape velocity" associated with the intermolecular forces of attraction. In an *ideal* gas, the intermolecular forces are negligible, and the molecules behave like particles that are free except for occasional elastic collisions with each other, and with the walls of the container.

An ideal crystalline solid is the exact opposite of an ideal gas, in the sense that the atoms are tightly bound to one another in a regular periodic lattice by very strong attractive forces, as illustrated in Figure 1.1. Within the crystal, neighboring atoms are so close together that their external electron distributions are starting to overlap and interact; in effect, the atoms are in contact with one another. In this condensed state, the density of matter is much greater than that of gases at room temperature and atmospheric pressure. A gram mole of a crystalline solid typically occupies a volume of only 10 to 100 milliliters, and the atoms are only 2 Ångströms or so (1Å = 10^{-10}m) apart. Under these circumstances, the energy of the system is mostly negative potential energy associated with the attractive forces between individual atoms. Though the atoms may have some thermal kinetic energy, this is only a small part of their total energy. The total energy of the system is therefore negative, which is simply another way of saying that the particles remain bound to well-defined equilibrium positions. The only effect of the thermal kinetic energy the particles may have is to make them oscillate about their equilibrium positions. In an *ideal* crystal these oscillations are harmonic motions whose amplitude is much smaller than the interatomic spacing. Since the ideal crystal is so simple physically, its properties are also easy to calculate. Partially for this reason, but also because the ideal crystal model is quite adequate for many purposes, we shall find it useful as the basis of much of our forthcoming work.

It is important, however, to understand that many solids do not conform to the ideal crystal model described above. First of all, lattice imperfections such as lattice vacancies and extra interstitial atoms may be present, along with other defects in the regular periodic structure of the crystal. In many cases, there may be large regions of nearly perfect crystalline order, each having a different lattice orientation, separated by thin, highly disordered boundary regions. Such substances are referred

4

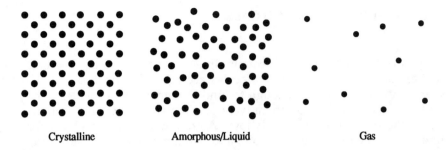

Crystalline   Amorphous/Liquid   Gas

Figure 1.1 Two-Dimensional schematic representation of crystalline solids, amorphous materials or liquids, and gases. In gases, the atoms can be much further apart than shown above.

to as *polycrystalline* materials. Ordinary metals, in the "as prepared" state, for example, are usually polycrystalline. Fortunately, the ideal crystal model provides a description of these materials that is satisfactory for many purposes. In certain other solid materials, the atoms are arranged more or less randomly. The resulting structure has none, or very little, of the long-range regularity of an ideal crystal. Materials of this type are called *amorphous* substances. Glass is a typical example of an amorphous material. Sometimes amorphous solids can be regarded as supercooled liquids of enormous viscosity. In many cases, the ideal crystal model still suffices to give a rough, though useful, description of their properties. Amorphous materials are important in electronics and materials engineering, though we shall not attempt to treat them in detail in this book.

Liquids resemble solids in that their density and interatomic spacing are much closer to those of crystalline substances than gases. In liquids, however, there is none of the geometric regularity of the crystalline solid, the atoms or molecules being randomly arranged, as in an amorphous solid. To attain the liquid state, however, you must raise the temperature of a solid until it melts. In doing this, one increases the kinetic energy of the atoms, which in the crystalline state is purely vibrational. As the temperature rises, the amplitude of atomic vibrations in the crystal increases until it finally approaches the interatomic spacing. At this point, the atoms attain enough kinetic energy to break loose from their former positions of equilibrium and move more or less freely past one another. They are still bound to one another in a dense, compact phase, but they now have translational as well as vibrational kinetic energy. In this state, atoms can move around more or less freely within the substance, even though they cannot generally escape to infinity. The substance has now melted and become a liquid. Solids and liquids are often collectively referred to as *condensed matter,* and what used to be referred to as solid-state physics is now more frequently called condensed-matter physics in view of the fact that solids and liquids are both condensed phases characterized by small interatomic distances and high density. The fact that this book retains the earlier designation in its title merely reflects the fact that it is largely concerned with crystalline substances.

Obviously, you can convert a crystalline solid first to a liquid and finally to a gas or vapor, by progressively raising the temperature. At a given temperature, for example room temperature, different substances may exist in any of these three possible states. Under these conditions, what determines whether any given material is solid, liquid, or gas, is the *strength* of the attractive forces between atoms or molecules. In gases, these forces are weak, in crystalline solids, they are strong. What determines how strong they are in any given substance is a complex question, which can be answered fully only in the context of quantum mechanics. Indeed, the answer to this question is one of the main things you can learn by studying solid-state physics. It is premature, however, to try to answer it now.

In addition to crystalline materials, we shall have to spend some time and effort studying the properties of ideal free-particle gases. This may seem surprising, because gases are physically at the opposite extreme from crystalline materials. However, the electrical properties of conducting substances can be understood only by observing that the valence electrons of their atoms are essentially free within the crystal. These electrons can be visualized as forming a free-particle *gas* within the substance, a gas which is confined by the external surfaces of the crystal. In order to understand the electrical behavior of conducting materials, therefore, it is necessary to study the properties of this "free-electron gas". These properties, as we shall see later, are similar in many ways to those of ordinary ideal monatomic gases.

1.3 LATTICES, UNIT CELLS, AND CRYSTAL SYMMETRY

Real crystal lattices are, of course, three-dimensional structures. The simplest of these is the lattice of points having integer coördinates (h,k,l) in an orthogonal cartesian coördinate system. Such a system can be thought of as being composed of cubic cells as basic structural units. This lattice is illustrated in Figure 1.2; it is called a simple cubic lattice. Three-dimensional structures are difficult to portray on paper, and are also somewhat complicated geometrically. Frequently, however, their basic geometry, and also the basic physics connected with them, can be adequately described with reference to two-dimensional, or even one-dimensional models, which are much simpler to portray, to visualize, and to analyze mathematically. There are situations in which this kind of simplification is not possible, but when it is valid, it is extremely helpful; in this book it will be frequently employed.

Figure 1.2(b) illustrates a two-dimensional crystal lattice which can be used to portray the basic geometry of ideal crystals. The parallelogram ABCD may be chosen as a *unit cell* of the crystal; the cell itself is in turn determined by the *basis vectors* **a** and **b**. It is clear from the diagram that the entire crystal can be mapped out by translating the unit cell along the **a**- and **b**-directions by integral multiples of those vectors. Thus, any lattice point in the crystal is located with respect to an origin at A by a vector **R** of the form

$$\mathbf{R} = h\mathbf{a} + k\mathbf{b} \ , \tag{1.3-1}$$

where h and k are integers. Moreover, in an infinite lattice, a point P, located with respect to A by vector $\mathbf{r}_p$, is carried by the transformation $\mathbf{r}_q = \mathbf{r}_p + \mathbf{R}$, where **R** is any vector of the form (1.3-1), into a point Q whose surroundings are geometrically identical in all respects to those of P. This property, called *translational invariance* can be regarded as defining geometrically what is meant by a crystal lattice. It is obvious that this procedure can be extended to define unit cells and basis vectors in three-dimensional lattices. Translational invariance is illustrated in Figure 1.2(b),

6

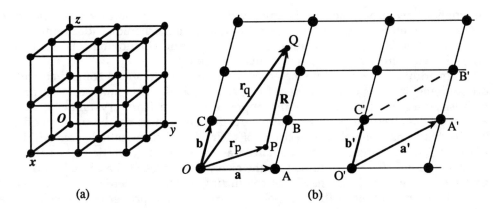

Figure 1.2 (a) Cubic lattice cells generated by points in an orthogonal cartesian coördinate system whose coördinates are all integers. (b) Two-dimensional unit cells and basis vectors.

where the lattice vector **R** (equal to 0**a** + 2**b** in this instance), translates the point P to a new location Q. It is evident that the physical surroundings of P and Q are the same, and that there is a point with these same surroundings in every unit cell of the crystal. We are thus led to suggest the following definitions:

> *Unit Cell*: A region of the crystal defined by three vectors, **a**, **b**, and **c**, which, when translated by a vector displacement consisting of a sum of integral multiples of these vectors, reproduces a similar region of the crystal.
> *Basis Vectors*: A set of linearly independent vectors **a**, **b**, and **c** which can be used to define a unit cell.
> *Primitive Unit Cell*: The smallest unit cell, in volume, that can be defined for a given lattice.
> *Primitive Basis Vectors*: A set of linearly independent vectors that can be used to define a primitive unit cell.

It should be observed that unit cells can be defined in more than one way. For example, in Figure 1.2(b), the most obvious--and sensible--choice of a unit cell is OABC. However, the larger cell OO′C′C could also be used inasmuch as it will map out the whole crystal by appropriate translations defined by its set of basis vectors OO′ and OC. This cell is non-primitive, since it is larger than the primitive cell OABC. The cell O′A′B′C′, defined by the basis vectors **a**′ and **b**′ might also be used. In this case, the unit cell can be seen to be equal in area to OABC; it is therefore *also* a primitive unit cell. It is also important to remember that the basis vectors of a crystal lattice *are not unit vectors*. Instead, they are dimensional vectors whose magnitudes are those of the interatomic spacing along the crystal axes. Moreover, it should be apparent that the lattice points of a three-dimensional lattice are described by a lattice vector **R** of the form

$$\mathbf{R} = h\mathbf{a} + k\mathbf{b} + l\mathbf{c} \; , \qquad\qquad (1.3\text{-}2)$$

where h, k, and l are integers. Finally, the property of translational invariance is also clearly valid in three dimensional crystals.

1.4 CRYSTAL STRUCTURES IN THREE DIMENSIONS

The study of crystal symmetry and general three-dimensional crystal geometry is full of subtle and complex details. Indeed, the subject constitutes an entire subfield of solid-state physics called *crystallography*, to which many scientists have devoted their entire lives. It is important to know some of the basic facts and terminology of this subject to develop an understanding of the physical properties of crystalline materials, but fortunately, a brief overview is all that is needed at the outset. We shall therefore present only a very elementary treatment of this subject. You should understand this clearly, and not be put off by the fact that our discussion leaves many seemingly important questions unanswered. The answers to these questions are simply a matter for more advanced study, and involve issues peripheral to the primary objectives of this text. Also, you will be presented with some results that are merely stated, with no attempt at derivation, nor even detailed explanation in some cases. Again, the facts are all you need to know at this point, the complex and difficult arguments for their validity being irrelevant to our present objectives.

Initially, one can show--with considerable difficulty--that there are exactly 14 ways of arranging points in space such that the physical surroundings of each lattice point is the same. This is the same as saying that if your crystal is made up of spherically symmetric atoms (whose symmetry properties are the same as those of point objects) you can draw only 14 different unit cells. These 14 arrangements are referred to as *Bravais lattices*, and are illustrated in Figure 1.3. They can be further subdivided into seven *crystal systems*, each of which is characterized by a unique symmetry property, such as invariance under rotation through given angles about certain axes, or under inversion, an operation in which a vector **r** from the cell origin to a lattice point is repaced by –**r**. These crystal systems are listed, along with their unit cell descriptors and characteristic symmetry elements, below Figure 1.4, which illustrates the notation pertaining to the size and shape of the unit cell.

If only spherically symmetric atoms were involved, there would be only 14 possible crystal structures. In general, however, lattice points may represent not only a single atom, but a group of atoms, or an entire molecule. The overall symmetry properties of a crystal will thus generally depend not only upon the symmetries of the Bravais lattice itself, but also on the symmetry properties of the atom or group of atoms at the lattice sites with reference to the lattice points themselves. When this added complication is taken into account, the number of possible crystal structures increases to 230. One now begins to see why crystallography is such a complicated business.

We are fortunate, however, that most important electronics materials, as well as many metals and alloys form crystals whose unit cells have mutually orthogonal axes. Indeed, most of these materials have cubic unit cells. This simplifies their geometry significantly, and allows those whose interest is confined to substances such as these to proceed without getting much further concerned with problems

(*Text continues on page 10*)

8

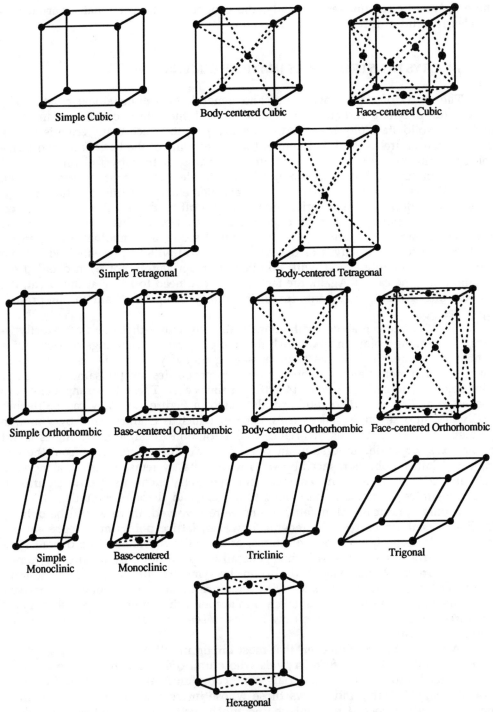

Figure 1.3 The 14 Bravais lattices

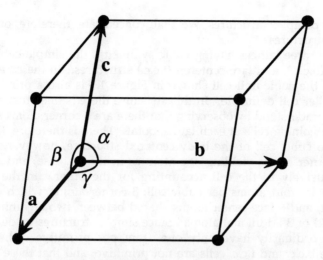

Figure 1.4. Notation for dimensions and angles within the unit cell of a crystal.

THE SEVEN CRYSTAL SYSTEMS

System	Unique Symmetry Element	Bravais Lattice	Unit Cell
Triclinic	None	Simple	$a \neq b \neq c$ $\alpha \neq \beta \neq \gamma \neq 90°$
Monoclinic	One 2-fold rotation axis*	Simple Base-centered	$a \neq b \neq c$ $\alpha = \beta = 90° \neq \gamma$
Orthorhombic	Three mutually orthogonal 2-fold rotation axes	Simple Base-centered Body-centered Face-centered	$a \neq b \neq c$ $\alpha = \beta = \gamma = 90°$
Tetragonal	One 4-fold rotation axis	Simple Body-centered	$a = b \neq c$ $\alpha = \beta = \gamma = 90°$
Cubic	Four 3-fold rotation axes (cube diagonals)	Simple Body-centered Face-centered	$a = b = c$ $\alpha = \beta = \gamma = 90°$
Hexagonal	One 6-fold rotation axis	Simple	$a = b \neq c$ $\alpha = \beta = 90°$ $\gamma = 120°$
Trigonal	One 3-fold rotation axis	Simple	$a = b = c$ $\alpha = \beta = \gamma \neq 90°$

* The term *n*-fold rotation axis refers to invariance under a rotation of 360/*n* degrees about some specific axis.

related to more complex structures. We shall concentrate, therefore, on a few simple but important structures.

There are three lattices having cubic symmetry, the simple cubic (s.c.), body-centered cubic (b.c.c.), and face-centered (f.c.c.) structures. In the case of the simple cubic structure, the cubic unit cell shown in Figure 1.3 is also a primitive cell, since there is no smaller cell definable. In this structure there is one atom per unit cell, a fact that can be understood by observing that there are 8 corner atoms shared equally between eight adjoining cells at each lattice point. There is therefore 8(1/8) = 1 atom per cell. In the cubic cell of the body-centered structure, however, there are two atoms, the 8 corner atoms yielding one atom as in the s.c. case, and a central atom belonging exclusively to the cell accounting for the other. In the face-centered structure, there are four atoms per cubic cell; 8 corner atoms, which contribute one atom to the cell, and 6 face-center atoms shared between two adjoining cells, which contribute 6(1/2) or 3 additional atoms. Since simple structures made up of a single atomic species ordinarily have only one atom per primitive cell, one is led to suspect that the b.c.c. and f.c.c. cells are not primitive, and that these structures can be defined by a smaller structural unit. This turns out to be true; the primitive cells for these two lattices are illustrated in Figure 1.5. Each of these primitive cells contains only one atom.

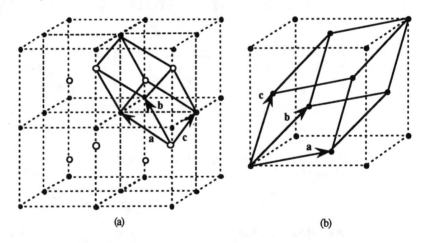

(a)   (b)

Figure 1.5 Primitive unit cells for (a) the body-centered and (b) the face-centered cubic structures. In (a) the atoms are all the same despite the fact that those at the centers of the cells are highlighted to clarify spatial relationships.

For most purposes it is more convenient to use the larger cubic cell, in view of the simplicity of coördinate geometry in orthogonal systems. Occasionally, however, we shall encounter applications where it is essential to use the primitive cell. We shall identify these situations whenever they occur. The f.c.c. primitive cell can be readily identified as a trigonal unit cell in which the angles α, β, and γ are all 60°. For this particular angle the trigonal lattice exhibits cubic symmetry, and reduces to the f.c.c.

In the simple cubic lattice, each atom is clearly surrounded by 6 nearest neighbors. The number of nearest neighbor atoms is referred to as the *coördination number* of the structure. Simple cubic thus has a coördination number of 6. The b.c.c. structure is easily seen to have a coördination number of 8, while for f.c.c., the coördination number is 12, the nearest neighbor distance being along the face diagonals. Structures with few nearest neighbors are relatively "open" in character, while those in which each atom is surrounded by many neighboring atoms are comparatively densely packed. The coördination number is therefore directly related to the density with which atoms are arranged within the crystal. The largest possible coördination number is 12; structures in which each atom is surrounded by 12 nearest neighbors are therefore referred to as *close-packed* configurations. The f.c.c. lattice is the most common example of such a structure.

Within the unit cell, the positions occupied by atoms, and other points also, are often described by cell coördinates defined as fractional parts of the basis vectors **a**, **b**, and **c**. For example, the body-center atom in the b.c.c. cubic cell would have cell coördinates $(1/2, 1/2, 1/2)$, while the topmost face-center atom in Figure 1.5(b) would have cell coördinates $(1/2, 1/2, 1)$.

When equal spheres are packed into a container, the densest packing is obtained by first inserting a bottom layer in which each sphere is surrounded by a hexagonal array of 6 nearest neighbors. On top of this, one may put a similar layer, using the triangularly disposed interstices between spheres in the bottom layer to hold the spheres in the upper one. It is evident that in such an arrangement, each sphere in the bottom layer will be in contact with three spheres in the layer above. In the interior of a close-packed array of spheres, therefore, each sphere is in contact with 12 nearest neighbors; six in its own layer, three in the layer above, and three in the layer below.

There are two different structures having this property of close packing, in which the coördination number is 12, and they differ only in the manner in which the close packed layers are stacked upon one another. In the first, the spheres in the third layer are positioned directly above those in the first, those in the fourth are directly above those in the second, etc., resulting in a layer stacking that can be designated as ABABAB.... This structure turns out to have hexagonal symmetry, and is referred to as *hexagonal close-packed*. When you start the third layer of the packed array, however, you find that instead of positioning the third-layer spheres directly above those in the first layer, you can place them in another set of sites, in which they are not directly above either first-layer or second-layer spheres. Designating these sites as C-positions, one can then form the repetitive sequence ABCABCABC... as an alternate stacking pattern In this structure, layers 1, 4, 7..., 2, 5, 8..., and 3, 6, 9... are directly above one another. This arrangement turns out to be the face-centered cubic lattice, a structure we have already identified as close-packed. In f.c.c. the close-packed layers lie in planes normal to the *diagonal* of the cubic f.c.c unit cell. These structures are illustrated in Figure 1.6.

The simple cubic lattice is the simplest structure nature has provided for the formation of crystals. One might therefore expect that many substances crystallize in this manner. In fact, the reverse is true; there are only a few substances that form simple cubic lattices. The reason is that the attractive forces that act between the atoms or molecules of most substances make it energetically favorable for the atoms to be closer together than they would be in the s.c. lattice, whose coördination number is only 6. They therefore tend to assume more densely-packed structures, such as b.c.c. and f.c.c. On the other hand, if density of packing were the only factor at work, there would be only two possible structures--the ones illustrated in Figure 1.6. In reality, though density of packing is often significant, other factors can also be important.

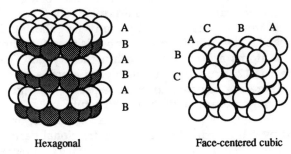

Hexagonal   Face-centered cubic

Figure 1.6 Hexagonal and cubic close-packed structures

The diamond lattice, illustrated in Figure 1.7(a), provides an excellent example of this ambivalence. Silicon and germanium, as well as diamond, crystallize in this structure. It is a very "open" lattice, with a coördination number of only 4. Despite this fact, diamond, silicon, and germanium are hard, strong, stable materials which exhibit little tendency to undergo phase changes into more densely packed crystalline structures. The reason is simple; carbon atoms have a strong tendency to form covalent electron-pair bonds with one another. These electron-pair carbon-to-carbon linkages are, in fact, what hold most organic molecules together. The tetravalent character of the carbon atom imparts a natural tetrahedral geometry to the covalent bonds that surround each atom This tetrahedral geometry is perfectly accommodated by the diamond structure. Indeed, the tetrahedral units of which it is composed are its most obvious geometrical feature. So despite the low density of packing, carbon crystallizes in this form, as do its sister elements silicon and germanium, which like carbon occupy column IV of the periodic table. It is of course true that there exists another crystalline form of carbon, but graphite is no more densely packed than diamond, and valency is also the predominant mechanism in its structural makeup.

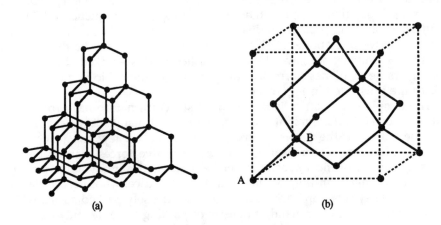

(a)   (b)

Figure 1.7 (a) The diamond structure (b) The diamond structure fitted into a cubic unit cell.

The diamond lattice turns out to have cubic symmetry, a fact not at all apparent from the diagram shown in Figure 1.7(a). In this diagram, the electron-pair bonds are shown as solid lines connecting nearest-neighbor atoms. Figure 1.7(b) illustrates how this structure can be fitted into a cubic unit cell. It can be regarded as two interpenetrating f.c.c. lattices, one based on an origin at A, the other based on B. Another way of looking at it is as a b.c.c. lattice with many of its atom sites vacant. The diamond lattice is not a Bravais lattice, since it can be regarded as an f.c.c. structure having the two-atom group AB on the lattice points rather than a single atom at each point. The bond length AB in the diamond structure is equal to one-quarter of the cubic cell diagonal.

The so-called III-V intermetallic compounds are also important electronic materials. They are composed of equal numbers of atoms from columns III and V of the periodic table, and thus have an *average* of four valence electrons per atom. They therefore satisfy the valency requirements of a tetrahedrally coördinated structure, and in fact crystallize in a lattice very similar to the diamond structure. The arrangement of atoms in this structure is identical to that of the diamond structure, the column III atoms occupying the f.c.c. sites based on A, the column V atoms occupying B sites. In this so-called *zincblende* structure, the two different atomic species are on alternate neighboring diamond-lattice sites, each column III atom being surrounded by four tetrahedrally disposed column V atoms (and vice-versa) so as to satisfy the bonding requirements of four covalent electron-pair bonds, which need a total of eight electrons. Gallium arsenide (GaAs) is the most important substance having this configuration, though other III-V semiconductors such as InSb, InP, and GaP have been used in electronic applications.

The structures of two simple ionic salts, NaCl and CsCl are illustrated in Figure 1.8. The NaCl structure has alternating sodium and chlorine atoms at the lattice points of a simple cubic lattice. The structure can also be viewed as two interpenetrating f.c.c. lattices, one of which is composed entirely of sodium atoms, the other

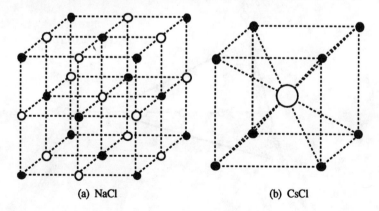

(a) NaCl   (b) CsCl

Figure 1.8 The sodium chloride and cesium chloride structures.

entirely of chlorine atoms. The CsCl structure is essentially body-centered, with cesium atoms at body centers and sodium at cube corner sites. Many other ionic crystals are found to crystallize in one or the other of these configurations.

14

1. 5 CRYSTAL PLANES, DIRECTIONS, AND MILLER INDICES

If you look at a three-dimensional crystal model, or at illustrations such as Figures 1.2(a), 1.3, 1.5, 1.6 1.7, or 1.8(a), you will notice that there are certain clearly defined planes, densely populated with atoms, that run through the crystal in various directions. The two-dimensional line traces of these planes in the plane of the page are also easily seen in the leftmost drawing of Figure 1.1, particularly when the figure is viewed from a small angle to the page and the page rotated about a vertical axis to display the structure from various directions. The atoms lying in the plane of the cube faces of cubic unit cells render these crystal planes highly visible, but other prominent planes making various angles with the cell faces can also be observed. For example, in cubic cells, atoms lying in planes normal to face diagonals and to the cell diagonals are also clearly visible. There are other less prominent families of planes, making odd angles to the cell faces, and less densely populated with atoms, which can also be distinguished. Indeed, there is a whole hierarchy of planes of this sort within the crystal lattice.

These sets of planes are involved in a number of important physical processes that occur in crystals. For example, the diffraction of X-rays is an important tool for chemical analysis and determination of the lattice structure of crystalline solids. X-ray diffraction, however, can be visualized as involving reflection of X-rays from various sets of crystal planes, in such a way that outgoing beams reflected from adjacent planes of any such set interfere constructively. This process, which we shall consider in detail in the next chapter, is referred to as *Bragg reflection*. Bragg reflection is also involved in the diffraction of electrons and neutrons by crystals. In analyzing diffraction phenomena, the orientation and spacing of the families of crystal planes must obviously play an important part. It is of some interest, therefore to study the geometry of crystal planes within the lattice.

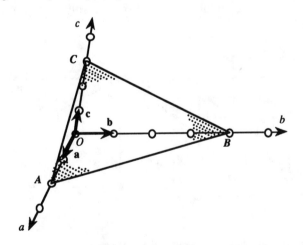

Figure 1.9 A (634) plane in a crystal lattice.

The orientation of crystal planes within the lattice is specified by a set of three integers referred to as the *Miller indices* of the planes. The Miller indices of crystal planes such as those illustrated in Figure 1.9 can be obtained as follows:

(1) Take the origin at any lattice point in the crystal, and coördinate axes in the directions of the basis vectors of the unit cell.

(2) Locate the intercepts of a plane belonging to the desired system along each of the coördinate axes, and express them as integral multiples of the respective basis vectors along the crystal axes.

(3) Take the *reciprocals* of these numbers, and multiply through by the smallest factor that will convert them to a triad of integers $(h, k, l,)$ having the same ratios. The quantity (hkl) is the required set of Miller indices for this system of planes.

Figure 1.9 illustrates a crystal plane whose intercepts are at twice the atomic spacing along the a-axis, at four times the atomic spacing along the b-axis, and at three times the atomic spacing along the c-axis. The Miller indices of the family of which this plane is a member are obtained by taking the reciprocals of these numbers, that is $(1/2, 1/4, 1/3)$, and converting this to the smallest possible integer triad by multiplying by 12, writing the result (without commas) as (634). In arriving at the Miller indices, the tacit assumption that no other plane of the system intersects any of the atoms along the line segments OA, OB, and OC in Figure 1.9 is usually made.

In any structure, a given set of crystal planes has a geometry characterized by some specific arrangement and spacing of atoms, and adjacent planes of the set have a characteristic interplanar spacing which depends on the Miller indices. There may be certain sets of crystal planes, moreover, whose Miller indices differ by permutation of indices or signs, yet which have the same interplanar spacing, and whose atoms all have the same geometrical arrangement. Such sets of crystal planes are said to be *crystographically equivalent*. The planes which define all the faces of the cubic cell in the s.c., b.c.c., and f.c.c. structures, for example, are all crystallographically equivalent. In *orthogonal* structures, the planes formed by assigning all possible permutations of minus signs to the Miller indices:

$$(hkl), (\bar{h}kl), (h\bar{k}l), (hk\bar{l}) ,$$

are all crystallographically equivalent. There are only 4 such permutations, because when the signs of all three indices are reversed, the resulting plane is not merely equivalent but is parallel--which is viewed as crystallographically *identical*--to the original one. Incidentally, you should note that negative Miller indices are conventionally written with the minus sign above the index, rather than before it. In *cubic* structures, all sets of planes reprersented by permutations of the three Miller indices among themselves (for example, (hkl), (hlk), (klh), etc.) are also crystallographically equivalent.

When a plane is parallel to one or two of the crystal axes, the corresponding intercepts will be at infinity. Since the reciprocal of an infinite quantity is zero, the Miller indices derived from these intercepts will likewise be zero. The situation can be understood with reference to Figure 1.9. When the point C recedes to infinity along the c-direction, the plane rotates about line AB until it is parallel to the c-axis. The intercepts are then $(2, 4, \infty)$, and the Miller indices are now (210). Subsequently, if point B recedes to infinity along OB, the plane rotates about a line normal to the ab-plane through A until it is normal to the a-axis. The intercepts are now $(2, \infty, \infty)$, and the Miller indices become (100). As noted above, the Miller indices of a particular set of planes are enclosed within ordinary parentheses. A complete set of crystallographically equivalent planes of which (*hkl*) is a member is written using curly brackets, thus: {*hkl*}.

It is possible also to assign numerical indices to directions within the crystal lattice. The indices of a *direction* in a crystal are expressed as a set of integers having the same ratios as the components of a vector from one lattice point to another, expressed as multiples of the respective basis vectors. Thus, the indices of a vector of the form $h\mathbf{a} + k\mathbf{b} + l\mathbf{c}$ is written--using square brackets--as [*hkl*]. Directions having different indices may be crystallographically equivalent in the same sense as crystal planes. Normals to crystallographically equivalent planes are crystallographically equivalent directions. However, except in cubic crystals, the [*hkl*] direction is not necessarily normal to the (*hkl*) plane. The complete set of crystallographically equivalent directions that includes [*hkl*] is written, using angle brackets, as <*hkl*>. The orthogonality of the direction [*hkl*] to the plane (*hkl*) in cubic lattices provides a strong motivation for using cubic rather than primitive cells whenever possible for the b.c.c. and f.c.c. structures.

From Figure 1.9, it might appear that the spacing between adjacent planes of the (*hkl*) system is the distance between the origin and the plane which is shown. This is not true, however, because the origin can be taken at any lattice point of the crystal, which means, in effect, that *a plane of the (hkl) system must pass through every lattice point*, as illustrated in Figure 1.10 For this reason, the spacing between adjacent planes is ordinarily smaller than the interatomic spacing.

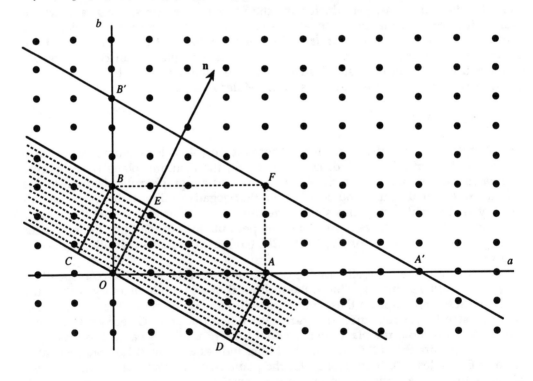

Figure 1.10. A family of (340) planes in an orthogonal crystal. The slanted lines represent the intersections of the planes, which are normal to the page, with the *ab*-plane of the unit cell.

In the figure, a set of (340) planes is shown. These planes are parallel to the c-axis of the crystal, and therefore normal to the page. There are in this example only two nonzero Miller indices. This simplifies the subsequent analysis, but still permits a more general result to be inferred. Let m and n be the number of interatomic spacings between OA and OB, respectively; in the case illustrated, $m = 4$ and $n = 3$. The Miller indices are obtained by taking the reciprocals of these numbers and multiplying by the smallest factor needed to obtain a pair of integers. If m and n have no common factor, this number will simply be the factor mn. We shall (again for simplicity) assume this to be the case, initially at least. The Miller indices will then be given by

$$h = \frac{mn}{m} = n \qquad \text{and} \qquad k = \frac{mn}{n} = m \ . \tag{1.5-1}$$

Now consider the area $OBFA$. Our usual scheme of assigning atoms to cells informs us that there are mn atoms in this region. Since region $ABCD$ clearly has the same area as $OBFA$, it must also contain mn atoms. But since exactly one plane of the system intersects each atom of the crystal, there must be mn planes within $ABCD$. If you count the number of planes along OE in the figure, you will see that this is correct. Since all these planes intersect both of the crystal axes illustrated above, and since there are m atom spacings along OA, and n along OB, the distances d_a and d_b between intercepts of *adjacent* planes along the respective crystal axes are

$$d_a = \frac{ma}{mn} = \frac{a}{h} \qquad \text{and} \qquad d_b = \frac{nb}{mn} = \frac{b}{k} \ . \tag{1.5-2}$$

There is still the question of what happens when the multiplying factor used to arrive at the Miller indices is not precisely mn. This occurs whenever m and n have a common factor. In the example shown in Figure 1.10, such a situation would have arisen had the plane $A'B'$ rather than AB been chosen initially to define the Miller indices. If we now let $m = \alpha m'$ and $n = \alpha n'$, where α is an integral common factor, (1.5 - 1) yields $h = \alpha m'$ and $k = \alpha n'$; substituting these values into (1.5 -2), however, leaves this expression unchanged. It may also be noted that though an orthogonal system has been used for simplicity in the figure, there is nothing in the equations written above that depends on the choice of such a system. The results are valid in any system.

It is possible to carry out the calculation outlined above for a family of planes having three nonzero Miller indices, and which are therefore not parallel to any of the crystal axes. A full description of this calculation, and a rigorous treatment of cases where two, or all three, of the indices have a factor in common is tedious, time-consuming, and in the end leads to no unexpected results. The case where the three indices have no common factor is assigned as a problem for the reader, who should in any event have no trouble in accepting the result that in general, the spacing between the intercepts of adjacent (hkl) crystal planes along the three crystal axes is given by

$$d_a = \frac{a}{h} \ , \qquad d_b = \frac{b}{k} \ , \qquad \text{and} \qquad d_c = \frac{c}{l} \ . \tag{1.5-3}$$

The actual interplanar spacing, d_{hkl} can now be obtained by calculating the scalar product of the vector $\mathbf{d}_a = \mathbf{a}/h$ with a unit vector $\mathbf{n}$ normal to the planes. In fact, we can write

$$d_{hkl} = \frac{\mathbf{n} \cdot \mathbf{a}}{h} = \frac{\mathbf{n} \cdot \mathbf{b}}{k} = \frac{\mathbf{n} \cdot \mathbf{c}}{l} \ . \tag{1.5-4}$$

In *orthogonal* systems having one atom per cell, this spacing can be stated more explicitly by noting that the (hkl) plane closest to the origin has intercepts a/h, b/k, c/l, along the three axes. If the axes are orthogonal, the equation of this plane in cartesian coördinates can be written as

$$f(x,y,z) = \frac{x}{(a/h)} + \frac{y}{(b/k)} + \frac{z}{(c/l)} = 1 \ . \tag{1.5-5}$$

This is the equation of a surface--a plane in this case--having the form $f(x, y, z) =$ constant. A vector normal to such a surface can be found by calculating the gradient of the function $f(x, y, z)$, and if this gradient is divided by its own magnitude, the result will be the unit normal vector $\mathbf{n}$. We can thus write,

$$\nabla f = \mathbf{i}_x \frac{\partial f}{\partial x} + \mathbf{i}_y \frac{\partial f}{\partial y} + \mathbf{i}_z \frac{\partial f}{\partial z} = \mathbf{i}_x \frac{h}{a} + \mathbf{i}_y \frac{k}{b} + \mathbf{i}_z \frac{l}{c} \ , \tag{1.5-6}$$

where $\mathbf{i}_x$, $\mathbf{i}_y$, and $\mathbf{i}_z$ are *unit* vectors along the cartesian axes, which now coincide with the crystal axes. Thus,

$$\mathbf{n} = \frac{\nabla f}{|\nabla f|} = \frac{\mathbf{i}_x(h/a) + \mathbf{i}_y(k/b) + \mathbf{i}_z(l/c)}{\sqrt{\dfrac{h^2}{a^2} + \dfrac{k^2}{b^2} + \dfrac{l^2}{c^2}}} \ . \tag{1.5-7}$$

The distance d_{hkl} between adjacent planes can now be obtained from (1.5-4) as the scalar product of this vector and the vector $\mathbf{a}/h$., which in the cartesian system has only an x-component, and can be written as $\mathbf{i}_x a/h$. The result is

$$d_{hkl} = \frac{1}{\sqrt{\dfrac{h^2}{a^2} + \dfrac{k^2}{b^2} + \dfrac{l^2}{c^2}}} \ . \tag{1.5-8}$$

1.6 THE RECIPROCAL LATTICE

When a beam of X-rays--or particles such as electrons--is directed at a crystal, it is observed that a complex system of outgoing diffracted beams in various directions is produced by Bragg reflection from the numerous sets of crystal planes in the lattice. If these diffracted beams gave direct information about the crystal lattice itself, there would be no need for this section, but instead the information they convey is most directly related to another lattice referred to as the *reciprocal lattice* of the crystal. The real space lattice of the crystal must then be inferred from the reciprocal lattice by a set of transformation equations which define the geometrical relationship between the two lattices. There are many other instances in which the reciprocal lattice turns out to be a useful construct, so it will be advantageous to introduce it at this point even though its full utility may not be immediately apparent.

In defining the unit cell of the reciprocal lattice it is necessary to start with the *primitive* unit cell of the direct space lattice of the crystal. If $\mathbf{a}$, $\mathbf{b}$, and $\mathbf{c}$ are primitive basis vectors of the direct lattice, a set of primitive basis vectors $\mathbf{a}^*$, $\mathbf{b}^*$, and $\mathbf{c}^*$ of the reciprocal lattice will be generated by the following relations:

$$\mathbf{a}^* \cdot \mathbf{a} = \mathbf{b}^* \cdot \mathbf{b} = \mathbf{c}^* \cdot \mathbf{c} = 1 \qquad (1.6\text{-}1)$$

and $\quad \mathbf{a}^* \cdot \mathbf{b} = \mathbf{a}^* \cdot \mathbf{c} = \mathbf{b}^* \cdot \mathbf{c} = \mathbf{b}^* \cdot \mathbf{a} = \mathbf{c}^* \cdot \mathbf{a} = \mathbf{c}^* \cdot \mathbf{b} = 0 \;. \qquad (1.6\text{-}2)$

From (1.6-2), since the scalar product of $\mathbf{a}^*$ with both $\mathbf{b}$ and $\mathbf{c}$ is zero, $\mathbf{a}^*$ is perpendicular to both $\mathbf{b}$ and $\mathbf{c}$, and thus to the plane determined by them. It is therefore in the direction of the vector $\mathbf{a} \times \mathbf{b}$, and can therefore be written as a multiple of that vector,

$$\mathbf{a}^* = A(\mathbf{b} \times \mathbf{c}) \;, \qquad (1.6\text{-}3)$$

where A is a scalar constant. This constant can be evaluated using (1.6-1), whereby

$$\mathbf{a}^* \cdot \mathbf{a} = A(\mathbf{b} \times \mathbf{c}) \cdot \mathbf{a} = 1 \;. \qquad (1.6\text{-}4)$$

Solving for A and substituting its value into (1.6-3), we find

$$\mathbf{a}^* = \frac{\mathbf{b} \times \mathbf{c}}{\mathbf{a} \cdot \mathbf{b} \times \mathbf{c}}$$

In the same way, it can be shown that $\qquad\qquad\qquad\qquad\qquad\qquad\qquad (1.6\text{-}5)$

$$\mathbf{b}^* = \frac{\mathbf{c} \times \mathbf{a}}{\mathbf{a} \cdot \mathbf{b} \times \mathbf{c}} \qquad \text{and} \qquad \mathbf{c}^* = \frac{\mathbf{a} \times \mathbf{b}}{\mathbf{a} \cdot \mathbf{b} \times \mathbf{c}} \;.$$

Using the same methods, one can also obtain inverse transformations, of the form

$$\mathbf{a} = \frac{\mathbf{b}^* \times \mathbf{c}^*}{\mathbf{a}^* \cdot \mathbf{b}^* \times \mathbf{c}^*} \;. \qquad (1.6\text{-}6)$$

The remaining inverse transformations can obviously be written merely by interchanging starred and unstarred symbols in (1.6-5).

For a simple cubic lattice of interatomic spacing a, $\mathbf{a} = a\mathbf{i}_x$, $\mathbf{b} = a\mathbf{i}_y$, $\mathbf{c} = a\mathbf{i}_z$. If these vectors are substituted into equations (1.6-5), the result is

$$\mathbf{a}^* = (1/a)\mathbf{i}_x \;, \qquad \mathbf{b}^* = (1/a)\mathbf{i}_y \;, \qquad \text{and} \qquad \mathbf{c}^* = (1/a)\mathbf{i}_z \;. \qquad (1.6\text{-}7)$$

This is another simple cubic structure, of lattice spacing $1/a$. From this, it is evident that the s.c. lattice is self-reciprocal. Note, however, that the dimensions of the reciprocal lattice are reciprocal distances. The units are those of the propagation constants of waves, suggesting that vectors in the reciprocal lattice might naturally be associated with the propagation vectors of diffracted radiation.

Consider now the case of a b.c.c. direct lattice, such as the one shown in Figure 1.5(a). For the primitive cell illustrated there, assuming the x-direction toward the reader, the y-direction to the right, and the z-direction upward, the primitive basis vectors are

$$\mathbf{a} = \frac{L}{2}(\mathbf{i}_x - \mathbf{i}_y + \mathbf{i}_z), \quad \mathbf{b} = \frac{L}{2}(-\mathbf{i}_x - \mathbf{i}_y + \mathbf{i}_z), \quad \mathbf{c} = \frac{L}{2}(\mathbf{i}_x + \mathbf{i}_y + \mathbf{i}_z), \tag{1.6-8}$$

where L is the edge of the cubic cell. Substituting these into (1.6 - 5), performing the indicated vector algebra, and simplifying, one may obtain the reciprocal lattice vectors

$$\mathbf{a}^* = \frac{1}{L}(\mathbf{i}_x - \mathbf{i}_y), \quad \mathbf{b}^* = \frac{1}{L}(-\mathbf{i}_x + \mathbf{i}_z), \quad \mathbf{c}^* = \frac{1}{L}(\mathbf{i}_y + \mathbf{i}_z). \tag{1.6-9}$$

These are easily identified as primitive basis vectors of an f.c.c. structure, like the one illustrated in Figure 1.5(b). Though different from the basis vectors in that diagram, they are identical to the equivalent set of basis vectors that would stem from choosing an origin at the face-center atom at the bottom of the cell. In a similar way, one can show that the reciprocal lattice associated with the f.c.c. structure is a b.c.c. lattice. Other reciprocal structures can be exhibited in the same way.

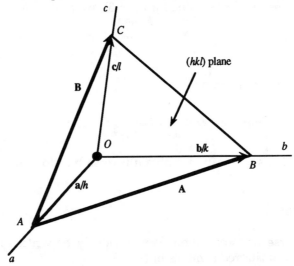

Figure 1.11 Direct lattice vector geometry for the derivation of Equations (1.6 - 11) and (1.6 - 13).

The geometries of the direct and reciprocal lattices are related by the fact that a vector $\mathbf{r}^* = h'\mathbf{a}^* + k'\mathbf{b}^* + l'\mathbf{c}^*$ from the origin to any lattice point of the reciprocal lattice is normal to the (hkl) plane of the *direct* lattice, where (hkl) and $(h'k'l')$ are identical except (possibly) for the presence of a common factor N, so that

$$\frac{h'}{h} = \frac{k'}{k} = \frac{l'}{l} = N .$$

(1.6-10)

This can be proved with reference to Figure 1.11, which illustrates the (hkl) plane adjacent to the origin, which is chosen at a lattice point. Clearly, both vectors $\mathbf{A}$ and $\mathbf{B}$ lie in the (hkl) plane. Then,

$$\mathbf{r}^* \cdot \mathbf{B} = \mathbf{r}^* \cdot [(\mathbf{c}/l) - (\mathbf{a}/h)] = (h'\mathbf{a}^* + k'\mathbf{b}^* + l'\mathbf{c}^*) \cdot [(\mathbf{c}/l) - (\mathbf{a}/h)] = \frac{l'}{l} - \frac{h'}{h} = 0,$$

and

(1.6-11)

$$\mathbf{r}^* \cdot \mathbf{A} = \mathbf{r}^* \cdot [(\mathbf{b}/k) - (\mathbf{a}/h)] = (h'\mathbf{a}^* + k'\mathbf{b}^* + l'\mathbf{c}^*) \cdot [(\mathbf{b}/k) - (\mathbf{a}/h)] = \frac{k'}{k} - \frac{h'}{h} = 0.$$

The vector $\mathbf{r}^*$ is clearly perpendicular to two independent vectors, $\mathbf{A}$ and $\mathbf{B}$, which lie in the (hkl) plane. It must therefore be perpendicular to the plane itself. Moreover, if $\mathbf{n}$ is a unit vector perpendicular to the plane, we may write $\mathbf{n} = \mathbf{r}^*/r^*$, and the distance between adjacent (hkl) planes can be expressed, using (1.6-1), as

$$d_{hkl} = \frac{\mathbf{n} \cdot \mathbf{a}}{h} = \frac{\mathbf{a} \cdot \mathbf{r}^*}{hr^*} = \frac{\mathbf{a} \cdot (h'\mathbf{a}^* + k'\mathbf{b}^* + l'\mathbf{c}^*)}{hr^*} = \frac{N}{r^*} .$$

(1.6-12)

The magnitude of the vector $\mathbf{r}^*$ is now seen to be directly related to the reciprocal of the interplanar spacing in the direct lattice by

$$r^* = \frac{N}{d_{hkl}} ,$$

(1.6-13)

where N is the integer defined by (1.6-10).

1.7 INTERATOMIC FORCES IN CRYSTALS

We are now at the end of our survey of crystallography, and can profitably look more closely at the interatomic forces that hold crystals together and ensure the stability of condensed matter. These forces have already been mentioned, but only in a very cursory way. This discussion will be more detailed, though by no means exhaustive. Indeed, we shall return to this subject again and again to develop a deeper and more quantitative understanding of what is still an important and active research area in condensed-matter physics.

The first fundamental interparticle force we learn about in elementary physics is gravity, which is usually presented as a macroscopic force between relatively massive bodies, but is naturally present on the atomic level also. However, its effects on this level are generally negligible, for it is many orders of magnitude weaker than the electromagnetic forces which are of primary importance in holding crystals together. The simplest of these electromagnetic interactions is the electrostatic force between charged particles. The electrostatic force, as defined by Coulomb's law, is like gravity, an inverse square interaction, but may be either attractive or repulsive, depending on the signs of the charges. On the atomic level, however, the way in which this simple classical force acts is governed by the requirements of quantum theory and chemical valency, which is in itself a quantum effect. These requirements modify to a significant extent electrostatic interactions in the atomic realm.

Chemical valency is an aspect of atomic structure arising directly from the periodic table of the elements. The periodic table and the concept of valence were in everyday use long before quantum theory was developed, but the basic justification of these ideas rests upon fundamental principles of atomic physics which in turn follow directly from quantum mechanics. At this point we must rely heavily upon classical notions of chemical valence, but as we progress the connections with quantum mechanics will become increasingly evident.

Ionic crystals typically unite elements from column I and column VII of the periodic table. The most common substance of this type is sodium chloride, NaCl. In sodium atoms the outer valence electron is loosely bound, and the atom is easily ionized, while chlorine atoms have an extremely strong affinity for electrons that will complete their valence octet and transform them into negative ions. Such substances are ionized not only in aqueous solution, but also in their crystalline form. In the NaCl crystal illustrated in Figure 1.8, then, there are monovalent positive ions on Na sites and monovalent negative ions on Cl sites. Acting on any given ion, there are repulsive forces from other ions of like sign as well as attractive ones from oppositely charged ions. Since all the nearest neighbors to any given ion are of opposite sign, however, the resultant interaction is attractive, and the crystal is in fact bound together by these forces. As the electron distributions of neighboring atoms begin to overlap--that is as the atoms begin to touch one another--repulsive forces begin to develop and to oppose the effect of simple electrostatic attraction, until a final equilibrium is reached in which the ions are typically a few Ångströms apart. In NaCl, the equilibrium interatomic distance is about 2.8Å, i.e., 2.8×10^{-10}m. Ionic substances are usually transparent to visible light; moreover, they exhibit a strong peak in optical reflectivity at a well-defined frequency in the far infrared. They are usually poor electrical conductors at room temperature. They have relatively high melting points and low vapor pressures, and they often crystallize in the compact NaCl and CsCl structures.

In Column IV, in the center of the periodic table, we find the tetravalent elements carbon, silicon, germanium, and tin. These elements have little or no tendency to form ions, either in aqueous solution or in the crystalline state. Instead, they tend to share their valence electrons with one another, forming covalent electron-pair bonds between neighboring atoms. We have already mentioned these properties in our previous study of the diamond lattice, in which these elements tend to crystallize. Unlike ionic substances, there is no transfer of charge from one atom to another in covalent crystals; since electrons are shared equally, the atoms are electrically neutral. Quantum theory shows that electron-pair covalent bonds can be very strong and stable links between covalent atoms. Crystals of diamond, silicon, and germanium are therefore very hard and strong, though somewhat brittle. They are relatively stable substances with high melting points. They are typically transparent to infrared radiation, though opaque to ultraviolet and (with the obvious exception of diamond) visible light. The infrared reflectivity peak mentioned in connection with ionic crystals is no longer observed. Germanium, silicon, and diamond, as a direct result of their covalent bonding, are semiconductors. In the pure form they exhibit a limited electrical conductivity that increases with temperature, particularly at high temperatures, and is moreover strongly influenced by the addition of minute quantities of certain types of impurity atoms. The nearest-neighbor interatomic distance--the distance AB in Figure 1.7--is, for germanium 2.45Å, for silicon 2.35Å, and for diamond 1.54Å.

It thus appears that covalency is a way of life in the center of the periodic table, while ionic behavior is the norm at the edges. These two diametrically opposed scenarios, however, are not mutually exclusive. While I-VII compounds are highly ionic, and group IV elements are exclusively covalent, there is a *mixture* of ionic and covalent bonding in the intermediate II-VI and III-V compounds, the former being primarily ionic though somewhat covalent, the latter mostly covalent in character, though slightly ionic. In II-VI compounds, such as ZnS, electron transfer from zinc to sulfur atoms is not quite complete; though the valence electrons reside mostly on sulfur sites, there is a slight tendency for them to be shared with zinc atoms, and to be found on zinc sites. In III-V materials like GaAs, the substance is mostly covalent in character, with a strong network of electron-pair bonds in place to bind the atoms together. These compounds are semiconductors which crystallize in the zincblende structure, whose form is almost identical to that of the diamond lattice. The sharing of electrons between the two atomic species is not quite symmetrical, however, for there is a small net positive charge associated with gallium sites and a corresponding negative charge on arsenic atoms.

Metallic substances present a physical picture entirely different from ionic and covalent materials. In ionic and covalent crystals, electrons are mostly immobile, being either tightly bound to the ions or tied up in a network of covalent pair bonds. In metallic crystals, however, the valence electrons are no longer associated with any particular atomic site, but are free to move at large within the crystal. In effect, they form a free-particle gas for which the crystal serves as a container. The electronic properties of the crystal are then primarily those of the gas of mobile electrons within it. The crystal is held together by a net electrostatic attraction between the positively charged immobile lattice ions and the gas of negatively charged electrons; the net attractive interaction arises in somewhat the same way as in ionic materials, except that the negative charges are no longer regularly spaced, but are randomly distributed. Since the valence electrons are free to move in the direction of an applied electric field, metallic substances conduct electricity freely. They are also good conductors of heat, and display high optical surface reflectivity and strong optical absorption within the material; these properties are also directly related to the presence of the the free electron gas.

Still another type of crystal binding is found in crystals of solid organic substances, such as naphthalene or benzoic acid. In these molecular crystals, the lattice sites are occupied by complete molecules which are electrically neutral. Neutral molecules, however, may posess intrinsic electric dipole moments if their internal charge distribution is asymmetric. Moreover, even molecules which have no intrinsic or permanent electric dipole moment can exhibit fluctuating *instantaneous* dipole moments arising from momentary fluctuations of the electronic charge distribution within the molecule. These instantaneous dipole configurations can induce oppositely directed dipole moments in neighboring molecules, much as a point charge or dipole can induce an image charge or image dipole of opposite sign in a nearby conductor. The force between an inducing dipole and the induced dipole is attractive, and can therefore act to bind the crystal together, in spite of the fact that the time-average dipole moment of the molecules may be zero. Binding forces that arise in this manner are referred to as *Van der Waals forces*. Since these forces are between dipoles rather than charged particles, they are much weaker than the binding forces in ionic crystals. Molecular binding is therefore comparatively weak, resulting in crystals that have relatively low melting points. Inert gases like neon and argon in the solid state also form crystals bound by Van der Waals forces.

When the energy difference between two different possible structures is relatively small, and when a significant potential energy barrier must be overcome to transform one into the other, it may be possible for both forms to exist as stable configurations at the same temperature and pressure. This phenomenon is referred to as *allotropy*, and the two different configurations are called *allotropes*, or *allotropic forms*. In such instances, of course, one form will be thermodynamically stable, while the other is metastable--that is, theoretically unstable with respect to the other, but inhibited from making a transformation by the potential energy barrier which must be surmounted. Two of the most familiar examples are carbon and tin. In the case of carbon, the allotropic forms are graphite and diamond, the latter being metastable under normal conditions. In regard to tin, the two allotropes are referred to as gray tin and white tin--or, sometimes, α- and β-tin. At room temperatures, the familiar "white" metallic tin, which has a tetragonal lattice, is the thermodynamically stable form, but below 286.4K the gray form, which crystallizes in the diamond structure, becomes the stable allotrope. Gray tin is another group IV covalent semiconductor, with properties similar to silicon and germanium. In this regard it is as strikingly different from the metallic white form as diamond is from graphite.

There are also substances whose long-range order lacks the property of translational invariance and is instead based on a polyhedral ordering scheme. Such substances, referred to as *quasicrystals*, sometimes display fivefold rotational symmetry, which is geometrically impossible in translationally invariant space lattices.

In this discussion, and in the preceding material, it is apparent that crystal lattices--and atoms as well--are built on the scale of Ångström units. The table of crystal properties and cell sizes below should make this fact even more evident. It is also important to recognize that a connection between the macroscopic properties of crystalline substances and the microworld of the lattice is provided by Avogadro's number, $N_a = 6.022 \times 10^{23}$ mole^{-1}, which gives the number of molecules or atoms per gram-mole. This fact is useful in working many of the exercises that follow.

REFERENCES

J. S. Blakemore, *Solid State Physics* (2nd edition), Saunders, Philadelphia (1974).

C. A. Wert and R. M. Thomson, *Physics of Solids* (2nd edition), McGraw-Hill, New York (1970).

C. Kittel, *Introduction to Solid State Physics* (4th edition), Wiley, New York (1971).

H. J. Goldsmid (ed.), *Problems in Solid State Physics*, Pion Ltd., London (1968).

M. A. Omar, *Elementary Solid State Physics*, Addison-Wesley, Reading MA (1975).

W. L. Bragg, *The Crystalline State*, Vol. I, Bell & Sons, London (1955).

F. Seitz, *Modern Theory of Solids*, McGraw-Hill, New York (1940).

PHYSICAL DATA FOR SIMPLE CRYSTALLINE SOLIDS

Substance	Lattice	Cell edge, Å	Density, g/cm^3	M. P., K	B.P., K
IONIC					
NaCl	NaCl	5.64	2.17	1074	1686
KCl	NaCl	6.29	1.98	1049	subl.
NaBr	NaCl	5.95	3.20	1028	1663
KBr	NaCl	6.58	2.75	1003	1708
NaI	NaCl	6.46	3.67	924	1577
KI	NaCl	7.05	3.13	959	1603
CsCl	CsCl	4.11	3.99	919	1563
AgCl	NaCl	5.55	5.56	728	1823
AgBr	NaCl	5.77	6.47	705	dec.
COVALENT and III-V					
C(diam)	diamond	3.56	3.51	4300	5500
Si	d	5.42	2.328	1685	2628
Ge	d	5.62	5.323	1231	3103
α-Sn	d	6.46	5.76	503	2540
GaAs	zincblende	5.64	5.32	1510	dec.
GaP	z	5.45	4.13	1750	dec.
InSb	z	6.48	5.78	798	dec.
InP	z	5.87	4.79	1330	dec.
METALLIC					
Na	bcc	4.29	0.97	371	1156
K	bcc	5.20	0.86	337	1047
Cu	fcc	3.62	8.92	1356	2840
Ag	fcc	4.09	10.5	1235	2485
Au	fcc	4.08	19.3	1337	3080
Fe	bcc	2.87	7.86	1808	3023
Al	fcc	4.04	2.70	933	2740
Pb	fcc	4.95	11.34	601	2013
β-Sn	tetr	5.83, 3.18	7.28	508	2540
VAN DER WAALS					
Ar	fcc	5.43 (4K)	1.66 (4K)	84.0	87.5
Ne	fcc	4.52 (4K)	1.45 (4K)	24.5	27.2
Kr	fcc	5.59 (20K)	3.19 (20K)	116.6	120.9
Xe	fcc	6.20 (88K)	3.66 (88K)	161.3	166.1

PROBLEMS

1. The density of copper is 8.92 g/cm^3, and its molar mass is 63.54 g/mole. Using these data, and elementary principles of physics and chemistry, calculate the nearest-neighbor interatomic spacing between atoms in the f.c.c lattice of copper. Compare your answer with the value calculated from the data in the above table.

2. The molar mass of argon is 39.95 g/mole. Assuming that argon is an ideal gas at normal temperature and atmospheric pressure, calculate the density of argon at atmospheric pressure and temperature 300K. How many atoms per unit volume are there under these conditions, assuming a monatomic gas? What is the average distance between atoms under these conditions? Compare these answers with those obtained for crystalline copper in Problem 1.

3. From the data in the above table, calculate the interatomic spacing (distance AB in Figure 1.7) in crystalline silicon. How many atoms are there per unit volume (cm^{-3})?

4. A cubic crystal's cubic cell edge is 3.6Å. Write an expression for a lattice vector from an atom at the origin to one 2 cells away along the a-axis, 4 cells away along the b-axis, and 6 cells distant along the c-direction. What is the length of this vector, and what are the angles it makes with the three crystal axes?

5. Work problem 4 for a monoclinic lattice where the cell edges are $a = 2$Å, $b = 3.6$Å, $c = 2.4$Å, and where the angle between the a- and b-axes is 60°.

6. When substances which normally crystallize in the b.c.c. or diamond structures are subjected to very high hydrostatic pressure, a phase transition to an f.c.c. structure sometimes occurs. Can you suggest a qualitative physical explanation for this fact?

7. Using the three-dimensional lattices shown in Figure 1.3 as a starting point, show that in two dimensions, the number of possible Bravais lattices is reduced to 5. Show explicitly the geometry of these five lattices.

8. Crystal lattices having five-fold rotational symmetry--that is, which are translationally invariant under rotations of 360/5 or 72 degrees about some axis--do not occur in nature. Can you give a geometrical explanation for this observation?

9. Show that a face-centered tetragonal arrangement of atoms is the same as a body-centered tetragonal lattice like the one shown in Figure 1.3, in which the base of the unit cell is √2/2 times that of the face-centered cell. Why are the face-centered and body-centered *cubic* lattices different?

10. Considering the atoms to be hard spheres of equal radii in contact along the line between nearest neighbors, find the fraction of the volume of the unit cell occupied by the atoms for the s.c., b.c.c., f.c.c., and diamond lattices.

11. With respect to an atom at the origin, a crystal plane intersects an atom two atomic spacings away along the a-axis, an atom four atomic spacings away along the b-axis, and an atom five atomic spacings away along the c-axis of the crystal. Find the Miller indices of this plane.

12. In a simple tetragonal crystal, the unit cell dimensions are $a = b = 1.80$Å, $c = 2.40$Å. Find the spacing between adjacent (111) planes and adjacent (523) planes in this crystal.

13. For the crystal structure described in the preceding problem, find the distance between adjacent atoms along the [111] direction and along the [523] direction.

14. In a face-centered cubic crystal, the spacing between adjacent (221) planes is 1.20Å. The molar mass of the atoms is 60g/mole. What is the density of this substance in the crystalline state?

15. Prove that in a cubic crystal the [*hkl*] direction is orthogonal to the (*hkl*) plane.

16. In an orthogonal lattice, derive an expression for the angle between the [*hkl*] direction and the normal to the (*hkl*) plane.

17. Derive the intercept spacings given in Equation (1.5 - 3) for a three-dimensional orthogonal lattice. You may assume that there are no integer factors common to any pair of atom spacings or Miller indices.

18. Draw simple sketches illustrating the {100}, {110}, and {111} planes in a cubic unit cell.

19. How many equivalent {111} planes are there in a cubic lattice? How many equivalent {122} planes? How many equivalent {123} planes?

20. What would the answers to the preceding problem be for an orthorhombic lattice?

21. Obtain an expression for the number of atoms per unit area in an (*hkl*) plane, in terms of the lattice parameters and interplanar spacing.

22. Find the reciprocal lattice for a two-dimensional simple square lattice of interatomic spacing a. Observe that you cannot define vector cross products in two dimensions.

23. Find the reciprocal lattice for a two-dimensional hexagonal array like the one in the base plane of the hexagonal structure illustrated in Figure 1.3.

24. Show that the face-centered cubic lattice has a body-centered cubic reciprocal lattice, using methods similar to those employed in Section 1.6.

25. Find the potential energy of binding between a chlorine atom and its nearest neighbor sodium atoms in the sodium chloride crystal. Express your answer in units of electron-volts (eV) per atom. Recall that $1 \text{ eV} = 1.602 \times 10^{-19}$ joule.

26. Show, using classical electrostatics, that the potential energy of an induced Van der Waals molecular dipole in an external inducing dipole field is proportional to r^{-6}, where r is the separation between dipoles. *Hint*: Recall that the potential energy of a point dipole in an external field is given by the scalar product of the dipole moment and the local external field.

27. Compare the electrostatic and Newtonian gravitational forces (a) between two electrons (b) between an electron and a proton (c) between an electron and a singly charged uranium 238 ion.

CHAPTER 2

WAVES, DIFFRACTION, AND X-RAY ANALYSIS

2.1 INTRODUCTION

In classical physics, it is natural to make a sharp distinction between waves and particles. In mechanics, one usually begins by stating the laws of motion as they apply to mass particles, that is, to localized bodies of finite mass so small that they can be regarded as mathematical points having no size or structure. The mechanics of systems of such particles, including rigid bodies of macroscopic size, can then be developed in a rational and straightforward way. This description can also be extended to deformable bodies, and even to liquids and gases.

In electromagnetic theory, the starting point is usually a discussion of electrical forces between point charges, which are also particles in the sense of classical mechanics. In this case, however, it is found that their interactions ultimately lead to the radiation of energy as electromagnetic *waves*. In sharp contrast with particles, waves are not localized spatially, and though they possess momentum and energy, they have no mass save that associated relativistically with their energy. Unlike mechanical disturbances such as sound waves, which need a tangible propagating medium, electromagnetic waves can travel through empty space, and require no material medium for their propagation. Finally, quantum physics has led to the realization that matter itself has a wavelike character, and that elementary particles like electrons, though they may act as particles under certain conditions, must most generally be described by a theory in which they often behave like waves.

It is necessary, therefore, to understand some of the more important aspects of wave propagation, concerning not only electromagnetic waves and the "matter waves" of quantum physics, but also the acoustical waves that propagate vibrational energy through crystal lattices wherein the atoms oscillate about their equilibrium lattice sites. In contrast to the more exotic waves associated with electromagnetism and quantum physics, these waves can be understood in terms of ordinary Newtonian mechanics and linear elasticity theory. All of these wave phenomena play an important part in describing the physical behavior of solids, and it is therefore essential initially to review some basic facts about wave propagation, particularly in regard to interference, diffraction, and dispersion of sinusoidal waves. In this chapter, after revisiting these topics, we shall study Bragg reflection and X-ray diffraction. In subsequent chapters, we shall find a knowledge of wave propagation useful in studying acoustic waves in crystal lattice, in developing basic quantum theory, and in understanding the wavelike behavior of matter on the atomic scale.

2.2 FUNDAMENTALS OF WAVE PROPAGATION

A rigorous definition of wave motion is hard to formulate. For our purposes, however, we may regard waves as self-propagating periodic disturbances that transport energy and momentum with no net transport of matter. Waves need not be of sinusoidal form, though sinusoidal or *harmonic* waves are the simplest examples of wave phenomena. Fortunately, more complex periodic waveforms--square or sawtooth waves, for example--can ordinarily be written as a Fourier series of sinusoidal component waves, using standard Fourier analysis. We shall therefore restrict our attention primarily to sinusoidal waves. These waves usually appear as solutions of mechanical, electrodynamic, or quantum equations of motion in the form of linear partial differential equations. Such equations have the property that two or more solutions can be added together to produce a sum which also satisfies this same partial differential equation. This property is known as the principle of *superposition*, a term that is operationally synonymous with addition.

A wave equation is any partial differential equation that has solutions of the form

$$u(x,t) = A\sin(kx - \omega t) \qquad \text{or} \qquad u(x,t) = Ae^{i\varphi} = Ae^{i(kx-\omega t)} \quad . \qquad (2.2\text{-}1)$$

In this expression, u can be any physical parameter that can display wave properties, for example, the magnitude of the electric field of a light wave. Such a parameter is a function of the two variables x and t. In the above expression the wave propagates along the positive x-direction. The parameter k is referred to as the *propagation constant*, while ω is the angular frequency in rad/sec. The quantity φ, defined as

$$\varphi = kx - \omega t \qquad (2.2\text{-}2)$$

is an angular variable referred to as the *phase* or *phase angle* of the wave, which defines its periodicity. At any fixed time, if x increases by an amount λ, equal to a single wavelength, the phase angle must change by 2π. Therefore, $k\lambda = 2\pi$. Also, at any given position, when a time equal to the period T of a single oscillation elapses, the phase angle must also change by 2π, which requires that $\omega T = 2\pi$. It is thus apparent that

$$k = 2\pi / \lambda \qquad \text{and} \qquad T = 2\pi / \omega \quad . \qquad (2.2\text{-}3)$$

The angular frequency ω (rad/sec) is related to the linear frequency f (Hz) by $\omega = 2\pi f$.

At every point x the function $u(x, t)$ defines harmonic oscillations of angular frequency ω. If these oscillations are in the direction of propagation, the wave is said to be *longitudinal*, while if they are normal to the propagation direction, the wave is *transverse*. Sound waves in air are longitudinal in character, while electromagnetic waves are transverse. The angular orientation of the direction of oscillation in the plane normal to the propagation direction describes the *polarization* of a transverse wave. Longitudinal waves do not exhibit the phenomenon of polarization.

Elementary courses often leave the impression that there is a single wave equation that can represent any physically possible wave phenomenon. Actually, however, there are many different linear partial differential equations that have solutions of the form of propagating sinusoidal waves, each of which may define a wave motion with a distinctly different physical character. It is important to understand this fact, because we shall have to deal with several different kinds of "wave equations" in our later studies. The most common wave equation--the one seen most frequently in elementary physics texts--has the form

$$\frac{\partial^2 u}{\partial x^2} = K^2 \frac{\partial^2 u}{\partial t^2} \quad , \tag{2.2-4}$$

for a wave propagating along the x-direction. The quantity K^2 is a constant involving the physical parameters that describe the properties of the propagating medium or system. For a wave propagating along a string, for example, $K^2 = \rho / \tau$, where ρ is the linear density (kg/m) and τ the tension, while for an electromagnetic wave in free space, $K^2 = \varepsilon_0 \mu_0$, where ε_0 is the dielectric permittivity and μ_0 the magnetic permeability of free space. We shall see later how equations such as this are derived from fundamental physical principles.

The velocity of propagation can be visualized as the speed at which the crests and troughs of the wave advance. These points are points of constant phase, points where the phase angle has values such as $\pi/2$, $3\pi/2$, $5\pi/2$, etc., and they move as the wave advances with a velocity referred to as the wave's *phase velocity*. This velocity can be expressed in terms of ω and k by setting the phase angle given by (2.2 - 2) equal to a constant, to obtain what is in effect the equation of motion for a point of constant phase. Setting this phase angle equal to the constant φ_0 and solving for x, we obtain

$$x = \frac{\omega}{k}t + \frac{\varphi_0}{k} = v_p t + x_0 \quad . \tag{2.2-5}$$

This equation expresses motion with constant velocity, starting at point $x = x_0$. The phase velocity is clearly given by

$$v_p = \frac{\omega}{k} \quad . \tag{2.2-6}$$

With the aid of (2.2 - 3), this can also be written as $v_p = f\lambda$.

The existence of wave solutions for any given partial differential equation can be established simply by substituting a trial solution of the form $u = A\exp[i(kx - \omega t)]$ into the equation. If the equation is a valid wave equation, the resulting expression will be *independent* of the variables x and t, and will simply define a relationship between ω and k that must be satisfied if wave solutions are to exist. This relation is referred to as the *dispersion relation*. In the case of the wave equation (2.2 - 4), if we assume solutions of this form, we find by direct differentiation and substitution that

$$\frac{\partial^2 u}{\partial x^2} = -k^2 u \qquad \text{and} \qquad \frac{\partial^2 u}{\partial t^2} = -\omega^2 u \quad ,$$

giving

$$-k^2 u = -\omega^2 K^2 u \quad , \quad \text{or} \qquad \omega = \frac{k}{K} \quad . \qquad (2.2\text{-}7)$$

The dispersion relation in this case is a very simple one, which informs us that that ω and k are directly propotional to one another. Another way of interpreting this is to note that the phase velocity ω/k has the constant value $1/K$ *independent of frequency or wavelength*. This important physical fact emerges naturally from the dispersion relation, and demonstrates the point that the dispersion relation conveys vital information about how waves propagate. It is important to note also that this simple dispersion relation arises from the equally simple form of the wave equation (2.2 - 4). Wave equations having a more complex form will generally have more complicated dispersion relations, in which the phase velocity is no longer constant, but will depend upon ω or k. Under these circumstances the phase velocity is a function of frequency or wavelength. We shall soon encounter several examples of waves of this type. Electromagnetic waves in free space, however, obey wave equations of the form (2.2 - 4), in which K^2 has the value $\varepsilon_0 \mu_0$, giving a phase velocity

$$v_p = c = \frac{1}{\sqrt{\varepsilon_0 \mu_0}} \quad . \qquad (2.2\text{-}8)$$

The fact that the sum of two solutions of a linear wave equation like (2.2 - 4) is itself a solution has already been mentioned. The importance of this fact can hardly be overstated, since it is the basis of the entire theory of interference and diffraction. The reader should now be able to verify by direct substitution that an arbitrary sum of wave solutions of the form (2.2 - 1), each of arbitrary frequency and wavelength, satisfies (2.2 - 4), provided that all of them satisfy the dispersion relation.

We shall soon find that it is sometimes necessary to work with waves that propagate not along one of the coördinate axes, but along an arbitrary direction in space. Under these circumstances, the wave amplitude will be a function of all three space coördinates as well as time. A propagating wave may now be written as an expression similar to (2.2 - 1) having the form

$$u(x, y, z, t) = A e^{ik_x x} e^{ik_y y} e^{ik_z z} e^{-i\omega t} = A e^{i\varphi} \quad . \qquad (2.2\text{-}9)$$

In this expression, the three parameters k_x, k_y, and k_z replace the single parameter k that appears in (2.2 - 1). If any two of the space variables are held constant, while the third is allowed to vary, the phase angle φ in the above equation will vary linearly with distance along the coördinate direction corresponding to the third variable at a rate determined by the k-parameter associated with this variable. The wave amplitude given by (2.2 - 8) therefore varies sinusoidally along each coördinate direction with a wavelength--measured along that coördinate direction--determined by its related k-parameter.

Suppose that the wave described by the above equations is observed at some particular instant of time. Under these circumstances, you can describe a set of surfaces on which all points have the same phase by setting φ, as well as t, constant in (2.2 - 9). These surfaces are by definition *wavefronts*. In this case the equation of the wavefronts is, at the given time t,

$$k_x x + k_y y + k_z z - \omega t = \varphi = const. \tag{2.2-10}$$

Since this is the equation of a set of planes, the wavefronts are planar, and (2.2 - 8) describes what are usually designated as *plane waves*. Along any direction lying in the plane wavefronts the phase is invariant, but along any other direction, the phase will vary sinusoidally with distance, according to (2.2 - 8). This sinusoidal variation will be most rapid in a direction *normal* to the surfaces of constant phase, i.e., the wavefronts. This property defines the *direction of propagation*. A vector normal to the wavefronts, whose equation as given by (2.2 - 9) has the form $f(x, y, z) = $ constant, can be written as the gradient of the function on the left side of the above equation, which is also the gradient of the phase angle φ. This vector is of the form

$$\mathbf{k} = \nabla\varphi = \mathbf{i}_x k_x + \mathbf{i}_y k_y + \mathbf{i}_z k_z \quad . \tag{2.2-11}$$

The vector $\mathbf{k}$, as defined by the gradient of the phase angle, is referred to as the *propagation vector* of the wave. According to the two above equations, and the properties of the gradient, its direction is that in which the phase advances most rapidly as a function of distance, and its magnitude is the rate of change of the phase angle along this direction. These characteristics determine what we perceive to be the direction along which the wave "travels".

It is now apparent that the quantities k_x, k_y, and k_z are simply the components of the propagation vector along the coördinate axes, and that the magnitude of this vector can be written in terms of these quantities as

$$k^2 = k_x^2 + k_y^2 + k_z^2 \quad . \tag{2.2-12}$$

Moreover, since the rate of advance of the phase angle with distance s along the direction of the vector $\mathbf{k}$ can be written as $d\varphi = k\, ds$, and since φ changes by 2π as s advances a distance equal to the wavelength λ, , it is clear that

$$k = \frac{2\pi}{\lambda} \quad . \tag{2.2-13}$$

Also, since the quantity $k_x x + k_y y + k_z z$ on the left side of (2.2 - 10) can be identified as the scalar product of the vector $\mathbf{k}$ with a position vector $\mathbf{r}$ (components x, y, z) which locates an arbitrary point having these coördinates, we can write (2.2 - 9) in a simpler form that we shall find quite useful:

$$u(\mathbf{r}, t) = A e^{i(\mathbf{k}\cdot\mathbf{r} - \omega t)} = A e^{i\varphi} \quad . \tag{2.2-14}$$

It is important to observe that the frequency is always regarded as an inherently real and *positive* quantity. The propagation constant k in (2.2 - 1), however, can be negative, or even complex. When k is negative, the propagation direction is reversed, and a wave of the form (2.2 - 1), for example, will travel along the $-x$ direction. Similarly, replacing the vector **k** with **-k** reverses the signs of all the components of the propagation vector, which likewise reverses the direction of propagation. When k is complex, the wave is exponentially attenuated, the imaginary part of k playing the role of an exponential attenuation factor.

The solutions (2.2 - 9) or (2.2 - 14) can be shown by direct substitution to satisfy the partial differential equation

$$\nabla^2 u = \frac{\partial^2 u}{\partial x^2} + \frac{\partial^2 u}{\partial y^2} + \frac{\partial^2 u}{\partial z^2} = K^2 \frac{\partial^2 u}{\partial t^2} \quad , \tag{2.2-15}$$

where K^2 is a constant, provided that the dispersion relation

$$\omega = \frac{1}{K}\sqrt{k_x^2 + k_y^2 + k_z^2} = \frac{k}{K} \tag{2.2-16}$$

is satisfied. The mathematical work is exactly analogous to that illustrated in connection with (2.2 - 6). The wave described by (2.2 - 9) differs from the one described by (2.2 - 1), which propagates along the x-direction, only by the choice of a different coördinate system. Since this can have no effect on the phase velocity, the expression ω/k still gives the phase velocity correctly. From (2.2 - 16) it is therefore evident that the phase velocity is $1/K$, as in the earlier case. It is equally apparent from the above equation that the dispersion relation is also the same in both cases.

2.3 INTERFERENCE AND DIFFRACTION PHENOMENA

Classical particles cannot overlap; two mass particles cannot be in the same place at the same time. With waves, however, the situation is quite different. When two waves encounter one another, they can combine and interact with one another. Such interactions can also occur when waves encounter physical barriers that partially obstruct propagation. These wave interactions are referred to as interference and diffraction. *Interference* refers primarily to effects associated with encounters between two or more independently propagating waves, while diffraction phenomena occur when waves impinge on physical obstacles to their propagation. Mathematically, similar methods are used to describe these two classes of phenomena, and the fine distinction between the terms *interference* and *diffraction* mentioned above is not always strictly observed.

In the simplest cases, the different interacting wave amplitudes are solutions of a linear partial differential equation, which according to the superposition property discussed in the preceding section, can merely added at every point (with due concern for phase differences) to give the total amplitude. We shall be concerned almost exclusively with waves of this type.

The interference of light waves was first observed by Thomas Young in 1801. In Young's experiment, plane monochromatic wavefronts are incident on two very narrow slits in an otherwise opaque screen, as illustrated in Figure 2.1. The slits are parallel, of essentially equal width, and separated by a known distance a, which is assumed to be much larger than the slit width, though it may be quite small on a macroscopic scale. In this arrangement, the slits are in effect separate sources of light which have a fixed phase relationship with one another. Waves of wavelength λ originate at each of the slits and impinge on a screen at a distance L from the sources. The distance L is assumed to be much larger than the distance a between the slits. At point P on the screen, the path lengths between the two sources and the observation point differ by an amount $a\sin\theta$, as illustrated below. If this path difference is zero or an integral number of wavelengths, the two separate waves arriving at P will add up constructively, "in phase", so to speak. Under these circumstances a maximum light intensity will be observed at the observation point. However, when the path difference is $1/2, 3/2, 5/2, 7/2$... times the wavelength λ, the two contributions are out of phase by $180°$ (or an equivalent angle), and the two amplitudes will add to zero. At these points, which are interspersed between the intensity maxima, the screen will be totally dark. One observes, therefore, a series of *interference fringes* on the screen, whose spacing is almost uniform for small angles, and whose appearance is illustrated in Figure 2.2. Mathematically, the condition for an intensity maximum is

$$n\lambda = a\sin\theta \qquad\qquad (n = 0, 1, 2, 3,...) \qquad , \qquad\qquad (2.3\text{-}1)$$

while for a minimum,

$$(n+\tfrac{1}{2})\lambda = a\sin\theta \qquad\qquad (n = 0, 1, 2, 3,...) \qquad . \qquad\qquad (2.3\text{-}2)$$

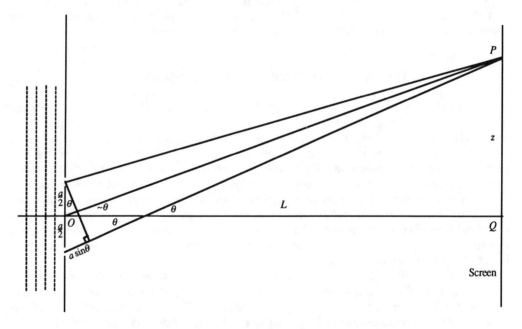

Figure 2.1 Interference of light waves emerging from two narrow slits separated by a distance a The distance from the lower slit to point P is greater than that from the upper slit to P by $a\sin\theta$.

Assuming that a and λ are given, equations (2.3 - 1) and (2.3 - 2) define values of the angle θ for each value of the integer n . The direction of the intensity maxima and minima observed on the screen with reference to the normal OQ are defined by angle POQ in the diagram. It is evident from the figure that this angle is not exactly the same as θ, but when the distance L is much larger than the distance a between the two slits, the two angles are very nearly equal, and their difference can be neglected. Thus, the above equations can be regarded as giving values of angle POQ. The distances z between the interference maxima and minima and the axis OQ are easily calculated from the relation

$$z = L \tan POQ \cong L \tan \theta \quad . \tag{2.3-3}$$

Figure 2.2 Double-slit interference fringes (Computer simulation).

The angular separation of interference fringes observed in Young's experiment is ordinarily very small, because of the short wavelength of visible light and the difficulty of preparing very narrow and very closely spaced slits. For He-Ne laser light of wavelength 6328Å, and slits for which $a = 0.20$mm, the slit separation is several hundred wavelengths. This means that for relatively small values of n, the values of $\sin\theta$ given by the above equations are small, and the approximation

$$\sin \theta = \tan \theta = \theta \tag{2.3-4}$$

will be valid. The angular spacing between adjacent maxima or minima ($\Delta n = 1$) given by (2.3 - 1) or (2.3 - 2) is then $\lambda/a = 0.00316$ rad, or 0.181°. On a screen 1.0m from the slits, the linear spacing between fringes would be 3.16mm. Moreover, the angular separation of the fringes depends *inversely* on the distance between the slits. In order for any observable pattern to be seen, therefore, the ratio λ/a cannot be too small. This is why Young's experiment in precisely the form described above is not easy to perform. Interference effects such as these can be observed between coherent monochromatic sources of radio waves, microwaves, X-rays, and sound waves. Electrons and other "particles" can display similar interference effects under certain conditions. Indeed, the existence of such phenomena is compelling evidence of the need for a wavelike description of elementary particles.

Suppose now that one of the two slits in Young's experiment is blocked, so that light waves can pass through only a single slit. Superficially, one might think that all the interference fringes would vanish, leaving only an evenly illuminated screen. What is observed, however, is a series of dark and light bands, much more widely spaced than the interference fringes in Young's experiment. The intensity of the illuminated regions also falls off sharply on either side of the relatively bright (and wide) central intensity maximum. The appearance of the pattern, shown in Figure 2.3, is quite different from the interference pattern of Figure 2.2.

Figure 2.3 Single-s;it diffraction pattern (Computer simulation).

The features observed in this pattern can be understood as arising from inter-ference of light passing through *different parts* of a single slit, rather than from two separate sources. In this situation, incident waves experience a single aperture that partially obstructs their progress--an example normally classified as diffraction rather than interference, even though interference is called upon for its interpretation. The appropriate geometry is now as illustrated in Figure 2.4. In Young's interference experiment it is assumed that the two slits are of equal width, and that their spacing *a*

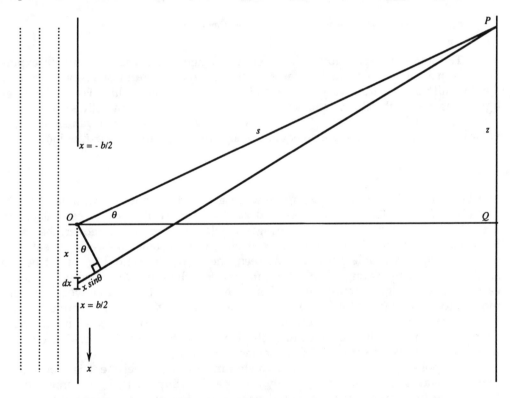

Figure 2.4 Geometry of single-slit diffraction experiment.

is much larger than the slit width. As long as these conditions are satisfied, the slit width itself is immaterial, and does not even appear in the previous equations.

In the single slit case shown directly above, however, the slit width *b* has now become very important. In this situation, it is necessary to calculate the wave amplitude at a given observation point P due to light entering a small element of the slit of width dx, and to integrate this quantity over the entire width of the source slit. If s is the distance between the center of the slit and the observation point, the differential wave amplitude du from light entering the element of width dx at a distance x from the center of the slit will be

$$du = A\sin(ks - kx\sin\theta - \omega t)dx \quad . \tag{2.3-5}$$

This expression must now be integrated over the entire slit, from $x = -b/2$ to $x = b/2$. In setting up the integral, it is advantageous to express the phase angle shown above as the sum of two angles, one depending on the variable of integration x, the other independent of that variable. In this way, the required integral can be written as

$$u = A\sin(ks - \omega t)\int_{-b/2}^{b/2}\cos(kx\sin\theta)dx + A\cos(ks - \omega t)\int_{-b/2}^{b/2}\sin(kx\sin\theta)dx \ . \tag{2.3-6}$$

In this expression, the second integral involves the integration of an odd function of x over an interval centered on the origin, which yields zero. The other integral is easily evaluated, giving

$$u = Ab\sin(ks - \omega t)\frac{\sin(\tfrac{1}{2}kb\sin\theta)}{\tfrac{1}{2}kb\sin\theta} \ . \tag{2.3-7}$$

The intensity of a wave, defined as incident energy per unit area per unit time, is proportional to the *square* of its amplitude, time-averaged over an integral number of periods. Therefore, the intensity of light striking the screen can be expressed as

$$I = I_0\frac{\sin^2(\tfrac{1}{2}kb\sin\theta)}{(\tfrac{1}{2}kb\sin\theta)^2} \ , \tag{2.3-8}$$

where I_0 is a constant incorporating the quantity Ab in (2.3 - 7) and the time-average of the square of $\sin(ks - \omega\tau)$.

Since in the limit $x \to 0$, $\sin x / x \to 1$, there is a bright central maximum at point Q on the screen. Elsewhere. the diffracted intensity is given by the above expression. Again, there will be points where the intensity is zero, separated by brighter regions, whose maximum intensity in this case falls off rapidly with increasing θ due to the factor in the denominator of (2.3 - 8). The intensity minima are associated with values of θ that cause the sine function in the numerator of this expression to vanish. This will happen when

$$\tfrac{1}{2}kb\sin\theta = \pi b\sin\theta / \lambda = n\pi \ ,$$

or, $n\lambda = b\sin\theta$ $(n = 1,2,3,...)$ $\tag{2.3-9}$

This looks like (2.3 - 1), which expresses the interference criterion for Young's two-slit interference experiment. Note, however, that the above equation is for diffraction intensity minima, while (2.3 - 1) locates interference maxima. Also, of course, the above equation contains the slit width b, which is much smaller than the distance a which separates the two slits in Young's experiment. This means that the angular separation between successive minima in the single-slit diffraction pattern is much larger than the separation of interference maxima or minima in the two-slit pattern. So, although there are similarities between the two patterns, there are also significant differences, as illustrated by Figures 2.2 and 2.3. These differences are also present in similar situations involving the diffraction and interference of electrons, as we shall see later.

2.4 X-RAY DIFFRACTION AND THE BRAGG EQUATION

One of the principal ways of determining the lattice structure of crystalline substances is through the analysis of X-ray diffraction patterns. Structural and other information about crystals can also be inferred from similar patterns obtained from the diffraction of electron beams. Moreover, the behavior of atomic electrons within metals, insulators, and semiconductors is strongly influenced by the *internal* diffraction of these electrons within the substance itself. It is therefore important for many reasons to study the physics of these diffraction processes. We shall concentrate initially on the diffraction of X-rays, though our findings will be applicable to other diffraction phenomena as well.

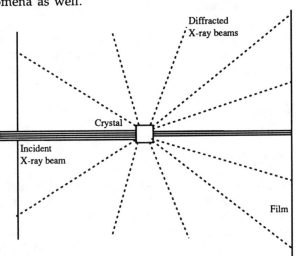

Figure 2.5 Von Laue's experiment for observing the diffraction of X-rays by crystals.

X-rays were discovered by Wilhelm Röntgen in 1895. They are electromagnetic waves much like visible light except that they have much shorter wavelength and much higher photon energies. They are usually produced in a high-vacuum electron tube wherein electrons are thermionically emitted from a filament cathode, and accelerated toward a metallic anode by a potential difference of 10 kilovolts or more. Such electrons have enough kinetic energy to remove inner-shell electrons from the atoms of the anode. When electrons return to the empty inner-shell atomic energy levels the energy they lose is emitted as a quantum of electromagnetic energy in the X-ray region of the spectrum.

According to quantum therory, the energy of a quantum of electromagnetic radiation is related to its wavelength by Planck's relation,

$$E = hf = hc / \lambda \ , \qquad (2.4\text{-}1)$$

where E is the energy and h is Planck's constant, whose value is 6.626×10^{-34} joule-sec. An electron accelerated by a potential difference V_0 acquires energy eV_0 where e is the electronic charge, equal to 1.602×10^{-19} coul. Such an electron, in an X-ray tube across which a 10 kilovolt accelerating voltage exists, can according to (2.4 - 1) excite the emission of an X-ray quantum of wavelength as short as

$$\lambda = \frac{hc}{eV_0} = \frac{(6.626 \times 10^{-34})(2.998 \times 10^{8})}{(1.602 \times 10^{-19})(1.0 \times 10^{4})} = 1.24 \times 10^{-10} \text{m. , or } 1.24 \text{Å} \ . \qquad (2.4\text{-}2)$$

These X-ray quanta have enough energy to remove electrons from the atoms, and to excite them out of the crystal, into the surrounding vacuum. This process, called the photoelectric effect, will be discussed in more detail in a later chapter. It occurs only when the entire quantum energy is taken up by a single atom. More frequently, X-rays interact with the crystal as a whole, by electromagnetic processes somewhat similar to those which govern the reflection and refraction of visible light.

In sharp contrast to visible light, whose wavelengths are thousands of times greater than the interatomic distances in crystal lattices, however, X-rays have wavelengths as small as, or even smaller than the nearest-neighbor distances in crystals. This strongly influences the way in which they interact with the substance, and as a result, there are significant differences in the behavior of X-rays and visible light in crystals, even though both are electromagnetic waves of otherwise similar character.

The wavelength defines the scale of the physical effects that occur when light or other electromagnetic energy encounters matter. A cubic volume whose side is of the order of the wavelength of visible light contains billions of atoms. Its interaction with matter under these conditions can be understood in terms of a model in which the substance is viewed as a homogeneous dielectric medium with an appropriate dielectric constant. In this model, Maxwell's equations lead to the ordinary laws of refraction and reflection, in which the refractive index is directly related to the dielectric constant. The phase velocity of the refracted wave is found to be c/n, where c is the free-space speed of light and n the index of refraction. Physically, these effects arise from the fact that the ordinary electrostatic boundary conditions on the fields at the surfaces of the dielectric medium must be satisfied at all times.

In the case of X-rays, a cubic volume of the size of the wavelength contains at most a few atoms. Under these circumstances, the physical picture applicable to longer wavelength radiation is obviously no longer valid. Instead, we must adopt a model in which X-rays are scattered in all directions by *each atom* of the substance. In this model, the crystal cannot be treated as a continuous dielectric medium. Radiation penetrates the crystal with no significant reduction in phase velocity, and there is no clearly defined specular reflection from the surface. The classical refractive index is now very close to unity, and the incoming radiation is merely scattered in all directions by every atom of the crystal. In an arbitrarily chosen direction, the scattering contributions from different atoms will usually add up with different phases, the resultant intensity in such a direction being *zero*. However, there are certain directions in which atomic scattering contributions from every atom in the crystal are in phase. In these directions there will be an intense scattered beam--a diffracted beam, actually, since the crystal acts much like a diffraction grating under these circumstances. As a result, a pattern of sharp, discrete diffraction maxima is obtained using the experimental scheme illustrated in Figure 2.5. This experiment was conceived by Max von Laue in 1912.

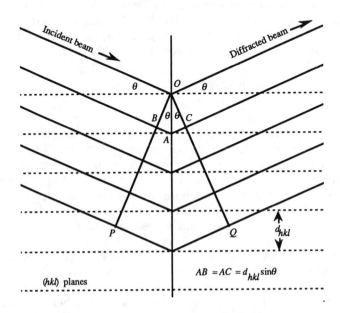

Figure 2.6 Schematic diagram illustrating Bragg picture of X-ray diffraction in crystalline materials.

These results were interpreted by W. L. Bragg in 1912 as in-phase specular reflections from all possible (hkl) crystal planes in the lattice. This interpretation in terms of *Bragg reflection* is illustrated in Figure 2.6, in which incoming beams are assumed to be reflected by the familiar law of optical reflection from a certain set of lattice planes. If the incoming beams make an angle θ with the planes, as illustrated, the outgoing beams reflected from adjacent planes will be in phase whenever the path difference $AB + AC$ equals an integral number of wavelengths. Under these conditions, the individual scattered beams will contribute to outgoing plane wavefronts like OQ, all of whose elements are in phase. Since $AB = AC = d_{hkl}\sin\theta$, the condition for constructive interference of all these outgoing beams is given by the *Bragg relation*

$$N\lambda = 2d_{hkl}\sin\theta \ , \tag{2.4-3}$$

where N is a positive integer. To understand what this equation implies, note that in general λ and d_{hkl} are fixed by experimental realities, and that the minimum value of N is unity. Also, observe that $\sin\theta$ can never be larger than unity. If the Bragg relation is viewed as predicting a number of values of θ for which diffraction is possible, it is evident that when $N\lambda/2d_{hkl} > 1$, no diffracted beams will be observed. Therefore, if the wavelength is too large, Bragg reflection can never occur. This is in agreement with the previously discussed idea that the wavelength of incoming radiation must be small if effects other than those associated with normal optical reflection/refraction phenomena are to be present. Also, when Bragg reflection is possible, the smaller the wavelength, the more orders of diffraction (as defined by possible integer values of N) will be observed. Finally, to obtain diffraction from closely spaced planes having high Miller indices, it is necessary to employ smaller X-ray wavelengths than would be needed for planes such as (100), (110), or (111).

As an example, consider the case of (111) planes in a crystal of aluminum exposed to monochromatic Cu(Kα) radiation of wavelength 1.540Å. Al has an fcc structure with cube edge $a = 4.04$Å. The spacing between adjacent (111) planes is one-third of the cube diagonal, or 2.335Å. According to the Bragg equation, possible diffraction angles are given by

$$\sin\theta = \frac{N\lambda}{2d_{111}} = \frac{N(1.540)}{(2)(2.335)} = \frac{1.540N}{4.67} = 0.3298 \qquad (N = 1)$$

$$= 0.6595 \qquad (N = 2)$$

$$= 0.9892 \qquad (N = 3) \ .$$

For $N = 4$, $\sin\theta$ exceeds unity and there can therefore be no diffraction for $N > 3$. So there will be three observable diffracted beams, at angles $\theta = 19.3°$, $41.3°$, and $81.6°$, corresponding to the inverse sines of the numbers shown above. For families of planes much closer together than those considered in this example, there may be no observable Bragg reflections; in such cases, the calculated value of $\sin\theta$ would exceed unity even for $N = 1$. X-rays of shorter wavelength must then be used. If tungsten radiation W(Kα) for which $\lambda = 0.2090$Å is substituted in the above calculations, it can be shown that no less than 22 diffracted beams will be emitted from (111) planes of Al, and that planes spaced as closely as $d = \lambda/2 = 0.1045$Å can be probed.

The Bragg picture of X-ray diffraction has the advantage of simplicity, and offers considerable insight into the geometry of the diffraction process. It therefore provides a good starting point for discussing this phenomenon. On the other hand, it introduces the picture of specular reflection from crystal planes as an *ad hoc* assumption with little or no physical justification, and provides no foundation for carrying out more detailed investigations of the diffraction process. These problems can be resolved by undertaking a more detailed analysis based only on the assumption that every atom in the crystal scatters incident X-radiation in all directions, and that the scattering from every atom has the same intensity and angular radiation pattern. The geometry related to this calculation is shown in Figure 2.7.

In Figure 2.7(a), radiation is incident from the left along the direction of the incoming unit vector n_i. The radiation is scattered from two points located at O and P, whose separation is defined by a vector r, and the outgoing scattered radiation along some arbitrary direction defined by an outgoing unit vector n_f is considered. These unit vectors are in the same directions as the initial and final propagation vectors k_i and k_f. The incoming radiation is viewed as a parallel beam having plane wavefronts such as OB. The outgoing radiation is regarded as a similar beam, with wavefronts such as PQ. The path difference between radiation scattered at P and at O

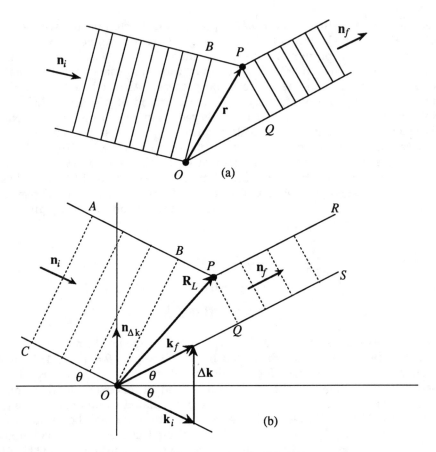

Figure 2.7 Geometry of X-ray scattering from two points O and P within a crystal.

is clearly OQ minus BP. The corresponding phase difference $\Delta\varphi$ is simply $2\pi/\lambda$ times the path difference; it can be expressed in terms of the incoming and outgoing unit vectors $\mathbf{n}_i$ and $\mathbf{n}_f$ as

$$\Delta\varphi = \frac{2\pi}{\lambda}(OQ - BP) = \frac{2\pi}{\lambda}(\mathbf{r}\cdot\mathbf{n}_f - \mathbf{r}\cdot\mathbf{n}_i) = \frac{2\pi}{\lambda}\mathbf{r}\cdot(\mathbf{n}_f - \mathbf{n}_i) \quad . \qquad (2.4\text{-}4)$$

This relationship is one that we shall find useful in solving several different problems. In the present context, incoming X-rays are scattered from two similar atoms located at the points O and P. The incoming and scattered beams are parallel monochromatic X-ray beams, whose initial and final propagation vectors are labeled $\mathbf{k}_i$ and $\mathbf{k}_f$ in the more detailed drawing shown in Figure 2.7(b). These vectors are, of course, parallel to the unit vectors $\mathbf{n}_i$ and $\mathbf{n}_f$. It is assumed that the scattering process does not bring about any change in wavelength. This means that the propagation vectors $\mathbf{k}_i$ and $\mathbf{k}_f$ have the same magnitude, which we may simply write as k. Physically, this amounts to assuming that the energy $hf = hc/\lambda$ of the X-ray photons is conserved in the scattering process. In this discussion the two outgoing beams are scattered by two atoms of the crystal. The vector OP connecting the two atoms must therefore be a lattice vector of the form (1.3 - 2). The axes in Figure 2.7(b) are oriented so as to depict the case of Bragg scattering, but this is only for simplicity, and does not influence the final result in any way. Incoming and outgoing plane wavefronts are shown as dotted lines; it is clear from the diagram that the path difference between radiation scattered at P along PR, and from O along OS is OQ minus BP. The phase difference $\Delta\varphi$ can therefore be written, as in the above equation,

$$\Delta\varphi = \frac{2\pi}{\lambda}(OQ - BP) = \frac{2\pi}{\lambda}\mathbf{R}_L \cdot \frac{\mathbf{k}_f - \mathbf{k}_i}{k} \quad . \tag{2.4-5}$$

In this expression, $\mathbf{R}_L$ is the lattice vector OP, while the incoming and outgoing unit vectors have been expressed as the respective $\mathbf{k}$-vectors divided by their own common magnitude $k = 2\pi/\lambda$. The radiation scattered from the two atoms in the direction shown will be in phase only if

$$\Delta\varphi = \mathbf{R}_L \cdot \Delta\mathbf{k} = 2\pi J \quad , \tag{2.4-6}$$

where $\Delta\mathbf{k} = \mathbf{k}_f - \mathbf{k}_i$, and J is an integer. If we now let

$$\mathbf{n}_{\Delta\mathbf{k}} = \frac{\Delta\mathbf{k}}{|\Delta\mathbf{k}|} \quad , \tag{2.4-7}$$

and observe from the diagram that

$$|\Delta\mathbf{k}| = 2k_i\sin\theta = \frac{4\pi\sin\theta}{\lambda} \quad , \tag{2.4-8}$$

we can write

$$\Delta\varphi = \frac{4\pi\sin\theta}{\lambda}\mathbf{R}_L \cdot \mathbf{n}_{\Delta\mathbf{k}} = 2\pi J \quad . \tag{2.4-9}$$

This is the condition for constructive interference of radiation scattered at angle θ from any two atoms in the crystal. In order that a diffraction maximum be observed, *radiation scattered by every atom in the crystal must interfere constructively*. If this condition is satisfied for $\mathbf{R}_L = \mathbf{a}$, $\mathbf{b}$, and $\mathbf{c}$, the unit cell basis vectors, then it will be satisfied for any linear combination $n_a\mathbf{a} + n_b\mathbf{b} + n_c\mathbf{c}$, thus for all possible lattice vectors $\mathbf{R}_L$. This statement assumes, of course, that all atoms in the crystal are on the lattice sites; the case where atoms are at other positions within the unit cell will be treated separately by a simple extension of this analysis. If (2.4 - 9) is not satisfied for any one of the choices $\mathbf{R}_L = \mathbf{a}, \mathbf{b}, \mathbf{c}$, the outgoing radiation scattered by different sets of atoms will not all have the same phase and the resultant amplitudes will add to zero when summed over all the atoms in a macroscopic crystal. Setting $\mathbf{R}_L$ in turn equal to $\mathbf{a}, \mathbf{b}$, and $\mathbf{c}$, one can therefore write a set of equations sometimes referred to as the *Laue equations*, which have the form

$$\left(\frac{2\sin\theta}{\lambda}\right)a\cos\alpha = h'$$

$$\left(\frac{2\sin\theta}{\lambda}\right)b\cos\beta = k' \tag{2.4-10}$$

$$\left(\frac{2\sin\theta}{\lambda}\right)c\cos\gamma = l' \quad ,$$

where h', k', l' are integers and α, β, γ are the angles between $\mathbf{n}_{\Delta k}$ and the **a-. b-,** and **c-** crystal axes.

Now consider the sets of crystal planes within the lattice. There are infinitely many such sets, and it is therefore reasonable to suppose that one of them is normal to the vector $\mathbf{n}_{\Delta k}$. If the Miller indices of this set are (hkl), then, from (1.5 - 4), it is clear that

$$\cos\alpha = hd_{hkl}/a, \qquad \cos\beta = kd_{hkl}/b, \qquad \cos\gamma = ld_{hkl}/c \quad . \tag{2.4-11}$$

Equations (2.4 - 10) and (2.4 - 11) can be combined to give

$$\frac{h'}{h} = \frac{k'}{k} = \frac{l'}{l} = \frac{2d_{hkl}\sin\theta}{\lambda} \quad . \tag{2.4-12}$$

From this, it is apparent that h', k', l' and h, k, l are identical except for some common factor. All these quantities, it will be noted, are integers; moreover, the Miller indices h, k, l have by definition no integer factor in common. Under these conditions, the only way integer triads of the form h', k', l' can be generated from the numbers h, k, l is by multiplying the latter triad by some integer factor N. This allows us, after eliminating direction cosines between equations (1.5 - 4) and (2.4 - 10), to write

$$\frac{h'}{h} = \frac{k'}{k} = \frac{l'}{l} = N = \frac{2d_{hkl}\sin\theta}{\lambda} \quad , \tag{2.4-13}$$

from which the Bragg relation follows immediately. Also, it is now evident that the vector Δk is normal to the (hkl) planes, and that the angle θ is the complement of the angle between this normal and the incoming and outgoing radiation. The Bragg picture of scattering is therefore verified.

Finally, from the relationships developed in Section 1.6, we know that the lattice vector $\mathbf{r}^*(h', k', l')$ of the reciprocal lattice is normal to the (hkl) plane of the direct lattice, and that its magnitude is $r^* = N/d_{hkl}$. We may now identify $\Delta k/2\pi$ as exactly this vector, since. (2.4 - 7), (2.4 - 8), and the Bragg relation allow us to write

$$\Delta\mathbf{k} = \mathbf{k}_f - \mathbf{k}_i = \frac{4\pi\sin\theta}{\lambda}\,\mathbf{n}_{\Delta k} = \frac{2\pi N}{d_{hkl}}\,\mathbf{n}_{\Delta k} = 2\pi\,\mathbf{r}^* \quad . \tag{2.4-14}$$

This can be more simply expressed as

$$\mathbf{k}_f = \mathbf{k}_i + \mathbf{G}^* \quad , \tag{2.4-15}$$

where $G^*(h', k', l')$ is any lattice vector of the *reciprocal* lattice multiplied by 2π. Equating the magnitudes of the vectors on both sides of this equation, and recalling that $k_f = k_i = k$, we find

$$2\mathbf{k}_i \cdot \mathbf{G}^* + G^{*2} = 0 \ . \tag{2.4-16}$$

Equations (2.4 - 15) and (2.4 - 16) can be regarded as vector forms of the Bragg relation, connecting experimentally determined diffracted beams defined by $\mathbf{k}_i$ and $\mathbf{k}_f$ with lattice vectors of the reciprocal lattice. It is true that the lattice so determined is the reciprocal lattice rather than the direct crystal lattice, but as shown in Section 1.6, it is not difficult to find the direct lattice when the reciprocal lattice is given. We shall also find these relations useful in other contexts, particularly in describing the behavior of electrons and acoustical waves in crystals.

2.5 DIFFRACTION BY REAL CRYSTAL LATTICES

So far, our description of X-ray diffraction has been based upon the assumption of scattering at the lattice points of an ideal crystal lattice. In reality, however, the atomic electrons that interact with incoming radiation to produce the diffraction pattern are not located at the lattice points themselves, but are described by a continuous *electron density distibution* about the lattice point. This density distribution expresses the probability that an electron will be found in a small volume element surrounding any given point in the neighborhood of the atomic nucleus, which for present purposes can itself be regarded as a point. The density distribution can be determined only by the laws of quantum mechanics. We shall see later how this is accomplished, but for now will simply regard it is a known quantity. In any case, we shall have to modify our calculations to account for the fact that X-rays are actually diffracted not by lattice points but by the "electron clouds" associated with the atoms. Also, we have assumed that the atoms are all located at lattice points, and that there are no atoms anywhere else within the unit cell. The analysis, therefore, is based on primitive cells containing one atom only, and does not account for structures having more than a single atom per unit cell, for example, bcc, fcc, and diamond.

We shall begin by considering scattering by an electron density distribution rather than a point atom. The density distribution can be described by a function $\rho(\mathbf{r})$ such that $\rho(\mathbf{r})dv$ is the probability that an electron will be found within the volume element dv. The electron density function, as determined quantum mechanically, must satisfy the condition

$$\int_v \rho(\mathbf{r})dv = Z \ , \tag{2.5-1}$$

where Z is the number of electrons associated with the electron cloud, that is, the atomic number of the substance. The integral is properly taken over the unit cell but since the electron density usually exhibits a rapid radial falloff, it is often a good approximation to integrate instead over all space.

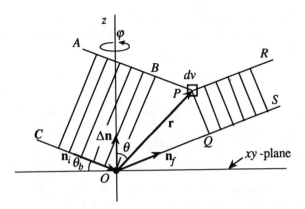

Figure 2.8 Scattering at the Bragg angle by an electron density distribution in the volume element dv.

The incoming radiation, assumed to be incident at the Bragg angle θ_b, is also assumed to be scattered in the volume element dv displaced from the origin by the vector $\mathbf{r}$, as illustrated in Figure 2.8. The angle θ in this discussion refers to the angle between this vector and the z-axis, which is taken to be normal to the (hkl) reflecting planes. Suppose now that the amplitude of radiation scattered by a *point electron* at the lattice point O along OS is expressed as $A\exp i(ks - \omega t)$, where s is measured along OS. The ratio of the radiation amplitude scattered by the density element dv to that scattered by a point electron at the origin, which we shall call df, can now be written

$$df = \frac{Ae^{i(ks-\omega t)+i\varphi_r} \cdot \rho(\mathbf{r})dv}{Ae^{i(ks-\omega t)}} = \rho(\mathbf{r})e^{i\varphi_r} \quad , \tag{2.5-2}$$

where φ_r is the difference in phase between radiation scattered at points P and O. However, according to (2.4 - 4), this phase difference is

$$\varphi_r = \frac{2\pi}{\lambda}\mathbf{r}\cdot(\mathbf{n}_f - \mathbf{n}_i) = \frac{2\pi}{\lambda}\mathbf{r}\cdot\Delta\mathbf{n} \quad . \tag{2.5-3}$$

From Figure 2.8, the magnitude of the vector $\Delta\mathbf{n}$ is $2\sin\theta_b$, while the angle between $\mathbf{r}$ and $\Delta\mathbf{n}$ is θ. Therefore, the scalar product in the above equation can be evaluated, and the expression can now be written as

$$\varphi_r = \frac{4\pi}{\lambda} r\sin\theta_b\cos\theta = \mu r\cos\theta \quad , \tag{2.5-4}$$

where

$$\mu = \frac{4\pi\sin\theta_b}{\lambda} \quad . \tag{2.5-5}$$

The scattered radiation amplitude is evaluated by substituting (2.5 - 4) into (2.5 - 2), and integrating over the volume elements using spherical coordinates r, θ, and φ, where φ is the azimuthal angle shown in Fig. 2.8. It is assumed, of course, that the electron density $\rho(\mathbf{r})$ is known. It is difficult to perform this integration in general;

however, if the electron density is independent of the angles θ and φ, the calculation is simpler, and the integral can often be evaluated. In this case, $\rho(\mathbf{r}) = \rho(r)$, and the integral becomes

$$f(\mu) = \int_0^{2\pi} \int_0^{\pi} \int_0^{\infty} \rho(r) e^{i\mu r \cos\theta} r^2 \sin\theta \, dr \, d\theta \, d\varphi \quad . \tag{2.5-6}$$

This can be integrated fairly easily over the angular variables. Since the integrand is independent of φ, the integral over this angle contributes only a factor of 2π. The integral over θ is evaluated by setting $x = \cos\theta$, $dx = -\sin\theta \, d\theta$. The expression is then easily integrated and evaluated at the limits, giving an expression in which the exponential factors can be written as a sine function, the final result being

$$f(\mu) = \int_0^{\infty} 4\pi r^2 \rho(r) \frac{\sin \mu r}{\mu r} dr \quad . \tag{2.5-7}$$

The quantity $f(\mu)$ is called the *atomic scattering factor*. It represents the ratio of the radiation amplitude actually scattered in the direction predicted by the Bragg relation, to that which would have been caused by a point scattering center with the charge of an electron at a lattice point. The atomic scattering factor affects only the *intensity* of the scattering, not the directions of diffracted beams, which are simply those suggested by the Bragg picture. Since the argument μ contains the Bragg angle, however, the intensity factor will depend on this quantity as well as on the electron density. Also, since the atomic scattering factor contains information about the electron density distribution function, it can be helpful in experimentally verifying theoretical predictions regarding this distribution. From the form of the above equation, it is evident that the electron density can be regarded as a Fourier transform of the atomic scattering factor.

So far, we have assumed that our unit cell has atoms only at its corners. This means that we are restricted to unit cells containing only one atom. If we are to understand diffraction patterns associated with crystals having cells containing more than a single atom, like the cubic bcc and fcc cells, we must take into account the interaction of radiation scattered by the various atoms within the unit cell. This can be accomplished in a way similar to that employed in the preceding analysis.

For the diffracted beam with indices (h', k', l'), which may contain a common integer factor, as described in the preceding section in connection with (2.4 - 10), we shall denote the ratio of the radiation amplitude scattered at the usual Bragg angle by an entire unit cell to that scattered by a point electronic charge at the origin by the symbol $F(h', k', l')$. Then, we can write

$$F(h',k',l') = \sum_i f_i e^{i\varphi_i} = \sum_i f_i e^{2\pi i (\mathbf{r}_i \cdot \Delta \mathbf{n})/\lambda} \quad , \tag{2.5-8}$$

where $\mathbf{r}_i$ is the vector from the origin to the i-th atom in the cell, f_i the atomic scattering factor for this atom, and φ_i the phase difference between radiation scattered from atom i and the origin. You will recall that the phase differences are given by (2.4 - 4) or (2.5 - 3). The sum is taken over all the atoms in the unit cell. If we write the coördinates of the i-th atom (x_i, y_i, z_i) as fractional parts of the cell edges a, b, and c, (as explained in Chapter 1, p. 11), then

$$\mathbf{r}_i = x_i \mathbf{a} + y_i \mathbf{b} + z_i \mathbf{c} \quad . \tag{2.5-9}$$

Also, according to (2.4 - 10)

$$\mathbf{a} \cdot \Delta\mathbf{n} = 2a \sin\theta_b \cos\alpha = h'\lambda$$

$$\mathbf{b} \cdot \Delta\mathbf{n} = 2b \sin\theta_b \cos\beta = k'\lambda \tag{2.5-10}$$

$$\mathbf{c} \cdot \Delta\mathbf{n} = 2c \sin\theta_b \cos\gamma = l'\lambda \quad ,$$

allowing us to express (2.5 - 8) finally as

$$F(h',k',l') = \sum_i f_i e^{2\pi i (h'x_i + k'y_i + l'z_i)} \quad . \tag{2.5-11}$$

When all atoms of the crystal are identical, all the f_i have the same value f. Under these conditions, (2.5 - 11) can be written simply as

$$F(h',k',l') = fS$$

where

$$S = \sum_i e^{2\pi i (h'x_i + k'y_i + l'z_i)} \quad . \tag{2.5-12}$$

The total amplitude is now given as the product of the atomic scattering factor f and a factor S governed by the geometrical arrangement of atoms within the unit cell, which is referred to as the *geometrical structure factor*. For crystals in which all the atoms in the unit cell are not identical, no such separation is possible, and the more general expression (2.5 - 11) must be used. Together, these expressions allow one to predict the effect of the electron density distribution within the atoms, as well as the arrangement of atoms within the unit cell, on the intensity of the diffracted beams whose pattern is inferred from the Bragg relation or the Laue equations. In particular, in cases where the geometrical structure factor is zero, certain diffracted beams that would otherwise be observed will be missing. It should be noted, however, that the observed intensity of the scattered radiation is given by the *square* of the amplitude (or for complex amplitudes by the square of its absolute value) rather than the amplitude itself.

These results can be readily understood by considering two specific examples. First, we shall examine the form of the atomic scattering factor for an atom having a *constant* electron density ρ_0 for $r < R$, and zero density for $r > R$. This means that the electron distribution is a spherical charge cloud of radius R and uniform charge density ρ_0. This is an admittedly crude simplification, in some ways at odds with what is predicted by quantum theory, but it will give a good idea of the scattering factor's usual form. The total electron population Z is then given by the product of electron density and volume, so that

$$Z = \tfrac{4}{3} \pi R^3 \rho_0 \quad , \qquad \text{or} \qquad \rho_0 = \frac{3Z}{4\pi R^3} \quad . \tag{2.5-13}$$

Substituting this information into (2.5 - 7), we obtain

$$f(\mu) = \frac{3Z}{(\mu R)^3} \int_0^R (\mu r) \sin(\mu r) \, d(\mu r)$$

$$= 3Z \left[\frac{\sin \mu R - \mu R \cos \mu R}{(\mu R)^3} \right] \tag{2.5-14}$$

as the atomic scattering factor. The limits of integration are from zero to R, since the electron density is zero for larger values of R. The function in brackets approaches the value $1/3$ as μR approaches zero, so that in this limit $f(\mu)$ tends to the value Z, equal to the number of valence electrons per atom. Since μ is directly proportional to the Bragg angle θ_b, this limit corresponds to that of small Bragg angles. As the Bragg angle increases, the value of f given by the expression above decreases as shown in the plot in Figure 2.9. Of course, at some value of the argument μR, the Bragg angle will reach 90°; beyond that point, the function (2.5 - 14) has no meaning in the given experimental context. The scattering factor for more realistic electron density distributions exhibits some of the same characteristics as the one plotted below; in all instances its initial value (as plotted) is unity, and at large values of the argument, it approaches zero. The information about the form of the electron density therefore resides in the finer details, a fact that somewhat restricts the usefulness of the scattering factor for accurately determining this density.

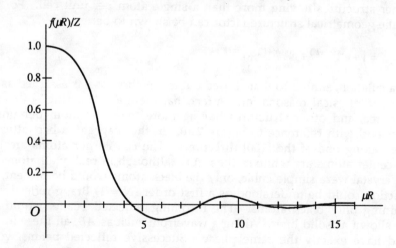

Figure 2.9 Structure factor of spherical atom of radius R with constant electron density.

As a second example, we shall now consider X-ray diffraction from a body-centered cubic crystal. It is, of course, possible to use the primitive cell shown in Figure 1.5 as a basis for discussion, but for a number of reasons, primarily the fact that the cell is non-orthogonal, this turns out to be extremely difficult. It is therefore advantageous to use the cubic bcc unit cell, despite the fact that it contain two atoms.

That complication is taken care of by the geometrical structure factor. Taking the origin at the corner of the unit cell, the center atom is described by the cell coördinates of eq. (2.5 - 12) by $(x_i, y_i, z_i) = (1/2, 1/2, 1/2)$. This accounts for one of the atoms; the other atom can be accounted for by including only one of the eight corner atoms in the cell (for example the corner atom at the origin, whose coördinates are (0, 0, 0)), and regarding the other seven as belonging to neighboring cells. If this *ad hoc* procedure is followed, eq. (2.5 - 12) gives the geometric structure factor as

$$S = 1 + e^{i\pi(h'+k'+l')} \quad . \tag{2.5-15}$$

The simple method used in getting this result can be justified by writing the contribution from all eight corner atoms explicitly according to (2.5 - 12), multiplying each by a factor 1/8, and adding them all together to obtain (with the inclusion of a body-center atom), the result given above. The work is purely algebraic, and is suggested as an exercise for the reader.

When the sum $h' + k' + l'$ is an even number, the second term in the above equation has the value +1, and the result $S = 2$ is obtained. When this sum is an *odd* integer, however, it has the value −1, and the structure factor is zero. According to (5.2 - 12) this means that the amplitude of outgoing scattered radiation will be zero, and that no diffracted beam will be observed. Thus, many of the diffraction maxima observed for a simple cubic structure will be missing in the X-ray diffraction pattern of a bcc structure having the same cubic cell dimensions. For example, the (100) diffraction maximum is absent in the bcc pattern, as is the (111) maximum, although the (200) and (222) beams--the second order maxima associated with these planes, for which $N = 2$ in the Bragg equation--will be observed. Similar effects are encountered in other structures having more than a single atom per unit cell. For the fcc structure, the geometrical structure factor can be shown to be

$$S = 1 + e^{i\pi(k'+l')} + e^{i\pi(h'+l')} + e^{i\pi(h'+k')} \quad . \tag{2.5-16}$$

The calculation, similar to that carried out for the bcc case, is assigned as an exercise.

The physical reasons for the fact that there are "missing" diffraction maxima in bcc, fcc, and other structures having more than one atom per unit cell can be understood with reference to Figure 2.10. In the diagram, a bcc lattice is shown as viewed along one of the [100] directions. The cell corner atoms are black and the body-center atoms are white in the figure, although in reality all atoms are identical. If the crystal were simple cubic, only the black atoms would be present, and the (100) diffraction could be understood as a first order ($N = 1$) Bragg reflection from planes containing only black atoms. The incoming reflected beams would then be only those shown as solid lines. Along a wavefront such as AB, all these incoming beams would have exactly the same phase. Successive reflected beams would differ in phase by 2π radians, as shown by the solid outgoing beams. These beams are in phase, and combine constructively to form outgoing diffracted wavefronts such as CD. The relative phase of each reflected beam is shown in the diagram.

In the bcc structure, crystal planes (containing white atoms) are interposed between the original (100) planes of the original simple cubic lattice of black atoms. Incoming X-rays can now undergo Bragg reflection from these planes as well as the original ones populated by black atoms. There are now outgoing beams shown as dotted lines in the figure interposed between the original diffracted beams, whose phases are odd multiples of π radians, as illustrated. The outgoing beams are no longer all in phase. In fact, neighboring pairs of outgoing reflected beams can now be regarded as interfering *destructively* with one another, contributing to an outgoing

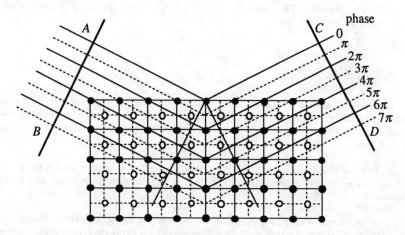

Figure 2.10 Schematic representation of Bragg diffraction from (100) planes in a bcc crystal. X-rays are incident from the left, and are reflected from (100) planes to form outgoing wavefronts like CD.

wavefront with zero amplitude. There is therefore no observed Bragg reflection. In the case of the second-order (200) reflection, the ingoing and outgoing beams are incident at a steeper angle to the crystal, and all the path differences are twice as large as those illustrated above. This means that the outgoing phase differences, such as those shown along CD, have double the values shown in the figure, and the outgoing beams again all interfere constructively, forming an observable (200) diffraction maximum. Similar physical arguments can be made to explain other missing Bragg reflections in crystals having more than a single atom per unit cell.

It would be going too far to say that wave phenomena is all there is to condensed matter physics, but it should now be apparent that wave interactions play an important part in the experimental analysis of crystal structures. A detailed understanding of interference and diffraction has allowed us not only to derive the simple picture of Bragg reflection, but also to develop some understanding of the intensities of X-ray diffraction maxima and their usefulness in determining electron density distributions and the geometry of complex crystal structures. We shall find many more uses for this understanding in our subsequent study of crystalline and amorphous materials.

REFERENCES

W. H. Bragg, *An Introduction to Crystal Analysis*, G. Bell & Sons, London (1928).

W. L. Bragg, *The Crystalline State*, Vol. I, G. Bell & Sons, London (1955).

A. Taylor, *X-Ray Metallography*, John Wiley & Sons, New York (1961).

M. J. Buerger, *Contemporary Crystallography*, McGraw-Hill, New York (1970).

B. E. Warren, *X-Ray Diffraction*, Addison-Wesley, Reading MA (1969).

M M Woolfson, *An Introduction to X-Ray Crystallography*, Cambridge University Press, Cambridge (1970).

H. A. Hauptmann, *The Phase Problem of X-Ray Crystallography*, Physics Today, Vol. 42/11, p. 24 (November, 1989).

PROBLEMS

1. Find the numerical value of the velocity of light in free space from the electrostatic and magnetic permittivities of this medium. Show that the index of refraction is equal to the square root of the relative dielectric permittivity in a transparent dielectric with magnetic permeability equal to that of free space.

2. Review the definition of *transverse* and *longitudinal* waves, and cite several examples of each. Can you suggest examples of systems that will propagate transverse and longitudinal waves simultaneously?

3. A transverse wave propagates in the x-direction along an elastic string. Its amplitude in meters is described by $u(x, t) = 0.05 \sin(4.0x - 160t)$, where t is expressed in seconds.. The string has mass density 0.012 kg/m. Find the wavelength, the frequency, the phase velocity, and the tension in the string. What is the maximum velocity and maximum acceleration of any point on the string?

4. A wave's amplitude in meters is described by $A\exp(0.6x + 0.8y + 1.20z - 270t)$, where t is in seconds. (a) Write an expression for the propagation vector of the wave. (b) What is the wavelength? (c) What is the phase velocity? (d) Describe the propagation vector in terms of its magnitude and the angles it makes with the three coördinate axes.

5. An electromagnetic wave's electric vector E lies in the xy-plane, making an angle of 30° with the positive x-axis. The magnetic vector also lies in the xy-plane, The wave propagates in free space, at a frequency of 10,000MHz. If the magnitude of E is 12.0v/m, write an expression for the propagation vector k and the vector E as a function of x, y, z, and t. What is the wavelength?

6. Show that if a harmonic wave propagating along the x-direction has a complex propagation constant, whose real and imaginary parts are k_r and k_i, respectively, the wave must have the form of an undamped propagating wave whose propagation constant is k_r, multiplied by an exponential attenuating factor in which the attenuation factor is k_i. Note that the frequency ω is a real positive quantity.

7. Show that the partial differential equation

$$\frac{\partial^2 u}{\partial x^2} = \alpha^2 \frac{\partial u}{\partial t} + K^2 \frac{\partial^2 u}{\partial t^2}$$

where α^2 and K^2 are constants, has solutions like those described in the preceding problem. Find the dispersion relation, and from it derive equations giving the real and imaginary parts of k as functions of the angular frequency ω.

8. Show that a general solution of the partial differential equation (2.2 - 4), containing two arbitrary functions of x and t, can be written as $u(x, t) = f(x - vt) + g(x + vt)$, where f and g are the arbitrary functions and $v = 1/K$. Describe the physical character of this solution.

9. Write an expression for the displacement of an atom from its equilibrium position in the lattice during the passage of a longitudinal acoustic wave of maximum amplitude 1.0×10^{-12}m, wavelength 2.5×10^{-9}m, and frequency 1.2×10^{12}Hz, propagating in the <221> direction in a cubic crystal.

10. Assuming that the wave defined in the preceding problem is a plane wave, write the equation of its wavefronts and verify the relation $\mathbf{k} = \nabla \varphi$.

11. Light of wavelength 5890Å is incident on two identical parallel slits of width 0.01mm and spacing 0.50mm. A ground glass screen is placed behind the slits, at a distance of 1.0m, as illustrated in Figure 2.1. Is the central point Q now brightly illuminated or dark? What is the spacing between adjacent maxima or minima of intensity on the screen? What is the distance between the central point Q on the screen and the third intensity minimum from that point?

12. In the situation described in the preceding problem, one slit is blocked, so that light passes through only a single slit. Is the central point Q now bright or dark? What is the distance now between Q and the third dark band from that point along the screen? What is the intensity ratio between a point 15° off the central axis and the point where maximum intensity is observed.

13. Monochromatic light is incident on two identical slits spaced a distance 0.60mm apart. A system of fringes is observed on a screen at a distance 60cm behind the slits, in which 24 fringes occupy a measured distance of 1.152cm. What is the wavelength of the incident light? (This is an experiment that allows you to measure the wavelength of light with a ruler!)

14. What slit configuration is needed in Young's experiment to produce an interference pattern in which the angular separation of adjacent minima is 1°?

15. Discuss the appearance of the observed single-slit diffraction pattern (a) when the slit width is much larger than the light wavelength (b) when the slit width is only a few times the wavelength (c) when the slit width is smaller than the wavelength.

16. What slit width is needed to produce a single-slit diffraction pattern in which the angular separation of the first intensity minima on either side of the central maximum is 1°, using monochromatic incident light of wavelength 5600Å (560nm)?

17. Monochromatic X-rays of wavelength 1.540Å (0.1540nm) are diffracted by (100) planes of a NaCl crystal, whose structure is illustrated in Figure 1.8, and in which the nearest-neighbor interatomic spacing is 2.80Å (0.280nm). How many diffracted beams will be observed, and what angles do they make with these crystal planes?

18. What is the minimum voltage needed to produce X-rays that will produce observable diffraction in the crystal described in the preceding problem?

19. A third-order diffraction maximum is observed from the (111) planes of a copper crystal, using X-rays of wavelength 0.862Å (0.0862nm). The incident and diffracted beams are observed to be at an angle of 38.26° to the planes. Find the distance between adjacent (111) planes in copper. If copper has an fcc lattice, what is the edge length of the cubic unit cell?

20. A first-order Bragg reflection is observed at an angle of 23.5° to a set of crystal planes. What angle will the second-order reflection make with these planes?

21. Find a general expression relating the m-th order and n-th order Bragg reflection angles for X-rays diffracted from a given set of crystal planes.

22. A simple orthorhombic crystal has an orthogonal unit cell whose dimensions are $a = 2.0$Å, $b = 3.0$Å, $c = 4.0$Å (0.2, 0.3, 0.4nm). X-rays of wavelength 0.40Å (0.040nm) are diffracted by (311) lattice planes. How many diffracted beams can be observed, and at what Bragg angles will they be found?

23. Show that in a simple cubic lattice, the diffraction of X-rays can be described by the equation

$$n\lambda \sqrt{h^2 + k^2 + l^2} = 2a\sin\theta$$

where a is the nearest neighbor interatomic distance. Show also that this relation can be obtained from equation (2.4 - 16).

24. The orthogonal unit cell of a simple tetragonal crystal has dimensions $a = b = 2.0\text{Å}$ (0.20nm), $c = 3.0\text{Å}$ (0.30nm). It is desired to observed at least 5 orders of diffraction from the (322) planes of this crystal. What is the minimum accelerating voltage needed to produce X-rays that will staisfy this requirement? Assuming that X-radiation corresponding to a voltage 10% higher than this minimum is employed, at what Bragg angles will these five diffracted beams be detected?

25. Show that the atomic scattering factor for a crystal composed of atoms having Z valence electrons whose electron density function has the form

$$\rho(r) = \frac{Z}{2\pi R^2 r} \qquad (0 < r < R)$$

$$= 0 \qquad (r > R)$$

is given by

$$f(\mu) = 2Z\frac{1 - \cos\mu R}{(\mu R)^2} \quad .$$

Make a rough plot of this function in terms of the variable μR.

26. Show that the atomic scattering factor for a crystal composed of atoms having Z valence electrons whose electron density function has the form

$$\rho(r) = \frac{Z}{\pi r_0^3}e^{-2r/r_0}$$

can be expressed as

$$f(\mu) = \frac{Z}{\left(1 + \left(\frac{1}{2}\mu r_0\right)^2\right)^2} \quad .$$

Make a rough plot of this function in terms of the variable μr_0. Hint: In the integral to be evaluated, express the sine function in terms of imaginary exponentials before integrating.

27. Show that the geometrical structure factor for the fcc lattice is given by (2.5 - 16). Which of the following X-ray reflections will be missing: (100), (110), (111), (200), (220), (221), (211), (210), (321)?

28. Show that the fcc structure factor (2.5 - 16) can be found by including in the calculation all atoms in the fcc unit cell, assigning weighting factors 1/8 for corner atoms, 1/4 for edge atoms, and 1/2 for face-center atoms.

29. Find the geometrical structure factor for the base-centered orthorhombic lattice shown in Figure 1.3 on p. 8. Which of the X-ray reflections listed in problem 27 will be absent for this structure?

30. Find the geometrical structure factor for the cubic cell of the diamond lattice described in Section 1.4. Be sure to take account of both atoms in the cell. Which of the X-ray reflections listed in Problem 27 will be missing for this structure?

31. Consider the body-centered CsCl structure of Figure 1.8(b), in which the two atomic species have different atomic scattering factors f_a and f_b. Write the scattered X-ray amplitude $F(h',k',l')$ for this structure, and show that the diffracted beams for which the sum $h' + k' + l'$ is odd have intensity smaller than those for which the sum is even by a factor

$$\frac{I_{odd}}{I_{even}} = \left(\frac{f_b - f_a}{f_b + f_a}\right)^2 .$$

32. Write the scattered X-ray amplitude $F(h',k',l')$ for the NaCl structure of Figure 1.8(a), in which the two atomic species have different atomic scattering factors f_a and f_b. Show that this result can be interpreted as the product of the body-centered amplitude found in the preceding problem and the fcc geometric structure factor given by equation (2.5 - 16).

CHAPTER 3

SOUND WAVES, DISPERSION RELATIONS, AND LATTICE VIBRATIONS

3.1 INTRODUCTION

In this chapter--and in succeeding chapters--there will be more about waves. The purpose now is to extend our current knowledge of wave motion, and to apply it to sound or acoustical waves in crystalline solids. This may not seem to be a very exciting objective, but its importance will soon become apparent. The sound waves of interest, moreover, are not those in the audio spectrum, but are of much higher frequency, billions of times higher than that of audible sound.

In the atmosphere, which approximates an ideal gas, sound waves (regardless of their practical and aesthetic relevance to everyday life) are phenomena that play a role of relatively minor importance in the physics of the gaseous medium in which they travel. In a gas, the energy of the atoms or molecules is largely translational kinetic energy; it is this energy that enables us to sense the temperature of the gas, and that contributes most significantly to the internal energy, specific heat, thermal conductivity, and other thermal properties of the substance. Also, in an ideal gas, the molecules interact with one another only through elastic collisions of very short duration; most of the time they act like free and independent particles. So, for a variety of reasons, the physics of gases, at least on an elementary level, is most easily described in terms of particles and particle interactions.

Solid materials, however, differ significantly from gases in that their atoms are tightly coupled to one another by strong interatomic forces. In these substances, the thermal kinetic energy of the atoms manifests itself as *vibrational* energy of motion, which because of the strong coupling between neighboring atoms is propagated throughout the material as *waves*. These waves are simply acoustical or sonic waves which in some ways resemble ordinary sound waves in gases. In crystals, however, thermal energy is carried by these waves, and the thermal properties of materials depend critically upon their behavior. Moreover, external excitations like light can also excite acoustic waves in crystal lattices. So, in crystalline materials, acoustical waves play an important part in determining the physical properties of the substance. One of our primary objectives, therefore, must be to understand how sound waves propagate in crystals and other solid materials.

In order to fully appreciate this subject, it is also necessary to understand in some detail the forces that bind the atoms of a crystal together. It therefore makes sense to begin by considering the simplest kind of interatomic forces as a specific example. These forces are encountered in ionic crystals, wherein most of the binding energy comes from simple electrostatic interactions between charged ions.

3.2 INTERATOMIC FORCES IN IONIC CRYSTALS

Ionic substances like NaCl, KCl, or AgBr are bound together mostly by electrostatic forces between ions formed by the transfer of valence electrons from positive metal atoms to those of electronegative elements such as the halogens. If this were the whole story, however, it would be favorable energetically for the atoms of the crystal to get closer and closer together, and ultimately to overlap. The lowest energy configuration would then be a "collapsed phase" in which positive and negative ions would form a plasma of incredibly small volume and astronomically high density. The electrostatic binding energy of this curious substance, would be, in principle, minus infinity! Actually, of course, nothing like this ever occurs. Instead, we have crystalline materials in which the atoms find stable positions of equilibrium corresponding to nearest-neighbor distances of a few Ångströms.

The binding energy, or *cohesive* energy of these materials is the energy needed to separate the crystal into independent ions at large distances from one another. While it isn't possible to measure this energy directly, it can be calculated quite accurately from measured thermodynamic and spectroscopic data. The results, for a number of typical ionic substances, are as follows:

MEASURED BINDING ENERGY FOR IONIC CRYSTALS

Substance	Energy, (kcal/mole)	(eV/molecule)
NaCl	−182.8	−7.92
KCl	−164.4	−7.12
NaBr	−173.3	−7.51
KBr	−156.2	−6.77
NaI	−166.4	−7.21
KI	−151.5	−6.56.

These energies have negative signs, which reflects the fact that the resultant forces between atoms are attractive rather than repulsive. They are large compared to the thermal kinetic energy per atom, which at room temperature is only about 0.037 eV per atom. This accounts for the fact that ionic crystals are stable configurations, with high melting points and low vapor pressures. However, these cohesive energies are finite, and they are far smaller than what one might expect for a dense collapsed plasma like the one mentioned above.

What prevents atoms and crystals from collapsing are the effects of quantum physics. Without them, atoms, molecules, and condensed phases like crystals, as we know them, could not exist. Quantum theory--or rather the physical character of microscopic systems, as described by quantum theory--implies, for electrons and atoms, the existence of a state of lowest, though *still finite* energy, as well as possible states of the system having higher energies. The lowest energy state is called the *ground state*, while the higher energy states are referred to as *excited states* of the system. In general, these states are of discrete, sharply defined energy, separated by energy intervals in which stable configurations of the system simply cannot exist. Often, however, particularly in situations where the laws of classical physics are applicable, the allowed states are very closely spaced in energy--so closely as to form, in effect, a continuum of possible energies. Even so, there will always be a ground state of finite energy.

Quantum theory predicts that any atom in its ground state has an electron density distribution of some definite size and shape surrounding the nucleus. This configuration is associated with the lowest-energy property of the ground state, and if it is distorted in any way, the energy of the new configuration will always be *greater* than the unperturbed ground-state energy. This increase in energy is perceived as a repulsive force exerted by the system on its surroundings. In effect, the atom resists external efforts to compress it into a smaller volume. or to alter its normal "shape" in any way. In a crystal, this kind of repulsive force begins to act between neighboring atoms or ions when their electron clouds start to overlap, and increases very rapidly until it balances any attractive forces that are present. This results in an equilibrium state in which the *total* force on any atom is zero, and in which the potential energy of any atom is a minimum. An exact quantitative description of this force is difficult to formulate, but it is clear that it must be repulsive, and that it must increase much more rapidly with decreasing interatomic distance than the attractive forces that predominate when the atoms or ions are far apart.

The "electron clouds" of positive and negative ions like Na^+ and Cl^- are spherically symmetric in free space. In the actual crystal, they are slightly distorted by the repulsive forces mentioned above, but are still roughly spherical. As previously stated, the exact form of the repulsive force between ions is hard to calculate, but its effect can be approximated by assuming that it varies with distance as some large inverse power of interionic spacing. This idea was first put forth by Otto Madelung in 1910, and discussed in more detail by Max Born in 1923. In view of the nearly spherical form of the ionic charge distributions, the attractive electrostatic forces between ions have the same form as the coulomb force between point charges. These ideas suggest that we can write a good approximate expression for the potential energy of interaction U_{ij} between any two ions, of the form

$$U_{ij} = \pm \frac{q^2}{4\pi\varepsilon_0 r_{ij}} + \frac{A}{r_{ij}^b} \quad , \qquad\qquad (3.2\text{-}1)$$

where q is the ionic charge, r_{ij} is the distance between ions i and j, and A and b are constants. The first term is the coulomb potential energy, while the second describes the repulsive potential energy, for which it is assumed that the exponent b is much greater than unity. It should be noted also that positive energies are associated with repulsive forces, while negative energies correspond to attractive interactions. The total energy of the system, referred to as the cohesive energy, is the sum of all the energies of interaction between all ion pairs. Since the interaction terms ij and ji represent the same energy--the mutual potential energy of interaction between the two atoms--you get *twice* the cohesive energy if you simply sum over all ion pairs indexed by i and j in (3.2 - 1). To get the right answer for the cohesive energy, therefore, you must multiply this sum by a factor of one-half. This point should be remembered, for it will turn up frequently in future work.

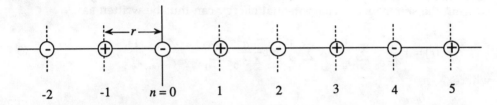

-2   -1 $n = 0$ 1   2   3   4   5

Figure 3.1 One-dimensional model of an ionic crystal.

We shall first consider the one-dimensional crystal model illustrated in Figure 3.1. This model is oversimplified in many ways, but suffices to illustrate the important physical effects that are observed. In the figure, we see a system consisting of N positive ions and N oppositely charged negative ions. There are thus $2N$ ions or N diatomic molecules in the crystal. Taking the origin at one of the negative ions, the potential energy of this ion can be written as a sum of potential energy terms of the form of (3.2 - 1), accounting for the energy of interaction of this ion with all the other ions in the system. This sum can be written as

$$U_0 = -\frac{q^2}{4\pi\varepsilon_0 r}\cdot 2\left[1 - \tfrac{1}{2} + \tfrac{1}{3} - \tfrac{1}{4} + \dots\right] + \frac{A}{r^b}\cdot 2\left[1 + \tfrac{1}{2^b} + \tfrac{1}{3^b} + \tfrac{1}{4^b} + \dots\right]$$

$$= -\frac{\alpha q^2}{4\pi\varepsilon_0 r} + \frac{A}{r^b}\zeta_b \quad , \tag{3.2-2}$$

where α and ζ_b represent the quantities in brackets in the upper equation (factors of 2 included). So far, we have counted once (and only once) energies involving atom zero and all other atoms in the chain. The quantity α can be evaluated by observing that the power series expansion of the function $\ln(1 + x)$ is

$$\ln(1+x) = x - \frac{x^2}{2} + \frac{x^3}{3} - \frac{x^4}{4} + \dots \quad . \tag{3.2-3}$$

The series for α in (3.2 - 2) is obtained by setting x equal to unity in (3.2 - 3). It therefore follows that in this example,

$$\alpha = 2\ln 2 = 1.3863 \quad . \tag{3.2-4}$$

In these calculations, negative energies are attractive, while positive energies are repulsive. The total coulomb energy is attractive because ions exerting attractive electrostatic forces on any given ion are closer on the average than those exerting repulsive forces. Nearest neighbors, for example, always exert attractive electrostatic forces on any ion. The second series in the expression above is more difficult to evaluate, and the constants A and b are still undetermined. As we shall see, however, it is possible to calculate the cohesive energy without summing this series or explicitly evaluating the constant A.

In a three-dimensional lattice, the total potential energy U_i of the i-th ion can be determined by summing (3.2 - 1) over j, the summation being taken over all the other atoms in the crystal. This means that the term for which $i = j$ must be excluded from the summation. The potential energy can thus be written as

$$U_i(r) = \pm \frac{q^2}{4\pi\varepsilon_0} \sum_{j(\neq i)} \frac{1}{r_{ij}} + A \sum_{j(\neq i)} \frac{1}{r_{ij}^b} = \pm \frac{q^2}{4\pi\varepsilon_0 r} \sum_{j(\neq i)} \frac{1}{x_{ij}} + \frac{A}{r^b} \sum_{j(\neq i)} \frac{1}{x_{ij}^b} \quad , \tag{3.2-5}$$

where

$$x_{ij} = \frac{r_{ij}}{r} \quad . \tag{3.2-6}$$

The x_{ij} are dimensionless quantities which express the distance between any two ions in the lattice in terms of the nearest-neighbor spacing r. In the one-dimensional example considered previously, these numbers are integers, but this is not so in two or three dimensions. Equation (3.2 - 5) can be written more simply as

$$U_i(r) = -\frac{\alpha q^2}{4\pi\varepsilon_0 r} + \frac{A\zeta_b}{r^b} \quad , \tag{3.2-7}$$

where

$$\alpha = \sum_j \mp \frac{1}{x_{ij}} \quad , \tag{3.2-8}$$

and

$$\zeta_b = \sum_j \frac{1}{x_{ij}^b} \quad . \tag{3.2-9}$$

The quantity α is referred to as the *Madelung constant*. In the one-dimensional lattice considered above, it has the value 2(ln2) or 1.3863. In three dimensions this is no longer true. The Madelung constant then has a value determined by the arrangement of atoms in the lattice, and must be calculated for the particular structure at hand. For an NaCl structure of spacing r, there are 6 nearest neighbor ions at a distance r from any given ion, 12 next-nearest neighbors at $\sqrt{2}$ times this distance, 8 third-nearest neighbors at $\sqrt{3}$ times this distance, etc. The series representing the sum over inverse distances along a linear chain in (3.2 - 2) is now replaced by a more complicated summation over a three-dimensional lattice, of the form

$$\alpha = 6 - \frac{12}{\sqrt{2}} + \frac{8}{\sqrt{3}} - \cdots \quad . \tag{3.2-10}$$

The sum is taken ultimately over all lattice points, succeeding terms involving 4th, 5th, 6th, neighbors, and so on *ad infinitum*. The signs are positive for neighbor ions opposite in sign to the ion at the origin and negative for ions of the same sign. Unfortunately, the series does not converge very rapidly and is therefore difficult to sum by brute force. This was a matter of concern before the era of digital computers, and certain tricks have been invented to improve convergence. These are no longer of any great interest, and we need only note that for the NaCl structure, the Madelung constant α has the value 1.7476. For other structures, it is different, but may be calculated in the same way.

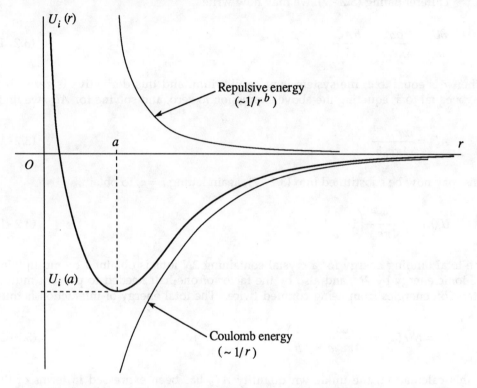

Figure 3.2 Plot of the potential energy of a single ion under the influence of forces exerted by all other ions in a one-dimensional ionic array of interionic spacing r. The total energy is exhibited as the sum of electrostatic and repulsive interionic energies.

It has not so far been assumed that r is the *equilibrium* interatomic spacing. In fact, r is a *variable* which has been introduced to allow us to evaluate the potential energy of a single ion under the influence of forces exerted upon it by all other ions in the crystal. The dimensions of the crystal lattice scale with this variable; when r varies, the entire lattice expands or contracts isotropically. If r is very large, both terms in (3.2 - 2) approach zero, so the total potential energy is zero in the limit of infinite interionic spacing. At large but finite interatomic spacing, the repulsive term is small in comparison to the coulomb energy, since for large r, $1/r^b$ is much less than $1/r$. So for large, interionic distances, the energy U_i will be negative. Conversely, in the limit of small r, the positive repulsive energy must be larger than the coulomb energy, and the total energy is thus positive in the limit of small ionic spacings. At some intermediate atomic spacing, the energy must exhibit a minimum. These features can be observed in Figure 3.2, in which the total ionic energy, represented by the bold curve, can be regarded as the sum of the two ingredients depicted by the lighter curves. At the minimum of the function U_i, located at the point $r = a$, the ion will be in equilibrium. At this point the derivative of the potential energy is zero, and the resultant force on the ion is likewise zero. This means that the quantity a is the equilibrium interatomic spacing of the crystal, and the equilibrium ionic binding energy must be $U_i(a)$, as illustrated.

Differentiating (3.2 - 7), we may now write

$$\frac{\partial U_i}{\partial r} = \frac{\alpha q^2}{4\pi\varepsilon_0 r^2} - \frac{b A \zeta_b}{r^{b+1}} \quad . \tag{3.2-11}$$

When r is equal to a, the system is at equilibrium, and this derivative is zero. Setting r equal to a, equating the above expression to zero, and solving for $A\zeta_b$, we find

$$A\zeta_b = \frac{\alpha q^2 a^{b-1}}{4\pi\varepsilon_0 b} \quad , \tag{3.2-12}$$

This may now be substituted into (3.2 - 7), again letting $r = a$, to obtain,

$$U_i(a) = -\frac{\alpha q^2}{4\pi\varepsilon_0 a}\left(1 - \frac{1}{b}\right) \quad . \tag{3.2-13}$$

The total binding energy for a crystal containing $2N$ ions is obtained by multiplying the ionic energy by $2N$, and also by the factor of one-half needed to prevent mutual interction energies from being counted twice. The total energy of interaction is thus

$$U_0 = NU_i(a) = -\frac{N\alpha q^2}{4\pi\varepsilon_0 a}\left(1 - \frac{1}{b}\right) \quad . \tag{3.2-14}$$

In this calculation, the unknown quantity $A\zeta_b$ has been expressed in terms of the lattice spacing a, which can be found from X-ray diffraction measurements.

For KCl, the nearest neighbor distance as determined by X-ray diffraction is 3.145Å (0.3145nm). Using this value, and setting N equal to Avogadro's number, we find that $-N\alpha q^2/4\pi\varepsilon_0 a$ equals -7.72×10^5 joule/mole, or -184.5 kcal/mole. You will note that this is somewhat larger than the figure -164.4 kcal/mole shown in the above table of experimentally determined energies. The difference can be attributed to the factor $[1 - (1/b)]$. For KCl, it appears that this factor should be $164.4/184.5$, which suggests that $b = 9.2$. This is encouraging, for it is in agreement with the previously stated idea that the exponent b must be substantially larger than unity. In itself, it does not prove the validity of the Born-Madelung calculation, but it shows that it is at least self-consistent. When other ionic substances are analyzed in the same way, a consistent picture emerges as shown in the table below.

It is clear from these data that the Born-Madelung calculation is supported by experimental evidence provided that the exponent b in the expression for the repulsive energy has a value of about 9.0. In the least consistent of these examples (NaI), the choice $b = 9.0$ gives a binding energy that differs from the experimentally determined result by only about 4%. Thus, the picture we have used leads to a reasonably accurate description of binding energies and interatomic forces in ionic substances. We have chosen the value $b = 9$ simply because it provides an optimal fit for all the available data. It is possible, however, to do even better by calculating b in terms of the *compressibility* of each material, a quantity which can be determined experimentally. We shall not present the details of this calculation; they are assigned as an exercise.

BINDING ENERGIES AND REPULSIVE EXPONENTS

Crystal	a, Å	$-\dfrac{N\alpha q^2}{4\pi\varepsilon_0 a}\dfrac{\text{kcal}}{\text{mole}}$	U_0 (expt) $\dfrac{\text{kcal}}{\text{mole}}$	$1 - (1/b)$	b
NaCl	2.82	205.7	−182.8	0.887	9.0
NaBr	2.98	195.0	−173.3	0.887	9.0
NaI	3.23	179.6	−166.4	0.926	13.6
KCl	3.15	184.5	−164.4	0.891	9.2
KBr	3.29	176.4	−156.2	0.885	8.7
KI	3.52	164.6	−151.5	0.920	12.6

It should be noted that these calculations are quantitatively valid only for ionic crystals. The interatomic forces that bind covalent and metallic substances cannot be expressed as simply as those in ionic crystals, and a calculation of cohesive energy for these materials is much harder--so much so, that we shall not attempt a quantitative treatment. The point of this discussion has not been so much a treatment of ionic binding *per se*, as its use as an example of how forces between atoms can act to bind any crystalline material together. *Quantitatively*, the forces in covalent and metallic substances differ from those in ionic materials, but *qualitatively* they are similar in that they lead to an atomic potential energy of the form shown in Figure 3.2. Thus, many of the physical properties described by the ionic model can be associated with crystalline materials in general.

3.3 FORCES ON VIBRATING ATOMS

So far, we have concentrated on the equilibrium configuration of an ionic lattice that is somewhat representative of crystalline materials in general. It is clear physically, however, that atoms may *vibrate* about their equilibrium positions when their total energy exceeds the equilibrium energy. Since the lattice sites are positions of minimum potential energy, when a single atom is displaced slightly from its lattice site, in any direction, its potential energy must increase. There must then be a net force on it equal to *minus* the gradient of the potential energy. This means that the force is opposite the direction of displacement from equilibrium. It is, in effect, a *restoring force* similar to that exerted by a spring, and the motion of the atom about the equilibrium site must therefore be oscillatory.

In general, however, the motion of atoms in the crystal lattice does not take place this simply. The preceding discussion is framed in terms of a single atom in motion with all others fixed in place. In reality, however, *all* the atoms in the lattice are in motion, and the vibrational motion of each atom is strongly affected by that of of its neighbors because of the strong forces each atom experiences from others nearby. It is clear that the individual atomic oscillations are not independent of one another, but are *coupled* by strong interatomic forces. Independent harmonic oscillators have a unique frequency of vibration, given by the square root of the force constant divided by the mass. When coupling between oscillators is introduced, however, the picture changes sharply. Now, there are a number of possible vibrational frequencies, closely related to the number of oscillators. If there are a great many oscillators, the number of possible frequencies is also large, and the allowed frequencies of vibration are very closely spaced. Under these circumstances, the effect of the interatomic coupling is to cause *waves* to propagate through the crystal lattice. In some ways, these waves resemble sound waves in gases, but in many respects they are quite different. Sound waves in crystals. for example, can be transverse as well as longitudinal, and their velocity can depend on the wavelength.

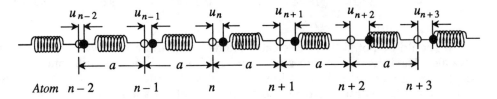

Figure 3.3 One-dimensional dynamical model of a crystal, viewed as a line of equal masses m with equiibrium spacings a, coupled together with ideal springs whose Hooke's-law force constant is β The equilibrium positions of the atoms are shown as white circles, while the instantaneous positions of the vibrating atoms at some given time are shown as black circles. The positions of each atom with respect to its equilibrium position is a time-vatying quantity denoted by the symbol u with an appropriate subscript.

The problem of the dynamics of atomic oscillations is more difficult than the Born-Madelung calculation of the equilibrium configuration. Therefore, we shall confine our analysis of this problem to a one-dimensional lattice of equal masses coupled together by interatomic forces that depend only on the distances between atoms. Since the lattice is in motion, these distances will no longer be integral multiples of the lattice constant, but will vary with time and with position within the crystal. In principle, the atomic displacements could be either transverse or longitudinal. We shall assume for simplicity that they are longitudinal, and show later that transverse displacements can be treated using the same approach. Also, we shall assume that the amplitude of the atomic oscillations is small compared to the equilibrium lattice spacing. Since the average thermal kinetic energy of the atoms is, as mentioned previously, much less than the equilibrium cohesive energy per atom, this is a realistic assumption except, perhaps, near the melting point.

This is beginning to sound like a difficult problem. After all, nobody has ever been able to solve the problem of three gravitating masses, and here we have an essentially *infinite* number of masses, all coupled together, and all exerting forces on each other--forces that are much more complicated than the force of gravity! We shall see, however, that despite these intimidating complexities, the problem can be solved fairly easily if you don't simply surrender at the beginning. There are some things going for us; all the masses are the same, they all exert similar forces on one another, and their equilibrium sites are regularly spaced.

If we make the additional assumption that only coupling forces between nearest neighbor atoms are significant, and that these forces are accurately described by Hooke's law, then the equations of motion of any atom can be written quite simply. These rather drastic simplifications are not always valid, and in any case need some detailed justification, which will be provided later. If we accept them, however, it is clear that we can model the behavior of a one-dimensional chain of coupled atoms as a set of masses coupled together by ideal springs, as illustrated by Figure 3.3. This model allows us to write an equation for the forces acting on the n-th atom, of the form

$$F_n = \beta(u_{n+1} - u_n) - \beta(u_n - u_{n-1}) = \beta(u_{n+1} + u_{n-1} - 2u_n) \ . \tag{3.3-1}$$

In this expression, β is the Hooke's-law force constant, and the subscripted u-symbols refer to the instantaneous displacements of the atoms from their respective equilibrium positions, as illustrated in Figure 3.3. The picture suggests that atom n experiences a force along the positive x-direction proportional to the extension of the "spring" on its right, $u_{n+1} - u_n$, and a similar force directed along the negative x-axis proprtional to the extension $u_n - u_{n-1}$ of the spring on its left, which leads immediately to (3.3 - 1). This model neglects the fact that atom n experiences forces not only from nearest neighbors, but also from more distant atoms, and also gives no information about the force constant β. Finally, it relies on a mechanistic view of the crystal that, though often very useful, can also sometimes be misleading.

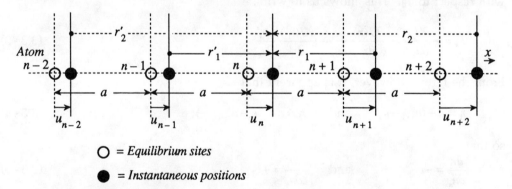

O = *Equilibrium sites*

● = *Instantaneous positions*

Figure 3.4. One-dimensional lattice illustrating the equilibrium sites and actual positions of several atoms at some arbitrary time. The positive directions associated with displacements from equilibrium and distances involved in force interactions are indicated by the directions of the arrows.

A more accurate picture of the lattice is shown in Figure 3.4, which is similar to Figure 3.3 without the springs. The white circles show the equilibrium lattice sites, while the dark circles represent a snapshot of the actual positions of the vibrating atoms at some instant of time. For simplicity, we use a one-dimensional picture, since it illustrates quite well most of the physical features of interest.

We must now focus our attention on atom n, and determine the instantaneous forces exerted on it by other atoms. In an ionic lattice, these forces will be given by a potential energy of the form (3.2 - 1), or, in one dimension, (3.2 - 2). This potential energy is written as a series of terms that arise from forces between nearest neighbor atoms, second neighbors, third neighbors, and so on. In the equilibrium case, we were able to handle all these interactions at once, but now we shall have to take them one at a time. It is important, however, to observe that all these forces depend on distance in the same way--a way that always involves a *single* function of interatomic distance such as (3.2 - 1). In non-ionic materials, (3.2 - 1) can no longer be used, but in any case, one function $U(r)$ suffices to define the potential energy of interaction between the atom n and all sets of neighbors, at distances shown as r_1, r'_1; r_2, r'_2; etc., in the diagram. The total energy of interaction U_n between atom n and all other atoms of the lattice therefore always has the form,

$$U_n = [U(r_1) + U(r'_1)] + [U(r_2) + U(r'_2)] + \dots \quad .$$

(3.3 - 2)

In this expression, the first term in brackets gives the potential energy of interaction between ion n and its two nearest neighbors. The quantities r_1 and r'_1 are the distances shown in Figure 3.4. The second term refers to the energy of interaction between ion n and its second neighbors, at distances shown by the dotted arrows in the figure. There will be similar terms for more distant sets of atoms. The function U is always the same; it is only the distance arguments that differ from term to term. At first, let us consider only nearest neighbor forces and for now drop the others. This leaves only the first term in (3.3 - 2).

The force on atom n is minus the derivative of the potential energy with respect to the displacement. In this case it is advantageous to express the displacement of the atom with reference to its equilibrium position, and to take this derivative with respect to u_n. This allows us to write,

$$F_n = -\frac{\partial U_n}{\partial u_n} = -\frac{\partial U(r_1)}{\partial r_1}\frac{\partial r_1}{\partial u_n} - \frac{\partial U(r'_1)}{\partial r'_1}\frac{\partial r'_1}{\partial u_n} \quad .$$

(3.3 - 3)

From the figure, however, it is apparent that

$$r_1 = a + (u_{n+1} - u_n) \quad \text{and} \quad r'_1 = a + (u_n - u_{n-1}) \quad ,$$

(3.3 - 4)

so that

$$\frac{\partial r_1}{\partial u_n} = -1 \quad \text{and} \quad \frac{\partial r'_1}{\partial u_n} = +1 \quad .$$

(3.3 - 5)

Substituting these results into (3.3 - 4) now yields,

$$F_n = \frac{\partial U(r_1)}{\partial r_1} - \frac{\partial U(r'_1)}{\partial r'_1} \quad .$$

(3.3 - 6)

This equation gives the force on the n-th atom as a function of the distances r_1 and r'_1. At equilibrium, all atoms are on lattice sites, and $r_1 = r'_1 = a$. The two terms in the above equation can be expanded about this equilibrium point in Taylor's series, of the form

$$\frac{\partial U(r_1)}{\partial r_1} = \left(\frac{\partial U(r_1)}{\partial r_1}\right)_a + \left(\frac{\partial}{\partial r_1}\frac{\partial U(r_1)}{\partial r_1}\right)_a (r_1 - a) + \ldots$$

$$\frac{\partial U(r_1')}{\partial r_1'} = \left(\frac{\partial U(r_1')}{\partial r_1'}\right)_a + \left(\frac{\partial}{\partial r_1'}\frac{\partial U(r_1')}{\partial r_1'}\right)_a (r_1' - a) + \ldots \quad . \tag{3.3-7}$$

Since we assume that the vibrational amplitudes are small compared with the equilibrium interatomic spacing a, higher order terms in the series may be neglected. Substituting these expressions into (3.3 - 6) and expressing the displacements $r_1 - a$ and $r_1' - a$ in terms of the u-parameters as indicated by (3.3 - 4), we find for the total force on the n-th atom,

$$F_n = \left(\frac{\partial U(r_1)}{\partial r_1}\right)_a - \left(\frac{\partial U(r_1')}{\partial r_1'}\right)_a + \left(\frac{\partial^2 U(r_1)}{\partial r_1^2}\right)_a (u_{n+1} - u_n) - \left(\frac{\partial^2 U(r_1')}{\partial r_1'^2}\right)_a (u_n - u_{n-1}) + \ldots \quad . \tag{3.3-8}$$

The sum of the first two terms in this equation is zero, because the same result is obtained from differentiating $U(r)$ with respect to r and setting r equal to a, as from differentiating $U(r')$ with respect to r' and setting r' equal to a. For similar reasons, the second derivatives in the two remaining terms, evaluated at $r = r' = a$, are also equal. The result, finally, can be written as

$$F_n = \beta_1(u_{n+1} - u_n) - \beta_1(u_n - u_{n-1}) = \beta_1(u_{n+1} + u_{n-1} - 2u_n) \quad , \tag{3.3-9}$$

where

$$\beta_1 = \left(\frac{\partial^2 U(r_1)}{\partial r_1^2}\right)_{r_1=a} . \tag{3.3-10}$$

This is the same result as that given by the "spring model" of (3.3 - 1). Now, however, further information relating the force constant to the interatomic potential energy of the atom in the equilibrium state has been obtained. It must be noted that this is only a first-order approximation to the true force on the n-th atom, because only interactions with nearest neighbors have been accounted for. However, it should now be apparent that forces from more distant atoms can be taken account of in a similar way by including terms of higher order in (3.3 - 2)

If one goes through precisely the same calculation, using forces and potential energies of interaction between atom n and the *second* neighbors $n + 2$ and $n - 2$, expressed in terms of the distances r_2 and r_2', one can obtain a force correction for second neighbor interactions of the same form as (3.3 - 9). In this calculation, the distances between atom n and the second neighbors can be written as

$$r_2 = 2a + (u_{n+2} - u_n) \qquad \text{and} \qquad r_2' = 2a + (u_n - u_{n-2}) \quad . \tag{3.3-11}$$

Also, the Taylor's expansions must be made about equilibrium sites at $r_2 = r_2' = 2a$. Otherwise, everything is exactly the same. When this second-neighbor force is added to the force obtained from the original calculation, the result will be

$$F_n = \beta_1(u_{n+1} + u_{n-1} - 2u_n) + \beta_2(u_{n+2} + u_{n-2} - 2u_n) \quad , \tag{3.3-12}$$

where

$$\beta_2 = \left(\frac{\partial^2 U(r_2)}{\partial r_2^2}\right)_{r_2 = 2a} . \tag{3.3-13}$$

Forces from more distant sets of atoms yield higher correction terms of the same form, and the exact force on the n-th atom can be expressed as an infinite series of such terms. Of course, this leads to equations of motion that are incredibly complex and difficult to solve. Fortunately, however, the force constants β_n usually diminish rapidly as more distant interactions are included, and higher-order terms quickly become insignificant. Indeed, for many purposes only the nearest-neighbor interaction need be considered. Since most of the important physical effects introduced by interatomic coupling are adequately illustrated by the inclusion of only nearest-neighbor forces, we shall largely limit our further discussions to this case. The calculation of higher-order contributions is of some importance, however, for without it we could never know to what extent their effect is felt, and how far the simple but frequently employed "spring models" can be trusted.

The one-dimensional ionic lattice discussed at the beginning of Section 3.2 can be used to verify these statements quite simply. For nearest-neighbor atoms at a distance r_1, the potential energy is

$$U(r_1) = -\frac{q^2}{4\pi\varepsilon_0 r_1} + \frac{A}{r_1^b} . \tag{3.3-14}$$

Differentiating twice with respect to r_1 and setting r_1 equal to a. we find

$$\beta_1 = \left(\frac{\partial^2 U(r_1)}{\partial r_1^2}\right)_a = -\frac{2q^2}{4\pi\varepsilon_0 a^3} + \frac{b(b+1)A}{a^{b+2}} . \tag{3.3-15}$$

However, the constant A can be written in terms of the lattice spacing a by (3.2 - 12), giving

$$\beta_1 = \frac{q^2}{4\pi\varepsilon_0 a^3}\left[-2 + \tfrac{1}{2}\alpha(b+1)\right] . \tag{3.3-16}$$

In writing the above expression, we have used the value 2.0 for the quantity ζ_b that appears in (3.2 - 12). This quantity is actually twice the sum of the second series in eq. (3.2 - 2), but since we have already shown that b is roughly 9.0, it is clear that the sum of this series will be very close to unity. Now, substituting the values $b = 9$ and $\alpha = 2\ln2 = 1.3863$, we find

$$\beta_1 = \frac{(4.93)q^2}{4\pi\varepsilon_0 a^3} . \tag{3.3-17}$$

An idea of the numerical value of this interatomic force constant may be obtained by substituting $a = 3.15 \times 10^{-10}$m, corresponding to KCl, into the above equation The result is $\beta_1 = 3.64$N/m $= 3.64 \times 10^{-9}$N/Å.

A similar calculation for the second-neighbor force constant yields the result

$$\beta_2 = \frac{q^2}{4\pi\varepsilon_0 a^3}\left[\frac{1}{4} + \frac{\alpha(b+1)}{2^{b+3}}\right] = \frac{(0.252)q^2}{4\pi\varepsilon_0 a^3} \quad . \tag{3.3-18}$$

The force constant for second neighbor interactions is in this example smaller than the first-neighbor force constant by a factor of about 20. For many purposes, this means that second (and higher) order interactions can be neglected entirely.

The force equations (3.3 - 1), (3.3 - 9) and (3.3 - 12) are easily transformed into equations of motion for the atoms simply by equating force to mass times acceleration. The study of these equations of motion, and the properties of their wave-like solutions is next on our agenda.

3.4 LONGITUDINAL WAVES IN CONTINUOUS LINEAR ELASTIC MEDIA

Waves most often arise as solutions of equations of motion in the form of partial differential equations. One of the simplest of these is the equation describing longitudinal acoustic waves in a linear elastic medium that is completely homogeneous and isotropic. To show how such waves can arise, let us consider the case of a long bar of such a substance, of uniform cross section, oriented parallel to the x-axis of a cartesian coördinate system. In a sample like this, elastic deformations can propagate as longitudinal waves travelling in the x-direction.

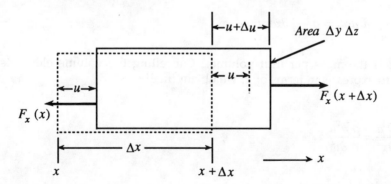

Figure 3.5 Instantaneous displacement and extensional strain of a volume element shown in the unstrained equilibrium state by the dotted rectangle, and in a strained condition at some instant of time by the solid rectangle.

Consider an element of such a linear elastic substance of length Δx and rectangular cross section $\Delta y \Delta z$, as illustrated in Figure 3.5. In the unstrained state. the element, as shown by the dotted rectangle, extends from x to $x + \Delta x$. In the presence of a stress, an elastic elongation (or compression) is produced, the left end of the element then being displaced a distance u along the x-direction, while the right end is displaced a distance $u + \Delta u$. If the medium has linear elastic properties, the stress and the resulting strain are, according to Hooke's law, directly proportional. The strain s is defined as the elastic deformation per unit length, which can be written as

$$s(x,t) = \lim_{\Delta x \to 0} \frac{\Delta u}{\Delta x} = \frac{\partial u}{\partial x} \quad . \tag{3.4-1}$$

The stress is defined as the force per unit cross-sectional area. The coördinate u is a vibration amplitude associated with an element whose equilibrium position is at some point x. The quantity u is therefore a function of position x and time t. In a linear elastic substance, the force at point x acting on an element such as the one shown will be, according to Hooke's law,

$$F(x) = Ys(x)\Delta y \Delta x \quad , \tag{3.4-2}$$

where Y is Young's modulus. At point $x + \Delta x$, the force will be

$$F(x + \Delta x) = Ys(x + \Delta x)\Delta y \Delta z \quad . \tag{3.4-3}$$

The resultant force on the element is therefore

$$F(x + \Delta x) - F(x) = Y\frac{s(x + \Delta x) - s(x)}{\Delta x}\Delta x \Delta y \Delta z = ma_x \quad , \tag{3.4-4}$$

where m is the mass and a_x the acceleration. In the differential limit, however, this can be written as

$$Y\frac{\partial s}{\partial x}dxdydz = \rho\frac{\partial^2 u}{\partial t^2}dxdydz \quad , \tag{3.4-5}$$

where ρ is the mass per unit volume. Cancelling the volume elements and using (3.4 - 1) to express s in terms of u, we obtain finally,

$$\frac{\partial^2 u}{\partial x^2} = \frac{\rho}{Y}\frac{\partial^2 u}{\partial t^2} \quad . \tag{3.4-6}$$

This can be recognized as a wave equation of the same simple form as that obtained for sound waves in ideal gaseous media or electromagnetic waves in free space. If we subsititute into this equation a plane wave solution of the usual form,

$$u(x,t) = Ae^{i(kx - \omega t)} \quad , \tag{3.4-7}$$

we find that the equation is satisfied so long as the *dispersion relation*

$$\omega = k\sqrt{\frac{Y}{\rho}} \tag{3.4-8}$$

is satisfied. This dispersion relation implies a phase velocity

$$v_p = \frac{\omega}{k} = \sqrt{\frac{Y}{\rho}} \quad, \tag{3.4-9}$$

which is a completely independent of frequency or wavelength. A wave having this property is said to be free from dispersion, or dispersionless. Transverse waves similar in all respects to these longitudinal waves can also be excited in solid substances having linear elastic properties. In this case the instantaneous deformation of the medium is in shear rather than extension or compression; as a result, the phase velocity contains the shear modulus in place of Young's modulus. We shall rely primarily on examples involving longitudinal waves, though a discussion of transverse waves will be given in another section.

3.5 PHASE VELOCITY, GROUP VELOCITY, AND DISPERSION

So far, we have spoken only of the phase velocity of waves. It is also possible to define--in a rather different way--a physically useful velocity for waves referred to as the *group velocity*. To see what this means, let us consider the case of two sinusoidal wave trains having the same amplitude, but slightly different frequencies and wavelengths. Let the first wave have frequency ω and propagation constant k, and the second, frequency $\omega + d\omega$ and propagation constant $k + dk$. We may write these two wave disturbances as

$$u_1 = A\cos(kx - \omega t) \quad, \tag{3.5-1}$$

$$u_2 = A\cos[(k + dk)x - (\omega + d\omega)t] \quad. \tag{3.5-2}$$

Superposing these waves, we can write for the total amplitude,

$$u_1 + u_2 = A[\cos(kx - \omega t) + \cos[(k + dk)x - (\omega + d\omega)t]] = A[\cos\alpha + \cos\beta] \quad. \tag{3.5-3}$$

From elementary trigonometry, however,

$$\cos\alpha + \cos\beta = 2\cos\tfrac{1}{2}(\alpha - \beta)\cos\tfrac{1}{2}(\alpha + \beta) \quad, \tag{3.5-4}$$

while from (3.5 - 3), we have

$$\alpha + \beta = 2kx - 2\omega t + x\,dk - t\,d\omega \cong 2(kx - \omega t) \quad, \tag{3.5-5}$$

and

$$\alpha - \beta = t\,d\omega - x\,dk \quad. \tag{3.5-6}$$

In (3.5 - 5) the terms containing differentials can be neglected in comparison with the others, though in (3.5 - 6), there are no "others", and the differential quantities are significant. Substituting these results into (3.5 - 3), we obtain finally,

$$u_1 + u_2 = 2A\cos(kx - \omega t)\cos(\tfrac{1}{2}t\,d\omega - \tfrac{1}{2}x\,dk) \quad . \tag{3.5-7}$$

This superposition can be regarded as a wave of the same frequency and wavelength as u_1 multiplied by a sinusoidal envelope of very much longer wavelength $4\pi/dk$, as shown in Figure 3.6.

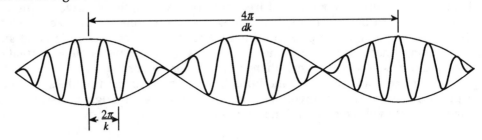

Figure 3.6 Wave train formed by superposing two sinusoidal waves of slightly different frequency and wavelength.

This long-wavelength envelope is *also* a wave having a characteristic phase velocity. The equation of motion of the point of zero phase of the envelope wave is,

$$t\,d\omega - x\,dk = 0 \quad ,$$

or, $\qquad x = \dfrac{d\omega}{dk}t = v_g t \quad .$ (3.5-8)

The phase velocity of the envelope is therefore $d\omega/dk$, or v_g. This velocity is called the *group velocity* associated with the wave (3.5 - 1). It can be shown that the energy of the wave is propagated with the group velocity. Physically, this can be understood if we observe that the propagating medium is very nearly at equilibrium in the region close to a node of the envelope. It is therefore difficult for energy to be propagated past such a point, and the energy of the wave moves with the velocity of the envelope itself. For a standing wave, there is no net energy transport, and the group velocity in this case is zero.

For elastic waves in a homogeneous, isotropic medium, as discussed above, the phase and group velocity are identical, according to (3.4 - 8), (3.4 - 9), and (3.5 - 8). This will always be true when ω depends *linearly* on k, because then ω/k and $d\omega/dk$ are always the same. Such waves are said to be non-dispersive. The term *dispersion* refers to any situation wherein the phase and group velocities are different, and any propagating medium in which this is true is referred to as a dispersive medium. In dispersive media, the phase and group velocities are not constant, but depend upon frequency. Moreover, it must be remembered that in such media, the time-honored idea that frequency times wavelength is constant is *no longer valid*. One of the easiest ways to become confused about the material we are now going to discuss is to ignore this fact!

Electromagnetic waves in vacuum are non-dispersive, since their dispersion relation has same form as that of elastic waves in a homogeneous medium. In dielectric media, however, the phase velocity of light waves (and thus the refractive index of the medium) depends on frequency; such media are therefore dispersive in regard to electromagnetic propagation. Conducting media are also dispersive for electromagnetic waves. As we shall soon see, acoustic waves traveling in a medium composed of discrete atoms bound to one another by Hooke's law forces also exhibit the phenomenon of dispersion.

The effects associated with propagation in dispersive media can be illustrated by an example involving the wave solutions of the partial differential equation

$$\frac{\partial^4 u}{\partial t^4} + \alpha^2 \frac{\partial^2 u}{\partial t^2} + \beta^2 \frac{\partial^2 u}{\partial x^2} = 0 \quad , \tag{3.5-9}$$

where α^2 and β^2 are positive constants. This equation has no apparent physical significance, but it demonstrates very well the ways in which dispersion can affect wave propagation. For solutions having the character of traveling waves, if we assume wave solutions of the form $u(x, t) = A \exp i(kx - \omega t)$, we can write

$$\frac{\partial^2 u}{\partial x^2} = -k^2 u \quad , \qquad \frac{\partial^2 u}{\partial t^2} = -\omega^2 u \quad , \quad \text{and} \qquad \frac{\partial^4 u}{\partial t^4} = \omega^4 u \quad . \tag{3.5-10}$$

Substituting these results into (3.5 - 9) and dividing by u, we get the dispersion relation

$$\omega^4 - \alpha^2 \omega^2 - \beta^2 k^2 = 0 \quad , \tag{3.5-11}$$

from which,

$$\omega^2 = \tfrac{1}{2} \left[\alpha^2 + \sqrt{\alpha^4 + 4\beta^2 k^2} \right] \quad . \tag{3.5-12}$$

In this dispersion relation, the positive sign of the radical must be chosen, since the choice of the negative sign leads to imaginary frequencies. In this context, it is important to remember that ω is by definition real and positive, while k may be negative or in some circumstances even complex. The "standard" form of the dispersion relation expresses ω as an explicit function of k, as above. In this case, however, the dispersion relation is unnecessarily complex when written this way, and it makes our work easier to solve (3.5 - 11) for k as a function of ω, to obtain

$$\beta k = \pm \omega \sqrt{\omega^2 - \alpha^2} \quad . \tag{3.5-13}$$

If this equation is divided on both sides by ω, the reciprocal of the phase velocity appears on the left, and it is then easy to show that

$$v_p = \frac{\omega}{k} = \frac{\beta}{\sqrt{\omega^2 - \alpha^2}} \quad . \tag{3.5-14}$$

The group velocity can be most easily obtained by differentiating (3.5 - 13) to obtain $dk/d\omega$, then taking the reciprocal. The result is

$$v_g = \frac{d\omega}{dk} = \frac{\beta\sqrt{\omega^2 - \alpha^2}}{2\omega^2 - \alpha^2} \quad . \tag{3.5-15}$$

First of all, it is to be noted that neither the phase velocity nor the group velocity is constant. Instead, both are functions of frequency--or of wavelength, if you substitute k for ω from (3.5 - 13). Also, the phase and group velocities are no longer equal. Even more remarkable, however, is the fact that no traveling wave whose frequency is less than $\omega = \alpha$ can be propagated in this system! This can be seen from the dispersion relation (3.5 - 13). In this expression, if k is real, the right side of the equation equals α^2 when k is zero, and becomes larger when k has any other value,

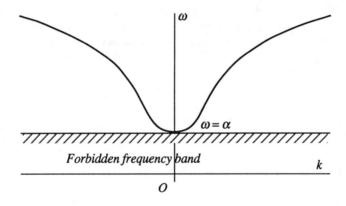

Figure 3.7 A plot of the dispersion relation associated with wave equation (3.5 – 9).

positive or negative. This is illustrated in Figure 3.7 which shows a plot of ω versus k. This system is in effect a *high-pass wave filter*; it propagates frequencies greater than $\omega = \alpha$ without attenuation, but will not propagate frequencies below this "cut-off" limit as unattenuated traveling waves. From another perspective, its action is similar to that of an electromagnetic waveguide, a device which likewise refuses to transmit radiation below a certain cutoff frequency. Though the physical mechanisms responsible for this behavior are in this case not apparent, their action is vividly portrayed in the dispersion relation.

3.6 ACOUSTIC WAVES IN ONE-DIMENSIONAL MONATOMIC LATTICES

We now return to the problem of the one-dimensional chain of equal masses, coupled together by interatomic forces, as illustrated in Figure 3.4. We shall include only nearest-neighbor interactions, and assume that vibrational amplitudes are always small compared to the lattice spacing a. Then, as we have already seen, the force on the n-th atom is given by (3.3 - 9). Equating force to mass times acceleration, we obtain

$$F_n = m\frac{\partial^2 u_n}{\partial t^2} = \beta(u_{n+1} + u_{n-1} - 2u_n) \quad , \tag{3.6-1}$$

where the force constant is now written simply as β. For a traveling wave solution of the form (3.5 - 10), the second time derivative can be written as $-\omega^2 u_n$, which leads to an equation of motion of the form

$$-m\omega^2 u_n = \beta(u_{n+1} + u_{n-1} - 2u_n) \quad . \tag{3.6-2}$$

An equation of motion of this form can clearly be written for every atom in the crystal. For a crystal containing N atoms, we therefore obtain (in place of the usual partial differential equation) a set of N coupled difference equations of the above form. This difference arises because we now have a system of discrete vibrating atoms instead of a continuous isotropic medium. These equations cause no insurmountable mathematical problems; they act in most ways very much like a single partial differential equation, and can be solved by similar methods. The u-parameters are vibrational amplitudes associated with atomic equilibrium sites, the x-coördinate of the n-th site (with reference to an origin at the distant left end of the lattice) being written as na. We may thus write for each vibrating atom, wavelike solutions of the form

$$u_n = Ae^{i(kx_n - \omega t)} = Ae^{i(kna - \omega t)} \quad ,$$

$$u_{n+1} = Ae^{i[k(n+1)a - \omega t]} = e^{ika}u_n \quad , \tag{3.6-3}$$

and $\quad u_{n-1} = Ae^{i[k(n-1)a - \omega t]} = e^{-ika}u_n \quad .$

Substituting these expressions into (3.6 - 2) and cancelling u_n, we find the dispersion relation,

$$\omega^2 = \frac{\beta}{m}(2 - e^{ika} - e^{-ika}) = \frac{2\beta}{m}(1 - \cos ka) \quad . \tag{3.6-4}$$

From elementary trigonometry, however,

$$2\sin^2\frac{\theta}{2} = 1 - \cos\theta \quad , \tag{3.6-5}$$

which allows us finally to write,

$$\omega = \sqrt{\frac{4\beta}{m}}\sin\left|\frac{ka}{2}\right| = \omega_m\sin\left|\frac{ka}{2}\right| \quad , \tag{3.6-6}$$

where

$$\omega_m = \sqrt{4\beta/m} \quad . \tag{3.6-7}$$

The absolute value signs are written in (3.6 - 6) merely to indicate that ω must be regarded as positive whatever the sign of k may be. In the future, we shall usually omit them for simplicity, but it should be observed that the frequency must always have a positive sign.

This dispersion relation is plotted in Figure 3.8. It is to be noted, first of all, that unlike the homogeneous isotropic medium treated in Section 3.4, this system is *dispersive*. The dispersion is solely due to the fact that it is not infinitesimally subdivisible but is composed of discrete atomic masses. In any event, unlike sound waves in gases, sound waves in crystal lattices are dispersive. Moreover, since the sine function cannot be greater than unity, there is an *upper limit* ω_m to the frequency of acoustic waves that will propagate in the lattice. In this respect it somewhat resembles the curious system of Section 3.5, except that in this case the lattice acts as a *low-pass filter* for sound waves, rather than a high-pass filter. In this treatment, we have assumed that the waves are longitudinal. Transverse waves are similar, except for the fact that the force constant β and the "cutoff frequency" ω_m are not the same for transverse and longitudinal waves, as we shall see later.

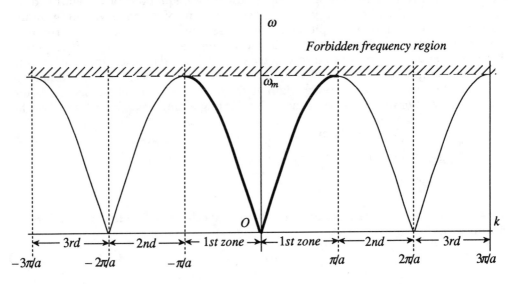

Figure 3.8 Plot of the dispersion relation for the one-dimensional monatomic lattice. The heavily accented part of the curve is within the first Brillouin zone.

The phase and group velocities can now be determined in the usual way. If we divide both sides of (3.6 - 6) by k, we obtain the phase velocity, which is best written in the form

$$v_p = \frac{\omega}{k} = a\sqrt{\frac{\beta}{m}} \left| \frac{\sin\frac{1}{2}ka}{\frac{1}{2}ka} \right| = v_0 \left| \frac{\sin\frac{1}{2}ka}{\frac{1}{2}ka} \right| \quad , \tag{3.6-8}$$

where

$$v_0 = a\sqrt{\beta / m} \quad . \tag{3.6-9}$$

The group velocity is found by differentiating ω with respect to k, which gives

$$v_g = v_0 \left| \cos\frac{1}{2}ka \right| \quad . \tag{3.6-10}$$

In the limit of long wavelengths, k approaches zero, $\sin(ka/2) \cong ka/2$. and the dispersion relation can be closely approximated by

$$\omega = ka\sqrt{\beta / m} = v_0 k \quad . \tag{3.6-11}$$

This is the same dispersion relation we associate with dispersionless propagation. It is also apparent that in this limit both phase and group velocities have very nearly the constant value v_0. Therefore, for long wavelengths and low frequencies, wave propagation is almost dispersionless, and is practically identical to that described in Section 3.4 for perfectly homogeneous media. It is only when the wavelengths are relatively short, and when frequencies are no longer small on the scale of ω_m that dispersion is appreciable. Since the maximum frequency ω_m is given by (3.6 - 7), while v_0 is defined by (3.6 - 9), we can write the cutoff frequency in the form

$$\omega_m = \frac{2v_0}{a} \quad . \tag{3.6-12}$$

Since the long-wavelength sound velocity is easily determined, we are now able to calculate the cutoff frequency ω_m. Typical sound velocities in crystals are of the order of 5000 m/s, while interatomic spacings are of the order of 3.0Å (0.3nm). If these figures are substituted into (3.6 - 12) we find a cutoff frequency of 3.3×10^{13} rad/sec, or 5.3×10^{12}Hz--five *trillion* oscillations per second. The smallest value of k at which this frequency is attained is $k = \pi/a$, at the upper edge of the boldly accented part of the dispersion curve shown in Figure 3.8. This corresponds to a wavelength equal to *twice the interatomic distance a*. Thus, long waves propagate much like sound waves in a perfectly homogeneous medium. Under these circumstances, the wavelength spans a distance of many times the interatomic spacing, and the wave does not sense the discrete atomicity of the material. It is only when the wavelength begins to be comparable to the distance between atoms--more precisely, to twice this distance--that the structure of the lattice announces its presence through the phenomenon of dispersion. This means that effects that concern only long wavelength or low frequency are not affected by dispersion; an example is the propagation of sound at ordinary audio or ultrasonic frequencies. When shorter waves or higher frequencies are significant, however, as they are for the thermal and optical properties of crystals, effects related to dispersion are very important and must be accounted for.

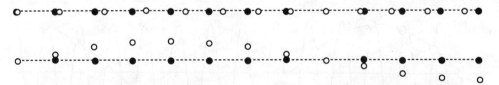

Figure 3.9 Atomic motions in longitudinal (top) and transverse (bottom) waves in one-dimensional lattices. Black circles represent atomic equilibrium sites, while white circles depict actual positions of atoms at some given time. For clarity, the amplitude of oscillatory motion is exaggerated in this diagram. In reality, the oscillation amplitude is small in comparison with the interatomic spacing.

The motion of the atoms themselves is given by (3.6 - 3), which shows that each atom oscillates harmonically with a common frequency ω related to the propagation constant by the dispersion relation (3.6 - 6). Each osciilator's phase differs from that of its nearest neighbors by the angle ka. As one proceeds along the chain, the phase of the oscillations changes from one atom to the next by this amount, and when the cumulative phase change amounts to 2π radians, an entire wavelength has been traversed. For longitudinal and transverse waves, this motion is illustrated in Figure 3.9. It will be observed that the geometry of transverse motion is easier to visualize than the longitudinal case. It is therefore convenient to use diagrams in which transverse displacements are illustrated, even though the actual displacements may be longitudinal. We shall frequently employ this practice.

The wavelength illustrated in Figure 3.9 is considerably larger than the interatomic spacing, and the phase difference ka between adjacent atoms is quite small. As the wavelength decreases, k becomes larger, and this phase difference increases, finally reaching 180° when $k = \pi/a$. At this point, the frquency has risen to the maximum possible value ω_m, as shown in Figure 3.8. Now adjacent atoms oscillate in opposite directions, up and down for transverse waves, toward and away from each other for longitudinal waves.

The dispersion relation, illustrated in Figure 3.8, seems to indicate that for any given frequency less than ω_m, there are many possible values of k, and therefore many possible wavelengths. A line drawn parallel to the k-axis within the band of allowed frequencies, for example, will intersect the dispersion curve at many points, each of which defines a possible value of k. Each of these values corresponds to a wavelength that is consistent with a solution of the form (3.6 - 3) and a dispersion relation of the form (3.6 - 6). The longest of these wavelengths corresponds to the smallest possible values of k, that is, the two that lie within the region of the k-axis designated in Figure 3.8 as the "first zone". The next smallest values of k will lie within the region referred to in the figure as the "second zone", and so on. There are in principle, an infinite number of allowed values of k, an infinite number of wavelengths, and an infinite number of "zones", for any possible frequency. The physical significance of these multiple solutions is illustrated in Figure 3.10.

It is apparent from this diagram that more than one harmonic wave can be fitted to a given sinusoidal arrangements of atomic displacements. The two longest possible waves are shown in the figure, but an infinite sequence of such waves of successively shorter wavelength can also be drawn to reproduce precisely the same displacements at any time. For clarity, transverse displacements are shown in the figure, but the same possiblity exists for a sinusoidally arranged sequence of longitudinal displacements like the one shown in Figure 3.9.

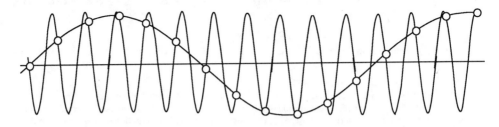

Figure 3.10 A given sinusoidal arrangement of transverse atomic displacements can be represented equally well by two harmonic waves having different wavelengths, as illustrated. Harmonic waves of even shorter wavelength can be drawn through the atoms as arranged above, giving representations of smaller wavelength than either of those shown in this diagram.

In this situation, it is evident that any possible harmonic motion of the atoms can be described using a value of k within the first zone of Figure 3.8, corresponding to a wavelength less than infinity but *larger than twice the interatomic spacing*. The additional representations having wavelength smaller than twice the interatomic distance are merely alternative mathematical descriptions of exactly the same physical situation, inasmuch as they all give the same atomic displacements at every instant of time. All the physics of the problem is therefore encompassed by the first zone-- the first *Brillouin zone*, as it is usually designated, after the French physicist Léon Brillouin, who first rigorously analyzed the details of these problems. We need therefore consider explicitly only the part of the dispersion relation within the first Brillouin zone--the part that is heavily accented in Figure 3.8.

The rest of the dispersion relation, the parts within the 2nd, 3rd, and higher Brilouin zones, can in this problem be safely ignored. In other cases, notably the treatment of free electrons as propagating quantum mechanical "matter waves", this is no longer possible, and the dispersion relation in the higher zones need not be an exact repeat of what lies within the first zone. It will be noted that the Brillouin zones are defined in a k-space which is essentially the same as that associated with the reciprocal lattice. In this example, the periodicity of the space lattice is defined by the interatomic distance a, while the reciprocal lattice is of periodicity $1/a$, which has the same dimensions as k. Each zone illustrated in Figure 3.8 occupies a distance $2\pi/a$ along the k-axis. Moreover, all the branches of the dispersion relation lying in the higher zones can be made to coincide with those in the first by translations of *integral multiples* of this distance along the k-direction. These phenomena all have their origin in the property of translational invariance associated with the direct lattice of the crystal.

The propagation of waves in a chain of discrete masses can be understood physically as a process in which a propagating wave is partially reflected by each of the masses. The waves reflected from neighboring atoms traverse paths that differ in length by twice the interatomic spacing a. They will therefore interfere constructively when this path difference equals an integral number of wavelengths, or when

$$N\lambda = 2a \qquad (N = 1,2,3,...) \ . \tag{3.6-13}$$

This is easily identified as the Bragg equation in one-dimensional form, wherein the scattering angle is necessarily 90°, so that $\sin\theta = 1$. Partial waves reflected from individual atomic masses, will thus undergo Bragg reflection when the propagation constant $k = 2\pi/\lambda$ has the values $N\pi/a$. These values correspond exactly to the boundaties of the Brillouin zones on the k-axis in Figure 3.8. The waves propagated by the lattice therefore undergo Bragg reflection by the lattice itself at the boundaries of the Brillouin zones. This property can actually be used to define the zone boundaries. Brillouin zones may be defined this way in two and three dimensions, and are useful in describing how waves are propagated in lattices of higher dimensionality. In all instances they are found to possess the symmetry of the reciprocal lattice. We shall postpone further discussion of Brillouin zones in two and three dimensions, however, until the need arises.

Plots of the phase velocity and group velocity versus wavelength are shown in Figures 3.11 and 3.12. It is clear that these two quantities are quite different unless the wavelength is large compared with the interatomic spacing. The phase velocity does not exhibit the periodic behavior of the dispersion relation and the group velocity, but it must be remembered that the phase velocity is a purely geometric concept, and that the wave's energy is propagated with the group velocity. Measurements of wave velocity ordinarily yield the group velocity rather than the phase velocity, and the wave's interaction with its physical environment is also in general governed by the group velocity. This peculiar behavior of the phase velocity has therefore no profound physical significance.

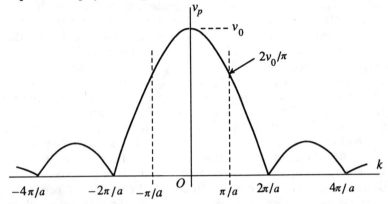

Figure 3.11 Phase velocity of wavwes in a linear monatomic lattice plotted as a function of propagation constant k.

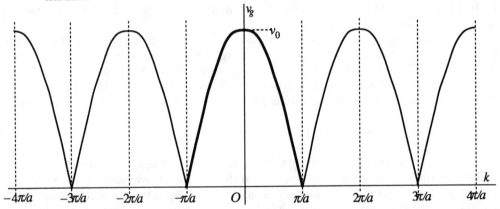

Figure 3.12 Group velocity of waves in a linear monatomic lattice as a function of propagation constant k. The heavily accented part of curve is within the first Brillouin zone.

The application of these one-dimensional calculations to three-dimensional crystals obviously has to be approached with some caution. It is often useful to view the "interatomic spacing" a as a spacing d_{hkl} between adjacent planes belonging to some specific family in a three-dimensional lattice, the propagation direction being normal to these planes, as illustrated in Figure 3.13.

Waves much longer than the interatomic spacing are propagated much like those in a homogeneous medium, at an essentially constant velocity and with no measurable dispersion. This "dispersionless range", however, extends to frequencies that are very high by conventional standards. It is only when the frequency approaches ω_m that dispersion is important. Since the cutoff frequency is about 10^{13} Hz in most substances, even the highest acoustic frequencies that can be generated in the laboratory (of the order of 1000MHz) are still very close to the origin on the scale of the dispersion relation as shown in Figure 3.8.

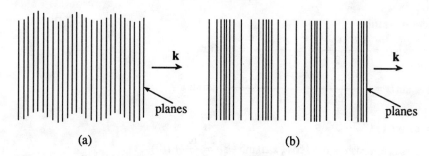

(a)   (b)

Figure 3.13 Propagation of (a) transverse and (b) longitudinal waves in a three-dimensional crystal. The direction of propagation is normal to the crystal planes that are illustrated.

In the crystal, when dispersion sets in, the group velocity becomes substantially less than it is in the dispersionless limit. Under these conditions, the effect of the partial reflections by atomic masses can be understood in terms of a "refractive index" v_0/v_g which can be significantly larger than unity. When the frequency approaches the cutoff frequency at which Bragg reflection occurs, the group velocity gets quite small, and this refractive index becomes very large. For frequencies *above* the cutoff frequency, waves cannot be propagated without attenuation. The substance then becomes *totally reflecting* to incident acoustic energy, and behaves much like a totally reflecting optical medium.The properties of the system in this range of frequencies will be discussed in the next section.

3.7 EFFECTS AT FREQUENCIES ABOVE THE CUTOFF FREQUENCY

Suppose now that oscillations are somehow excited at a frequency greater than the cutoff frequency ω_m. The equations of motion are the same as before, so equation (3.6 - 1) is still valid. If any kind of wave solutions are to exist, the subsequent development through (3.4 - 7) must also be valid. The difference is that now the left side of the dispersion relation (3.6 - 6) is greater than ω_m, so that the quantity $\sin(ka/2)$ must be larger than unity. The sine function is less than or equal to unity for all *real* values of its argument, so we are led to suspect that ka must be a complex quantity with a nonzero imaginary part. Since a is real, we are forced to assume that the propagation constant k is a complex quantity which we shall now write,

$$k = k_r + ik_i \quad . \tag{3.7-1}$$

We must now write the amplitude u_n as

$$u_n = Ae^{i[(k_r+ik_i)na-\omega t]} = Ae^{i(k_r na-\omega t)}e^{-k_i na} \quad . \tag{3.7-2}$$

From this it is evident that solutions in this range of frequencies must be damped waves having an exponential attenuation coefficient k_i. Also, we must now write (3.6 - 6) as

$$\frac{\omega}{\omega_m} = \sin\tfrac{1}{2}(k_r + ik_i)a = \sin\tfrac{1}{2}k_r a \cos\tfrac{1}{2}ik_i a + \cos\tfrac{1}{2}k_r a \sin\tfrac{1}{2}ik_i a \quad . \tag{3.7-3}$$

However, since

$$\cos ix = \frac{e^{i(ix)} + e^{-i(ix)}}{2} = \frac{e^x + e^{-x}}{2} = \cosh x$$

$$\tag{3.7-4}$$

and $\quad \sin ix = \dfrac{e^{i(ix)} - e^{-i(ix)}}{2i} = -\dfrac{1}{i}\cdot\dfrac{e^x - e^{-x}}{2} = i\sinh x \quad,$

we can write (3.7 - 3) as

$$\sin\tfrac{1}{2}k_r a \cosh\tfrac{1}{2}k_i a + i\cos\tfrac{1}{2}k_r a \sinh\tfrac{1}{2}k_i a = \frac{\omega}{\omega_m} + i(0) \quad . \tag{3.7-5}$$

The quantities on both sides of this equation can be equal only if their real and imaginary parts are separately equal. Therefore, one can write

$$\sin\tfrac{1}{2}k_r a \cosh\tfrac{1}{2}k_i a = \frac{\omega}{\omega_m} \tag{3.7-6}$$

and $\quad \cos\tfrac{1}{2}k_r a \sinh\tfrac{1}{2}k_i a = 0 \quad .$ $\tag{3.7-7}$

The function $\sinh x$ is zero only when $x = 0$. In (3.7 - 7) this would require that k_i be zero, which in turn implies that k is a real quantity. As we know, however, when ω/ω_m is greater than unity, k cannot be real. Therefore, in order that (3.7 - 7) be satisfied, we must have $\cos(k_r a/2) = 0$, or $k_r a = \pm\pi, \pm3\pi, \pm5\pi$, etc. But then, $\sin(k_r a/2)$ must have the value ±1 in equation (3.7 - 6). Choosing the plus sign, we find,

$$\frac{\omega}{\omega_m} = \cosh\tfrac{1}{2}k_i a \quad, \tag{3.7-8}$$

or, taking the inverse hyperbolic cosine of both sides,

$$k_i = \frac{2}{a}\cosh^{-1}\frac{\omega}{\omega_m} \quad . \tag{3.7-9}$$

Choosing the minus sign leads to no other solution, since the cosh function cannot be negative.

As demonstrated by (3.7 - 2), k_i is the attenuation coefficient; its reciprocal represents a distance within which the wave amplitude is reduced by a factor of $1/e$. The attenuation factor is plotted as a function of frequency in Figure 3.14. For frequencies below the cutoff frequency, the attenuation factor is zero, since the imaginary part of k is zero in that frequency range. Above the cutoff frequency, the attenuation factor is given by (3.7 - 9); starting from zero at $\omega = \omega_m$ it rises rapidly with frequency as illustrated. For a frequency 1.0% greater than the cutoff value, $\omega/\omega_m = 1.01$, and $\cosh^{-1}(1.01) = 0.1413$. For a lattice in which the interatomic spacing has the typical value 3.0Å (0.3nm), this leads to a value for the attenuation coefficient of $9.42 \times 10^8 \text{m}^{-1}$, whose reciprocal is $1.06 \times 10^{-9}\text{m}$, or 10.6Å. For this frequency, then, waves are attenuated in amplitude by a factor $1/e$ in a distance corresponding to only about three times the atomic spacing. Therefore, waves of practically any frequency that exceeds ω_m are very strongly attenuated by the lattice.

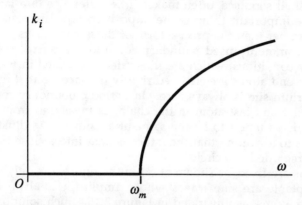

Figure 3.14 The attenuation coefficient for waves on a monatomic lattice plotted as a function of frequency. Since the propagation constant k has no imaginary part for frequencies less than the cutoff frequency, the attenuation factor is zero in that frequency range.

The question of what happens to the energy of attenuated waves above the cutoff frequency can be resolved by noting that there are no energy loss mechanisms whatever in the equations of motion we have written for this system. All the forces are conservative, and for small amplitudes are similar to those exerted by ideal Hooke's law springs. There is no friction, nor any other mechanism for dissipating energy. Therefore, if energy is not transmitted by the system, it has to be reflected. We may conclude from this that the "damping" process corresponds to an internal reflection--total reflection in a lattice of appreciable thickness--rather than any kind of dissipative attenuation. If the "crystal" is very thin, however, that is, if the total number of atoms is not very large, some energy may be propagated through the system and leak out the other side, particularly at freqencies not far above cutoff.

3.8 BOUNDARY CONDITIONS, NORMAL MODES, AND THE DENSITY OF VIBRATIONAL STATES

Thus far, we have considered only solutions of the wave equation. In most situations, there are requirements that solutions satisfy not only an equation of motion, but *also* certain boundary conditions at the surfaces of the sample. We shall see that the effect of imposing boundary conditions on the wave equation is ordinarily to limit the possible frequencies or wavelengths to a finite--though ordinarily very large--set of discrete values.

In the preceding analysis, the lattice has usually been viewed as containing a very large number of atoms, though a critical examination will reveal that no such assumption has been made explicitly. The wave solutions and dispersion relations we have found, are therefore valid no matter how large--or small--the number of atoms in the lattice may be. From this point on, we shall assume that there are exactly N atoms in the lattice; this number is ordinarily, though *not necessarily* very large. The boundary conditions, in a one-dimensional lattice are applied to the first and last atoms in the chain. The exact choice of boundary conditions is somewhat arbitrary, and as we shall soon see, often makes little difference in a lattice containing many atoms. The important thing is the imposition of some reasonable set of boundary conditions rather than the precise form of those conditions.

The two most commonly used boundary conditions are *fixed end* conditions and *periodic* boundary conditions, which are illustrated illustrated in Figure 3.15. In the fixed-end case, the end atoms are clamped rigidly in place, so that their displacement from the equlibrium site is always zero. In periodic boundary conditions, the displacement of the first and last atom in the chain, as measured from the respective equilibrium sites, is assumed to be the same at all times. As illustrated in the diagram, this amounts to assuming that the lattice is bent into a closed curve, which may for simplicity be regarded as a circle.

If the end atoms are fixed, as shown at (a) in the figure, the only harmonic solutions that are acceptable are sine waves whose amplitude is always zero at the coördinates of the end atoms, as illustrated in Figure 3.16. Such solutions are standing waves, composed of two travelling waves going in opposite directions, with propagation constants k and $-k$. These solutions have the form,

$$u(x,t) = Ae^{ikx}e^{-i\omega t} + Ae^{-ikx}e^{-i\omega t} = (2A\cos kx)e^{-i\omega t} \quad . \tag{3.8-1}$$

In this expression, moreover, not all values of k can be accepted; only those giving zero displacement at the end atoms can be used, as shown in Figure 3.16. This leads to a *discrete* set of solutions that satisfy both the equations of motion (3.6 - 2) and the fixed-end boundary conditions, a set which includes only a finite number of allowed wavelengths. These conditions apply to both transverse and longitudinal waves.

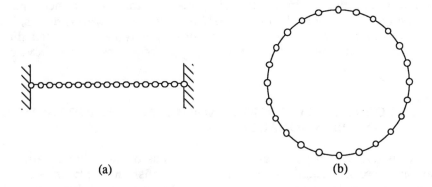

(a)   (b)

Figure 3.15 Schematic representation of (a) fixed-end and (b) periodic boundary conditions as applied to a one-dimensional monatomic lattice.

It is clear from Figure 3.16 that for a monatomic lattice of length L, only waves of wavelength $2L, 2L/2, 2L/3,$, etc. satisfy fixed-end boundary conditions. The smallest wavelength that could normally exist in the first Brillouin zone is $\lambda = 2a$. The fixed-end boundary conditions prohibit the excitation of this mode, however, since

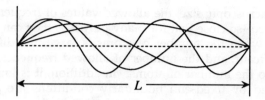

Figure 3.16 Sinusoidal waves that satisfy fixed-end boundary colnditions in a one-dimensional lattice.

it requires *every* atom of the system, including those at the ends, to be in motion. Since the length L can be expressed in terms of the interatomic spacing a as

$$L = (N-1)a \quad , \tag{3.8-2}$$

the possible wavelengths as illustrated in the figure must be

$$\lambda = 2L, \frac{2L}{2}, \frac{2L}{3}, \frac{2L}{4}, \cdots \frac{2L}{(N-2)} \quad . \tag{3.8-3}$$

In this expression, the sequence has to be terminated at the point shown, since the next shortest wavelength would be $2L/(N-1)$, which according to (3.8 - 2) is the same as $2a$, and must therefore be excluded. There are thus a total of $N-2$ solutions of the wave equations in the first zone that satisfy fixed-end boundary conditions. These solutions can be indexed in terms of possible values of k simply by setting k equal to $2\pi/\lambda$ in (3.8 - 3), to obtain.

$$k = k_n = \frac{\pi}{L}, \frac{2\pi}{L}, \frac{3\pi}{L}, \frac{4\pi}{L}, \cdots \frac{(N-2)\pi}{L}$$

$$= \frac{\pi}{(N-1)a}, \frac{2\pi}{(N-1)a}, \frac{3\pi}{(N-1)a}, \frac{4\pi}{(N-1)a}, \cdots \frac{N-2}{N-1} \cdot \frac{\pi}{a} \quad . \tag{3.8-4}$$

Corresponding to the possible values of k there are discrete frequencies ω_n given by (3.6 - 6) as

$$\omega_n = \omega_m \sin \frac{\pi}{2(N-1)}, \ \omega_m \sin \frac{2\pi}{2(N-1)}, \ \omega_m \sin \frac{3\pi}{2(N-1)}, \cdots \omega_m \sin \frac{N-2}{N-1} \cdot \frac{\pi}{a} \quad . \tag{3.8-5}$$

Physically, several points should be noted. First, it should be observed that the imposition of boundary conditions has transformed a continuous range of possible wavelengths and frequencies into one that is *quantized*, that is, into one in which only a set of discrete frequencies and wavelengths is allowed. Quantization is a word most frequently used with reference to quantum theory, but it should be apparent that it has the same meaning--and the same importance--with reference to many problems in classical physics.

Also, it is significant that the number of allowed frequencies and wavelengths is closely related to the number of atoms. For a chain containing only a few coupled atoms, the number of allowed frequencies or wavelengths is small, and they are widely spaced along their respective axes. but when the number of atoms is large, as it is in systems of macroscopic size, the allowed values of frequency and wavelength are very closely spaced--so close that for many purposes they can be treated as a continuum. Moreover, when the number of atoms is large, the difference between N and $N - 2$ is insignificant, and the number of allowed frequencies and wavelengths is essentially equal to the number of atoms. In addition, it is important to note that the solutions allowed by fixed-end boundariy conditions are all standing waves consisting of a superposition of two travelling waves having equal amplitude and k-values equal in magnitude, but opposite in sign. Finally, one should observe that the allowed values of k are *equally spaced* along the k axis, but that because of the nonlinear character of the dispersion relation, this is not true of the allowed values of frequency on the ω-axis.

Steady-state solutions of the wave equation (or other equations of motion) that also satisfy an appropriate set of boundary conditions, like those derived above, are often referred to as the *normal modes* of the oscillatory system. The allowed values of k and ω given above define the set of normal modes of oscillation for a one-dimensional monatomic lattice with fixed-end boundary conditions.

The case of periodic boundary conditions can be treated by this same approach, but is a bit more difficult because of differences that exist between chains containing even and odd numbers of atoms. It is important to treat the case of periodic boundary conditions in detail, however, because boundary conditions of this form are very simple to use, and usually furnish the simplest mathematical route to soving problems that would otherwise be unnecessarily difficult and complex. We shall therefore ordinarily use periodic boundary conditions. The case of periodic boundary conditions differs from that of fixed-end conditions also in that these boundary conditions allow *traveling waves* to propagate; in fact, traveling waves are the primary excitations under periodic boundary conditions, though standing waves can also exist under the proper conditions.

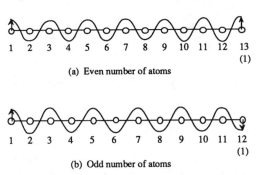

(a) Even number of atoms

(b) Odd number of atoms

Figure 3.17 Periodic boundary conditions applied to chains containing even and odd numbers of atoms. At (a), a wave of wavelength twice the atomic spacing satisfies periodic boundary conditions with no difficulty in a chain of 12 atoms, as shown by the arrows representing atomic displacements of atoms 1 and 13, which are equivalent. At (b), where the chain contains 11 atoms, the propagation of a wave of this wavelength implies that equivalent atoms 1 and 12 must move in opposite directions at the same time. Such a mode therefore cannot propagate in a chain having an odd number of atoms.

The case of periodic boundary conditions is illustrated in Figure 3.17, which shows two lattices, one containing an even number of atoms (12 in the diagram), the other having an odd number (11). It is as if the circular chain illustrated in Figure 3.15(b) has been cut and laid out in a straight line. Atom 13 at (a) in the above diagram and atom 1 are equivalent, and their displacements must be equal at all times. They must in fact be regarded as the same atom, as in Fig. 3.15(b). Similar remarks apply to atoms 1 and 12 at (b) above. For an even number of atoms, there is no problem in exciting the smallest allowed wavelength ($\lambda = 2a$) in the first zone. In this case the displacements of the equivalent atoms 1 and 13 are automatically the same. This is not true in a chain having an odd number of atoms, where, as shown at (b) above, the two atoms regarded as equivalent must move in opposite directions for a wave having this wavelength. In fact, such a wave cannot be excited, and this mode must be excluded for an odd number of atoms. Moreover, in both instances, the *longest* wave that can be excited is now (for similar reasons) no longer $2L$, but L, The allowed wavelengths are therefore,

$$\lambda = L, \frac{L}{2}, \frac{L}{3}, \frac{L}{4}, \cdots 2a = L, \frac{L}{2}, \frac{L}{3}, \frac{L}{4}, \cdots \frac{L}{\frac{1}{2}N} \quad , \qquad (N \text{ even}) \qquad (3.8\text{-}6)$$

the length of the lattice being now related to the spacing by $L = Na.$, as shown in the figure. For odd values of N, the wavelengths are the same, except that the last term in the sequence must be excluded, the series of numbers in the denominators running only to the integer value $(N - 1)/2$. Therefore, we find

$$\lambda = L, \frac{L}{2}, \frac{L}{3}, \frac{L}{4}, \cdots \frac{L}{\frac{1}{2}(N-1)} \quad , \qquad (N \text{ odd}) \quad . \qquad (3.8\text{-}7)$$

Corresponding to these wavelengths, as before, are allowed values of k. In this case, however, since traveling waves can propagate in either direction, each wavelength is associated with *two* possible values of k, one positive, the other negative. The allowed values of k are therefore,

$$k = k_n = \pm\frac{2\pi}{L}, \pm\frac{4\pi}{L}, \pm\frac{6\pi}{L}, \cdots \pm\frac{N\pi}{L}$$

$$= \pm\frac{\pi}{a}\cdot\frac{2}{N}, \pm\frac{\pi}{a}\cdot\frac{4}{N}, \pm\frac{\pi}{a}\cdot\frac{6}{N}, \cdots \pm\frac{\pi}{a}\cdot\frac{N}{N} \quad , \quad (N \text{ even}, \ L = Na) \quad , \qquad (3.8\text{-}8)$$

and $\quad k = k_n = \pm\frac{2\pi}{L}, \pm\frac{4\pi}{L}, \pm\frac{6\pi}{L}, \cdots \pm\frac{(N-1)\pi}{L}$

$$= \pm\frac{\pi}{a}\cdot\frac{2}{N}, \pm\frac{\pi}{a}\cdot\frac{4}{N}, \pm\frac{\pi}{a}\cdot\frac{6}{N}, \cdots \pm\frac{\pi}{a}\cdot\frac{N-1}{N} \quad , \quad (N \text{ odd}, \ L = Na) \quad . \qquad (3.8\text{-}9)$$

From this, it is apparent that for N even, there are N traveling wave solutions that satisfy periodic boundary conditions, while for N odd, there are $N - 1$ such solutions. The allowed frequencies can be calculated as before, from (3.6 - 6)

The physical points noted in regard to the solutions satisfying fixed-end conditions will be found to be valid here also. In particular, for small values of N, there are only a few widely-spaced allowed values of k and ω--values, moreover, that may be quite different from those associated with fixed-end boundary conditions for that same value of N. For such systems, the boundary conditions have a lot to do with determining the character of allowed vibrational modes. If the number of atoms is large, however, the allowed values of k and ω are very closely spaced, and the number of solutions is essentially equal to the number of atoms. The allowed values of k are again equally spaced along the k-axis. Thus, when there are very many atoms, it makes little difference physically what kind of boundary conditions are imposed. So it makes sense to use those that are easiest for purposes of calculation, which usually means periodic boundary conditions.

Sometimes it is important to know the density with which closely spaced allowed values of k or ω are packed along their respective axes in the dispersion relation plot. The number of allowed values of k or ω per unit distance along their respective axes is referred to as the vibrational *density of states* $g(k)$ or $g(\omega)$, as the case may be. The quantity $g(\omega)d\omega$ thus represents the number of allowed vibrational modes in a differential frequency range $d\omega$ about some given frequency ω. This situation is illustrated in Figure 3.18, which also shows some of the differences between systems containing only a few coupled atoms and those in which there are a very large number. Periodic boundary conditions are used in this example, so that the allowed k-values extend from $-\pi/a$ to $+\pi/a$.

Since the allowed k-values are equally spaced, and (if the number of atoms is large) the number of allowed states is essentially the same as the number of atoms, there will be N allowed states in a distance $2\pi/a$ along the k-axis. This means that the number of states per unit distance has the constant value $Na/2\pi$. By definition,

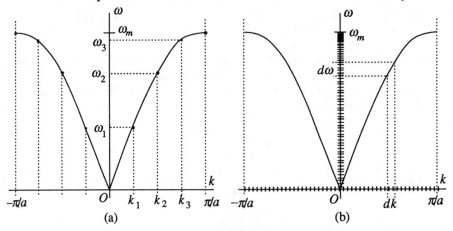

Figure 3,18 Allowed vibrational states of monatomic one-dimensional systems in which there are (a) very few, and (b) very many atoms. Periodic boundary conditions are assumed. At (a) there are only a few isolated vibrational states, while at (b) the allowed states are so closely spaced as to form a quasi-continuous distribution. In this case, the number of states and the number of atoms can be regarded as equal, though this is not necessarily so in (a). Note that the allowed values of k are equally spaced in both cases.

this is the density of states $g(k)$. In a small interval dk along the k-axis, such as the one shown in Figure 3.18(b), the number of states will therefore be,

$$g(k)dk = \frac{Na}{2\pi}\,dk \quad .$$

(3.8-10)

From the diagram, it is clear that the number of states in the interval $d\omega$ along the ω-axis, which is equal to $g(\omega)d\omega$, is exactly the same as the number of states in dk. Therefore,

$$g(\omega)d\omega = g(k)dk = \frac{Na}{2\pi} dk = \frac{Na}{2\pi} \frac{dk}{d\omega} d\omega \quad .$$

(3.8-11)

The quantity $dk/d\omega$ is the reciprocal of the group velocity (3.6 - 11), which allows us, with the help of (3.6 - 12), to write

$$g(\omega)d\omega = \frac{N}{2\pi} \frac{2}{\omega_m \cos\frac{1}{2}ka} d\omega \quad .$$

(3.8-12)

However, according to the dispersion relation (3.6 - 6),

$$\sin\tfrac{1}{2}ka = \frac{\omega}{\omega_m}, \quad \text{and} \quad \cos\tfrac{1}{2}ka = \frac{\sqrt{\omega_m^2 - \omega^2}}{\omega_m} \quad .$$

(3.8-13)

Substituting this into (3.8 - 12), we may finally write the density of states $g(\omega)$ as

$$g(\omega)d\omega = \frac{N}{\pi} \frac{d\omega}{\sqrt{\omega_m^2 - \omega^2}} \quad .$$

(3,8-14)

For frequencies small compared to ω_m, $g(\omega)$ has the nearly constant value $N/\pi\omega_m$, As dispersion sets in with increasing frequency, $g(\omega)$ increases, becoming very large near the cutoff frequency. These features are easily seen to be consistent with Figure 3.18(b). The density-of-states concept is very useful in solid-state physics; we shall encounter it in later chapters in several different contexts.

3.9 TRANSVERSE WAVES IN CRYSTAL LATTICES

Our treatment of waves in periodic lattices has been framed largely in terms of longitudinal waves, though the possibility of exciting transverse waves has frequently been mentioned. When the picture of coupled ideal harmonic oscillators is valid--that is, when interatomic forces act like ideal springs--longitudinal and transverse modes can propagate independently of one another. They differ only in that transverse waves are polarized, and that their velocity may differ from that of longitudinal waves having the same wavelength.

A realistic description of transverse waves in periodic lattices arising from any simple model of interatomic forces is too complex to be presented in detail here. We shall therefore merely show that wave equations of the same form as those already obtained for longitudinal waves hold for small transverse oscillations of a linear chain of masses where Hooke's law forces act between neighboring atoms. We shall also investigate the differences between longitudinal and transverse wave propagation mentioned above.

One of the main differences between transverse and longitudinal oscillations of harmonically coupled masses is that the effective force constants for longitudinal and transverse motions are not the same. This can be understood most simply in reference to the situation illustrated in Figure 3.19, where a single mass is attached by ideal springs to two rigid supports so that it can oscillate either longitudinally or transversely. These springs can be regarded as having an unstretched equilibrium length l_0, and having been stretched to length a in being fastened to the mass in its equilibrium position. In the crystal lattice, this situation can arise when one atom is free to move, all others being held fixed in their lattice sites.

If this atom is displaced longitudinally, in the x-direction, the situation is very simple. At equilibrium, equal and opposite forces act on the mass. Since their sum is zero, they do not have to be considered explicitly. When the mass is displaced horizontally a distance x, as shown, both springs exert additional negatively directed force components whose magnitude is βx, where β is the force constant of each of the springs. The equation of motion can therefore be written

$$F_x = m\ddot{x} = -2\beta x \quad ,$$

or, $\quad m\ddot{x} = -\beta_l x \quad ,$ $\qquad\qquad$ where $\quad \beta_l = 2\beta \quad .$ $\qquad\qquad$ (3.9 - 1)

In the above expression, the overdots represent differentations with respect to time.

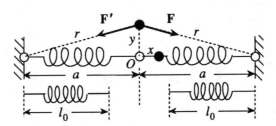

Figure 3.19 Longitudinal and transverse displacements of a mass constrained by two ideal springs connected to fixed supports as shown. White circles represent equilibrium positions, while the black dots illustrate instantaneous positions of the oscillating mass.

Equation (3.9 - 1) represents a simple harmonic oscillation in the x-direction with an effective longitudinal force constant 2β. The frequency of this oscillation is therefore

$$\omega_l = \sqrt{\beta_l / m} = \sqrt{2\beta / m} \quad .$$ $\qquad\qquad$ (3.9 - 2)

For transverse oscillations, the problem is more complex. For a vertical displacement of the mass, the vertical force components for springs stretched to length r will be,

$$F_t = m\ddot{y} = 2F\sin\theta = -2\beta(r - l_0)\frac{y}{r} \quad ,$$ $\qquad\qquad$ (3.9 - 3)

where θ is the acute angle between the vector $\mathbf{F}$ in the diagram and the horizontal. For small transverse displacements, the distances r and a are very nearly the same, which allows this equation to be written

$$F_t = m\ddot{y} \cong -2\beta y\left(1 - \frac{l_0}{a}\right) = -\beta_t y \quad , \tag{3.9-4}$$

where the effective *transverse* force constant is given by

$$\beta_t = 2\beta\left(1 - \frac{l_0}{a}\right) \quad . \tag{3.9-5}$$

Again, this may be related to a transverse oscillation frequency by

$$\omega_t = \sqrt{\beta_t / m} = \sqrt{\frac{2\beta}{m}\left(1 - \frac{l_0}{a}\right)} \quad . \tag{3.9-6}$$

It is clear from this that the transverse oscillation frequency is not the same as the longitudinal frequency. This difference in transverse and longitudinal frequencies is also present in a periodic lattice of equal masses coupled by nearest-neighbor Hooke's law forces, which we shall now consider. Its effect will be seen as a difference in the velocities with which transverse and longitudinal waves of the same wavelength propagate in the lattice.

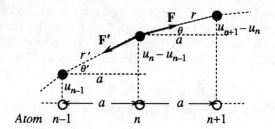

Figure 3.20 A periodic lattice of transversely oscillating masses coupled together by nearest-neighbor Hooke's law forces. White circles represent equilibrium lattice sites, while black dots represent instantaneous positions of oscillating atoms. The transverse displacements shown above are exaggerated for clarity; in reality they are small compared to the interatomic spacing a.

A series of equal masses oscillating transversely about the equilibrium sites of a monatomic one-dimensional lattice is illustrated in Figure 3.20. The masses are assumed to be coupled by Hooke's law forces acting between nearest-neighbor atoms, forces between more distant atoms being neglected. It will be assumed also that the transverse displacements u_n are all small compared with the lattice spacing a. The forces **F** and **F'**, though of interatomic origin, are analogous to the tension in a set of ideal springs between neighboring atoms, which for accuracy as well as simplicity are omitted from the diagram. These forces depend upon the instantaneous interatomic spacings r and r'. When $r = r' = a$, the system is at equilibrium, and the two forces are equal and opposite. Otherwise, they act in such a way as to make the masses oscillate transversely about their respective equilibrium sites. With the aid of Figure 3,20 and the binomial expansion, the quantities r and r' can be expressed as

$$r = \sqrt{a^2 + (u_{n+1} - u_n)^2} = a\sqrt{1 + \left(\frac{u_{n+1} - u_n}{a}\right)^2} \cong a\left[1 + \frac{1}{2}\left(\frac{u_{n+1} - u_n}{a}\right)^2\right] \quad , \tag{3.9-7}$$

$$r' = \sqrt{a^2 + (u_n - u_{n-1})^2} = a\sqrt{1 + \left(\frac{u_n - u_{n-1}}{a}\right)^2} \cong a\left[1 + \frac{1}{2}\left(\frac{u_n - u_{n-1}}{a}\right)^2\right] \quad . \tag{3.9-8}$$

From this, it is clear that r and r' differ only by the *square* of a quantity that, under the assumption of small oscillations, is much less than unity. Therefore, to first order in the oscillation amplitudes, r and r' can be set equal to a.

The transverse y-components of the forces $\mathbf{F}$ and $\mathbf{F'}$ can now be written as

$$F_y = F\sin\theta = F(r)\frac{u_{n+1} - u_n}{r} \quad \text{and} \quad F_r' = -F'\sin\theta' = -F'(r')\frac{u_n - u_{n-1}}{r'} \quad . \tag{3.9-9}$$

Now, using a Taylor's expansion about $r = a$, we can write

$$F(r) = F(a) + \left(\frac{\partial F}{\partial r}\right)_a (r - a) + \cdots \quad . \tag{3.9-10}$$

Since the difference between r and a is of the order of the square of the small quantity $(u_{n+1} - u_n)/a$, only the first term is significant: also, by the same reasoning, $F(r)$ can be replaced by $F(a)$ in (3.9 - 9). Likewise, $F(r')$ can be replaced by $F(a)$. In the same spirit, we can replace r and r' by a in the denominators in (3.9 - 9), which can then be written as

$$F_y = F(a)\frac{u_{n+1} - u_n}{a} \quad \text{and} \quad F_r' = -F(a)\frac{u_n - u_{n-1}}{a} \quad . \tag{3.9-11}$$

Summing the transverse force components and setting them equal to mass times transverse acceleration, we obtain finally

$$F_n = m\frac{\partial^2 u_n}{\partial t^2} = \beta_t(u_{n+1} + u_{n-1} - 2u_n) \quad , \tag{3.9-12}$$

with $\beta_t = \dfrac{F(a)}{a}$. $\tag{3.9-13}$

This has the same form as the equation of motion (3.6 - 1) for longitudinal waves, except that the transverse force constant β_t appears in place of the longitudinal force constant. It is clear also that the transverse force constant's form differs from that of its longitudinal counterpart, as in the simple examples worked previously.

The dispersion relation for transverse waves can be calculated in exactly the same way as that already described for longitudinal waves. The result is the same, except that the transverse force constant appears in place of the longitudinal force constant. We find, therefore, that the dispersion relation is

$$\omega = \sqrt{\frac{4\beta_t}{m}}\left|\sin\tfrac{1}{2}ka\right| = \omega_{mt}\left|\sin\tfrac{1}{2}ka\right| . \qquad (3.9\text{-}14)$$

The phase and group velocities are also given by expressions of the same form as those obtained previously, except for the appearance of the transverse force constant. It should also be noted that it is possible to measure long-wavelength sound velocities for transverse waves as well as longitudinal waves in crystals. The transverse force constant can be calculated from these measured velocities using (3.6 - 9), which is valid for both transverse and longitudinal waves.

It is also possible to excite simultaneously *two* independent transverse modes, with mutually perpendicular polarization directions, for any given wavelength and any given propagation direction. In Figure 3.20, for example, it would be possible to have transverse oscillations perpendicular to the plane of the page, as well as those shown in the plane. Indeed, there could also be oscillations in planes at angles to the page ranging between zero and 90°, though these could be expressed as linear superpositions of the two polarizations referred to initially. In three-dimensional lattices, the transverse force constants for these two polarizations need not be the same, so there can be two separate transverse propagation modes with different dispersion relations, cutoff frequencies and phase and group velocities. For certain symmetrical cases the two directions of polarization for the transverse modes will be crystallographically equivalent, and their dispersion relations will then be identical. The situation is illustrated in Figure 3.21, in which both longitudinal and transverse dispersion relations are plotted. Fortunately, the difference between longitudinal (L) and transverse (T) force constants is often not very large. This means that the contributions of L and T waves in some cases (for example, the calculation of specific heat) are nearly equal. In other instances, however, the difference can be of considerable importance.

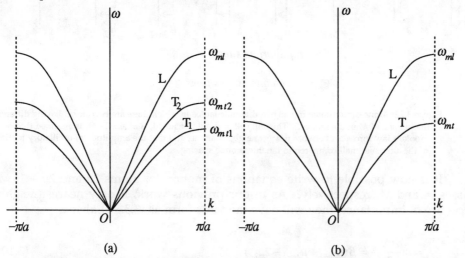

(a) (b)

Figure 3.21 Dispersion relations for longitudinal (L) and transverse (T) waves in periodic lattices. In the most general case (a) the force constants for the two possible transverse modes are not the same, and there are two separate branches to the transverse dispersion curve. The diagram (b) illustrates a symmetric case in which the transverse force constant is isotropic and the two transverse branches coincide. An example of this situation would arise when transverse waves propagate along the (100) direction in a cubic lattice.

It is possible to investigate lattice dispersion curves experimentally using data obtained from experiments in which neutrons are inelastically scattered by the crystal lattice. The results are generally in good agreement with theoretical predictions, particularly when effects arising from second- and third-neighbor interactions are considered.

3.10 THE LINEAR DIATOMIC LATTICE

So far, we have discussed wave propagation in the context of lattices containing only a single atomic species. In general, there may be several atoms in the unit cell, each of different mass. The simplest example of this complexity occurs in ionic crystals, where there are two atomic species of different mass. This case can be discussed by a simple extension of the one-dimensional model used in the preceding section, in which it is assumed that the atoms in the chain can have masses m and M, which alternate as illustrated in Figure 3.22. In this discussion, it will always be assumed that $M > m$. It will also be assumed that only nearest-neighbor Hooke's law forces are present. We shall consider initially longitudinal oscillations of amplitude small in comparison with the interatomic spacing, though it should be clear from the preceding section that results of the same form follow for the transverse case. It should be observed that the unit cell of this lattice is of length $2a$. It is assumed that there are a total of $2N$ atoms in the lattice, N having mass m, and N with mass M.

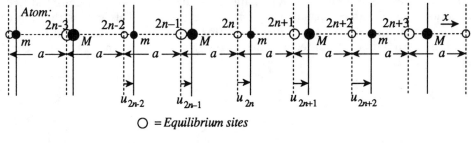

$\bigcirc$ = Equilibrium sites

$\bullet$ = Instantaneous positions

Figure 3.22 A one-dimensional model of a diatomic lattice in which there are two atoms having different masses m and M in the unit cell. The unit cell, it should be noted, is of size $2a$. It is assumed that Hooke's law forces act between nearest neighbor atoms, and that the amplitude of oscillatory motions of the atoms is small compared to the interatomic spacing.

It is now possible to write equations of motion for atoms $2n$ and $2n + 1$, with masses m and M, respectively. As in our previous work, if only nearest-neighbor forces are of importance, they will have the same form as (3.3 - 1), that is

$$F_{2n} = m\frac{\partial^2 u_{2n}}{\partial t^2} = \beta(u_{2n+1} + u_{2n-1} - 2u_{2n}) \tag{3.10-1}$$

and $\quad F_{2n+1} = M\frac{\partial^2 u_{2n+1}}{\partial t^2} = \beta(u_{2n+2} + u_{2n} - 2u_{2n+1}) \quad .$ \hfill (3.10-2)

We shall again assume wave solutions of the same general form as those given by (3.6 - 3). In view of the fact that the two atoms have different masses, however, it makes sense to assume that their oscillation amplitudes may not be the same. It is therefore reasonable to assume that

$$u_{2n} = A e^{i(2kna - \omega t)} \quad \text{and} \quad u_{2n+1} = B e^{i(k[2n+1]a - \omega t)} \quad . \tag{3.10-3}$$

In these equations, the coefficient of k in the exponent represents the x-coördinate of the lattice site of each atom. In the same spirit, we can also write,

$$u_{2n+2} = A e^{i(k[2n+2]a - \omega t)} = u_{2n} e^{2ika} \quad , \tag{3.10-4}$$

and

$$u_{2n-1} = B e^{i(k[2n-1]a - \omega t)} = u_{2n+1} e^{-2ika} \quad . \tag{3.10-5}$$

Using the above equations to eliminate u_{2n+2} and u_{2n-1} from (3.10 - 1) and (3.10 - 2), and evaluating the time derivatives of u_{2n} and u_{2n+1} from (3.10 - 3), the equations of motion can now be expressed as

$$(m\omega^2 - 2\beta)u_{2n} + \beta(1 + e^{-2ika})u_{2n+1} = 0 \quad , \tag{3.10-6}$$

and

$$\beta(1 + e^{2ika})u_{2n} + (M\omega^2 - 2\beta)u_{2n+1} = 0 \quad . \tag{3.10-7}$$

We now have two equations for the two amplitudes u_{2n} and u_{2n+1}. They are homogeneous equations, in view of the zeros on the right side, and their only explicit solution is $u_{2n} = u_{2n+1} = 0$. This is the *only* possible solution if the determinant of the coefficients on the left side is not zero. For other solutions to exist, the determinant must vanish. Under these circumstances, both equations yield a single consistent solution for the ratio u_{2n+1}/u_{2n}. Setting the determinant equal to zero leads at once to the dispersion relation. Alternatively, both equations can be solved for u_{2n+1}/u_{2n} and the two results equated. The result, in either case, is,

$$\begin{vmatrix} m\omega^2 - 2\beta & \beta(1 + e^{-2ika}) \\ \beta(1 + e^{2ika}) & M\omega^2 - 2\beta \end{vmatrix} = (2\beta - m\omega^2)(2\beta - M\omega^2) - 4\beta^2 \cos^2 ka = 0 \quad . \tag{3.10-8}$$

The trigonometric identity $1 + \cos 2ka = 2\cos^2 ka$ has been used to arrive at the final form of this expression. It can be written more explicitly by expanding the product on the left and collecting powers of ω to obtain

$$\omega^4 - \frac{2\beta(m + M)}{mM}\omega^2 + \frac{4\beta^2 \sin^2 ka}{mM} = 0 \quad . \tag{3.10-9}$$

This may now be solved as a quadratic in ω^2 to give the dispersion relation as

$$\omega^2 = \frac{\beta(m + M)}{mM}\left[1 \pm \sqrt{1 - \frac{4mM \sin^2 ka}{(m + M)^2}}\right] \quad . \tag{3.10-10}$$

There are now two separate branches of the dispersion relation, corresponding to the two possible choices for the sign of the radical in this equation. A plot of this dispersion relation, shown in Figure 3.23, illustrates the two separate solutions, which are labeled ω_- and ω_+ respectively. The lower branch looks much like the dispersion curve for a monatomic lattice, and is referred to as the *acoustical* branch The upper branch is quite different in appearance, and is referred to as the *optical* branch, because waves belonging to this section of the dispersion curve can be excited by electromagnetic radiation of optical frequency. Between the two separate parts ot the dispersion curve is a band of frequencies where no undamped traveling wave solutions exist. The only solutions that can be found in this frequency range have complex values of k and are exponentially damped, much like the solutions above the cutoff frequency in the monatomic lattice. Solutions for frequencies greater than the maximum optical branch frequency (at $k = 0$) are also of this kind. This lattice's behavior as a wave filter is more complicated than that of the monatomic lattice; there are now two frequency bands in which waves can be propagated without attenuation. If m and M are nearly equal, the gap between these two bands becomes quite small, and disappears entirely when $M = m$. The unit cell size then changes discontinuously from $2a$ to a, and the dispersion relation reduces to the one obtained previously for the monatomic case.

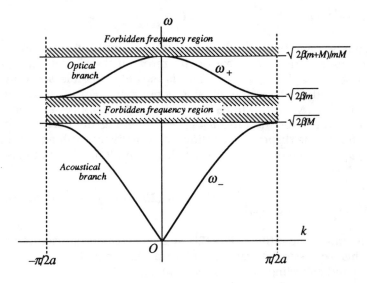

Figure 3.23 Dispersion curve for the diatomic linear lattice with nearest neighbor Hooke's law forces. Note that since the size of the unit cell is now $2a$, the first Brillouin zone extends from $-\pi/2a$ to $\pi/2a$.

Because the length of the lattice cell in this example is $2a$, the edges of the first Brillouin zone are at $k = \pm \pi/2a$, as shown in the figure. If these values are substituted into the dispersion relation (3.10 - 10), it is apparent that at the zone boundaries,

$$\omega_-(\pi/a) = \sqrt{2\beta/M}, \quad \text{and} \quad \omega_+(\pi/a) = \sqrt{2\beta/m} . \qquad (3.10\text{-}11)$$

The optical branch frequency in the long wavelength limit is obtained simply by setting $k = 0$ in (3.10 - 10), and choosing the plus sign for the radical. The result is,

$$\omega_+(0) = \sqrt{\frac{2\beta(m+M)}{mM}} \quad , \tag{3.10-12}$$

as shown in the diagram. For the acoustic branch, this procedure gives $\omega_-(0) = 0$, in agreement with the illustration. For long acoustic waves, k (and ω) will be small, though not zero. In this case, it is easiest to start with the dispersion relation in the form given by (3.10 - 9). Since the term containing the fourth power of ω decreases with decreasing ω more rapidly than the quadratic term, it can be neglected in this limit; moreover, $\sin ka$ can be approximated by ka. Equation (3.10 - 9) then becomes

$$\omega_-(k) \cong ka\sqrt{\frac{2\beta}{m+M}} \quad . \tag{3.10-13}$$

The phase velocity of long acoustic branch waves follows at once as

$$v_0 = \frac{\omega_-}{k} = a\sqrt{\frac{2\beta}{m+M}} \quad . \tag{3.10-14}$$

The ratio u_{2n+1}/u_{2n} can be calculated from (3.10 - 7) and (3.10 - 3) as

$$\frac{u_{2n+1}}{u_{2n}} = \frac{\beta(1+e^{2ika})}{2\beta - M\omega^2} = \frac{B}{A} \cdot e^{ika} \quad , \tag{3.10-15}$$

from which

$$\frac{B}{A} = \frac{\cos ka}{1 - \dfrac{M\omega^2}{2\beta}} \quad . \tag{3.10-16}$$

For long wavelengths, k is small, and the quantities $\exp(ika)$ and $\cos ka$ in the two above equations approach unity. In this limit, the acoustic branch frequency approaches zero, and the ratio B/A is unity. Therefore, both atoms in the cell move in the same direction with essentially the same amplitude and phase, much like neighboring atoms in a monatomic lattice. The optical branch frequency approaches the value $\omega_+(0)$ given by (3.10 - 12) in the long wavelength limit; in this case (3.10 - 16) yields

$$\frac{B}{A} = -\frac{m}{M} \quad . \tag{3.10-17}$$

From this, it is obvious that neighboring atoms move in *opposite* directions, so that the center of mass of the unit cell (and the crystal as a whole) remains fixed. Atomic oscillations of this kind can be excited in ionic crystals, in which the two atoms in the unit cell bear equal and opposite charges, by electric fields which exert equal and opposite forces on the charged ions. In particular, as we shall see in the next section, they can be excited by the sinusoidally varying electric fields associated with electromagnetic radiation in the infrared region of the spectrum.

We have considered explicitly only longitudinal waves, but as in the monatomic case, it is possible for the diatomic lattice to propagate two independent transverse waves in all respects similar except for different harmonic force constants. So there can be three separate acoustic-mode waves, one longitudinal and two transverse, and three separate optical-mode waves. There are thus generally *six* branches to the dispersion relation, which in analogy with the monatomic case, are abbreviated LA, TA_1, TA_2, LO, TO_1, and TO_2. Some of the physical effects arising from external excitation of optical mode waves will be discussed in the next section.

3.11 OPTICAL EXCITATION OF LATTICE WAVES IN IONIC CRYSTALS

The metal and halogen ions in a crystal like NaCl have equal and opposite charges. In these crystals, the oscillating electric field of a transverse electromagnetic wave whose propagation vector is in the positive x-direction in Figure 3.22 can excite transverse optical mode vibrations, since it exerts equal and opposite transverse forces on the ions, which move them in the manner already described for long-wavelength transverse optical mode lattice waves. In this section, we shall consider a diatomic linear lattice like that of the previous section, in which alternate atoms of mass m and M have charges $+q$ and $-q$, respectively. A transverse electromagnetic wave whose electric vector lies in the plane of the page propagates to the right as suggested above. The frequency of this wave is designated as ω_0 and the maximum value of its oscillating electric field as E_0 Its wavelength is assumed to be much larger than the interatomic spacing a. This means that k is much smaller than π/a, and allows us to use the simplifying assumption $k \cong 0$ in the equations of motion. Since the interatomic spacing is only a few Ångströms, this assumption is a good one for wavelengths in the infrared, visible, and even much of the ultraviolet region of the spectrum.

In this situation, each atom experiences an oscillating transverse force of magnitude $\pm qE_0\exp(-i\omega_0 t)$, the sign depending on the sign of the ionic charge. The equations of motion for the two ionic species will differ from (3.10 - 1) and (3.10 - 2), however, only in the use of the transverse force constant β_t, and in the addition of a term describing the oscillating driving force to the right side of both equations. They may therefore be written,

$$F_{2n} = m\frac{\partial^2 u_{2n}}{\partial t^2} = \beta_t(u_{2n+1} + u_{2n-1} - 2u_{2n}) + qE_0 e^{-i\omega_0 t} \tag{3.11-1}$$

and $$F_{2n+1} = M\frac{\partial^2 u_{2n+1}}{\partial t^2} = \beta_t(u_{2n+2} + u_{2n} - 2u_{2n+1}) - qE_0 e^{-i\omega_0 t} \ . \tag{3.11-2}$$

The system is now under the influence of a sinusoidal excitation of frequency ω_0, which *forces* it to oscillate at that frequency. We can thus assume solutions of the form (3.10 - 3) in which $\omega = \omega_0$. Equations (3.10 - 4) and (3.10 - 5) are also valid, with this same minor change. As in the previous case, the equations of motion can now be expressed, in analogy with (3.10 - 6) and (3.10 - 7), as

$$(2\beta_t - m\omega_0^2)u_{2n} - \beta_t(1 + e^{-2ika})u_{2n+1} = qE_0 e^{-i\omega_0 t} \qquad (3.11\text{-}3)$$

and $\quad -\beta_t(1 + e^{2ika})u_{2n} + (2\beta_t - M\omega_0^2)u_{2n+1} = -qE_0 e^{-i\omega_0 t} \quad . \qquad (3.11\text{-}4)$

These are no longer homogeneous equations, and there is no problem in solving them explicitly for the amplitudes u_{2n} and u_{2n+1}. In doing so, it is convenient to use the approximation $k = 0$, setting $\exp(\pm 2ika) = 1$. The algebra is most easily handled by using determinants to solve the system of equations. One can show in this way that

$$u_{2n} = \frac{-qE_0/m}{\omega_0^2 - \omega_+^2(0)} e^{-i\omega_0 t} \quad \text{and} \quad u_{2n+1} = \frac{+qE_0/M}{\omega_0^2 - \omega_+^2(0)} e^{-i\omega_0 t} \quad , \qquad (3.11\text{-}5)$$

where $\omega_+(0)$ is the transverse optical mode frequency for $k = 0$, given by

$$\omega_+(0) = \sqrt{\frac{2\beta_t(m + M)}{mM}} \quad . \qquad (3.11\text{-}6)$$

The above equations predict a *resonance* at the frequency $\omega_0 = \omega_+(0)$, where the amplitudes of both atomic species become infinite. This is perhaps not surprising, since (3.11 - 6) is the natural frequency of transverse vibrations at $k = 0$. The fact that the amplitude is predicted to be infinite at this frequency can be traced to the absence of any mechanism for the dissipation of energy in this theory. The field continually pumps energy into the system, but since only conservative forces are considered, there is no way of getting rid of it in the above calculations. In reality, however, there are effects that limit the vibrational amplitudes near resonance to large but finite values. Since Maxwell's electromagnetic theory predicts that accelerated charges radiate electromagnetic energy, there can be strong *reradiation* of energy at the excitation frequency. This reemitted energy is observed as waves that are reflected and refracted by the substance. What happens near resonance can be explained in terms of a frequency-dependent dielectric constant, since the dielectric constant is proportional to the dipole moment of the unit cell, which is in turn proportional to the oscillation amplitudes. Since the dielectric constant determines the refractive index and the surface reflectivity, it is understandable that these properties will exhibit sharp variations near the resonant frequency. In particular, the reflected intensity can be expected to exhibit an easily observable maximum at this point. There are also internal processes which act to dissipate electromagnetic energy as heat, and which cause the optical absorption coefficient to display a peak near the resonant frequency.

These phenomena have been observed. Specifically, all ionic substances exhibit the expected optical absorption and reflection peaks near the frequency given by (3.11 - 6). These frequencies are in the far infrared, at wavelengths ranging between about 12.5μ for SiC and 233μ for TlBr. For NaCl, the absorption maximum is at 61μ. Continuous-spectrum infrared radiation, such as that emitted by a hot filament, will after reflection from an ionic crystal surface have a spectrum with a pronounced peak at the resonant frequency of the lattice. If the radiation experiences several such reflections, it becomes nearly monochromatic, because frequencies far from resonance are attenuated by a large factor in each reflection. Radiation produced in this manner is known by the German name *Reststrahlen*, whose English

equivalent is *residual radiation*. The phenomenon of optical-mode lattice resonance described above is thus usually called the Reststrahlen effect.

According to (3.9 - 13), the transverse force constant can be written $\beta_t = F(a)/a$.
It is clear from Figures 3.19 and 3.20 that $F(a)$ is merely the attractive force that holds
the atoms in place when the lattice is in equilibrium. In an ionic crystal, in which
only nearest-neighbor forces are considered, this is simply $q^2/4\pi\varepsilon_0 a^2$, so that

$$\beta_t = \frac{q^2}{4\pi\varepsilon_0 a^3} \quad . \tag{3.11-7}$$

For NaCl, the interatomic distance a is 2.82Å, or 2.82×10^{-10}m, which allows us to
caculate the value $\beta_t = 10.28$N/m for this material. Then, according to (3.11 - 6),
using known atomic mass values, we find

$$\omega_+(0) = \sqrt{\frac{(2)(10.28)(23+35.5)}{(23)(35.5)(1.66\times10^{-27})}} = 2.98\times10^{13}\text{rad / sec,}$$

and $\quad \lambda = \frac{2\pi c}{\omega} = 6.32\times10^{-5}\text{m} = 63.2\mu.$

This is in good agreement with the experimentally observed Reststrahlen
peak in the optical absorption, which is found at 61μ. Other ionic substances show
similar agreement between Reststrahlen frequencies determined experimentally
and calculated using this theory, as follows:

RESTSTRAHLEN ABSORPTION WAVELENGTHS IN IONIC CRYSTALS

Crystal	Reststrahlen wavelength λ, (μ)	
	(theory)	(experiment)
NaCl	63.2	61
KCl	86.0	70
NaBr	77.8	76
KBr	110.8	88
NaI	91.9	
KI	131.0	102
AgCl	86.0	100
AgBr	119.0	126.

The Reststrahlen effect can be observed only in crystals in which the atoms of
the lattice are ionized. It is essentially absent in the infrared spectra of covalent substances like Si and Ge, since there is no net charge associated with any atom of a
purely covalently bound crystal. The relative strength of the observed Restrahlen
effect is therefore a useful measure of the ionicity of the substance. In GaAs, for
example, a weak effect is observed, while in NaCl the observed changes in absorption and reflectivity are much stronger. We shall see in later chapters that there are
many other instances in which acoustic and optical mode lattice waves play an
important role in determining the physical properties of crystalline materials.

REFERENCES

L. Brillouin, *Wave Propagation in Periodic Structures*, McGraw-Hill, New York (1946); Dover Publications, New York (1953).

F. Seitz, *Modern Theory of Solids*, McGraw-Hill, New York (1940), Chapter 2.

J. M. Ziman, *Principles of the Theory of Solids*, 2nd Edition, Cambridge University Press, Cambridge (1972), Chapter 2.

R. E. Peierls, *Quantum Theory of Solids*, Oxford University Press, London (1955), Chapter 3.

R. H. Bube, *Electrons in Solids*, 2nd Edition, Academic Press, San Diego (1988), Chapters 2, 3.

M. Born and K. Huang, *Dynamical Theory of Crystal Lattices*, Oxford University Press,. Oxford (1956).

C. Kittel, *Introduction to Solid State Physics*, John. Wiley and Sons, New York, 2nd Edition (1956), Chapters 3-5; 3rd Edition (1966), Chapter 5.

PROBLEMS

1. Find the value of the parameter ζ_b in (3.2 - 2) for $b = 3$, $b = 6$, and $b = 9$.

2. The convergence of the Madelung series (3.2 - 10) can be improved by evaluating it over successively larger cubic cells centered on an atom at the origin. In these cells, electrical neutrality is insured by counting only the fractional part of the atomic volume that lies within the cell. Using this approach, show that the Madelung constant of a two-dimensional simple square lattice consisting of alternate positive and negative ions is approximately 1.607, using a square cell of side $4a$, where a is the nearest-neighbor interatomic distance.

3. The compressibility of a substance is defined as $K = - (\Delta V / \Delta P) / V$ in the limit $\Delta V \to 0$. Show from the first law of thermodynamics that $1 / K = V(\partial^2 U / \partial V^2)$ for an adiabatic process ($dQ = 0$), where U is the cohesive energy of the lattice. Show also that

$$\left(\frac{\partial^2 U}{\partial V^2} \right)_a = \frac{1}{36 N^2 a^4} \left(\frac{\partial^2 U}{\partial r^2} \right)_a .$$

4. Use the results of the preceding problem to show that the exponent b in (3.2 - 7) can be expressed in terms of the compressibility K by

$$b = 1 + \frac{4 \pi \varepsilon_0 \cdot 18 a^4}{K \alpha q^2} .$$

Calculate b for NaCl, using the measured values $K = 4.0 \times 10^{-11}$ N/m^2 and $a = 2.82 \times 10^{-10}$ m.

5. Show that the longitudinal force constant β for a monatomic linear lattice can be expressed in terms of Young's modulus by $\beta = Ya$.

6. Show that the wave equations

$$\frac{\partial^2 u}{\partial x^2} = K^2 \frac{\partial^2 u}{\partial t^2} \quad \text{and} \quad \frac{\partial^4 u}{\partial x^4} = K^4 \frac{\partial^4 u}{\partial t^4}$$

are both dispersionless, and that their dispersion relations are the same, assuming that ω and k are both real.

7. (a) Show that all the sinusoidal solutions of the equation $\partial^2 u/\partial x^2 = \alpha^2(\partial u/\partial t)$, where α is real, die out exponentially with time. This "inherently damped" equation is the equation for heat flow or diffusive transport of matter. (b) Show also that the similar equation $\partial^2 u/\partial x^2 = -i\alpha^2(\partial u/\partial t)$ can have undamped travelling wave solutions, but is inherently dispersive; write the dispersion relation. This equation has the form of the quantum wave equation for free particles.

8. Consider the wave equation

$$\frac{\partial^2 u}{\partial x^2} - i\alpha^2 \frac{\partial u}{\partial x} = -\beta^2 \frac{\partial^2 u}{\partial t^2} \quad ,$$

where α and β are real constants. (a) Find the dispersion relation. (b) Discuss conditions under which undamped wave solutions can--and cannot--be found. (c) Characterize the physical behavior of a system that propagates waves such as these.

9. Can dispersionless solutions be found for the wave equation

$$\frac{\partial^3 u}{\partial x^3} + \frac{1}{u^2}\left(\frac{\partial u}{\partial x}\right)^3 = -\beta^3 \frac{\partial^3 u}{\partial t^3} \quad ,$$

where β is real? Explain.

10. (a) Find the dispersion relation for the wave equation

$$\frac{\partial^2 u}{\partial x^2} - \beta^2 \frac{\partial^2 u}{\partial t^2} - \alpha^2 u = 0 \quad ,$$

where α and β are real constants. (b) Find the phase and group velocities. (c) Comment on the physical behavior of the system that propagates these waves.

11. Find the phase and group velocities associated with the wave solutions referred to in Problem 7(b).

12. Find the phase and group velocities of the waves that satisfy the equation

$$\frac{\partial^2 u}{\partial x^2} = K^2 \frac{\partial^6 u}{\partial t^6} \quad .$$

13. Find the phase and group velocities of the waves satisfying the wave equation

$$\alpha^2 \frac{\partial^3 u}{\partial x^3} - \beta^2 \frac{\partial u}{\partial x} = \frac{\partial u}{\partial t} \quad ,$$

where α and β are real constants. Comment on the physical behavior of the system that propagates these waves.

14. Longitudinal waves propagate along a linear monatomic lattice whose interatomic spacing is 3.6×10^{-10}m. The mass of the atoms is 56amu (1amu $= 1.6605 \times 10^{-27}$kg). The acoustic velocity in the long-wavelength limit is 5400 m/sec. Find (a) the cuttoff frequency ω_m, (b) the phase and group velocity at wavelength $4a$. (c) the phase and group velocity of waves at the cutoff frequency, (d) the longitudinal interatomic force constant. All interatomic forces are assumed to obey Hooke's law, and only nearest-neighbor interactions are significant.

15. Longitudinal sound waves propagate along the (100) direction in a monatomic simple cubic lattice ($a = 2.5$Å, $m = 32$amu). The interatomic Hooke's law force constant is 18 N/m. Find (a) the cut-

off frequency, (b) the velocity of long-wavelength longitudinal sound waves, (c) the phase and group velocity of longitudinal waves of wavelength 7.5Å. Only nearest-neighbor interactions are important.

16 . Longitudinal waves propagate in a monatomic linear lattice wherein m = 48amu and the interatomic spacing is 3.2×10^{-10}m. The long-wavelength velocity is 4800 m/sec. At a certain wavelength, the group velocity is determined to be 3200 m/sec. What is the phase velocity at this wavelength? What is the interatomic Hooke's law constant?

17. In a certain monatomic lattice of spacing $a = 3.0 \times 10^{-10}$m and mass m = 40amu, the longitudinal group velocity is 2700 m/sec. The cutoff frequency for longitudinal oscillations is 2.5×10^{13} rad/sec. What is the phase velocity of these waves? What is the interatomic Hooke's law constant and the long-wavelength longitudinal sound velocity?

18. Young's modulus for iron (m = 56amu, density 7.87 g/cm^3) is 2.18×10^{11}N/m^2. Calculate the velocity of sound at macroscopic wavelengths and estimate the cutoff frequency.

19. Transverse waves propagate in a monatomic linear lattice in which the interatomic spacing is 2.7×10^{-10}m; the interatomic Hooke's law constant for longitudinal motion is β_l = 20 N/m. The velocity of transverse waves in the long wavelength limit is half that of longitudinal waves. Find the transverse Hooke's law constant and the magnitude of equilibrium nearest-neighbor attractive forces.

20. Show that the time-average kinetic and potential energies of a single classical simple harmonic oscillator are the same, and are each equal to one-half the total oscillator energy, if evaluated over a time interval equal to an integral number of cycles, or long in comparison with a single period.

21. The average total energy of a harmonically bound atom in a linear monatomic lattice can be shown to be 0.025eV at room temperature (300K). Show that this energy corresponds to a longitudinal amplitude small in comparison with a typical interatomic spacing, using the results of the preceding problem along with the data v_0 = 5000 m/sec, m = 50amu, and $a = 2.5 \times 10^{-10}$m.

22. Consider a linear monatomic lattice like the one shown in Figure 3.15(a) containing eight atoms, the ones at each end being held fixed. Find the allowed wavelengths, k-values, and frequencies of oscillation for this system. Assume for ease of visualization transverse oscillations. Denote the length of the crystal as L, the atomic mass as m, and the Hooke's law force constant between neighboring atoms as β.

23. Work the previous problem for the case of traveling waves in a linear system containing eight harmonically coupled atoms in which periodic boundary conditions are imposed, so that the motion of atoms 1 and 9 are the same at all times.

24. Consider the case of longitudinal oscillations in a linear diatomic lattice having the characteristics of NaCl ($a = 2.82 \times 10^{-10}$m, m = 23amu, M = 35.5amu, long wavelength velocity 4800 m/sec). Find (a) the longitudinal interatomic force constant, (b, c, d) the frequencies associated with the upper boundary of the acoustical branch, and the lower and upper extermes of the optical branch of the dispersion relation, (e, f) the frequencies of acoustical and optical branch waves of wavelength $\lambda = 8a$.

25. In the lattice of the preceding problem, find the frequency of the LO mode having the same wavelength as an LA mode wave of frequency 1.60×10^{13}rad/sec.

26. In a certain diatomic linear lattice the width of the forbidden frequency region between the acoustical and optical branches is equal to the width, in frequency, of the optical branch. Find the mass ratio M/m for this lattice.

27. Show for the one-dimensional linear diatomic lattice of Section 3.10, that the long-wave optical mode frequency can be expressed as

$$\omega_+(0) = \frac{m+M}{\sqrt{mM}} \cdot \frac{v_0}{a} \ ,$$

where v_0 is the long-wavelength *acoustic mode* velocity.

28. (a) Show that the dispersion relation (3.10 - 9) for the linear diatomic lattice can be written in dimensionless form as

$$\Omega^4 - \Omega^2 + \tfrac{1}{4}\Omega_0^2 \sin^2 ka = 0 \ , \quad \text{where } \Omega = \omega / \omega_+(0) \ , \quad \Omega_0^2 = \frac{4\beta}{\bar{M}\omega_+^2(0)} \ , \quad \text{and } \bar{M} = \tfrac{1}{2}(m+M) \ .$$

(b) Show that this leads to a dispersion relation of the form
$$2\Omega_\pm^2 = -1 \pm \sqrt{1 - \Omega_0^2 \sin^2 ka} \ .$$

(c) Show also that
$$\Omega_0^2 = mM / \bar{M}^2 \ .$$

29. Find general expressions for the phase and group velocities of waves in the diatomic linear lattice of Section 3.10, as functions of the propagation constant k. Plot (roughly) the results. *Hint*: Use the results of the preceding problem.

30. For the diatomic lattice of Section 3.10, show that

(a) $\omega_+^2 + \omega_-^2 = \omega_+^2(0)$; (b) $\omega_+^2 - \omega_-^2 = \omega_+^2(0)\sqrt{1 - \dfrac{4mM\sin^2 ka}{(m+M)^2}}$; and (c) $\sin ka = \dfrac{\sqrt{mM}}{2\beta}\,\omega_+\,\omega_-$,

where $\omega_+ = \omega_+(k)$, $\omega_- = \omega_-(k)$.

31. How would you order the following materials (InP, CdS, Ge, KBr), with respect to the strength of the Reststrahlen effect they exhibit? Explain.

32. Can you suggest how *longitudinal* optical-mode vibrations might be excited by electromagnetic waves impinging on a one-dimensional linear diatomic lattice. How might these waves be excited in a three-dimensional crystal having the NaCl structure?

33. The Reststrahlen absorption peak for ZnS is observed at a wavelength of 35μ, as compared with 61μ for NaCl. The interatomic spacing in ZnS is 2.35 Å. Compare this observed wavelength with what one might expect from theory, and state whether it is, or is not, in reasonable agreement.

34. The Reststrahlen peak is observed for KCl at a wavelength of 70μ. Calculate the expected Reststrahlen wavelengths for KBr and KI, assuming that the interatomic force constant β_t is the same for all three substances. Are the results in good agreement with experiment?

35. Using the data in the preceding problem and the observed Reststrahlen wavelengths given in the table above, calculate the expected ratios of interatomic force constants for KBr and KI to that of KCl.

36. Derive the dispersion relation for longitudinal waves in a monatomic linear lattice of equal masses, in which Hooke's law forces between nearest neighbors and also *second* neighbors, are significant.

37. Derive the density-of-states function for longitudinal vibrational modes of the one-dimensional linear diatomic lattice of Section 3.10. Assume periodic boundary conditions, and use the dispersion relation (3.10 - 10).

38. Show that the forbidden frequency region between the acoustical and optical branches of the diatomic lattice dispersion relation (3.10 - 10) is of width $\Delta\omega$ given by

$$(\Delta\omega)^2 = \omega_+^2(0) - \frac{4\beta}{\sqrt{mM}} \quad .$$

39. Derive expressions for the attenuation coefficient of the exponentially damped traveling wave solutions in the diatomic lattice of Section 3.10 (a) for frequencies between the top of the acoustical branch and the bottom of the optical branch, and (b) for frequencies higher than $\omega_+(0)$.

40. Derive the following relationships between phase and group velocities:

(a) $\dfrac{v_g}{v_p} = \dfrac{k}{\omega} \cdot \dfrac{d(\ln \omega)}{d(\ln k)}$; (b) $\dfrac{dv_p}{dk} = \dfrac{v_g - v_p}{k}$;

(c) $\dfrac{dv_g}{dk} = \dfrac{1}{k}\left(1 - \dfrac{v_p}{v_g}\right)$; (d) $\dfrac{dv_g}{dv_p} = \dfrac{k}{v_g - v_p} \cdot \dfrac{d^2\omega}{dk^2}$.

CHAPTER 4

QUANTUM MECHANICS

4.1 INTRODUCTION

Someone once remarked "If you ask ten physicists what quantum mechanics is all about, you'll get at least eight different answers." There is some truth to this, possibly because quantum theory is still a developing subject. Those who study its foundations do not always agree on how it should be interpreted, or even about whether it is a complete and self-consistent description of physical reality. Fortunately, our objective is merely to acquire a working knowledge of the subject and to use it to solve simple problems in areas where it is fairly easy to use and interpret, and where it consistently yields answers in good agreement with experiment. We need not therefore be greatly concerned with philosophical questions. Nevertheless, a few general observations about the basic ideas of quantum physics are in order.

Classical mechanics asserts that if you know the forces acting on a system of particles, and if you are given proper information regarding its initial state, you can precisely determine its future development, and accurately predict the position and velocity of each particle at every instant of time. Moreover, it assumes that the system is independent of the observer, and that its evolution need not be affected in the least by efforts to obtain information about its state. Quantum mechanics *rejects* these conventionally "obvious" assertions. Therefore, when working with it, one must sometimes settle for a less detailed--though more generally valid--description of physical reality than that given by classical physics.

Quantum mechanics can sometimes yield precise answers to many problems. In general, however, it will tell you only the average value of many individual measurements made on a given dynamical system in a certain initial state. There is a uranium isotope of mass 230amu, for example. Like all isotopes of this element, it is radioactive, decaying by α-particle emission into a thorium isotope, in this case with an observed half-life of 20.8 days. The decay of each nucleus in a sample of this substance is an easily observable event, taking place during a very short and well-defined time interval, a click of the Geiger counter announcing the transformation.

Quantum mechanics permits you to calculate the half-life of an isotope like $_{92}U^{230}$, but will not predict when any given nucleus will decay, nor what set of internal circumstances causes it to disintegrate. Moreover, quantum theory denies the possibility of answering these questions, and asserts that any such decay is an *inherently random* event! The further conclusion that randomness is not only inherent in quantum mechanics, but in nature itself, may not be rigorously justified, but is generally accepted in contemporary physics. This inherent randomness can be traced to the *uncertainty principle*, and ultimately to the idea that the act of observation inevitably affects the outcome of most experiments--an idea that we shall soon discuss in greater detail.

When you use quantum theory, you must acquire a mindset different from that of classical physics; in particular, you sometimes have to accept what seems to be an incomplete description of system dynamics. Also, even when quantum theory permits an accurate knowledge of particle trajectories, for example, the sad fact is that they are usually very tough to calculate. But on the level of atoms, molecules, and elementary particles, only quantum theory can be trusted to give correct answers to dynamical problems. As you go to more massive particles and to larger systems, the classical and quantum pictures of reality differ less sharply, and on the scale of everyday macroscopic physics, they are essentially indistinguishable. It would be not only silly, but also incredibly difficult, to employ quantum theory to determine the trajectory of a baseball. The answer would be in any event essentially the same as that obtained from a much simpler classical calculation. One should therefore not sell classical mechanics short. Despite the fact that quantum theory provides the ultimate picture of physical reality, classical mechanics is often much simpler, and in its realm of applicability perfectly adequate. At the same time, it is important to understand that many features of the classical landscape--features that we simply take for granted, like the existing chemical elements and the compounds they form--are as they are and behave as they do because of quantum mechanics.

Solid-state physics is concerned with both macroscopic and microscopic phenomena, and therefore intermixes quantum theory and classical physics in a way that can sometimes be confusing. We have already used classical mechanics and electromagnetic theory to investigate phenomena (like lattice vibrations) that inhabit the "gray area" between the microworld and the realm of large-scale physics. Our conclusions can be justified by arguing that the masses of atoms in the crystal lattice are rather large on the scale of elementary particle masses, and that we have been concerned with the motion of these heavy atoms as a whole rather than with their internal structure and dynamics. Even so, despite the general validity of the picture that has been drawn, we shall find that quantum theory enables us to see it more clearly in many respects.

4.2 PLANCK'S THEORY OF BLACKBODY RADIATION

In 1899, classical mechanics, thermodynamics, and electromagnetism were regarded as a rigorous, comprehensive description of physical reality, which needed the repair of only two or three loose ends to be complete and self-consistent. The unsolved problems concerned inconsistencies in the transformation laws associated with the reference systems of mechanics and electromagnetism, the line spectra of excited atoms and molecules, and the spectrum of light emitted by bodies heated to incandescence. The pursuit of these "loose ends", however, finally unraveled the whole elaborately woven fabric of classical physics, and the resolution of these unco-öperative problems led finally to relativity and quantum physics. The story of relativity is interesting, but not entirely relevant to the study of condensed-matter physics, at least on an elementary level. Quantum theory, however, has been of fundamental importance in this subject area. Its story began with Max Planck's attempt to explain the spectral intensity distribution of continuous-spectrum radiation emitted by incandescent hot bodies. In the case of an "ideal radiator" of zero reflectivity and maximum emissivity, this emitted energy is called *blackbody radiation*.

Initial attempts at discussing this subject used classical thermodynamics to treat the radiation field, which was regarded as a system having thermodynamic properties like those of ordinary matter--temperature, pressure, volume, internal energy, entropy, etc. The radiation field was assumed to be in thermal equilibrium with the atoms of the radiator, which (like the atoms of our idealized crystal lattices) were modeled as classical simple harmonic oscillators. The laws of classical physics impose no restrictions on the amplitude, frequency or energy these oscillators can have. The results of these calculations are embodied in what is referred to as the *Rayleigh-Jeans law*, which predicted spectral intensities at longer wavelengths quite well, but suggested that in the short wavelength limit the spectral intensity and total emitted energy should become infinitely large. This so-called ultraviolet catastrophe was sharply at odds with the experimental findings illustrated in Figure 4.1. Until Planck came along, this was one of the loose ends of classical physics.

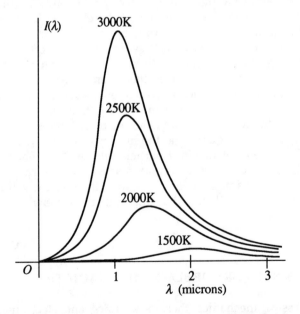

Figure 4.1 Schematic plot showing the spectral intensity distribution of radiation emitted by incandescent blackbody radiators at several temperatures. Note that the spectral intensity goes to zero in the short-wavelength limit, as well as at long wavelengths.

Max Planck was the classical physicist *par excellence*, steeped in the traditions of the subject, learned in its lore. In 1901, he found a way of describing the spectral intensity of blackbody radiation that was in excellent agreement with experimental observations, but which required the strange assumption that the oscillators in equilibrium with the radiation can have only certain discrete energies ε_n, given by

$$\varepsilon = \varepsilon_n = nhf_0 = n\hbar\omega_0 \quad , \quad (n = 0, 1, 2, 3, \dots) \quad , \tag{4.2-1}$$

where

$$\hbar = h / 2\pi \quad . \tag{4.2-2}$$

Here f_0 or ω_0 is the oscillator frequency, and h appears as a new universal physical constant, now known as *Planck's constant*, whose numerical value is

$$h = 6.626 \times 10^{-34} \text{ J sec} , \quad \text{and} \quad \hbar = h/2\pi = 1.0546 \times 10^{-34} \text{ J sec} .$$

An oscillator in undergoing transitions from one energy state to the next higher or lower state must now, in order to conserve energy, emit or absorb *quanta* of radiant energy $\Delta\varepsilon$ at the oscillator frequency, so that from (4.2 - 1),

$$\Delta\varepsilon = \hbar\omega_0 \quad . \tag{4.2-3}$$

These ideas allowed Planck to derive the formula

$$I(\lambda)d\lambda = \frac{2\pi hc^2}{\lambda^5} \cdot \frac{d\lambda}{e^{hc/\lambda kT} - 1} \tag{4.2-4}$$

for the radiated energy per unit area per unit time in the wavelength interval $d\lambda$ at wavelength λ. In this expression T is the absolute temperature of the radiating body and k is Boltzmann's constant, which is simply the molar ideal gas constant divided by Avogadro's number. Planck had no knowledge of the value of h; and had to find it by choosing a number that gave the best fit to the available experimental data. He found that the value 6.55×10^{-34} J–sec led to an almost perfect fit to the observations. This differs by only about one percent from the currently accepted value.

Planck struggled valiantly but without success to derive his radiation formula without making any assumption about discrete energy levels or quanta of radiant energy. Finally, and reluctantly, he gave up and published his findings, strange as they must have seemed then. Within a few years, however, they led to the solution of a number of other puzzling problems, and it soon became clear that Planck had uncovered a whole new world of physics--a world wherein the structure of atoms, molecules, and even the constituents of atomic nuclei were to be revealed.

4.3 EINSTEIN AND THE PHOTOELECTRIC EFFECT

When ultraviolet light falls upon the surface of a metal, it is found that electrons are expelled from the substance into a surrounding vacuum, where they may be collected at an anode and made to flow as a photocurrent in an external circuit, as illustrated in Figure 4.2. The maximum initial kinetic energy of these photoelectrons can be determined by placing a grid between the photoemitting cathode and the anode, and determining how much negative retarding voltage must be applied to it to reduce the photocurrent to zero. Experiments of this sort, using monochromatic light, show that if the incident light frequency is less than some well-defined threshhold value, there is no photoemission no matter how *intense* the light may be. For frequency ω greater than this threshhold frequency ω_0, photoelectrons are emitted in numbers proprtional to the incident light intensity, causing a photocurrent proportional to light intensity to flow in the external circuit. The maximum kinetic energy of these electrons can be measured by observing the retarding voltage φ_0 needed to reduce the photocurrent to zero, since this voltage creates a potential barrier of height qV_0 that electrons having charge q must surmount to reach the anode. This initial kinetic energy is found to be proportional to the frequency difference $\omega - \omega_0$.

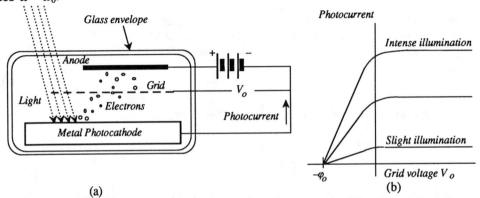

(a)   (b)

Figure 4.2 (a) Apparatus used to observe the photoelectric effect in metals. (b) A plot of observed current–voltage characteristic curves for several incident light levels. It is assumed that the incident light is monochromatic.

The existence of this threshhold frequency for the photoelectric effect was one of those puzzling little effects whose explanation had not been found within the framework of classical physics. In 1905, however, Albert Einstein proposed a simple explanation of the photoelectric effect using Planck's quantum hypothesis, and in doing so added some substance of his own to quantum theory.

According to Einstein, the valence electrons in the metal cathode have potential energy lower than electrons at rest in the surrounding vacuum; otherwise they would escape from the metal even if there were no illumination. The picture of electron energies must be somewhat like that illustrated in Figure 4.3. The energy difference between an electron with maximum potential energy in the metal and an electron at rest--that is, with zero kinetic energy--just outside the material, we shall write as $q\varphi_0$, The excitation potential φ_0 is a characteristic property of the metal called the *work function*. The electron must obtain energy $q\varphi_0$ from the incident light to be emitted as a photoelectron. According to Planck's hypothesis, a quantum of light will convey energy $\hbar\omega$, where ω is the light frequency. If the light frequency is below the threshhold frequency, the energy of the quantum of radiation is insufficient to excite the electron over the potential barrier at the surface of the metal into the vacuum. At the threshhold frequency, the energy of the light quantum is the same as the excitation energy, and we can write

$$\hbar\omega_0 = q\varphi_0, \quad \text{or} \quad \omega_0 = q\varphi_0/\hbar \; . \tag{4.3-1}$$

Above the threshhold frequency, the light quantum has more than enough energy to excite the electron into the vacuum. The energy in excess of the amount given by (4.3 - 1) appears as kinetic energy of the excited electron. Thus, the maximum kinetic energy of an electron excited by such a light quantum will be

$$\varepsilon_m = \hbar(\omega - \omega_0) = \hbar\omega - q\varphi_0 \; . \tag{4.3-2}$$

These predictions agree in every respect with the experimental results shown in Figure 4.2. Equation (4.3 - 1) predicts that the slope of a curve giving ε_m as a function of incident light frequency will be $h/2\pi$. The value of Planck's constant measured in this way is in excellent agreement with the value obtained by Planck from measurements of the spectral intensity of blackbody radiation. The photoelectric effect thus provides a striking verification of the quantum hypothesis in an area quite different from the original application.

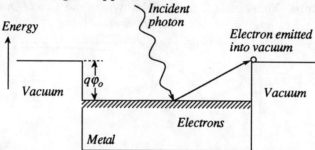

Figure 4.3 Representation of photoemission as a particle interaction in which a photon collides with a single electron, which acquires all the energy of the incident photon, and is excited as a photoelectron into the vacuum. The photon is absorbed in the interaction. In the drawing, the electron is shown as being emitted with zero kinetic energy, but if the incident photon energy is greater, it can be emitted with an initial kinetic energy greater than zero.

Einstein's analysis of this phenomenon assumes that it can be considered as a two-body *collision* in which the light quantum in giving up all its energy to a single electron, behaves much like a particle. Indeed, he gave the incident radiation quantum the Newtonian designation *photon*. This is perhaps the earliest example in which wave-particle duality--another inherent feature of quantum theory--was given explicit recognition.

4.4 THE SPECIFIC HEAT OF SOLIDS

We have so far regarded a crystal as an assembly of atoms held together by interatomic forces, whose net effect is to make them act as classical harmonic oscillators. This picture allows us to understand many simple properties of crystalline materials. The effect of increased thermal kinetic energy is to excite larger vibrational amplitudes, and thus to increase the total vibrational energy of the lattice.

It can be shown (as we shall see later) that if an assembly of classical harmonic oscillators has a Maxwell-Boltzmann distribution of energies, as predicted by elementary statistical theory, the average total energy per oscillator is $3kT$, where T is the absolute temperature and k is Boltzmann's constant, which can be regarded as the ideal gas constant per atom. If the vibrational energy accounts for all the internal energy of the crystal, its thermodynamic internal energy will be,

$$U = 3NkT \quad , \qquad\qquad\qquad (4.4\text{-}1)$$

where N is the number of oscillators. The heat capacity at constant volume, C_v, is the amount of internal energy needed to produce unit temperature change, which can be obtained by differentiating (4.4 - 1) to obtain

$$C_v = (\partial U / \partial T)_v = 3Nk \quad . \qquad\qquad\qquad (4.4\text{-}2)$$

For a mole of the substance, N is equal to Avogadro's number, and the product Nk, in view of the definition of k, is $3R$, where $R = 8.314\text{J/mole}$ is the molar gas constant. The molar heat capacity--or molar specific heat as it is more frequently called-- therefore has the constant value $3R = 24.94$ J/mole, independent of the material and of the temperature. This classical result is known as the *Law of Dulong and Petit*.

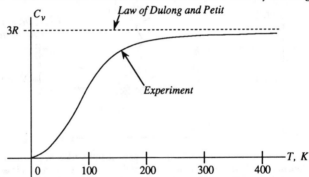

Figure 4.4 Experimentally determined specific heat of a typical crystalline solid as a function of temperature, in comparison with the prediction of the Law of Dulong and Petit.

As illustrated in Figure 4.4, the Law of Dulong and Petit, though in good agreement with experiment at and above room temperature, is not obeyed at low temperatures. At low temperatures, the observed specific heat of crystalline substances decreases, and approaches zero near absolute zero. Also, the experimental curve varies somewhat from one substance to another in regard to the temperature range in which the rapid decrease of specific heat occurs.

This discrepancy can be ascribed to Planck's idea that the energies of harmonic oscillators must be quantized in discrete energy levels

$$\varepsilon_n = n\hbar\omega \qquad (n = 0, 1, 2, 3, \ldots) \quad , \qquad\qquad\qquad (4.4\text{-}3)$$

where ω is the oscillator frequency given by classical mechanics. This leads, as we will show in more detail later, to an average oscillator energy different from the classical value $3kT$, and yields results for the specific heat of crystalline substances in good agreement with experimental results. This explanation was given by Einstein in 1911 and Debye in 1912. The quantum theory thus provides a simple explanation for still another effect that cannot be understood using the ideas of classical physics.

4.5 THE BOHR MODEL OF THE ATOM

Another problem of atomic physics that could not be solved by classical methods is that of the emission and absorption spectra of atoms and molecules. Classical physics provides no explanation for the sharply defined spectral lines observed in optical emission spectra of the elements, for example. From the time of Planck's initial discoveries, it appeared as though the answer might be given by quantum theory, but it was not until 1913 that Niels Bohr found a way of quantizing the hydrogen atom that described the spectrum of this element with impressive accuracy. This delay was partly due to the fact that the atomic nucleus was not discovered until 1910, when Rutherford's scattering experiments were performed. It was only then that the concept of an atom as a point nucleus surrounded by a swarm of electrons emerged.

In Bohr's model, which utilizes this picture, a single electron of mass m and charge q is assumed to move in a circular orbit around a much more massive nucleus bearing a positive charge Zq, where Z is an integer. The factor Z allows the theory to include not only hydrogen, (for which $Z = 1$), but also certain ionic species, like He+ ($Z = 2$), Li++ ($Z = 3$), Be+++ ($Z = 4$), etc., composed of a single electron and a massive positively charged nucleus.

In classical electrodynamics, accelerated charges like the "orbiting" electron always radiate energy in the form of electromagnetic waves. Classically, then, one would expect the electron to continually lose energy, spiralling inward toward the nucleus as its energy is depleted by radiation. Bohr, however, suggested that stable *non-radiative* states of the atom can exist, corresponding to circular electron orbits whose angular momentum L is quantized in integral multiples of $h/2\pi$, so that

$$L_n = mr_n^2 \omega_n = n\hbar, \quad (n = 1, 2, 3, \dots) \quad . \tag{4.5-1}$$

This quantization of angular momentum also quantizes the orbit radii and angular velocities as indicated in the above equation; the energy and linear velocity are also quantized. The allowed total energies, kinetic plus potential, can be written

$$\varepsilon_n = \tfrac{1}{2} mr_n^2 \omega_n^2 - \frac{Zq^2}{4\pi\epsilon_0 r_n} \quad . \tag{4.5-2}$$

In this equation, ε_n are the allowed energies of the system; the permittivity of free space in the second term is employs a different style of type for the letter epsilon to avoid confusion with the energies. This practice will be used routinely in any future case where confusion between these quantities can occur. The minus sign before the potential energy means that the coulomb force between electron and nucleus is attractive. We may now equate the coulomb force on the electron to mass times centripetal acceleration $r\omega^2$ to obtain

$$\frac{Zq^2}{4\pi\epsilon_0 r_n^2} = mr_n\omega_n^2 \quad . \tag{4.5-3}$$

The three equations above are simultaneous equations for the three unknowns r_n, ω_n, and ε_n. They are most easily solved by noting from (4.4 - 1) that

$$\omega_n = \frac{n\hbar}{mr_n^2} \quad , \tag{4.5-4}$$

and substituting this into (4.5 - 3) to obtain an explicit value for r_n. This can in turn be substituted into (4.5 - 2) to obtain, finally,

$$r_n = \frac{4\pi\epsilon_0 n^2\hbar^2}{mZq^2} \quad , \tag{4.5-5}$$

$$\omega_n = \frac{mZ^2q^4}{(4\pi\epsilon_0)^2 n^3\hbar^3} \quad , \tag{4.5-6}$$

and $\quad \varepsilon_n = -\frac{mZ^2q^4}{2(4\pi\epsilon_0)^2 n^2\hbar^2} \quad . \tag{4.5-7}$

Quantizing the angular momentum is now seen to quantize the orbit radii, the angular velocity, and the total energy of the system as well. The allowed energies are negative, corresponding to stable bound states of the electron. This fact is also reflected in finite values for the orbital radii. The lowest allowed energy, and the smallest orbital radius occurs when $n = 1$. This defines the *ground state* of the atom. Setting $n = 1$ in the above equations, these ground state parameters are found to be

$$r_1 = \frac{4\pi\epsilon_0 \hbar^2}{mZq^2} \tag{4.5-8}$$

and

$$\varepsilon_1 = -\frac{mZ^2q^4}{2(4\pi\epsilon_0)^2\hbar^2} \quad . \tag{4.5-9}$$

The quantity r_1, referred to as the *first Bohr radius*, roughly defines the size of the atom. For hydrogen, $Z = 1$, and these expressions yield the numerical answers

$$r_1 = \frac{(4\pi)(8.854\times10^{-12})(1.0546\times10^{-34})^2}{(9.110\times10^{-31})(1.602\times10^{-19})^2} = 5.293\times10^{-11}\text{m} = 0.5293 \text{ Å},$$

and $\quad \varepsilon_1 = -\frac{(9.110\times10^{-31})(1.602\times10^{-19})^4}{(2)(4\pi)^2(8.854\times10^{-12})(1.0546\times10^{-34})^2} = -2.181\times10^{-18}\text{J} = -13.62\text{eV}.$

The quantized orbital radii and allowed energies for hydrogen can be written most simply, with the aid of (4.5 - 8) and (4.5 - 9), as

$$r_n = n^2 r_1 \qquad \text{and} \qquad \varepsilon_n = -\frac{\varepsilon_1}{n^2} \ . \tag{4.5-10}$$

These energy levels are illustrated in Figure 4.5. Transitions between levels are accompanied by the emission or absorption of energy quanta, ordinarily in the form of photons. For a transition from an initial state m to a final state n, the frequency of the light quantum emitted or absorbed, according to Planck's hypothesis, is

$$\hbar\omega_{mn} = |\varepsilon_m - \varepsilon_n| = \varepsilon_1 \left| \frac{1}{n^2} - \frac{1}{m^2} \right| \ . \tag{4.5-11}$$

This equation--using all possible integer values for m and n--leads to a prediction for the optical spectrum of hydrogen that agrees closely with experiment. The Bohr quantization rule, which was simply a guess initially (a guess suggested possibly by the fact that Planck's constant has dimensions of angular momentum) is now seen to predict the observed spectrum of hydrogen.

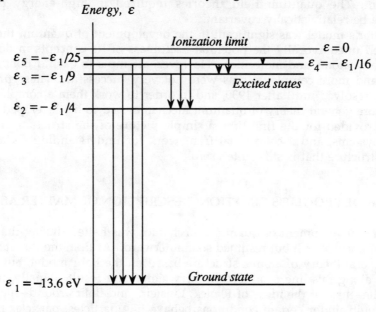

Figure 4.5 Energy level diagram for the hydrogen atom derived from the Bohr model. Vertical lines illustrate possible downward transitions from one state to another, each of which corresponds to an observed spectral line in the optical emission spectrum.

It is important to note from (4.5 - 10) that as the quantum number n becomes large, energy differences between adjacent states become small, and the allowed energy states become very closely spaced. In this limit, also, the orbital radii become very large. The limiting energy is zero, corresponding to an electron at infinity. This limit therefore corresponds to the ionized state of the atom. These features are also evident in Figure 4.5.

One more calculation is of some importance. Multiplying equation (4.5 - 5) by (4.5 - 6) gives the linear velocity v_n of the electron as

$$v_n = r_n \omega_n = \frac{Zq^2}{4\pi\epsilon_0 n\hbar} \quad . \tag{4.5-12}$$

Clearly, the linear velocity has the largest possible value in the ground state ($n = 1$). For hydrogen ($Z = 1$), this amounts to

$$v_1 = \frac{q^2}{4\pi\epsilon_0 \hbar} = \frac{(1.602 \times 10^{-19})^2}{(4\pi)(8.854 \times 10^{-12})(1.0546 \times 10^{-34})} = 2.187 \times 10^6 \text{m/sec} = 2187 \text{km/sec}$$

This is fast, but even so less than one percent of the speed of light. Bohr's theory, in which relativitistic effects are neglected, is therefore self-consistent in regard to this assumption, which suggests that a quantum theory of atoms, molecules, and crystalline materials adequate for many purposes can be formulated non-relativistically. It must be observed, however, that in the realm of nuclear and elementary particle physics, where particle energies are much higher, relativistic effects can be very important. The quantum field theories required in high-energy physics must therefore be relativistically covariant.

Bohr's model was significant in the development of quantum theory, because it showed unequivocally the potential usefulness of its concepts in describing the structure of atoms and molecules. However, attempts to extend Bohr's methods to helium and more complex atoms were not very successful. These problems were not fully resolved until after 1930, and in order to work them a completely new and much more general theory of quantum mechanics had to be developed. Still, Bohr's theory provided for the first time a simple picture of the structure of one-electron atomic systems, and a conceptual framework for understanding certain aspects of atomic structure that is still quite useful.

4.6 DE BROGLIE'S RELATION; DESCRIPTION OF MATTER AS WAVES

The development of quantum mechanics was halted during the period 1914-1918, by World War I, but resumed soon afterward. At first, the thrust was toward a more general theory of atomic structure based on the Bohr model, but several years of work along this line produced no very significant result. Finally, in 1924, Louis de Broglie--turning the ideas of Planck, Einstein, and Bohr around--suggested that if waves could under certain conditions behave like particles, particles might equally well act like waves.

An electron in one of Bohr's circular orbits can be thought of as having wave properties; specifically, it can be assigned a wavelength λ. Such a wave, travelling along a circular path of length $2\pi r$ will experience self-interference, which will be constructive only if the path length equals an integral number of wavelengths. We are thus led to suggest, using (4.5 - 5), that

$$n\lambda = 2\pi r_n = \frac{2\pi(4\pi\epsilon_0)n^2\hbar^2}{mZq^2} = \frac{nh}{\left(\dfrac{mZq^2}{4\pi\epsilon_0 n\hbar}\right)} \quad . \tag{4.6-1}$$

However, according to (4.5 - 12), this can be written as

$$\lambda = \frac{h}{mv_n} = \frac{h}{p} \quad , \tag{4.6-2}$$

where p is the linear momentum of the electron.

Considerations such as this led de Broglie to propose that the properties of matter can be described quite generally in terms of waves, and that the wavelength associated with a particle of linear momentum p must follow from the relation

$$p = \frac{h}{\lambda} = \frac{h}{2\pi} \cdot \frac{2\pi}{\lambda} = \hbar k \quad . \tag{4.6-3}$$

This is frequently referred to as the *de Broglie relation*. De Broglie did not succeed in developing his ideas into a comprehensive dynamical theory, but his suggestion led directly to the formulation of such a system of "wave mechanics" within a few years. De Broglie's relation suggests that a monoenergetic beam of electrons should be diffracted by a crystal lattice in exactly the same way as X-rays. For free electrons, energy is related to momentum by

$$\varepsilon = mv^2/2 = p^2/2m \quad , \qquad \text{or,} \qquad p = \sqrt{2m\varepsilon} \quad . \tag{4.6-4}$$

For such electrons, the Bragg diffraction condition can be written, employing the de Broglie relation, as

$$\frac{nh}{p} = \frac{nh}{\sqrt{2m\varepsilon}} = 2d_{hkl}\sin\theta \quad . \tag{4.6-5}$$

The diffraction of electrons by crystals was observed experimentally in 1927 by Davisson and Germer in the US and by G. P. Thomson in Britain. Their experiments also provided quantitative justification for the de Broglie relation as expressed by (4.6 - 5). It has since been shown that protons, positive and negative ions, neutral atoms, and other particles also exhibit the wavelike behavior predicted by the de Brogle relation.

4.7 WAVE MECHANICS

In 1926, Erwin Schrödinger developed a general theory of quantum mechanics, based upon the physical ideas embodied in the Planck and de Broglie relations. This theory is referred to as *wave mechanics*. It has been verified in many different experimental investigations, and has turned out to be the simplest and most useful general approach to quantum physics. Even so, its structure is abstract and mathematical, and to use it, you must master the abstract principles on which it is based.

Though quantum theory rejects many of the seemingly obvious assumptions of classical physics, it retains certain important classical concepts. In particular, the laws of *conservation of energy, momentum, and angular momentum* are accepted practically unaltered as basic assumptions of quantum mechanics. Also, the external mathematical formalism of quantum theory is based largely on the infrastructure of classical mechanics. It is difficult to imagine what form quantum physics would have taken had this framework not been available, but it is likely that it would have been a very different theory from that which is so familiar to physicists today.

In quantum theory there are no sharp distinctions between the wavelike and particle-like behavior of matter. However, in using wave mechanics, as a purely practical matter, it is useful to adopt the point of view than an object behaves as a wave unless you somehow force it to act as a particle.

In wave mechanics, the dynamics of what would be referred to as a particle in classical physics is described by a scalar function $\Psi(x, y, z, t)$, referred to as the *wave function*. This quantity is a solution of a wave equation often referred to as the *Schrödinger equation*. It is in general a *complex*, quantity and its physical significance is not easily described. You may, however, think of Ψ as the amplitude of "a wave associated with the particle". The *real* quantity $\Psi^*\Psi$ (or $|\Psi|^2$), where Ψ^* is the complex conjugate of Ψ, however, does have a simple physical interpretation as follows;

> $\Psi^*\Psi dv$ is the probability that the particle will be found in the volume element dv at time t.

Since there is unit probability that the particle will be *somewhere*, we must also require that

$$\int_v \Psi^*\Psi dv = 1 \quad , \tag{4.7-1}$$

where this *normalization integral* is evaluated over all space. One may now ask, "Why bother with Ψ at all; why not just find a wave equation for the physically defined quantity $\Psi^*\Psi$ and forget about Ψ altogether?" The answer is that although a wave equation for $\Psi^*\Psi$ can be written, it is nonlinear and therefore difficult to solve even in the simplest cases. Worse yet, $\Psi^*\Psi$, unlike Ψ, does not lend itself to the design of a formalism in which only linear operators, equations, and operations are needed. So, although Ψ is complex, and though its physical meaning isn't easily described, it greatly simplifies the mathematics of quantum theory. Like it or not, we must therefore use it.

The role of the dynamical variables of classical mechanics, like displacement, momentum, and energy, is played in quantum physics by *operators* that act on the wave function. Each of these classical dynamical quantities can be assigned an appropriate quantum-mechanical operator in wave mechanics.

> Physical measurements of the dynamical variable associated with any quantum mechanical operator can yield only values that are eigenvalues of the operator.

To understand what this means, you must know something about *eigenfunctions* and *eigenvalues*. Translated into English, these German words mean *characteristic functions* and *characteristic values*, an opaque academic terminology for a simple and frequently encountered mathematical problem.

This problem--referred to as an eigenvalue problem--arises in the solution of linear differential equations, and also in many other contexts. We are interested primarily in differential equations, but there are eigenvalue problems in matrix algebra, and other areas as well. Nearly all of the linear differential equations of physics can be written in the form

$$\underline{A}f = \alpha \cdot f \ . \tag{4.7-2}$$

In this expression, the underlined symbol $\underline{A}$ is a linear differential operator, which operates on a function f of space coördinates and time, while α is a constant. Any problem that can be written this way is an eigenvalue problem. The effect of the operator operating on f is to *regenerate* the function f multiplied by some constant α. Obviously, the operator operating on any old function will not regenerate the function in this manner. It will only work with certain functions--functions that satisfy the differential equation as defined by the above expression. These functions are referred to as *eigenfunctions* of the operator $\underline{A}$. Moreover, particularly when boundary conditions as well as the differential equation must be satisfied, proper solutions may not exist for all values of the constant α. Frequently, solutions can exist only for some discrete set of values, which we can write $\{\alpha_n\}$, where $n = 1, 2, 3$, etc. The values of α for which solutions can exist are called the *eigenvalues* of the operator $\underline{A}$ under the specified boundary conditions.

As an example consider the differential equation

$$\frac{d^2\varphi}{dx^2} = -\alpha^2\varphi(x) \ , \tag{4.7-3}$$

where boundary conditions $\varphi(0) = \varphi(L) = 0$ are specified. The general solution can be expressed as $A\sin\alpha x + B\cos\alpha x$, where α can have any real value, but when the boundary conditions are imposed, we see that in order for φ to be zero at $x = 0$, we must set $B = 0$. Even then, only a certain set of wavelengths can be permitted if the boundary condition at $x = L$ is to be satisfied. This requires us finally to write

$$\varphi_n(x) = A\sin\alpha_n x \ , \qquad \text{where} \quad \alpha_n = n\pi/L \quad (n = 1,2,3,\dots) \ . \tag{4.7-4}$$

The set of functions $\{\varphi_n(x)\}$ are the eigenfunctions of the operator d^2/dx^2 under the assumed boundary condition, while the set of values $\{\alpha_n\}$ define its eigenvalues. A knowledge of the operator and the boundary conditions enables us to find both the eigenfunctions and the eigenvalues. The boundary conditions are seen to be very important in defining the relevant eigenfunctions and eigenvalues in any given situation. We have seen similar examples in previous work, though they have not been presented in this context.

Though this discussion involves a differential operator, the operator $\underline{A}$ need not be of this type; any linear operator can generate an eigenvalue problem of this form, and any such operator can have eigenfunctions and eigenvalues. For example, matrices $\underline{\underline{M}}$ operating on vectors $\mathbf{v}$ such that $\underline{\underline{M}}\mathbf{v} = \alpha\mathbf{v}$, can have eigenvectors and eigenvalues. You should recall, finally, that a linear operator is defined as one having the property

$$\underline{A}(af + bg) = a\underline{A}f + b\underline{A}g \ , \tag{4.7-5}$$

where f and g are any two functions, and a and b are constants.

So far, we have said nothing about the form of a wave equation appropriate for describing the dynamics of a particle, but we are now positioned to see how it might be written. Any such equation must embody the Planck and de Broglie relations, and also include the classical definitions of potential and kinetic energy. For kinetic energy, this means $mv^2/2$ or $p^2/2m$, and for potential energy, $F_x = -\partial V/\partial x$. Let us start with the case of a free particle that moves in the x-direction. In this case the potential energy is zero since there are no forces, and the kinetic energy K is equal to the total energy ε. We therefore begin with

$$\varepsilon = \hbar\omega \ , \qquad p = \hbar k \ . \qquad \text{and} \qquad \varepsilon = K = p^2/2m \ ,$$

$$\text{or,} \qquad \hbar\omega = \frac{\hbar^2 k^2}{2m} \ . \tag{4.7-6}$$

The last of these equations has the form of a *dispersion relation*, which we shall require our wave equation to satisfy. First, however, we must find suitable operators to represent momentum, total energy and kinetic energy. We must also insist that the energy and momentum operators have eigenvalues $\hbar\omega$ and $\hbar k$, respectively, as suggested by the Planck and de Broglie relations.

For momentum, therefore, we must postulate an operator $\underline{p}$ which satisfies the eigenvalue equation

$$\underline{p}\varphi_p = \hbar k \varphi_p \ . \tag{4.7-7}$$

In this equation, φ_p are the eigenfunctions of an operator $\underline{p}$, which may conceivably operate on waves of the form $\exp i(kx - \omega t)$. Since $\partial[\exp(ikx)]/\partial x = ik\exp(ikx)$, we are led to suspect that suitable eigenfunctions of this operator might have this form, and that the operator itself is closely related to $\partial/\partial x$. In fact, if we define the operator as

$$\underline{p} = \frac{\hbar}{i} \frac{\partial}{\partial x} \ , \tag{4.7-8}$$

it is clear that (4.7-7) will be satisfied, that the eigenfunctions of $\underline{p}$ are of the form,

$$\varphi_p = e^{ikx} \ , \tag{4.7-9}$$

and that its eigenvalues are $\hbar k$, where k (in the absence of any boundary conditions) can have any real value, positive or negative.

In regard to the total energy, we must find an operator $\underline{\varepsilon}$, whose eigenvalues are given by the Planck relation $\varepsilon = \hbar\omega$, and which has the property that

$$\underline{\varepsilon}\varphi_\varepsilon = \hbar\omega \varphi_\varepsilon \ . \tag{4.7-10}$$

By reasoning similar to that used in the preceding case, it is clear that the operator

$$\underline{\varepsilon} = i\hbar \frac{\partial}{\partial t} \qquad (4.7\text{-}11)$$

substituted into (4.7 - 10) defines eigenfunctions

$$\varphi_\varepsilon = e^{-i\omega t} \quad , \qquad (4.7\text{-}12)$$

plus a set of eigenvalues $\hbar\omega$, where ω is any positive frequency. The reader should now be able also to show, using these same methods, that the operator $\underline{K}$ defined by

$$\underline{K} = -\frac{\hbar^2}{2m} \frac{\partial^2}{\partial x^2} = \frac{1}{2m} \underline{p}^2 \quad , \qquad (4.7\text{-}13)$$

has eigenfunctions $\exp(ikx)$ and eigenvalues $K = p^2/2m$ as defined by (4.7 - 6), and is therefore a suitable kinetic energy operator.

A free particle, in the absence of any prior knowledge of its position, can be expected to have a well-defined momentum and energy, but may be located in any interval dx with equal probability. If it is to be represented by a wave function, and if the interpretation of $\Psi^*\Psi$ as a probability density is valid, then we are forced to conclude that the only wave function that it can reasonably have is

$$\Psi(x,t) = Ae^{i(kx-\omega t)} \quad . \qquad (4.7\text{-}14)$$

For such a wave, the complex conjugate Ψ^* is $A^*\exp{-i(kx - \omega t)}$. Then, by the definition of $\Psi^*\Psi$ in terms of probability preceding equation (4.7 - 1), the probability $P(dx)$ of finding the particle in an interval dx along the x-axis, in this one-dimensional case, will be.

$$P(dx) = \Psi^*\Psi dx = A^*A dx = (const.)\cdot dx \qquad , \qquad (4.7\text{-}15)$$

which agrees with the description of a free-particle wave suggested above.

We must now seek a wave equation having the dispersion relation given by (4.7 - 6). For a wave of the form (4.7 - 14), we can write

$$\frac{\partial^2 \Psi}{\partial x^2} = -k^2 \Psi \text{ and } \qquad \frac{\partial \Psi}{\partial t} = -i\omega \Psi \quad . \qquad (4.7\text{-}16)$$

Multiplying the first of these equations by $-\hbar^2/2m$, and the second by $i\hbar$, it is clear that we can write such a wave equation as

$$-\frac{\hbar^2}{2m} \frac{\partial^2 \Psi}{\partial x^2} = i\hbar \frac{\partial \Psi}{\partial t} \quad . \qquad (4.7\text{-}17)$$

This is Schrödinger's equation for a free particle. By running the machinery in reverse, it is easy to see that it is satisfied by waves such as those described by (4.7 - 14), and that its dispersion relation is given by (4.7 - 6). Equally important, however, is the fact that the wave function (4.7 - 14) is not only a solution of the Schrödinger equation, but also (as one can verify by direct substitution) a solution of the eigenvalue problems (4.7 - 7) and (4.7 - 10). Therefore, the function (4.7 - 14) is simultaneously an eigenfunction of the energy operator and the momentum operator, and the eigenvalues are those expressed by the Planck and de Broglie relations. The physical consequences of these observations are that energy and momentum are *conserved quantities* for a free particle. This will be discussed more fully in a later section.

So far, we have considered only the case of a free particle, whose potential energy is zero. In general, however, particles can be acted upon by forces, whose effect can be described classically--and quantum mechanically as well--by a potential energy that depends only on the position of the particle. This potential energy $V(x)$ is related to the force component F_x by

$$F_x = -\frac{\partial V(x)}{\partial x} \quad . \tag{4.7-18}$$

Now, in order to write a reasonable wave equation, we must seek operators for the displacement x and the potential energy $V(x)$. Let us consider the displacement first. The operator representing the classical position or displacement must have eigenvalues that somehow correspond to physically measured positions of the particle. This remark bears the connotation that the particle *has* a sharply defined position-- that is, that it is sharply localized. The simplest position operator that can be suggested (and the right one, as we shall see), is a simple algebraic multiplication by the variable x itself, that is,

$$\underline{x} = x \cdot \quad . \tag{4.7-19}$$

To see why this is so, consider the eigenvalue problem,

$$\underline{x}\Psi = x \cdot \Psi = x_0 \Psi \quad , \tag{4.7-20}$$

where x_0 is an eigenvalue. Let us try to solve this equation for the eigenfunction Ψ. If x and x_0 are not equal, the only possible solution is $\Psi = 0$. If x and x_0 *are* equal, the value of Ψ at that point could be anything. Since Ψ is zero everywhere except when $x = x_0$, however, the only way the normalization integral (4.7 - 1) can have unit value is for Ψ to be *infinite* at $x = x_0$ in such a way that the integral over any interval that includes the singularity generates unit subtended area. The eigenfunction Ψ thus has a very odd form; it is zero except at a single point $x = x_0$, where its value is infinite. The integral of the function over any interval including the singularity, moreover, is unity. Such a function is referred to as a Dirac δ-function; we shall learn more about its properties in later work. For now, we need only observe that it is an eigenfunction of the operator $\underline{x}$, and that any eigenvalue x_0 corresponds to an observable, sharply defined position of the particle. It should also be noted that the eigenfunction gives a good representation of a particle having a precisely defined position, but does not resemble a traveling wave like that defined by (4.7 - 14). This seems like a very complex way of describing a simple situation, but it is the only way to fit the classical position variable into the formal structure of quantum theory.

A scalar function of position $f(x)$ can be associated with an operator in much the same way. Such an operator has eigenfunctions equal to zero except at a single point, exactly like those described above. It follows that one can define an operator for the potential energy similar to the displacement operator, of the form

$$\underline{V} = V(x) \cdot \quad . \qquad\qquad (4.7 \text{-} 21)$$

We are now at the point where we can write a wave equation for the general case in which the potential energy is no longer zero, but has the value $V(x)$. The wave equation for the free particle (4.7 - 17) can be expressed as an operator equation wherein the operator $\underline{K}$, operating on a wave function Ψ equals the total energy operator $\underline{\varepsilon}$ operating on Ψ. This operator equation reflects the fact that in classical mechanics, the kinetic energy of a free particle equals its constant total energy. For a particle acted on by forces defined by a potential energy, it is the *sum* of the kinetic and potential energy that remains constant and equal to the total energy. We may therefore replace the operator on the left side of (4.7 - 17) with an operator expressing the sum of these two energies, acting on the wave function Ψ. In classical physics, the sum of the kinetic and potential energies of a conservative system, expressed in terms of position and momentum, is often referred to as the *Hamiltonian* of the system. This nomenclature has persisted in quantum theory, where this operator is referred to as the Hamiltonian operator $\underline{H}$. It is in any event clear that this proced-ure leads to a wave equation of the form

$$-\frac{\hbar^2}{2m}\frac{\partial^2 \Psi}{\partial x^2} + V(x) \cdot \Psi(x) = i\hbar\frac{\partial \Psi}{\partial t} \quad , \qquad\qquad (4.7 \text{-} 22)$$

or,

$$\underline{H}\Psi = i\hbar\frac{\partial \Psi}{\partial t} = \underline{\varepsilon}\Psi \quad , \qquad\qquad (4.7 \text{-} 23)$$

where

$$\underline{H} = -\frac{\hbar^2}{2m}\frac{\partial^2}{\partial x^2} + V(x) \cdot \quad . \qquad\qquad (4.7 \text{-} 24)$$

This is the general form of Schrödinger's equation for a one-dimensional system.

For three-dimensional systems, there is a momentum operator for each car-tesian component of momentum. The operator $\underline{p}$ in (4.7 - 8) is therefore actually the operator $\underline{p}_x$ for the x-component of momentum, and will hereafter be written that way. The operators for the y- and z-components are the same except that the deriva-tives are taken with respect to the respective coördinates. The total momentum operator (like the classical momentum) has the character of a vector, and can be obtained by summing the three component operators times their respective cartes-ian unit vectors. It can therefore be expressed in terms of a gradient operator. The kinetic energy operator is found from the classical relation $K = (p_x{}^2 + p_y{}^2 + p_z{}^2)/2m$, and in operator form--derived using the above operators for the momentum components--is related to the Laplacian opreator, as shown in the table below, which lists most of the operators we shall need.

Dynamical Variable		Associated Operator
Position: x, y, z	$\rightarrow$	$\underline{x} = x \cdot$
	$\rightarrow$	$\underline{y} = y \cdot$
	$\rightarrow$	$\underline{z} = z \cdot$
Function of position: $f(x,y,z)$	$\rightarrow$	$\underline{f} = f(x,y,z) \cdot$
Momentum: p_x, p_y, p_z	$\rightarrow$	$\underline{p}_x = \dfrac{\hbar}{i}\dfrac{\partial}{\partial x}$
	$\rightarrow$	$\underline{p}_y = \dfrac{\hbar}{i}\dfrac{\partial}{\partial y}$
	$\rightarrow$	$\underline{p}_z = \dfrac{\hbar}{i}\dfrac{\partial}{\partial z}$
Vector momentum:	$\rightarrow$	$\underline{p} = i_x\underline{p}_x + i_y\underline{p}_y + i_z\underline{p}_z = \dfrac{\hbar}{i}\nabla$
Kinetic energy:	$\rightarrow$	$\underline{K} = \dfrac{1}{2m}(\underline{p}_x^2 + \underline{p}_y^2 + \underline{p}_z^2) = -\dfrac{\hbar^2}{2m}\nabla^2$
Potential energy:	$\rightarrow$	$\underline{V} = V(x,y,z) \cdot$
Total energy	$\rightarrow$	$\underline{\varepsilon} = i\hbar\dfrac{\partial}{\partial t}$
Hamiltonian	$\rightarrow$	$\underline{H} = \underline{K} + \underline{V}$

It is clear from this that the single-particle Schrödinger equation, in its most general form can be written as

$$-\frac{\hbar^2}{2m}\nabla^2\Psi + V(x,y,z)\cdot\Psi(x) = i\hbar\frac{\partial\Psi}{\partial t} \quad , \tag{4.7-25}$$

The wave equation (4.7-25) determines how "matter waves" are propagated. As we have seen in several previous examples, these waves must usually obey boundary conditions imposed by the geometry of the system in which they propagate. In the case of particle wave functions, these boundary conditions are quite simple. They ordinarily require that

Ψ and $\nabla\Psi$ must be everywhere continuous and single-valued, and Ψ must also satisfy the normalization condition (4.7 - 1).

As in previous examples, these boundary conditions play a very important role in determining the physical character of the allowed wave solutions. In this case, as mentioned previously, they largely determine the eigenvalues that express the physically observed values of energy, momentum, and other dynamical quantities.

In quantum theory, operators play the role of dynamical variables, and any physical measurement of the dynamical quantity represented by the operator must yield an eigenvalue of the operator. But the operators usually have *many* eigenvalues, often an infinite number of them. Suppose now that you have prepared a very large number of identical systems, each in the same initial state described by the wave function Ψ. Then, you start making measurements of the dynamical quantity you're interested in on each of them, one by one. If you are lucky--that is if the initial configuration of the systems is just right--you may obtain the same answer (that is, the same eigenvalue), time after time. You are happy, and conclude that quantum theory gives you precise answers, measurable to as many decimal places as you wish. If you are *not* lucky, however, you will always observe an eigenvalue of the operator, but not necessarily the *same* one for every system! You will get different answers for individual measurements, answers that can be interpreted only as some kind of mean value or *expectation value* that expresses the average of thousands of individual trials. If there is only a single system, and you can make only one measurement, quantum theory cannot generally predict its exact outcome, but only an expectation value. There is thus an *inherent uncertainty* associated with the result of any individual measurement, and all you can hope to know is the most probable outcome. Unfortunately, it is this situation that is most frequently encountered. We shall soon see what circumstances bring about the lucky situation first discussed, but for now that is irrelevant. Whether you are lucky or not, however, quantum theory *will* tell you the expectation value $<\alpha>$ associated with a measurement of the physical quantity represented by the operator $\underline{\alpha}$ for a particle whose wave function is Ψ. It is defined by a weighted average of $\underline{\alpha}\Psi$ of the form

$$\langle \alpha \rangle = \int_v \Psi^* \underline{\alpha} \Psi \, dv \ . \tag{4.7-26}$$

The expectation value of the momentum component p_x can be written, for example, as

$$\langle p_x \rangle = \int_v \Psi^* \left(\frac{\hbar}{i} \frac{\partial}{\partial x} \right) \Psi \, dv = \frac{\hbar}{i} \int_{-\infty}^{\infty} \Psi^* \frac{\partial \Psi}{\partial x} \, dx \ . \tag{4.7-27}$$

If Ψ is a free-particle wave function of the form (4.7 - 14), then $\partial \Psi / \partial x = ik\Psi$, and assuming that the normalization condition is satisfied, (4.7 - 27) gives the "lucky" invariant result $<p_x> = \hbar k_x$ = const., so that momentum is conserved. If there are forces acting, $V(x)$ is no longer zero. Then, in classical mechanics, momentum is no longer conserved, and becomes a time-varying quantity. In quantum theory, the function Ψ now cannot have the simple plane-wave form. In this more general case, since Ψ is a function of x, y, z, and t, and since the integral is taken over the whole system's space coördinates, the above expectation value will be (though independent of the space coördinates) a function of time, in agreement with classical mechanics. If one differentiates (4.7 - 27) with respect to time, one can in this case (and with some difficulty) express the right side of the equation, with the aid of Schrödinger's equation for Ψ, as an expectation value of the quantity $\partial V / \partial x$. This allows the above equation to be written as

$$\frac{d\langle p_x \rangle}{dt} = -\left\langle \frac{\partial V}{\partial x} \right\rangle = \langle F_x \rangle \ , \tag{4.7-28}$$

where F_x is the x-component of the classical resultant force. This can be recognized as a Newtonian equation of motion for expectation values, which verifies the fact that insofar as expectation values are concerned, quantum mechanics agrees with the classical equation of motion. The algebraic work involved in deriving this result is of no great significance, and is assigned as an exercise for the reader.

Though some further details will emerge in our later work, we have now presented most of the basic framework of Schrödinger's theory of wave mechanics. It should be understood that much of what has been discussed is pure hypothesis, not subject to rigorous proof other than by experimental investigation. Though most of this material is not only abstract, but also in sharp conflict with intuitive ideas based on classical physics, it has withstood rigorous experimental scrutiny and emerged unscathed. It therefore appears to be an accurate description of the physical world. The abstractness of this development, however, cannot be significantly reduced without sacrificing its generality; you must live with it if you are going to use quantum theory. Naturally, there may be many unanswered questions at this point; this need not cause undue concern. The rest of our work will be directed toward discussing specific examples and exploring the further implications of the theory developed above. In the course of this work, most of your questions will probably be answered. However, you may find it helpful to *revisit* this section frequently as you go along; in doing so you will strengthen your understanding of the inherently abstract ideas of quantum theory and become more accustomed to using them. Try it, you may like it!

4.8 THE TIME-DEPENDENCE OF THE WAVE FUNCTION

The wave function Ψ for a single particle is defined as a solution of the wave equation (4.7 - 25) that satisfies certain boundary conditions. Once it has been obtained, all the dynamical properties of the system follow directly from it. In order to get it, however, you must usually solve a complicated partial differential equation. This problem can be simplified by first determining the time-dependence of the wave function and eliminating it from the calculation, leaving only a time-independent equation to be solved. This can be done by assuming that solutions have a harmonic time-dependence which can be expressed as a factor $\exp(-i\omega t)$. We shall therefore begin by suggesting that the wave function has the form

$$\Psi(x,y,z,t) = \psi(x,y,z)e^{-i\omega t} \quad \text{, with } \omega = \varepsilon/\hbar \ . \tag{4.8-1}$$

This assumption may appear initially to be arbitrary, but as we shall see, it leads to no loss of generality. If it is now substituted back into (4.7 - 25), we find

$$-\frac{\hbar^2}{2m} \nabla^2 \psi + V(x,y,z)\,\psi(x,y,z) = \hbar\omega\,\psi = \varepsilon\psi \ , \tag{4.8-2}$$

or,

$$\underline{H}\,\psi = \varepsilon\,\psi \ . \tag{4.8-3}$$

The function ψ is a *time-independent* eigenfunction of the $\underline{H}$ operator, with eigenvalues $\varepsilon = \hbar\omega$. The factor $\exp(-i\omega t)$ has already been shown to be an eigenfunction of the energy operator having those same eigenvalues. The time-dependent wave function Ψ is therefore an eigenfunction of *both* operators, which share the common set of eigenvalues $\{\varepsilon\}$.

Equation (4.8 - 2) can be rewritten as

$$\nabla^2 \psi + \frac{2m}{\hbar^2}[\varepsilon - V(x,y,z)]\, \psi = 0 \quad . \tag{4.8-4}$$

This equation is called the *time-independent* Schrödinger equation. It is important to remember that in the above expression ε is so far unspecified. This equation can be solved for the time-independent wave functions ψ, regarding ε as an arbitrary constant. Subsequently, when boundary conditions are imposed, a set of eigenfunctions $\{\psi_n\}$ and energy eigenvalues $\{\varepsilon_n\}$ will be defined. The time-dependent eigenfunctions Ψ_n follow simply by multiplying ψ_n by the factor $\exp(-i\omega_n t)$, as suggested by (4.8 - 1) The details of these calculations will be illustrated by a series of examples worked out in forthcoming sections. In any event, these wave functions can now be written as

$$\Psi_n(x,y,z,t) = \psi_n(x,y,z)e^{-i\omega_n t} \quad , \text{ with } \qquad \omega_n = \varepsilon_n/\hbar \quad . \tag{4.8-5}$$

It is important now to observe that as a consequence of the above discussion, for eigenfunctions of the form (4.8 - 5), we can write

$$\Psi_n^* \Psi_n = \psi_n^* e^{i\omega_n t} \cdot \psi_n e^{-i\omega_n t} = \psi_n^* \psi_n \quad , \tag{4.8-6}$$

so that the quantities $\Psi_n^* \Psi_n$ and $\psi_n^* \psi_n$ are in this instance not only equal but also *time-independent*. Thus, the normalization property (4.7 - 1) is valid for either time-dependent or time-independent wave functions. If the operator $\underline{\alpha}$ has no explicit time dependence, the same statement applies to (4.7 - 26). These remarks are applicable, however, *only* to individual eigenfunctions ψ_n of the form (4.8 - 5), related to a single allowed energy eigenvalue ε_n.

Solutions of the form (4.8 - 5) are not the most general solutions of the time-dependent Schrödinger equation (4.7 - 25). More general solutions can be obtained by superposing solutions of the form (4.8 - 5) having different energy eigenvalues ε_n. For example, suppose that for some allowable energy ε_n, we solve the time-independent Schrödinger equation (4.8 - 7), to obtain a solution $\psi = \psi_n(x, y, z)$ Then, if we choose another possible energy ε_m, we will find a different solution ψ_m. These two solutions can be converted into two different solutions of the time-dependent Schrödinger equation, Ψ_m and Ψ_n, by multiplying each of them by the appropriate oscillatory time-dependent factor $\exp(-i\varepsilon t/\hbar)$. Since they are related to two different energy eigenvalues, however, these two factors will have *different* frequencies ω_m and ω_n, as defined in (4.8 - 5). Nevertheless, the arbitrary linear combination

$$\Psi(x,y,z,t) = c_m \Psi_m + c_n \Psi_n = c_n \psi_n(x,y,z)e^{-i\varepsilon_n t/\hbar} + c_m \psi_m(x,y,z)e^{-i\varepsilon_m t/\hbar} \tag{4.8-7}$$

is still a solution of the time-dependent Schrödinger equation, as you can verify by direct substitution, using the fact that that ψ_m and ψ_n satisfy (4.8 - 4). More generally still, any solution of the form

$$\Psi(x,y,z,t) = \sum_n c_n \Psi_n = \sum_n c_n \psi_n(x,y,z)e^{-i\varepsilon_n t/\hbar} \tag{4.8-8}$$

will satisfy the time-dependent Schrödinger equation. Returning now to (4.8 - 7), if we take the complex conjugate of both sides to obtain Ψ^*, and multiply the resulting expression by Ψ, we find

$$\Psi^*\Psi = (c_n\psi_n e^{-i\varepsilon_n t/\hbar} + c_m\psi_m e^{-i\varepsilon_m t/\hbar})(c_n^*\psi_n^* e^{i\varepsilon_n t/\hbar} + c_m^*\psi_m^* e^{i\varepsilon_m t/\hbar})$$

$$= c_n c_n^* \psi_n \psi_n^* + c_m c_m^* \psi_m \psi_m^* + c_m c_n^* \psi_m \psi_n^* e^{i(\varepsilon_n - \varepsilon_m)t/\hbar} + c_m^* c_n \psi_m^* \psi_n e^{-i(\varepsilon_n - \varepsilon_m)t/\hbar}. \tag{4.8-9}$$

In this expression, the first two terms are clearly real and time-independent. Moreover, the fourth term is the complex conjugate of the third. However, the sum of a complex number $x + iy$ and its conjugate $x - iy$ is the real quantity $2x$, that is, twice the real part of the complex number. If the complex number is expressed in polar form, this can be written as $2R\cos\theta$, where R is the polar magnitude and θ the phase angle. Therefore, we can write the above equation as

$$\Psi^*\Psi = c_n c_n^* \psi_n \psi_n^* + c_m c_m^* \psi_m \psi_m^* + 2\left|c_n c_m^* \psi_n \psi_m^*\right|\cos[(\varepsilon_n - \varepsilon_m)t/\hbar] \ . \tag{4.8-10}$$

It is now apparent that $\Psi^*\Psi$ is *no longer time-independent*, but has an oscillatory time dependence whose frequency depends on the energy differerence $\varepsilon_n - \varepsilon_m$. It is also clear that this will be true for more general superpositions of the form (4.8 - 8). Similar time dependences will be found for the expectation values of time-independent operators calculated using (4.7 - 26).

There is one other point that should be mentioned before we move on to other subjects. This has to do with the fact that the eigenvalues of operators associated with dynamical quantities, and their expectation values as given by (4.7 - 26), must be *real*, since they are the quantities observed in experiments. A real number has the property that it equals its own complex conjugate. If we take the complex conjugate of the expectation value shown in (4.7 - 26) and set it equal to the original expression, we find

$$\int_v \Psi^* \underline{\alpha} \Psi \, dv = \left(\int_v \Psi^* \underline{\alpha} \Psi \, dv\right)^* = \int_v \Psi(\underline{\alpha}\Psi)^* \, dv = \int_v (\underline{\alpha}\Psi)^* \Psi \, dv \ . \tag{4.8-11}$$

This relationship can be regarded as defining the class of operators $\underline{\alpha}$ whose eigenvalues and expectation values are real, and which can potentially represent dynamical variables in quantum theory. These operators are called *Hermitian* operators. All the operators we have so far encountered are Hermitian.

In summary, we have found that a wave function associated with a single allowed energy eigenvalue yields a time-independent probability amplitude $\Psi^*\Psi$. Under these conditions, the probability of finding the particle in any given volume element does not change with time. Such a state also exhibits time-independent expectation values (given by Eq. (4.7 - 26)) for physical quantities whose quantum operators have no explicit time dependence. Such states are referred to as *stationary states*, and their wave functions are called *stationary-state eigenfunctions*. You can also construct wave functions by superposing stationary-state solutions corresponding to *different* energy eigenvalues. These wave functions are valid descriptions of physically possible states of the system, but now the probability distributions they describe--and the expectation values of any other physcal quantities they define--are time-dependent. Some further consequences of these results will be discussed later.

4.9 THE FREE PARTICLE AND THE UNCERTAINTY PRINCIPLE

We can now discuss a simple method for finding the stationary-state eigenfunctions and energy eigenvalues of a single-particle system acted upon by known external forces. These time-independent eigenfunctions are all that is needed to provide a description of the system adequate for most purposes. All the pieces of this puzzle have been exhibited and studied; we now need only put them together. The rules for doing this are as follows;

1. Associate with the particle a complex wave function $\Psi(x, y, z, t)$

2. Associate with the dynamical variables position, momentum, kinetic energy, etc., the operators given in the table in the preceding section.

3. Form the Hamiltonian operator **H**, and write the Schrödinger equation in its time-independent form as $\underline{H}\psi = \varepsilon\psi$ or, as given by (4.8 - 4),

$$\nabla^2 \psi + \frac{2m}{\hbar^2}[\varepsilon - V(x,y,z)]\,\psi(x,y,z) = 0 \ ,$$

where
$$\Psi(x,y,z,t) = \psi(x,y,z)e^{-i\varepsilon t/\hbar} \ .$$

4. Solve this partial differential equation using as boundary conditions the requirement that the wave function and its gradient must be everywhere continuous and single-valued, and that the *normalization* condition

$$\int_v \Psi^* \Psi dv = 1 \ .$$

must be satisfied.

5. The energy eigenvalues and eigenfunctions are obtained from the above calculations. Additional information regarding the expectation values of physical quantities α represented by operators $\underline{\alpha}$ can be found from

$$\langle \alpha \rangle = \int_v \Psi^* \underline{\alpha} \Psi dv \ .$$

The mathematical details of this work can be complex. but the procedure outlined above is the same regardless of what mathematical problems appear. We shall begin by working the simplest possible problems, and continue with progressively more difficult examples, until we have finally outlined the wave mechanics of the hydrogen atom. The first, and simplest, of these examples concerns a free particle, one on which no forces act, and whose potential energy is therefore constant. In this case we can set V equal to zero. The time-independent Schrödinger equation then becomes

$$\nabla^2 \psi + k^2 \psi = 0 \ , \tag{4.9-1}$$

where

$$k^2 = 2m\varepsilon/\hbar^2 \ , \qquad \text{or,} \qquad \varepsilon = \hbar\omega = \frac{\hbar^2 k^2}{2m} \ . \tag{4.9-2}$$

Note that (4.9 - 2) defines the free-particle dispersion relation already encountered in (4.7 - 6). Consider first a purely one-dimensional situation in which the particle's motion is along the x-direction. Then the operator ∇^2 is simply d^2/dx^2, and solutions are of the form $\exp(\pm ikx)$. To get the time-dependent solutions, you need only multiply the time-independent solutions by $\exp(-i\omega t)$. In this case, then,

$$\psi(x) = Ae^{\pm ikx}, \qquad \text{and} \qquad \Psi(x,t) = Ae^{i(\pm kx - \omega t)} \ . \tag{4.9-3}$$

This wave function describes a plane wave propagating in the x-direction; its propagation vector is simply $\mathbf{i}_x k$. We have seen it before, as (4.7 - 14), where it was postulated on physical grounds as the only "reasonable" description of a free particle, and was used to infer the form of the free-particle Schrödinger equation. It is not surprising, therefore, that it is regenerated by running the machinery backwards. The plus sign before k corresponds to waves propagating along the positive x-direction, the minus sign to oppositely directed waves. For simplicity, we shall choose the plus sign in this discussion. This solution is continuous and differentiable everywhere, and in this sense satisfies the boundary conditions listed above in (4). Ordinarily, setting the normalization integral equal to unity would allow us to evaluate the constant A. Problems arise in doing this here, however; the quantity Ψ^* will be $A^*\exp{-i(kx-\omega t)}$, so that $\Psi^*\Psi = A^*A = |A|^2$. This means that the constant A must be infinitesimally small if the normalization integral is to have unit magnitude. Physically, the problem arises because the "boundaries" of the system are infinitely distant. Therefore, the particle can be anywhere in an infinite region with equal probability, which implies that the probabilty of finding it in any finite interval is, though constant, infinitesimal. The difficulty is confined to this single example, and its cause is simple. We can get around it by avoiding the explicit evaluation of the normalization integral, and simply assigning unit value to it wherever it appears. We have done this in the preceding section, where we showed that the expectation value of the momentum of a free particle can be written as

$$\langle p_x \rangle = \int_{-\infty}^{\infty} \Psi^* \left(\frac{\hbar}{i} \frac{\partial}{\partial x} \right) \Psi \, dx = \frac{\hbar}{i} \cdot ik_x \int_{-\infty}^{\infty} \Psi^* \Psi \, dx = \hbar k_x \ . \tag{4.9-4}$$

Using the energy operator instead of the momentum operator, we also find that

$$\langle \varepsilon \rangle = \hbar \omega \ . \tag{4.9-5}$$

In the more general three-dimensional case, we can show by direct substitution into (4.9 - 1) that solutions of the form

$$\psi(x,y,z) = A e^{ik_x x} e^{ik_y y} e^{ik_z z} \quad \text{or} \quad \Psi(x,y,z,t) = A e^{ik_x x} e^{ik_y y} e^{ik_z z} e^{-i\omega t} \tag{4.9-6}$$

where

$$k^2 = k_x^2 + k_y^2 + k_z^2 \ , \tag{4.9-7}$$

satisfy (4.9 - 1). We have seen previously that the quantities $k_x, k_y,$ and k_z form the components of a propagation vector $\mathbf{k}$, and that solutions of this form can be written as

$$\psi = A e^{i\mathbf{k}\cdot\mathbf{r}} \quad \text{or} \quad \Psi = A e^{i(\mathbf{k}\cdot\mathbf{r} - \omega t)} \ . \tag{4.9-8}$$

These wave functions describe plane waves propagating in the direction of the propagation vector. If you substitute them back into the time-dependent form of Schrödinger's equation (4.7 - 19), you will obtain the dispersion relation

$$\hbar \omega = \frac{\hbar^2}{2m}\left(k_x^2 + k_y^2 + k_z^2\right) = \frac{\hbar^2 k^2}{2m} \ . \tag{4.9-9}$$

From this one can see that the group velocity $d\omega/dk$ is $\hbar k/m$, or p/m. The phase velocity ω/k is one-half the group velocity, a fact that has little physical significance, since the rate at which the energy of the wave is propagated is determined by the group velocity. In this example, it is important to note that the Schrödinger equation can be satisfied for any positive value of energy ε, and for any real values of the components $k_x, k_y,$ and k_z. These eigenvalues are not further restricted by any more specific boundary conditions, so in this example there is a *continuous* range of possible energy and momentum eigenvalues.

The wave functions corresponding to any given energy are clearly traveling plane waves of infinite extent, waves that are not restricted in any way. The momentum components are precisely defined by the eigenvalues $k_x, k_y,$ and k_z, so that the particle momentum is accurately specified. Its *position*, however, is totally undefined; it can occupy any volume element with equal probability. The eigenfunctions themselves describe what we identify as waves, not particles. They can also depict a particle localized within some small region of space, but this can be accomplished only by *superposing* eigenfunctions having different momenta and energies.

A good example of a localizing process is the single-slit diffraction experiment described--in the context of light waves--in Section 2.3. There is no essential difference between the diffraction of light and the diffraction of a beam of electrons, represented quantum mechanically as plane waves. A beam of monoenergetic electrons incident on a slit of width Δz, as shown in Figure 4.6, will produce a diffraction pattern on a photographic film that cannot be distinguished from the pattern generated by an incident beam of monochromatic light. Both effects arise from the diffraction of waves by the slit, and both can be described by the analysis given in Section 2.3.

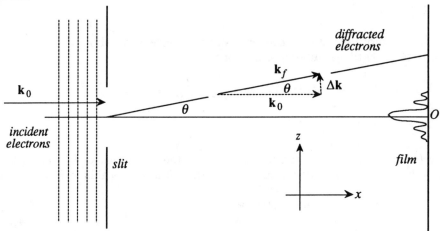

Figure 4.6 An incident beam of monoenergetic electrons is diffracted through a small angle by a narrow slit of width Δz and subsequently detected on a film. The slit width is exaggerated in this figure. Actually, the slit is very narrow, and the film very distant on the scale of the slit width.

In both cases, a diffraction pattern like that shown in Figure 2.3 will be observed. The intensity of the pattern as a function of the diffraction angle θ is given by equation (2.3 - 8), and the positions of intensity minima are described by (2.3 - 9). If there were no diffraction, the electrons would simply go through the slit parallel to the x-axis forming a sharp image of the slit on the film. The angle θ would then be *zero* for all electrons. As it is, however, the electrons are diffracted through various angles, resulting in a diffraction pattern that spreads out in the z-direction on either side of point O on the film. This pattern has a characteristic angular width defined by the angle θ within which the most intense part of the pattern is observed. The most intense part of the pattern is located within the central bright region of the pattern shown in Figure 2.3; according to this criterion, the angular width of the pattern can be defined--approximately--by the positions of the first intensity minima on either side of the central maximum at point O on the film.

What "happens" during the diffraction process isn't easy to describe--indeed, there's really no way to describe it, except to observe that the diffraction process can rotate the propagation vector of the incident electron beam, $\mathbf{k}_0$, through some angle θ. After diffraction, the propagation vector is $\mathbf{k}_f$, as shown in the diagram, the magnitudes k_0 and k_f being equal, since energy--as given by (4.9 - 9)--is conserved. If the angle θ is small, an assumption which we shall make for simplicity, the vector triangle in the figure is practically a right triangle, and we can write $\sin\theta \cong \Delta k / k_0$. From (2.3 - 9), we can now write the angles associated with diffraction minima as

$$n\lambda = \frac{2\pi n}{k_0} = (\Delta z)\sin\theta \cong \frac{(\Delta z)(\Delta k_z)}{k_0} \quad , \tag{4.9-10}$$

where Δz is the slit width. Regarding the angular width of the diffraction pattern as the width of the central "bright" region, we may set n equal to unity, to obtain

$$(\Delta z)(\Delta k_z) \cong 2\pi \ . \tag{4.9-11}$$

Multiplying by $\hbar$ and using the de Broglie relation, we can express this as

$$(\Delta z)(\Delta p_z) \cong 2\pi\hbar \ . \tag{4.9-12}$$

Since the width of the diffraction pattern has been defined by the somewhat arbitrary choice $n = 1$, it is clear that this relation is not very precise. We can therefore additionally neglect the factor 2π in the above equation, and replace the symbol "$\cong$" with the less definite "$\approx$", to be interpreted as "of the order of", to obtain finally,

$$(\Delta z)(\Delta p_z) \approx \hbar \ . \tag{4.9-13}$$

This expression suggests that our attempt to localize the position of the electrons within the limits defined by the slit width Δz, though successful, has introduced into the picture an uncertainty in the z-component of their momentum. In the absence of any attempt to define its position, the electron acts like a pure sinusoidal wave, whose k-vector, and momentum, are precisely defined. As illustrated in Figure 4.6, for example, an incoming electron has no well-defined position, but its momentum is precisely defined by the vector $\mathbf{k_0}$. In particular, the z-component of its momentum is exactly zero, since this vector has no z-component. Our attempt to localize it requires that it be diffracted through some angle that can be determined only in terms of an intensity distribution function that tells us only where electrons may--or may not--be detected. You can ascertain, after the fact, where an electron has landed, since it announces its presence as a tiny speck on the developed film. However, the electrons do not all arrive at the same point. The intensity distribution (2.3 - 8) gives information about the relative probability of finding electrons in given parts of the pattern, but no precise information about the path of any individual electron. There's no way that quantum theory will *ever* tell you that. We must conclude, therefore, that though we can't know what "happens" during a diffraction process that localizes an electron's z-coördinate, we can conclude that it must somehow introduce an inherently random *uncertainty* into the z-component of the particle's momentum. The uncertainty in momentum can be traced to the presence of the vector $\Delta \mathbf{k}$ in Figure 4.6--a vector needed to preserve conservation of momentum, which is required in quantum mechanics as well as classical physics.

This is one of the simplest examples of a more general principle inherent in quantum mechanics, which states that the components of position and momentum of a particle cannot be determined *simultaneously* with arbitrary precision, but must obey an "uncertainty relation" of the form (4.9 - 13). This phenomenon is known as the *Heisenberg uncertainty principle*. To determine the position of a particle like an electron you must first force it to *have* a position, by passing it through a slit as suggested above, or in some way that may seem superficially different but which accomplishes the same purpose. Indeed, when you postulate a wave function that isn't spread out over all space like an infinite plane wave, but exists in some region of space and is zero elsewhere, you are dealing not with a simple plane wave having a single well-defined wavelength, but with a wave function made up of a Fourier superposition of many waves, each having a different wavelength, and thus (according to de Broglie) a different momentum! As a result of this fact, the uncertainties Δz and Δp_z in the z-components of a particle's position and momentum in situations like the one shown above are *always* related by an uncertainty relation such as (4.9 - 13), and similar relations may be associated with the other cartesian components as well. These relations are not equalities, and thus an exact value of the product of the uncertainties cannot be determined. It can be shown, however that this product cannot be *less* than $\hbar/2$. It should be noted that the uncertainty relations connect only a given momentum component and the *same* component of the displacement. There is no uncertainty relation between x and p_z, or between p_x and z, for example, and there is nothing that prevents these pairs of components from being determined simultaneously with arbitrary precision.

The uncertainty principle can be expressed in another form, as a relation between an uncertainty $\Delta\varepsilon$ in energy and a corresponding time uncertainty Δt. This form can be exhibited by first multiplying Δp_z in (4.9 - 22) by $\Delta t/\Delta t$, to obtain

$$\left(\frac{\Delta p_z}{\Delta t} \cdot \Delta z\right) \Delta t \approx \hbar \ . \tag{4.9-14}$$

We may now observe that $\Delta p_z/\Delta t$ represents an average external force needed to create the uncertainty in momentum Δp_z, and that the quantity in parentheses is the work done in this process. But by the work-energy theorem, which follows from energy conservation, this work must correspond to a change in energy $\Delta\varepsilon$. Therefore, the Heisenberg uncertainty relation can also be expressed as

$$\Delta\varepsilon \cdot \Delta t \approx \hbar \ . \tag{4.9-15}$$

This derivation, though perhaps lacking in rigor, reveals clearly the physical factors that lead to the energy-time form of the uncertainty relation.

4.10 A ONE-DIMENSIONAL POTENTIAL WELL OF INFINITE DEPTH

Another simple example of an easily soluble quantum problem concerns a particle confined by a "potential well" of the form illustrated in Figure 4.7. In this system, the potential energy $V(x)$ is zero for $(0 < x < L)$ and infinite elsewhere. In this situation, classically, the particle experiences very strong forces at $x = 0$ and $x = L$ that prevent it from leaving the region bounded by these points. In classical mechanics, the problem is very simple; if the particle's total energy is zero, it remains at rest within the well, and if it is greater than zero, it moves back and forth between the two confining walls with momentum given by $p_x = \pm(2m\varepsilon)^{1/2}$.

To solve this problem quantum mechanically, we first write the time-independent Schrödinger equation as

$$\frac{d^2\psi}{dx^2} = \frac{2m(V-\varepsilon)}{\hbar^2}\psi \ . \tag{4.10-1}$$

Outside the well, where V is infinite, we can regard V as a large positive constant, which is allowed to approach infinity. Then, for any finite value of ε, the solutions

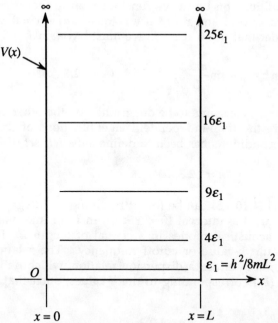

Figure 4.7 Potential energy diagram and energy levels for the infinite one-dimensional potential well of width L. Note that the smallest allowed energy is not zero, but has a finite positive value.

of the above equation can be of the form

$$e^{+\left(\sqrt{2m(V-\varepsilon)}/\hbar\right)x} \qquad \text{or} \qquad e^{-\left(\sqrt{2m(V-\varepsilon)}/\hbar\right)x} \ . \tag{4.10-2}$$

When V becomes very large, we must insist that the wave function remain finite. Therefore, we must *reject* any solution that gives an infinite wave function, and retain those that do not. But now, the solution you're left with--the one that does not become infinite--approaches *zero* as V becomes infinitely large. For $x > 0$, then, the first solution has to be discarded, and the second approaches zero; for $x < 0$, the second must be rejected, and the first approaches zero. Therefore, outside the well, the *only* solution that is acceptable is,

$$\psi = 0 \qquad (x < 0, x > L) \ . \tag{4.10-3}$$

This result agrees with the classical notion that the particle must be confined to the interior of the well. Indeed, the result seems so obvious that it might have been *assumed* rather than (as above) so tediously calculated. However, in quantum theory, it is dangerous to make naïve assumptions based on classical physics. Moreover, as we shall soon see, particles frequently show up in places where they're classically forbidden!

Inside the well, V is zero, and the solutions of (4.10 - 1) must be of the form

$$\psi = A\sin kx + B\cos kx \ , \qquad \text{where} \qquad k = \sqrt{\frac{2m\varepsilon}{\hbar^2}} \ . \tag{4.10-4}$$

The boundary conditions on the wave function require that it be continuous every-where--in particular at $x = 0$ and $x = L$. If ψ is to be zero at $x = 0$, we must require that $B = 0$. Then, in order that $\psi = 0$ at $x = L$, we must have $\sin kL = 0$, or, $kL = n\pi$. There-fore, we can write

$$\psi_n(x) = A_n \sin k_n x = A_n \sin \frac{n\pi x}{L} , \qquad (n = 1,2,3,...) . \qquad (4.10\text{-}5)$$

where A_n are arbitrary constants to be determined by the other boundary conditions. These functions are the time-independent eigenfunctions of the system. The effect of these boundary conditions has been to define a *discrete set* of allowed k-values,

$$k_n = n\pi / L , \qquad (n = 1,2,3,...) . \qquad (4.10\text{-}6)$$

The wave functions (4.10 - 5) can be found by fitting an integral number of loops of the sine function into the interval $(0 < x < L)$, in the same manner used to deter-mine the allowed acoustical modes in a crystal of length L. In this case, though, there is no maximum k-value or cutoff frequency. The relation between ε and k given by (4.10 - 4), is in effect, a dispersion relation, which defines a set of *discrete energy eigenvalues* $\{\varepsilon_n\}$ corresponding to the k-values, such that

$$\varepsilon_n = \frac{\hbar^2 k_n^2}{2m} = \frac{n^2 h^2}{8mL^2} . \qquad (n = 1,2,3,...) . \qquad (4.10\text{-}7)$$

Note that the final form of this expression utilizes h rather than "h-bar". The set of allowed energies--or "energy levels"--is illustrated in Figure 4.7. Observe also that the spacing between levels decreases with increasing particle mass and increasing L. Thus, in the realm of classical physics, the allowed energies will be so closely spaced as to behave like an energy continuum. Finally, it should be noted that the lowest allowed energy (corresponding to $n = 1$) is not zero, but has a finite value $h^2/8mL^2$. A particle therefore *cannot be at rest* in this system, but must have a finite "zero-point" kinetic energy! This strange behavior is quite common in quantum theory. Though it is not possible for a system to give up its zero-point energy, certain other effects associated with it have been observed and have provided indirect experimen-tal confirmation of its reality.

The coefficients A_n associated with the eigenfunctions ψ_n can be evaluated using the normalization condition (4.7 - 1). Thus, using (4.10 - 5), we can write

$$\int_{-\infty}^{\infty} \psi_n^* \, \psi_n \, dx = A_n^2 \int_0^L \sin^2 \frac{n\pi x}{L} \, dx = 1 , \qquad (4.10\text{-}8)$$

which allows us to evaluate A_n as

$$A_n = \sqrt{\frac{2}{L}} \qquad \text{(for all } n\text{) .} \qquad (4.10\text{-}9)$$

In this calculation we can use the time-independent eigenfunctions, since we are dealing with individual eigenstates of the system, as explained in Section 4.8, in reference to (4.8 - 6). In this example, the coefficient is the same for all values of n, though this is usually not true in other systems.

In general, not only the wave function but also its derivative must exist and be everywhere continuous. You will observe, however, that this problem has been solved without reference to the derivative of ψ. Indeed, the slope of ψ is *not* continuous at $x = 0$ and $x = L$, This formal violation of the rules arises from the infinite discontinuity of the potential $V(x)$ at these points, and causes no alarming problems; it is only a peculiarity of this particular example. If the potential outside the well is large but not infinite, the derivative of the wave function, though rapidly changing, becomes continuous in the neighborhood of these points. It should be noted also that the time-independent wave function is real, though when it is multiplied by the factor $\exp(-i\omega t)$ to convert it to the time-dependent form Ψ it becomes complex.

By writing the sine in exponential form and multiplying by $\exp(-i\omega t)$, the time-dependent wave function can be written as

$$\Psi_n(x,t) = \frac{A_n}{2i}\left(e^{i\left(\frac{n\pi x}{L}-\omega t\right)} - e^{i\left(-\frac{n\pi x}{L}-\omega t\right)}\right) . \tag{4.10-10}$$

The above expression exhibits the time-dependent wave function as a superposition of two travelling waves of equal amplitude propagating in opposite directions. This can be identified as a standing wave--a physical portrayal in harmony with the classical picture of a particle moving back and forth as it experiences periodic elastic collisions with the rigid walls of the confining potential well. Such a particle has a positive momentum half the time and a negative momentum of equal magnitude the other half. Under these circumstances you might guess that the expectation value $<p_x>$ associated with any eigenstate is zero, while the expectation value $<p_x^2>$ would be $\hbar^2 k_n^2$, The reader can confirm these conjectures by using the proper operators in the recipe for expectation values given by (4.7 - 26).

The probability density $\psi^*\psi$ is shown for the three eigenstates $n = 1, 2,$ and 7 in Figure 4.8. The curves are the squares of the sinusoidal eigenfunctions (4.10 - 5), since for real functions ψ^* and ψ are identical. There are some curious features to be noted. In the ground state ($n = 1$), the particle is most likely to be found in the neighborhood of $x = L/2$, and the probability of finding it near either of the walls is very small. For the state $n = 2$, the probability of finding it at $x = L/2$ is *zero*; Now it spends most of its time near $x = L/4$ and $x = 3L/4$. This is in sharp disagreement with the predictions of classical physics, which tell us that the probability associated with all coördinate elements is the same, as indicated by the horizontal dotted lines in all three diagrams. In (c), however, where $n = 7$, we observe that the probability density is beginning to oscillate rapidly with distance, so that--if you ignore the rapid fluctuations--the classical result is (in some average sense) being approached. However, in all these cases, there are certain points where the probability density is zero. If you insist a classical view of the motion as a particle phenomenon, you will be forced to the conclusion that it goes from one place to another without ever having visited certain points in between! This odd circumstance is an artifact of the classical mindset. If you regard the "particle" as a standing wave made up of a superposition of two oppositely directed travelling waves, the picture no longer seems so strange.

One should note, however, that in this problem the potential well that has been defined does act to *localize* the wave function within a region of length L. It is therefore forced to exhibit to some degree the behavior of a classical particle rather than a wave. In this regard the situation resembles the diffraction process discussed

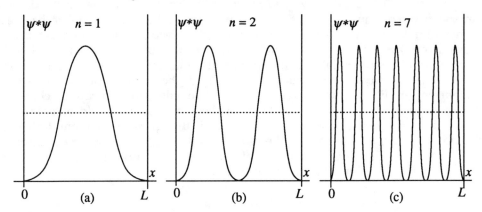

Figure 4.8 Probability density as a function of distance within the potential well of Section 4.10 for the eigenstates (a) n = 1, (b) n = 2, (c) n = 7. The dotted lines illustrate the classical probability density.

in the preceding section. Can we now conclude that the ground-state ($n = 1$) momentum $\hbar k_1 = \pi \hbar / L$ is precisely known, with zero uncertainty, and that the product of the uncertainties in position and momentum is therefore also zero, in violation of the uncertainty principle? The answer is no, of course. The reason has to do with the fact that in this example *momentum is not conserved*, since forces act on the particle every time it collides with the boundaries of the well and reverses direction. It is true that the magnitude of the x-component of momentum remains fixed, but its *sign* changes every time the particle collides with the well. There are therefore two possible answers that can result from a measurement of momentum--the one given above and its counterpart with a minus sign. So there is really an uncertainty in momentum $\Delta p_x = 2\pi \hbar / L$, and the product of these two uncertainties must be $(\Delta p_x)(\Delta x) = 2\pi \hbar$, as required by Heisenberg. This can also be understood by observing that the sinusoidal wave functions (4.10 - 4), though eigenfunctions of the Hamiltonian operator, are *not* eigenfunctions of the momentum operator. If the sine function is written in exponential form, it is evident that the wave function is a superposition of *two* momentum eigenfunctions having opposite signs. As we shall see later, this has the consequence that momentum is not a conserved quantity.

4.11 MORE WELLS AND BARRIERS

Another useful example, closely related to the one just discussed, is the case of a potential well of finite depth, as illustrated in Figure 4.9. The well is of width L, its "walls" being located at $x = \pm L/2$. The potential V within the well iz zero, while outside the potential energy is greater by an amount V_0. Classically, a particle of energy less than V_0 will be confined to the region $-L/2 < x < L/2$, while particles of greater energy will never be trapped inside the well.

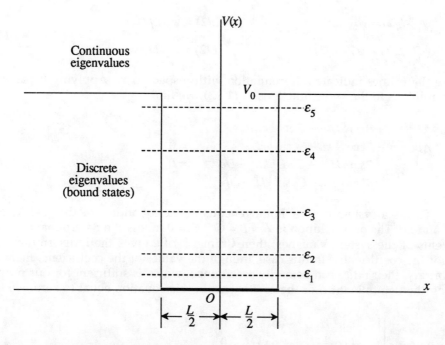

Figure 4.9 A potential well of finite width and depth. Classically bound particles have discrete energies. while classically free paricles have a continuous range of allowed energies.

Quantum mechanically, the stationary-state wave functions must satisfy the Schrödinger equation both inside and outside the well, so the wave function and its first derivative must be continuous at $x = \pm L/2$. Initially, we shall assume that the particle's total energy ε is less than V_0. Under these circumstances, we can write

$$\frac{d^2\psi}{dx^2} = -k^2\psi \ , \quad \text{where} \quad k^2 = \frac{2m\varepsilon}{\hbar^2} \ , \qquad (-L/2 < x < L/2) \ , \qquad (4.11\text{-}1)$$

and

$$\frac{d^2\psi}{dx^2} = \beta^2\psi \ , \quad \text{where} \quad \beta^2 = \frac{2m(V_0 - \varepsilon)}{\hbar^2} \qquad (x < -L/2, x > L/2) \ . \qquad (4.11\text{-}2)$$

The first equation has sinusoidal solutions, while those of the second are of the form $\exp(\pm\beta x)$. Since the wave function must remain finite at $\pm\infty$, we must reject any solution that becomes infinite at these points, and write

$$\psi_1 = Ae^{\beta x} \qquad\qquad (x < -L/2) \ ,$$

$$\psi_2 = B\sin kx + C\cos kx \qquad\qquad (-L/2 < x < L/2) \ , \qquad (4.11\text{-}3)$$

$$\psi_3 = De^{-\beta x} \qquad\qquad (x > L/2) \ .$$

The continuity of the wave function and its first derivative at $\pm L/2$ require that

$$\psi_1(-L/2) = \psi_2(-L/2) \ ; \qquad\qquad \psi_2(L/2) = \psi_3(L/2) \ ,$$

and

$$\psi_1'(-L/2) = \psi_2'(-L/2) \ ; \qquad\qquad \psi_2'(L/2) = \psi_3'(L/2) \ ,$$

(4.11-4)

where the primes indicate differentiation with respect to x. Applying these boundary conditions to the wave functions (4.11-3), we find

$$
\begin{aligned}
Ae^{-\beta L/2} + B\sin\tfrac{1}{2}kL - C\cos\tfrac{1}{2}kL &= 0 \\
A\beta e^{-\beta L/2} - Bk\cos\tfrac{1}{2}kL - Ck\sin\tfrac{1}{2}kL &= 0 \\
B\sin\tfrac{1}{2}kL + C\cos\tfrac{1}{2}kL - De^{-\beta L/2} &= 0 \\
Bk\cos\tfrac{1}{2}kL - Ck\sin\tfrac{1}{2}kL + D\beta e^{-\beta L/2} &= 0 \ .
\end{aligned}
$$

(4.11-5)

This is a system of four homogeneous linear equations for the coefficients A, B. C, and D. The only solution is $A = B = C = D = 0$ unless the determinant of the coefficients of the system vanishes; then Cramer's rule gives the indeterminate value $0/0$ for the coefficients. In this case, though the values of the coefficients themselves is arbitrary, their *ratios* can be easily ascertained, which is sufficient for our purposes. Setting the determinant Δ of the coefficients in this equation equal to zero. we find

$$
\Delta = e^{-\beta L}
\begin{vmatrix}
1 & \sin\tfrac{1}{2}kL & -\cos\tfrac{1}{2}kL & 0 \\
\beta & -k\cos\tfrac{1}{2}kL & -k\sin\tfrac{1}{2}kL & 0 \\
0 & \sin\tfrac{1}{2}kL & \cos\tfrac{1}{2}kL & -1 \\
0 & k\cos\tfrac{1}{2}kL & -k\sin\tfrac{1}{2}kL & \beta
\end{vmatrix}
= 0 \ .
$$

(4.11-6)

In this expression, a factor $\exp(-\beta L/2)$ has been extracted from the first and last columns of the determinant indicated in (4.11-5). The above determinant can now be expanded in minors to yield, finally, an equation of the form

$$k^2\sin\tfrac{1}{2}kL\cos\tfrac{1}{2}kL - k\beta\cos^2\tfrac{1}{2}kL + k\beta\sin^2\tfrac{1}{2}kL - \beta^2\sin\tfrac{1}{2}kL\cos\tfrac{1}{2}kL = 0 \ ,$$

or,

$$(k\sin\tfrac{1}{2}kL - \beta\cos\tfrac{1}{2}kL)(k\cos\tfrac{1}{2}kL + \beta\sin\tfrac{1}{2}kL) = 0 \ .$$

(4.11-7)

Dividing by $\cos^2\theta$, this can be written as

$$(k\tan\tfrac{1}{2}kL - \beta)(\beta\tan\tfrac{1}{2}kL + k) = 0 \ ,$$

(4.11-8)

where, as indicated by (4.11-2),

$$\beta^2 = \alpha^2 - k^2 \ , \qquad \text{with} \quad \alpha^2 = 2mV_0/\hbar^2 \ .$$

(4.11-9)

Equation (4.11-8) is satisfied when either of the two factors vanishes, that is, whenever

$$k\tan\tfrac{1}{2}kL = \sqrt{\alpha^2 - k^2} \qquad \text{or} \qquad -k\cot\tfrac{1}{2}kL = \sqrt{\alpha^2 - k^2} \ .$$

(4.11-10)

These equations define values of k--and therefore, as expressed by (4.11-1), energy eigenvalues, for which both Schrödinger's equation and the boundary conditions (4.11 - 4) are satisfied. To find these values explicitly it is necessary to solve equations (4.11 - 10) for k. Unfortunately, since they are transcendental equations, it

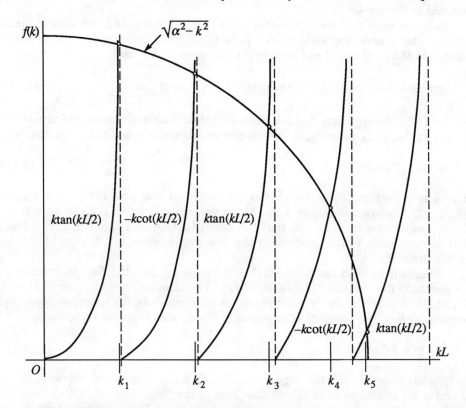

Figure 4.10 A plot of the functions on both sides of Equations (4.11 - 10). The intersections of the trigonometric curves with the circle are points where the transcendental relationships expressed by these equations are satisfied, and therefore represent the values of k for which solutions of Schrödinger's equation and the proper boundary conditions can be found. These points define the allowed energy eigenvalues of the system.

is impossible to do this algebraically. However, by plotting both sides of the equations separately as functions of k and observing where the intersections of the resulting curves occur, a graphical solution such as that illustrated in Figure 4.10 can be obtained. In this figure, the trigonometric functions give rise to curves with many branches, which approach vertical asymptotes at $kL = \pi, 2\pi, 3\pi, 4\pi, \ldots$, as illustrated. These branches represent, alternately, the functions on the left sides of the first and second equations in (4.10 - 11). The right side of both these equations, plotted as a function of k, gives the circular curve in the drawing, whose radius is α, a quantity related to the well depth V_0 by (4.11 - 9). The intersections of the circular curve with the trigonometric functions define a discrete finite set of k-values and energy eigenvalues for the system. As the depth V_0 of the well increases, the circle's radius expands, and more and more energy eigenvalues will join the set. But even if the well depth is very small there will be at least one energy eigenvalue defining a "bound state", that is, a discrete quantum state that describes a particle classically constrained to remain inside the well. Successive eigenvalues alternately cause one or the other of the two factors shown in (4.11 - 7) and (4.11 - 8) to vanish. In the specific case shown in the figure there are five bound states, whose energies are illustrated in Figure 4.9.

Suppose now that the first factor of (4.11 - 7) is zero, and the second factor is not zero. This means that $k\sin(kL/2) = \beta\cos(kL/2)$. Multiplying the first of the four equations in (4.11 - 5) by $-\beta$ and adding it to the second, we find,

$$B(k\cos\tfrac{1}{2}kL + \beta\sin\tfrac{1}{2}kL) = C(\beta\cos\tfrac{1}{2}kL - k\sin\tfrac{1}{2}kL) = 0 \ . \tag{4.11-11}$$

Since the factor multiplying B is not zero, it is clear that under these circumstances B is zero, and the wave function in the interior of the well, from (4.11 - 3) must be

$$\psi_2(x) = C\cos kx \ , \tag{4.11-12}$$

which is an *even* function of x. This is the situation that prevails for the eigenvalues $k_1, k_3, k_5, \ldots$ shown in Figure 4.10. Moreover, since $B = 0$, it is clear from the first and third equations in (4.11 - 5) that the coefficients A and D must now be equal, which in turn leads to the conclusion that the entire wave function (4.11 - 3) is an even function of x.

When the second factor in (4.11 - 7) vanishes, and the first is not zero, we must conclude that $k\cos(kL/2) = -\beta\sin(kL/2)$. The calculation leading to (4.11 - 11) is still valid, but now the factor multiplying B is zero, while the quantity multiplying C remains finite. The conclusion is now that $C = 0$, which allows us to write

$$\psi_2(x) = B\sin kx \ . \tag{4.11-13}$$

This is what happens for the eigenvalues $k_2, k_4, k_6, \ldots$ shown in Figure 4.10. The first and third equations of (4.11 - 5) now lead to the result $D = -A$, which shows that the wave function as a whole is an *odd* function of x. Thus, starting with an even eigenfunction of lowest energy, the eigenfunctions are alternately even and odd as you go up in energy, as illustrated in Figure 4.11. It can be shown that this is *always* the case when the potential $V(x)$ is, as in this example, an even function of x. As a result, the probability density $\psi^*\psi$ will then be (as you might expect on purely physical grounds) an even function of the coördinates. In the preceding section, where an infinitely deep well was considered, the origin was located at the edge of the well rather than the center to simplify the algebra. If it is moved to the center, so that the potential energy is an even function of x, you will observe that the eigenfunctions for that problem also exhibit this alternate even-odd property.

These characteristics are also evident in Figure 4.11, which shows the four lowest energy wave functions of the potential well shown in Figure 4.9 plotted as a function of x. An even more curious quantum mechanical effect, however, can also be observed. Classically, a particle bound by this potential is absolutely constrained to stay in the region $(-L/2 < x < L/2)$. There is no possibility of its ever being found outside that interval. Quantum mechanically, however, there is an exponentially decaying wave function associated with the classically forbidden regions beyond the boundaries of the well. This means that there is a finite--and easily calculated--probability of finding the particle in these classically forbidden regions. Moreover, since the potential energy is larger than the total energy ε_n in these regions, the kinetic energy of the particle is *negative* there, which suggests that its momentum is imaginary! This "leakage" of the wave function into classically forbidden regions is a characteristic feature of quantum mechanics, which leads to certain experimentally observable effects, which have provided evidence that this strange phenomenon is real.

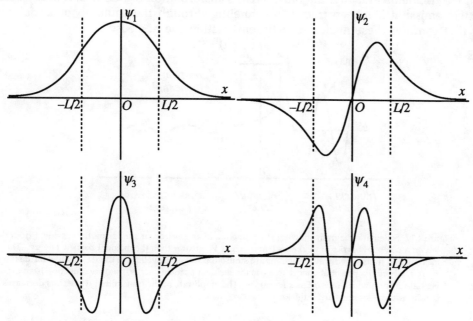

Figure 4.11 The first four wave functions of the potential well illustrated in Figure 4.9. Note the alternate even and odd character of the wave functions, and the "leakage" of the wave function into the classically forbidden regions of the x-axis.

The most conspicuous of these effects is referred to as quantum *tunneling*. This phenomenon is most easily observed when an electron is incident on a thin, but classically insurmountable barrier, like the one illustrated in Figure 4.12. This potential can be regarded as the inverse of the one considered in Figure 4.9. It is apparent from the work above that the solutions of the wave equation for a particle whose total energy is less than the barrier potential energy V_0, are similar to those written above in eq. (4.9 - 3)--sinusoidal in the classically allowed regions, and real exponential functions within the barrier. If the barrier is very thick, moreover, it is clear from the above work that the wave function within it is a decaying exponential which will fall essentially to zero within the barrier, thus assuring that there is no probability that the particle will "leak through". Such a barrier is impervious to the incident particle, in agreement with classical ideas. For a barrier of very small thickness (typically 10 to 100 Å), however, the exponential interior wave function will not have decayed to a negligible value at the far end of the barrier, which suggests that there is an appreciable probability that the particle will "tunnel through" and emerge in the classically allowed region on the opposite side of the barrier.

These tunneling phenomena can be observed as currents that can be made to pass through thin insulating layers separating metallic conductors. The "contact resistance" at connections between corroded or oxidized conductors can be attributed

144

to electron tunneling. It is also responsible for the phenomenon of field emission, in which electron currents are made to flow from a metal cathode into a surrounding vacuum by the application of a strong external electric field. It is also observed in the electrical breakdown of dielectrics and semiconductor rectifiers subjected to very high electric fields. Finally, the radioactive transformation of nuclei that decay by α-particle emission has been traced to tunneling through the coulomb potential barrier that confines these nuclear constituents within the nucleus.

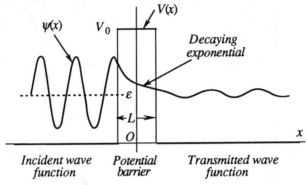

Figure 4.12 Schematic diagram showing the tunneling of an electron or similar particle incident from the left on a potential barrier of thickness L and height V_0 greater than the incident particle energy. The incident and transmitted wave functions are sinusoidal waves travelling to the right, while inside the barrier, where the potential energy exceeds the incident particle energy, the wave function is an exponential function which falls off as x increases. The amplitude of the transmitted wave thus decreases rapidly with increasing barrier thickness.

Another important effect can be illustrated by this example. For particle energies less than the well depth V_0, the above work shows that the wave equation and the required boundary conditions can be satisfied for a finite number of discrete energies, which define the energy levels of the system in this range of energies. For these energies, the particle cannot escape from the well according to classical physics.

Energies *greater* than V_0 define states in which the particle classically has enough energy to escape from the well and appear outside the region $-L/2 < x < L/2$. Under these conditions, the quantity β^2 in (4.11 - 2) is negative, and we can rewrite this equation as

$$\frac{d^2\psi}{dx^2} = k_0^2\psi \ , \quad \text{where} \ \ k_0^2 = -\beta^2 = \frac{2m(\varepsilon - V_0)}{\hbar^2} \quad (x < -L/2, x > L/2) \ . \quad (4.11\text{-}14)$$

The solutions of this equation are now sinusoidal rather than exponential. As before, since the potential is even, the solutions must be even or odd. For even solutions, we can write

$$\psi_2 = A\cos kx \qquad\qquad (0 < x < L/2) \ ,$$

$$\psi_3 = B\sin k_0 x + C\cos k_0 x \qquad (x > L/2) \ , \qquad\qquad (4.11\text{-}15)$$

$$\text{and} \quad \psi(-x) = \psi(x) \qquad\qquad (-L/2 < x < 0) \ .$$

Equating these wave functions and their derivatives at $x = L/2$, we obtain

$$\frac{B}{A}\sin\tfrac{1}{2}k_0 L + \frac{C}{A}\cos\tfrac{1}{2}k_0 L = \cos\tfrac{1}{2}kL \quad , \tag{4.11-16}$$

$$\frac{B}{A}k_0\cos\tfrac{1}{2}k_0 L - \frac{C}{A}k_0\sin\tfrac{1}{2}k_0 L = -k\sin\tfrac{1}{2}kL \quad . \tag{4.11-17}$$

These equations can now be solved for the ratios B/A and C/A, to give

$$\frac{B}{A} = \sin\tfrac{1}{2}k_0 L\cos\tfrac{1}{2}kL - \frac{k}{k_0}\cos\tfrac{1}{2}k_0 L\sin\tfrac{1}{2}kL \tag{4.11-18}$$

and

$$\frac{C}{A} = \cos\tfrac{1}{2}k_0 L\cos\tfrac{1}{2}kL + \frac{k}{k_0}\sin\tfrac{1}{2}k_0 L\sin\tfrac{1}{2}kL \quad . \tag{4.11-19}$$

It is possible to find these ratios for arbitrary values of k and k_0, thus for arbitrary energies and well depths. Therefore, a perfectly acceptable even wave function can be written for a particle of energy greater than V_0 *irrespective* of its energy and of the well depth. A similar calculation leads to the same conclusion if the wave function is assumed to be odd rather than even. Physically, this means that there is a *continuous range* of allowed energy eigenvalues for particles of energy greater than V_0. For particles of smaller energy, we have seen that the wave function must approach zero at large distances along the positive or negative x-direction. It is this condition that led to the requirement of discrete energy eigenvalues for a particle classically constrained to the interior of the well. Particles not so constrained need not satisfy this condition; instead, their wave functions need only behave like free-particle wave functions at plus or minus infinity. Their phase at large distances is therefore arbitrary, which lessens the restraints on the wave function as a whole, and permits Schrödinger's equation and all relevant boundary conditions to be satisfied, as shown above, for arbitrary energies. This result is true in general; particles classically "trapped" within any finite region of space have discrete energy eigenvalues, while those not so constrained have a continuous energy spectrum. In the context of this example, a particle of energy less than V_0 can have only discrete energies, while particles of greater energy have a continuous spectrum of allowed energies.

The above methods can be used to solve a variety of "barrier problems" related to tunneling, barrier penetration, and similar phenomena. Perhaps the simplest of these concerns the barrier illustrated in Figure 4.13(a). In this diagram, particles are incident on a potential barrier having the form of a step function of height V_0. The particles can either be scattered by the barrier into a reflected beam of equal but oppositely directed momentum, or they can continue along the positive x-direction, forming a transmitted beam in which the particle kinetic energy is reduced by the height of the barrier. These are the only possibilities that conserve energy in a strictly one-dimensional problem. The total wave function on the left of the barrier is therefore a sum of free-particle waves of positive and negative k, while the wave function on the right is simply a wave propagating to the right, whose propagation constant (though different from that of incident waves) is still positive. In an infinite one-dimensional system, there will be no waves returning from the far right unless another scattering barrier is present, which we assume not to be the case. We can write these free-particle wave functions as

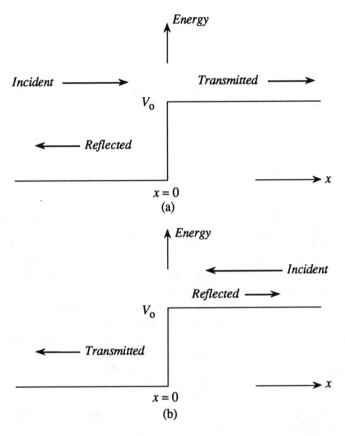

Figure 4.13 Particle wave functions incident on a potential barrier of height V_0. Arrows are in direction of the particle momentum as expressed by the propagation vector of the free-particle wave function. (a) Incident, reflected, and transmitted particle beams for a particle incident from the left. (b) The incident, reflected, and transmitted beams for a particle incident on the barrier from the right.

$$\psi_0(x) = Ae^{ik_0x} + Be^{-ik_0x} \quad , \qquad (x < 0) \ ,$$

and $\quad \psi_1(x) = Ce^{ikx} \quad , \qquad\qquad (x > 0) \ ,$ $\qquad\qquad$ (4.11-20)

with $\quad k_0^2 = \dfrac{2m\varepsilon}{\hbar^2} \quad$ and $\quad k^2 = \dfrac{2m(\varepsilon - V_0)}{\hbar^2} \ .$ $\qquad\qquad$ (4.11-21)

Observe that this notation is slightly different from that of the preceding example. The constants $A, B,$ and C express the amplitude of the incident, reflected and transmitted waves, respectively.

We now need only require that the wave functions ψ_0 and ψ_1 be equal and that their derivatives be the same at $x = 0$. This implies that

$$A + B = C$$

and $\quad ik_0 A + ik_0 B = ikC \quad .$ $\hspace{6cm}$ (4.11-22)

These equations can now be solved for the constants B and C in terms of A, to obtain

$$B = \frac{k_0 - k}{k_0 + k} \cdot A$$

and $\quad C = \dfrac{2k_0 A}{k_0 + k} \quad .$ $\hspace{6cm}$ (4.11-23)

It is now possible to determine a reflection coefficient and a transmission co-efficient that express the reflected and transmitted particle fluxes as fractions of the incident particle flux. The amplitudes of the wave functions themselves have no direct physical significance; we know, for example, that the particle densities are given by A^*A and B^*B rather than A and B . The quantities most easily determined in the present situation, however, are not particle densities, but rather the particle currents, or *fluxes*. Therefore, the reflection coefficients are most reasonably defined as the flux ratios mentioned above. The flux, as measured by the number of particles passing through unit area normal to the x-axis per unit time is proportional not only to the particle density, but also to the particle velocity or momentum. The greater the x-component of velocity, the more particles pass through the area element per second. This means that the particle flux J_x, can be defined as the particle density times the x-component of velocity, or

$$J_x = \rho \langle v_x \rangle = (\psi^* \psi) \cdot \frac{\hbar k_x}{m} \quad .$$ $\hspace{4cm}$ (4.11-24)

The reflection and transmission coeficients of the barrier defined as suggested above can thus be written

$$R = \frac{J_{xr}}{J_{xi}} = \frac{B^*B}{A^*A} \cdot \frac{k_0}{k_0} = \frac{B^2}{A^2} \quad ,$$ $\hspace{3cm}$ (4.11-25)

and $\quad T = \dfrac{J_{xt}}{J_{xi}} = \dfrac{C^*C}{A^*A} \cdot \dfrac{k}{k_0} = \dfrac{k}{k_0} \cdot \dfrac{C^2}{A^2} \quad .$ $\hspace{3cm}$ (4.11-26)

Substituting the values shown above for B and C in terms of A, this becomes

$$R = \left(\frac{k_0 - k}{k_0 + k} \right)^2$$ $\hspace{5cm}$ (4.11-27)

and $\quad T = \dfrac{4kk_0}{(k_0 + k)^2} \quad .$ $\hspace{5cm}$ (4.11-28)

It is easy to show from these equations that $R + T = 1$, as expected if particle flux is conserved. Using (4.11 - 21) to express k and k_0 in terms of ε and V_0, these equations can be written as

$$R = \left(\frac{\sqrt{\varepsilon} - \sqrt{\varepsilon - V_0}}{\sqrt{\varepsilon} + \sqrt{\varepsilon - V_0}} \right)^2$$

$$(\varepsilon > V_0) \qquad \qquad (4.11\text{-}29)$$

and $\quad T = \dfrac{4\varepsilon(\varepsilon - V_0)}{\left(\sqrt{\varepsilon} + \sqrt{\varepsilon - V_0} \right)^2}$.

In this development, we have assumed, of course, that the quantity $\varepsilon - V_0$ in (4.11 - 21) is positive, thus that the incident kinetic energy is greater than the barrier height. This need not be so, however. If it is not, then (as in the potential well of finite depth) the wave function for $x > 0$ becomes a real exponential rather than a sinusoidal function, the solution of Schrödinger's equation in this region being now

$$\psi_1(x) = Ce^{-\beta x} , \qquad \text{where} \qquad \beta^2 = \frac{2m(V_0 - \varepsilon)}{\hbar^2} . \qquad (4.11\text{-}30)$$

As before, there can be no growing exponential term in this solution, since the wave function must remain finite at infinity. The solution in the region $(x < 0)$ remains sinusoidal, as given by (4.11 - 21). Matching the wave function and its derivative at $x = 0$ as above, and solving for the coefficient B, we now find

$$B = A \left(\frac{1 - \dfrac{i\beta}{k_0}}{1 + \dfrac{i\beta}{k_0}} \right) \qquad \text{and} \qquad B^* = A^* \left(\frac{1 + \dfrac{i\beta}{k_0}}{1 - \dfrac{i\beta}{k_0}} \right) . \qquad (4.11\text{-}31)$$

The coefficient B is now complex, and we must use B^*B instead of B^2 in (4.11 - 25). You can find the complex conjugate B^* simply by replacing i by $-i$ in the expression for B--a procedure of quite general applicability. The expression for the reflection coefficient R in (4.11 - 25) then yields simply $R = 1$, independent of k_0 and β. Since reflection and transmission coefficients must add to unity, we conclude that $T = 0$. This follows also from the fact that for $\varepsilon < V_0$, the wave function rapidly approaches zero within the region $x > 0$. In any event, we obtain

$$R = 1$$

and $\quad T = 0 \qquad (\varepsilon < V_0)$. $\qquad (4.11\text{-}32)$

The results given by equations (4.11 - 29) and (4.11 - 32) are plotted against the incident particle kinetic energy ε in Figure 4.14. Below the barrier potential energy V_0, the transmission and reflectivity are energy-independent, but above this energy, the reflection coefficient decreases rapidly and the transmission rises, approaching the limits zero and unity, respectively, with increasing energy. Below the barrier energy, the barrier is penetrated to some extent by the exponentially decreasing wave function, though the transmission coefficient is always zero because of its infinite thickness.

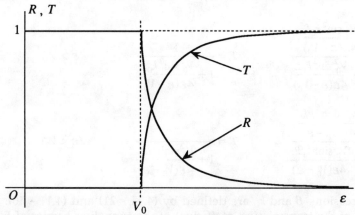

Figure 4.14 Reflection and Transmission coefficients of the step barrier of Figure 4.13(a) plotted as functions of incident particle energy. For energies less than the barrier height R is identically equal to unity and T is identically zero.

The same barrier can be approached by particles incident from the right rather than the left, as shown in Figure 4.13(b). In this case, there are also transmitted and reflected fluxes as illustrated in the diagram, and the transmission and reflection coefficients of the barrier can be calculated by the same procedure followed above. The calculation of these cofficients is assigned as an exercise for the reader.

A more realistic example involves the "tunneling barrier" shown in Figure 4.12. In this case there will be incident and reflected fluxes with kinetic energy ε in the region $x < 0$. For $\varepsilon > V_0$, there will also be incident and reflected sinusoidal waves in the region $0 < x < L$, whose propagation constant k is related to the kinetic energy $\varepsilon - V_0$. In the region $x > L$, there will be a single wave representing a transmitted flux of particles moving to the right, again with kinetic energy ε. The fluxes can all be written in terms of free-particle sinusoidal wave functions as in the above example; the wave functions and their derivatives can be equated at $x = 0$ and $x = L$ as usual. This leads to a set of four simultaneous equations, which can be solved for the ratios of the amplitudes of the waves described above to that of the incident wave function. Once these are known, the related fluxes and the transmission and reflection coefficients of the barrier can be found as in the preceding case.

For $\varepsilon < V_0$, the wave function in the region $0 < x < L$ will be composed of real exponentials of argument $\pm\beta x$, with β defined as above in terms of $V_0 - \varepsilon$. Both the growing and decaying exponential function must be retained in this case, since the exponential wave function is defined only in the barrier region and its behavior at $\pm\infty$ is therefore irrelevant. The same procedure of matching wave functions and their derivatives at the boundaries of the barrier region can be carried out, however, leading now to new expressions for transmission and reflection coefficients for incident particle energies less than the barrier height. Since the barrier is of finite thickness, the transmission coefficient is not zero, nor is the reflection coefficient unity. Instead, the transmission coefficient is now related to the tunneling probability.

The algebra demanded by these calculations is straightforward but relatively tedious, and will not be presented in detail here It is instead assigned as an exercise. One obtains for this tunneling barrier, the transmission and reflection coefficients

$$R = \frac{\dfrac{V_0^2 \sin^2 k_0 L}{4\varepsilon(\varepsilon - V_0)}}{1 + \dfrac{V_0^2 \sin^2 k_0 L}{4\varepsilon(\varepsilon - V_0)}} \quad , \qquad T = \frac{1}{1 + \dfrac{V_0^2 \sin^2 k_0 L}{4\varepsilon(\varepsilon - V_0)}} \qquad (\varepsilon > V_0) \qquad (4.11\text{-}33)$$

and

$$R = \frac{\dfrac{V_0^2 \sinh^2 \beta L}{4\varepsilon(v_0 - \varepsilon)}}{1 + \dfrac{V_0^2 \sinh^2 \beta L}{4\varepsilon(V_0 - \varepsilon)}} \quad , \qquad T = \frac{1}{1 + \dfrac{V_0^2 \sinh^2 \beta L}{4\varepsilon(V_0 - \varepsilon)}} \qquad (\varepsilon < V_0) \quad . \qquad (4.11\text{-}34)$$

In these expressions β and k_0 are defined by (4.11 - 21) and (4.11 - 30). Figure 4.15 shows a plot of the transmission coefficient of the tunneling barrier of Figure 4.12 as a function of incident particle energy. It is apparent that the transmission coefficient is no longer zero when $\varepsilon < V_0$, and that tunneling can therefore occur under these circumstances. The maxima and minima for $\varepsilon > V_0$ are resonances associated with the interference of the two free-particle waves in the barrier region.

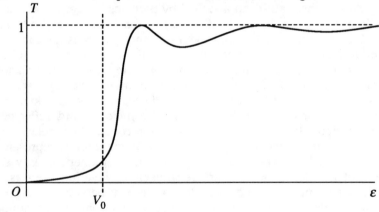

Figure 4.15 The transmission coefficient of the potential barrier shown in Figure 4.12 plotted as a function of incident kinetic energy.

4.12 THE QUANTUM HARMONIC OSCILLATOR

The harmonic oscillator is simplest example of an oscillatory system in the realm of classical mechanics. Moreover, there are many real physical systems whose motion is accurately predicted by this model. We have already used harmonic oscillator theory, for example, to discuss the atomic vibrations in crystal lattices. The harmonic oscilator is an equally important (and also exactly soluble) problem in quantum mechanics. Simple harmonic motion is always associated with a potential energy varying as the square of the distance from an equilibrium point of minimum energy. With respect to an origin at this point, the classical potential energy of a one-dimensional harmonic oscillator is $\beta x^2/2$, where β is the force constant and x the displacement. The potential has the form of a "parabolic well" of infinite depth, as Illustrated in Figure 4.16. The results of the preceding section suggest that for this system. there will be a discrete spectrum of allowed energies. Classically, a particle of mass m under the influence of this potential oscillates with a constant frequency ω equal to $(\beta/m)^{1/2}$. The classical potential energy $V(x)$ for this system can thus be written as

$$V(x) = \tfrac{1}{2}\beta x^2 = \tfrac{1}{2}m\omega^2 x^2 \quad . \tag{4.12-1}$$

We shall find the final form of this expression most useful for the quantum mechanical treatment of this system. Such a treatment begins by inserting this potential energy function into Schrödinger's equation (4.8 - 4) to obtain

$$\frac{d^2\psi}{dx^2} + \frac{2m}{\hbar^2}\left[\varepsilon - \tfrac{1}{2}m\omega^2 x^2\right]\psi(x) = 0 \quad . \tag{4.12-2}$$

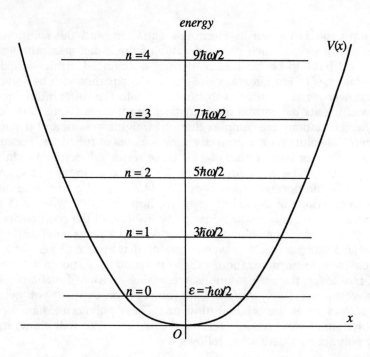

Figure 4.16 Parabolic potential well and the allowed energy levels associated with the one-dimensional quantum harmonic oscillator.

This can be put into a simpler form by making the following three transformations, most simply one at a time, in the following order: let

$$\alpha = m\omega/\hbar \ , \tag{4.12-3}$$

$$\varepsilon = (n + \tfrac{1}{2})\hbar\omega \ , \tag{4.12-4}$$

and $\quad \xi = x\sqrt{\alpha} \ . \tag{4.12-5}$

These substitutions transform (4.12 - 2) into

$$\frac{d^2\psi}{d\xi^2} + \left[(2n+1) - \xi^2\right]\psi(\xi) = 0 \ . \tag{4.12-6}$$

Finally, if we now make the additional substitution

$$\psi(\xi) = e^{-\xi^2/2}H(\xi) \ , \tag{4.12-7}$$

we can arrive at a differential equation for the function $H(\xi)$ of the form

$$\frac{d^2H}{d\xi^2} - 2\xi\frac{dH}{d\xi} + 2nH(\xi) = 0 \ . \tag{4.12-8}$$

This equation is known as Hermite's equation, and the solutions $H(\xi)$ are called Hermite functions. Each possible value of the index n--a number that does *not* at this point have to be an integer--defines a distinct Hermite function, which we can write as $H_n(\xi)$. For general values of n, the equation can be solved only by assuming a power series solution, substituting it into the differential equation, and evaluating coefficients by normal mathematical procedures for finding solutions of this sort. The calculations are complex though straightforward, and if the index n is not an integer, the solutions are perfectly *useless* as wave functions, because of their behavior at $x = \pm\infty$. For large values of $|\xi|$, these series solutions go to infinity more rapidly than $\exp(\xi^2)$. The wave function (4.12 - 7) thus diverges at $\pm\infty$, and it is impossible to satisfy the normalization condition (4.7 - 1). We therefore need not go through the calculations in detail. It happens, however, that when n is an integer, the series solutions have a remarkable property, in that all the coefficients of powers higher than ξ^n are *zero*. The solution now reduces to a *polynomial* of degree n in ξ. The polynomial solutions lead to wave functions that approach zero at $x = \pm\infty$, and impose no obstacle to normalization. These polynomials, known as *Hermite Polynomials* are, moreover, the *only* solutions acceptable as wave functions.

When you successively differentiate the function $\exp(-z^2)$ you get a series of polynomial factors times the original function. These polynomials are closely related to the polynomial solutions of Hermite's equation. We will show, in fact, that the series of polynomials defined as follows,

$$H_n(z) = (-1)^n e^{z^2}\frac{d^n}{dz^n}(e^{-z^2}) = (-1)^n e^{z^2}D^n e^{-z^2} \ , \tag{4.12-9}$$

are the polynomial solutions of Hermite's equation. We shall use the operator notation $D^n = d^n/dz^n$ and also (occasionally) use primes to denote differentiation with respect to the argument z in the development that follows. Finally, we shall find it helpful to employ the relation

$$D^n(zf) = nD^{n-1}f + zD^nf \; , \tag{4.12-10}$$

where f is a differentiable function of z. This is easily verified by differentiating the product zf three or four times and observing the results.

We begin by differentiating (4.12 - 9) with respect to z, to obtain

$$H_n'(z) = (-1)^n e^{z^2} D^{n+1} e^{-z^2} + (-1)^n \cdot 2ze^{z^2} D^n e^{-z^2} \; . \tag{4.12-11}$$

However, $D^{n+1} = D(D^n)$. Using this relation and then expanding the first term in the above equation with the aid of (4.12 - 10), we find

$$H_n'(z) = (-1)^n e^{z^2} D^n(-2ze^{-z^2}) + (-1)^n \cdot 2ze^{z^2} D^n e^{-z^2}$$

$$= (-1)^n e^{z^2}\left[-2nD^{n-1}e^{-z^2} - 2zD^n e^{-z^2}\right] + (-1)^n \cdot 2ze^{z^2} D^n e^{-z^2} \; ,$$

$$= 2n \cdot (-1)^{n-1} e^{z^2} D^{n-1} e^{-z^2} \; . \tag{4.12-12}$$

From the definition (4.12 - 9), however, this can be written in the form

$$H_n'(z) = 2nH_{n-1}(z) \; . \tag{4.12-13}$$

Also, from (4.2 - 11), with the aid of (4.2 - 9), we see that

$$H_n'(z) = 2zH_n(z) - H_{n+1}(z) \; . \tag{4.12-14}$$

If this is differentiated with respect to z, we obtain

$$H_n''(z) - 2zH_n'(z) - 2H_n(z) + H_{n+1}'(z) = 0 \; . \tag{4.12-15}$$

From (4.2 - 13), however, $H'_{n+1}(z) = 2(n + 1)H_n(z)$. Substituting this into (4.12 - 15) and simplifying, we finally arrive at

$$H_n''(z) - 2zH_n'(z) + 2nH_n(z) = 0 \; , \tag{4.12-16}$$

which is the same as Hermite's equation (4.12 - 8). The polynomials defined by equation (4.12 - 9) are therefore solutions of Hermite's equation. The above algebraic exercise is somewhat tedious, but it is not useless, for the identities (4.12 - 13) and (4.12 - 14) are useful in working with Hermite polynomials. Another useful identity,

$$H_{n+1}(z) - 2zH_n(z) + 2nH_{n-1}(z) = 0 \; , \tag{4.12-17}$$

follows from equating the right sides of (4.12 - 13) and (4.12 - 14).

Since polynomial solutions as given by (4.12 - 9) are defined only for integer values of n, and because the normalization condition cannot be satisfied by nonintegral values, there is a discrete set of allowed energy eigenvalues. From (4.12 - 4) it is clear that the energy eigenvalues $\{\varepsilon_n\}$ must be given by

$$\varepsilon_n = \left(n + \tfrac{1}{2}\right)\hbar\omega , \qquad (n = 0,1,2,3...) . \tag{4.12-18}$$

The eigenfunctions can now be obtained from (4.12 - 7) as

$$\psi_n(\xi) = N_n e^{-\xi^2/2} H_n(\xi) , \quad \text{with} \quad \xi = x\sqrt{\alpha} \quad \text{and} \quad n = 0,1,2,3... . \tag{4.12-19}$$

where N_n is a normalization constant, chosen to satisfy condition (4.7 - 1). These wave functions are illustrated in Figure 4.17(a-d), where the four eigenfunctions of lowest energy are plotted. As indicated by (4.12 - 19), their form is that of an algebraic polynomial H_n modulated by the exponential function $\exp(-\alpha x^2/2)$. It can be shown, with some difficulty, that the normalization constant N_n is given by

$$N_n^2 = \frac{1}{2^n n!}\sqrt{\frac{\alpha}{\pi}} . \tag{4.12-20}$$

The calculation, which we shall omit, proceeds along the same lines as that already illustrated for the case of the infinitely deep square well potential. As in the case of the infinitely deep square well, the time-independent wave functions are real; this is a general characteristic of one-dimensional bound-state systems.

The first few Hermite polynomials H_n, as obtained from (4.12 - 9) are

n	$H_n(z)$	$H_n(x\sqrt{\alpha})$
0	1	1
1	$2z$	$2x\sqrt{\alpha}$
2	$4z^2 - 2$	$4\alpha x^2 - 2$
3	$8z^3 - 12z$	$8(\alpha x^2)^{3/2} - 12x\sqrt{\alpha}$
4	$16z^4 - 48z^2 + 12$	$16\alpha^2 x^4 - 48\alpha x^2 + 12$
5	$32z^5 - 160z^3 + 120z$	$32(\alpha x^2)^{5/2} - 160(\alpha x^2)^{3/2} + 120x$.
$\vdots$	$\vdots$	$\vdots$

Higher polynomials are obtained using the identity (4.12 - 17)--a practical application of the "useless" algebra we performed. Direct substitution into Hermite's differential equation will convince you that these polynomials are valid solutions.

Figure 4.17(e) shows the probability density $\psi^*\psi$ for a quantum state of relatively high energy, for which $n = 11$, This curve exhibits many oscillations, whose amplitude is fairly small near the origin, and considerably larger near the extremes of the oscillatory part of the curve. As in previous cases we have discussed, there are a number of points where the probability density is zero. Since the oscillation amplitude is largest near the ends of the curve, it would appear from the definition of the probability density that there is a larger probability of finding the particle near the ends of its excursions from the origin than anywhere else. Since at large energies the quantum behavior of the particle resembles its classical behavior, it seems as though classical physics might in this case lead to a similar result.

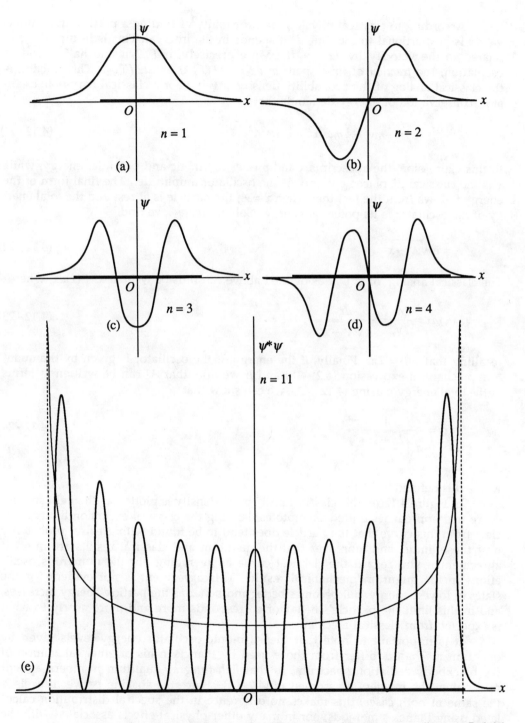

Figure 4.17 (a-d) Wave functions for the first four eigenfunctions of the harmonic oscillator. (e) Probability amplitude for the $n = 11$ eigenstate; light curve shows classical probability density. Classical amplitude limits are shown by the bold horizontal lines along the x-axes.

According to classical physics, the probability of finding a particle in an interval dx is proportional to the time dt it spends in the interval. This is in turn directly related to the velocity by $dx = v_x dt$. More precisely, if $T/2$ is the half-period of oscillation, the *fraction* of time spent in dx is $dt/(T/2)$ or $2dx/Tv_x$. This fraction is the classical analog of the probability density $\psi^* \psi dx$. For a classical harmonic oscillator, conservation of energy demands that

$$\varepsilon = \varepsilon_k + \varepsilon_p = \tfrac{1}{2}mv_x^2 + \tfrac{1}{2}m\omega^2 x^2 = \tfrac{1}{2}m\omega^2 A^2 \ . \tag{4.12-21}$$

In this expression, the subscripts k and p refer to kinetic and potential energy, while x is the classical displacement and A the oscillator amplitude. The final form of the energy follows from the fact that when $x = A$, the particle is at rest and the total energy of the oscillator is its potential energy. Solving for v_x, we find

$$v_x = \omega\sqrt{A^2 - x^2} \ . \tag{4.12-22}$$

The classical analog of $\psi^* \psi dx$ as defined above can thus be written as $P(x)dx$, where

$$P(x)dx = \frac{2dx}{Tv_x} = \frac{dx}{\pi\sqrt{A^2 - x^2}} \ , \tag{4.12-23}$$

recalling that $\omega T = 2\pi$. Finally, if the energy of the oscillator is given by the quantum mechanical expression (4.2 - 18) and if we note that A^2 can be written in terms of the total energy ε using (4,12 - 21), we can show that

$$P(x) = \frac{1}{\pi\sqrt{\dfrac{2n+1}{\alpha} - x^2}} \ , \tag{4.12-24}$$

where α is defined by (4.12 - 3).

In Figure 4.17(e), this classical probability density is plotted as the light smooth curve that approaches dotted asymptotes defining the classical excursion limits. It is clear from this curve that the particle does tend to be found with greatest probability near these limits, and moreover that the quantum and classical results are in good agreement if you regard the classical curve as averaging out the numerous oscillations in the quantum mechanical result. This agreement is not evident for the states of lowest energy, but becomes better and better as the particle energy increases, and in this limit the particle's behavior corresponds more and more nearly to what is expected from classical mechanics.

It is important to note that the harmonic oscillator energy levels given by quantum mechanics differ from those used by Planck in his original calculation of the blackbody radiation spectrum, in that *half-integral* quantum numbers appear rather than the integers n assumed in (4.2 - 1). Since the spacing between levels is the same in both cases, this makes no difference in the spectral distribution calculated using Planck's methods, nor in many other physical effects associated with the harmonic oscillator. It should be understood, however, that the harmonic oscillator's ground state $n = 0$ is not a state of zero energy, but has a zero-point energy

$$\varepsilon_0 = \tfrac{1}{2}\hbar\omega \ . \tag{4.12-25}$$

Quantum mechanics thus predicts that harmonic oscillators in their ground state are not at rest, but have a small finite zero-point oscillation amplitude. This observation also applies to the quantized vibrational modes of atoms in crystal lattices.

We shall find the quantum-mechanical harmonic oscillator model useful in a number of future discussions, particularly those involving the thermal properties of crystals. The model is also useful--as we shall soon see--because it illustrates in a simple way many of the mathematical results and physical characteristics associated with other more complicated quantum mechanical systems.

4.13 ORTHOGONALITY OF EIGENFUNCTIONS AND TIME DEPENDENCE OF EXPECTATION VALUES

Eigenfunctions of Schrödinger's equation satisfying the physical requirements for wave functions always exhibit the property of *orthogonality*. This means that in a one-dimensional system they always satisfy the condition

$$\int_{-\infty}^{\infty} \psi_m^* \psi_n \, dx = 0 \qquad (m \neq n)$$

$$= 1 \qquad (m = n) \ . \tag{4.13-1}$$

This relation expresses an inherent property of the eigenfunctions ascribable to the form of Schrödinger's equation and the boundary conditions; it is valid no matter what potential function $V(x)$ is chosen, or what mathematical form the eigenfunctions may have. The case $m = n$ should by now be familiar as the normalization condition on the wave function. In a three-dimensional system, a similar condition is satisfied, the integral (which now involves three space coördinates) being evaluated over the entire volume of the system.

The validity of the orthogonality condition can be demonstrated by writing Schrödinger's equation for ψ_n and ψ^*_m as

$$\frac{d^2\psi_n}{dx^2} - \frac{2m}{\hbar^2}\left[\varepsilon_n - V(x)\right]\psi_n(x) = 0 \tag{4.13-2}$$

and

$$\frac{d^2\psi_m^*}{dx^2} - \frac{2m}{\hbar^2}\left[\varepsilon_m - V(x)\right]\psi_m^*(x) = 0 \ . \tag{4.13-3}$$

The second of these equations follows from the first simply by taking the complex conjugate, noting that the energy eigenvalue and the potential energy $V(x)$ are both real quantities. If we now multiply the first equation by ψ^*_m, the second by ψ_n, subtract one from the other and integrate, we find

$$\int_{-\infty}^{\infty} \left[\psi_m^* \frac{d^2 \psi_n}{dx^2} - \psi_n \frac{d^2 \psi_m^*}{dx^2} \right] dx = \frac{2m}{\hbar^2} (\varepsilon_n - \varepsilon_m) \int_{-\infty}^{\infty} \psi_m^* \psi_n dx \ . \tag{4.13-4}$$

The integrand on the left side of this equation can be written as the derivative of the quantity $\psi_m^*(d\psi_m/dx) - \psi_n(d\psi_m^*/dx)$, so that (4.13 - 4) can be expressed as

$$\left[\psi_m^* \frac{d\psi_n}{dx} - \psi_n \frac{d\psi_m^*}{dx} \right]_{-\infty}^{\infty} = \frac{2m}{\hbar^2} (\varepsilon_n - \varepsilon_m) \int_{-\infty}^{\infty} \psi_m^* \psi_n dx \ . \tag{4.13-5}$$

For physically possible wave functions, ψ and $d\psi/dx$ both approach zero at $x = \pm \infty$. Therefore, the left side vanishes at both endpoints, and the quantity on the right side of (4.13 - 5) must always be equal to zero. When $m \neq n$, ε_m and ε_n are not the same, and therefore the integral must vanish. When $m = n$, the integral reduces to the normalization integral, which must have the value unity, but now $\varepsilon_n - \varepsilon_m$ is zero, so that the equation is still satisfied. We are thus left with the orthogonality condition as given by (4.13 - 1). The property of orthogonality is not restricted to Schrödinger's equation, but is also exhibited by the solutions of partial differential equations describing acoustic and electromagnetic waves, diffusion, heat flow, etc. It is easy to see that the sinusoidal eigenfunctions (4.10 - 5) associated with the infinite square-well potential satisfy the orthogonality condition, because of the well known (and easily demonstrated) fact that

$$\int_0^L \sin \frac{m\pi x}{L} \sin \frac{n\pi x}{L} \, dx = 0 \quad (m \neq n) \ . \tag{4.13-6}$$

It is less easy to see that eigenfunctions of more complex systems such as the harmonic oscillator oscillator satisfy this condition. From the above work, however, it is clear that they must do so, and that no detailed proof is needed for each example.

One of the important consequences of the orthogonality of eigenfunctions is that (subject to certain mathematical restrictions) an arbitrary function $f(x)$ can be expanded as an infinite series such functions.. The way to do this is easily understood. Let us assume that there are an infinite number of eigenfunctions, and that $f(x)$ can be written as a series of the form

$$f(x) = \sum_{n=0}^{\infty} a_n \psi_n(x) \ . \tag{4.13-7}$$

If we multiply this equation by ψ_m^* and integrate term by term, we obtain

$$\int_{-\infty}^{\infty} f(x) \psi_m^*(x) \, dx = \sum_{n=0}^{\infty} \int_{-\infty}^{\infty} a_n \psi_m^*(x) \psi_n(x) \, dx \ . \tag{4.13-8}$$

In the summation on the right, according to the orthogonality condition (4.13 - 1), all the integrals are zero except the one for which $n = m$, which yields the value of the coefficient a_m as

$$a_m = \int_{-\infty}^{\infty} f(x)\, \psi_m^*(x)\, dx \ . \tag{4.13-9}$$

The coefficients having been thus determined, the series (4.13 - 7) gives an explicit representation of $f(x)$ as a series of orthogonal eigenfunctions. Of course, it remains to be shown that this series is convergent, but it is possible to show that convergence to the desired function is obtained under most conditions encountered in physical problems. For the sinusoidal square-well eigenfunctions (4.10 - 5), this series turns out to be an ordinary Fourier sine series. For harmonic oscillator eigenfunctions of the form (4.12 - 19) similar expansions involving the Hermite polynomials can be written, and other systems give rise to still other expansions of this type.

For systems in which eigenvalues are continuous rather than discrete, the orthogonality of eigenfunctions still prevails, and it is still possible to represent an arbitrary function in terms of them. This representation is now no longer a series of discrete terms, but assumes the form of an integral--a Fourier integral in the case of free-particle systems. Although such representations are useful for many purposes, we shall not need them in our work, and will not discuss them in detail.

Linear combinations of eigenfunctions such as (4.13 - 7) are composed of individual terms containing stationary-state eigenfunctions corresponding to different energies. Although this sum satisfies the time-dependent Schrödinger equation, each of these eigenfunctions has a different time-dependence. The function it represents is therefore not time-independent. Thus, the function

$$f(x,t) = \sum_{n=0}^{\infty} a_n \Psi_n(x,t) = \sum_{n=0}^{\infty} a_n \psi_n(x) e^{-i\varepsilon_n t/\hbar} \tag{4.13-10}$$

is the same as that given by (4.13 - 7) at $t = 0$, but not for later times. You can thus construct a superposition of eigenfunctions that represents any given function at some given instant of time ($t = 0$ in the above example), but it will not *continue* to represent this same function as time elapses. A superposition wave function therefore cannot generally represent a stationary state of the system. You can "localize" a free-particle at time $t = 0$, for example, by superposing eigenfunctions of different energies in such a way that the superposition has a strong peak somewhere at $t = 0$. As time elapses, however, the effect of the different time dependences of individual terms will smear out the peak and make the resulting wave packet less and less "local" as time goes on. This same state of affairs has also been encountered in Section 4.8 in connection with (4.8 - 10). It is sometimes useful to regard an expansion like (4.13 - 10), in which time-dependent eigenfunctions appear, as one in which the coefficients themselves are time-dependent. Thus, in (4.13 - 10), we could define new coefficients as the product of a_n with the time-dependent exponential function.

This discussion leads naturally to a question which has been mentioned previously (though only partially answered) concerning when you can expect to be "lucky" in obtaining precise, reproducible answers from measurements of physical observables, and when you must settle for less well-defined averages or "expectation values". Consider a measurable physical quantity represented by a suitably defined operator $\underline{A}$. This operator defines a set of eigenfunctions $\Phi_n(x, t)$ and eigenvalues α_n, such that

$$\underline{A}\Phi_n = \alpha_n \Phi_n \ . \tag{4.13-11}$$

Now imagine a physical system whose state is described by a wave function $\Psi(x, t)$. If it should happen that Ψ is equal to one of the operator's eigenfunctions Φ_n, then, if the eigenfunctions Φ_n are normalized like wave functions, the expectation value $<A>$ of the physical observable will be,

$$\langle A \rangle = \int_{-\infty}^{\infty} \Psi^* \underline{A} \Psi \, dx = \int_{-\infty}^{\infty} \Phi_n^* \underline{A} \Phi_n \, dx = \alpha_n \int_{-\infty}^{\infty} \Phi_n^* \Phi_n \, dx = \alpha_n \ . \tag{4.13-12}$$

Under these circumstances any measurement of this physical observable will yield the precise value α_n, and there is *no possibility* of any other answer. The "expectation value" is not an average at all, but a precise determination--the only answer that can *ever* result from repeated measurements of this quantity made on identical systems in this state.

If the wave function $\Psi(x, t)$ is *not* one of the operator's eigenfunctions, it can be written as a series of the eigenfunctions Φ_n, of the form (4.13 - 10). This is possible because one can show that the property of orthogonality is associated not only with eigenfunctions of the Hamiltonian operator, but also with eigenfunctions of any *Hermitian* operator that satisfies condition (4.8 - 11), and which can therefore be used to represent a dynamical variable in quantum theory. The above expectation value can therefore be written as

$$\langle A \rangle = \int_{-\infty}^{\infty} \left[\sum_m c_m^* \Phi_m^* \right] \underline{A} \left[\sum_n c_n \Phi_n \right] dx = \sum_m \sum_n c_m^* c_n \int_{-\infty}^{\infty} \Phi_m^* \underline{A} \Phi_n \, dx \ . \tag{4.13-13}$$

In view of (4.13-11), the integrand above becomes $\alpha_n \Phi_m^* \Phi_n$, and the coefficient α_n can be taken outside the integral. Then, because of the orthogonality of the eigenfunctions Φ_n, all the integrals are zero except those for which $m = n$, giving finally

$$\langle A \rangle = \sum_n c_n^* c_n \alpha_n \ . \tag{4.13-14}$$

In this expression, the coefficients c_n and c^*_n could be time-dependent, as suggested above. Their time dependence need not be exponential as in (4.3 - 10), since the time-dependence of the eigenfunctions Φ_n can't be assumed to be the same as that of Schrödinger wave functions. Quantum theory suggests that any process of measurement *forces* the state of the system into one of the eigenstates, and thus yields a measurement of the observable equal to an eigenvalue α_n. Which of the eigenstates the system assumes is inherently random, as is the eigenvalue that turns up as the measured value of the physical quantity. One thing you can predict, however, is that the average or "expectation" value of a large number of measurements on such systems will be given by (4.13 - 14), and that it will generally be time-dependent.

The preceding discussion has been concerned with an arbitrary operator $\underline{A}$, whose eigenvalues correspond to the observable values of some unspecified physical quantity. Its applicability is therefore quite general. In practical problems like the examples worked out in previous sections, we are most often concerned with wave functions and energy eigenvalues. The wave functions of physical systems are eigenfunctions of the Hamiltonian operator. This operator is the sum of operators associated with the system's kinetic and potential energies, and in this sense is clearly related to its total energy; we have already seen that its eigenvalues represent the allowed energies. Indeed, as noted earlier in connection with eqs (4.8 - 1, 2, 3) these energy eigenvalues are eigenvalues not only of the $\underline{H}$ operator, but also of the time-dependent energy operator $i\hbar\partial/\partial t$. In view of this, we can conclude from the above discussion that when a system's wave function is a single eigenfunction Ψ_n of the $\underline{H}$ operator, a measurement of its energy can yield only the corresponding eigenvalue ε_n. If the wave function has the form of a superposition of eigenfunctions, as in (4.13 - 10), however, an inherently random energy eigenvalue will be observed, and a series of repeated observations will yield a set of eigenvalues whose expectation value is

$$\langle \varepsilon \rangle = \langle \underline{H} \rangle = \sum_n c_n^* c_n \varepsilon_n \ . \tag{4.13-15}$$

These conclusions are arrived at simply by replacing the operator $\underline{A}$ in the above discussion with the Hamiltonian operator $\underline{H}$, and its eigenfunctions with the eigenfunctions $\Psi_n(x, t)$ of the Hamiltonian. There is one important difference, however. Now, the time dependences of the coefficients c_n and c^*_n are of exponential form as in (4.13 - 10), and the product $c_n c^*_n$ is time-independent. So the expectation value of the energy is independent of time, and energy is a conserved quantity. In future work, it is useful to remember that the energy of a system in an eigenstate can be expressed as the expectation value of the Hamiltonian operator for that state.

Another significant result that follows from this work concerns the distribution of measured values of an observable about the expectation value. Is it most probable that measured values will be bunched closely about the expectation value, or will there be a large spread that ranges over values far removed from the average? This question can be answered by introducing an operator $\underline{\Delta A}$ defined so that

$$\underline{\Delta A} = \underline{A} - \langle A \rangle \ , \quad \text{and thus} \quad \left(\underline{\Delta A}\right)^2 = \underline{A}^2 - 2\underline{A}\langle A \rangle + \langle A \rangle^2 \ . \tag{4.13-16}$$

The operator $(\underline{\Delta A})^2$ represents the square of the difference between an individual measurement of the physical quantity associated with $\underline{A}$ and the average value of a large number of measurements made on an identical system in the same initial state. This difference expresses the deviation of any measured value from the statistical average; its average over all the measurements is referred to as the standard deviation σ. If we now write the expectation value of the above operator, recalling that $<A>$ is merely a constant, we can express the square of the standard deviation as

$$\sigma^2 = \left\langle \left(\underline{\Delta A}\right)^2 \right\rangle = \left\langle \underline{A}^2 \right\rangle - 2\langle A \rangle\langle A \rangle + \langle A \rangle^2 = \left\langle \underline{A}^2 \right\rangle - \langle A \rangle^2 \ . \tag{4.13-17}$$

It is easy to see from (4.13 - 11) and (4.13 - 12) that this quantity will be zero when the initial state wave function is an eigenfunction of the operator $\underline{A}$. Under these circumstances, there is no "statistical spread" and the same value is obtained from every measurement. If the initial state is not an eigenstate, however, there will be a spread of values whose standard deviation is given by (4.13 - 16).

It is possible to derive an expression for the time derivative of the expectation value of an operator by finding the time derivative of the general integral expression (4.13 - 12) for the expectation value. Such a time derivative can exist because of the time-dependence of the wave function, or because of the fact that the operator itself may depend explicitly on time. Most of the operators we encounter in quantum theory do not contain time explicitly, the conspicuous exception being the energy operator $\underline{\varepsilon}$. We shall proceed initially on the assumption that we are concerned with an operator $\underline{A}$ that has no *explicit* time dependence. Since the limits of the integral in (4.13 - 12) are fixed, we can get its time derivative as follows;

$$\frac{d\langle A \rangle}{dt} = \frac{d}{dt}\int_{-\infty}^{\infty}\Psi^*\underline{A}\Psi\,dx = \int_{-\infty}^{\infty}\frac{\partial\Psi^*}{\partial t}\underline{A}\Psi\,dx + \int_{-\infty}^{\infty}\Psi^*\frac{\partial}{\partial t}(\underline{A}\Psi)\,dx$$

$$= \int_{-\infty}^{\infty}\frac{\partial\Psi^*}{\partial t}\underline{A}\Psi\,dx + \int_{-\infty}^{\infty}\Psi^*\underline{A}\frac{\partial\Psi}{\partial t}\,dx \ . \tag{4.13-18}$$

Writing Schrödinger's equation and taking its complex conjugate, we now see that

$$\underline{H}\Psi = \left[-\hbar^2\frac{\partial^2}{\partial x^2}+V(x)\right]\Psi = i\hbar\frac{\partial\Psi}{\partial t} \ , \ \text{and} \ \ \underline{H}\Psi^* = -i\hbar\frac{\partial\Psi^*}{\partial t} \ . \tag{4.13-19}$$

Using these equations to express the time derivatives of Ψ and Ψ^* in terms of $\underline{H}\Psi$ and $\underline{H}\Psi^*$, we can write (4.13 - 18) as

$$i\hbar\frac{d\langle A \rangle}{dt} = -\int_{-\infty}^{\infty}\left(\underline{H}\Psi^*\right)(\underline{A}\Psi)\,dx + \int_{-\infty}^{\infty}\Psi^*\underline{A}\,\underline{H}\Psi\,dx \ . \tag{4.13-20}$$

The first of the two integrals on the right can be written as

$$\int_{-\infty}^{\infty}\left(\underline{H}\Psi^*\right)(\underline{A}\Psi)\,dx = \int_{-\infty}^{\infty}\left[-\frac{\hbar^2}{2m}\frac{\partial^2\Psi^*}{\partial x^2}+V(x)\Psi^*\right]\Omega(x,t)\,dx$$

$$= -\frac{\hbar^2}{2m}\int_{-\infty}^{\infty}\Omega\frac{\partial}{\partial x}\left(\frac{\partial\Psi^*}{\partial x}\right)dx + \int_{-\infty}^{\infty}V(x)\Psi^*\Omega\,dx \ , \tag{4.13-21}$$

where
$$\Omega(x,t) = \underline{A}\Psi(x,t) \ . \tag{4.13-22}$$

The first integral above may be integrated by parts letting $u = \Omega$, $dv = \partial(\partial\Psi^*/\partial x)dx$, $du = (\partial\Omega/\partial x)dx$ and $v = \partial\Psi^*/\partial x$, to obtain

$$-\frac{\hbar^2}{2m}\int_{-\infty}^{\infty}\Omega\frac{\partial}{\partial x}\left(\frac{\partial\Psi^*}{\partial x}\right)dx = -\frac{\hbar^2}{2m}\left[\Omega\frac{\partial\Psi^*}{\partial x}\right]_{-\infty}^{\infty} + \frac{\hbar^2}{2m}\int_{-\infty}^{\infty}\frac{\partial\Psi^*}{\partial x}\cdot\frac{\partial\Omega}{\partial x}\,dx \ . \tag{4.13-23}$$

Wave functions must be well behaved to the extent that the existence of the normalization integral (4.7 - 1) is guaranteed. This means that both the function and its derivative must approach zero for large values of $\pm x$. Therefore, the first term on the right side of the above equation vanishes. Noting this fact, and substituting the resulting expression into (4.13 - 21) gives,

$$\int_{-\infty}^{\infty} \left(\underline{H}\Psi^*\right)\left(\underline{A}\Psi\right)dx = \frac{\hbar^2}{2m}\int_{-\infty}^{\infty} \frac{\partial \Psi^*}{\partial x}\cdot\frac{\partial \Omega}{\partial x}dx + \int_{-\infty}^{\infty} V(x)\Psi^*\Omega\,dx \quad . \tag{4.13-24}$$

Now consider the integral of the quantity $\Psi^*\underline{HA}\Psi\,dx$ on the interval $(-\infty < x < \infty)$. This integral can be evaluated in exactly the same way as the one directly above, employing an integration by parts using $u = \Psi^*$, $dv = \partial(\partial\Omega/\partial x)dx$, $du = (\partial\Psi^*/\partial x)dx$, and $v = \partial\Omega/\partial x$. The result of this calculation is exactly the same as the expression shown on the right side of (4.13 - 24), which allows us to write

$$\int_{-\infty}^{\infty} \left(\underline{H}\Psi^*\right)\left(\underline{A}\Psi\right)dx = \int_{-\infty}^{\infty} \Psi^*\underline{A}\underline{H}\Psi\,dx \quad . \tag{4.13-25}$$

Substituting this result into (4.13 - 20) and identifying the two integrals as expectation values of the respective operators, we may finally write

$$\frac{d\langle A\rangle}{dt} = \frac{i}{\hbar}\langle \underline{HA} - \underline{AH}\rangle \quad . \tag{4.13-26}$$

From this we can see that if operators $\underline{A}$ and $\underline{H}$ commute--that is, if $(\underline{AH})\Psi$ and $(\underline{HA})\Psi$ are equal, the expectation value $<A>$ is constant, and therefore the physically observable quantity associated with $\underline{A}$ is *conserved*. Since, obviously, $\underline{H}$ commutes with itself, the associated dynamical quantity, in this case the total energy, is conserved. If $\underline{A}$ is regarded as the momentum operator $(\hbar/i)(\partial/\partial x)$, it is apparent that the operator commutes with the kinetic energy term in $\underline{H}$, but not with the potential energy $V(x)$, since $V(x)\partial\Psi/\partial x$ and $\partial(V\Psi)/\partial x$ are not equal. In general, therefore, momentum is not a conserved quantity. This is in line with what we know from classical mechanics; the momentum of a classical harmonic oscillator, for example, clearly varies sinusoidally during the course of a cycle. For a free particle, however, $V(x)$ *is* constant, and in this case the momentum operator does commute with $V(x)$, which allows us to conclude that (as expected) the momentum as well as the energy of a free particle is conserved.

In the preceding analysis, we assumed for simplicity that the time t did not appear explicitly in the operator $\underline{A}$. This is what allows us in (4.13 - 18) to express $\partial(\underline{A}\Psi^*)/\partial t$ as $\underline{A}(\partial\Psi^*/\partial t)$. If $\underline{A}$ depends explicitly on time, this is no longer true, and this derivative must be evaluated by the chain rule. The effect of this is to introduce a third term into (4.13 - 18), which has the form of the expectation value $<\partial\underline{A}/\partial t>$. If $\underline{A}$ is explicitly time dependent, therefore, this quantity must be added to the right side of (4.13 - 26). Also, we should note that though all calculations in this section refer to a one-dimensional system, they can be extended to three dimensions, and are valid in the three-dimensional world.

A final consequence of this discussion is that if an operator $\underline{A}$ has the same set of eigenfunctions as the Hamiltonian operator, the observable associated with operator $\underline{A}$ is a conserved quantity. This can easily be seen by assuming that the eigenfunctions Ψ_n of $\underline{\mathbf{H}}$ (whose eigenvalues are ε_n) are also eigenfunctions of $\underline{\mathbf{A}}$ with eigenvalues α_n. Then,

$$\underline{\mathbf{H}}\underline{\mathbf{A}}\Psi_n = \underline{\mathbf{H}}\,\alpha_n\Psi_n = \alpha_n\underline{\mathbf{H}}\Psi_n = \alpha_n\varepsilon_n \;,$$

and

$$\underline{\mathbf{A}}\underline{\mathbf{H}}\Psi_n = \underline{\mathbf{A}}\varepsilon_n\Psi_n = \varepsilon_n\underline{\mathbf{A}}\Psi_n = \varepsilon_n\alpha_n \;, \tag{4.13-27}$$

so that

$$(\underline{\mathbf{H}}\underline{\mathbf{A}} - \underline{\mathbf{A}}\underline{\mathbf{H}})\Psi_n = 0 \;. \tag{4.13-28}$$

This assures that the expectation value in (4.13 - 26) is zero if the wave function Ψ is an eigenfunction, and since it is true for all eigenfunctions, it is valid even when the wave function has the form (4.13 - 10).

4.14 THE HYDROGEN ATOM

All the examples previously discussed have been one-dimensional. They are useful not only for the insights on quantum physics they offer and the practice they provide in putting it to work, but also because they can sometimes be used as reasonable models for actual physical systems. Atomic systems, however, are not easily described by one-dimensional models. Indeed, complex atoms involve many-body interactions that cannot be solved exactly either classically or quantum mechanically. In the case of hydrogen and the related hydrogenic ions discussed in Section 4.5, however, one need solve only a two-body problem similar to the classical problem of two bodies subject to their mutual gravitation. In the case of hydrogen the two bodies are the electron and the proton and the interaction is electrostatic rather than gravitational, but since radial inverse square attractive forces are involved in both cases, the problem--at least on the classical level--is a familiar one. The classical potential energy of this inverse-square system can be written

$$V(r) = -\frac{q^2}{4\pi\epsilon_0 r} \;, \tag{4.14-1}$$

where q is the electronic charge and r the distance between the two particles. For simplicity, we shall discuss explicitly only the hydrogen problem, but answers concerning related hydrogenic ions can be obtained by replacing q^2 by Zq^2, where Zq is the charge of the ionic nucleus. Again in the interest of simplicity, we shall take the origin of coördinates at the proton. To avoid problems associated with the use of an accelerated reference frame, we should really use the center of mass of the system as the origin, but in view of the fact that the proton is 1836 times more massive than the electron, any errors arising from our choice of reference system will be small, and can in any event be corrected later. It is clear that since the potential energy is purely radial, it will be best to choose a spherical coördinate system (r, θ, φ), in which

$$\begin{aligned}
x &= r\sin\theta\cos\varphi \\
y &= r\sin\theta\sin\varphi \\
z &= r\cos\theta \;.
\end{aligned} \tag{4.14-2}$$

In this system, we must write the time-independent Schrödinger equation as

$$\nabla^2\psi + \frac{2m}{\hbar^2}\left[\varepsilon + \frac{q^2}{4\pi\epsilon_0 r}\right]\psi(r,\theta,\varphi) = 0 \ , \tag{4.14-3}$$

with $\quad \nabla^2\psi = \dfrac{1}{r^2}\dfrac{\partial}{\partial r}\left(r^2\dfrac{\partial\psi}{\partial r}\right) + \dfrac{1}{r^2\sin\theta}\dfrac{\partial}{\partial\theta}\left(\sin\theta\dfrac{\partial\psi}{\partial\theta}\right) + \dfrac{1}{r^2\sin^2\theta}\dfrac{\partial^2\psi}{\partial\varphi^2} \ . \tag{4.14-4}$

The form of the Laplacian shown above can be derived from the more familiar cartesian form by a straightforward (though tedious) coördinate transformation using the relations (4.14 - 2). The details, while not irrelevant, need not be presented here.

It is customary to use the method of separation of variables to solve linear partial differential equations like the one above. In this method, one assumes initially solutions of the form

$$\psi(r,\theta,\varphi) = R(r)\Theta(\theta)\Phi(\varphi) \ , \tag{4.14-5}$$

where $R(r)$ is a function of r alone, independent of θ and φ, while $\Theta(\theta)$ is a function of θ alone, and $\Phi(\varphi)$ is a function of φ alone. Substituting this solution into (4.14 - 4), noting that the partial derivatives of this function act--as total derivatives--on only one of these factors, one finds (after multiplying through by $r^2\sin^2\theta/R\Theta\Phi$),

$$\frac{\sin^2\theta}{R}\frac{d}{dr}\left(r^2\frac{dR}{dr}\right) + \frac{2mr^2\sin^2\theta}{\hbar^2}\left[\varepsilon + \frac{q^2}{4\pi\epsilon_0 r}\right] + \frac{\sin\theta}{\Theta}\frac{d}{d\theta}\left(\sin\theta\frac{d\Theta}{d\theta}\right) = -\frac{1}{\Phi}\frac{d^2\Phi}{d\Phi^2} = m^2. \tag{4.14-6}$$

The expression on the left above is independent of φ, and involves only the variables r and θ, while the second one depends only on φ, being completely independent of r and θ. Under these circumstances there is no way that the two expressions can be equal unless they are separately equal to some constant, denoted in the above equation (for reasons soon to be seen) by m^2. This constant is known as a separation constant. We now focus our attention on the second and third parts of this expression, which we can write as

$$\frac{d^2\Phi}{d\Phi^2} = -m^2\Phi(\varphi) \ . \tag{4.14-7}$$

This is a familiar equation whose solutions are of the form

$$\Phi_m(\varphi) = e^{\pm im\varphi} \ . \tag{4.14-8}$$

The total wave function ψ must clearly be single-valued. This requires that $\Phi(\varphi)$ be a single-valued function of the azimuthal angle φ. This condition can be satisfied only if $\Phi(\varphi)$ is a periodic function whose period is an integral multiple of 2π radians, which suggests that in (4.14 - 8) m must be an integer, that is,

$$m = 0,\pm1,\pm2,\pm3... \ . \tag{4.14-9}$$

The notation m^2 in (4.14 - 6) is now understandable, since it excludes imaginary values for m and solutions of the form $\exp(\pm m\varphi)$, which are never single-valued when φ is an angular variable. This separation constant is clearly quantized; it turns out to be one of several quantum numbers associated with the hydrogen atom.

Equation (4.14 - 6) can now be slightly rearranged, by transferring terms that depend only on r to one side, and terms that depend only on θ to the other, to read

$$\frac{1}{R}\frac{d}{dr}\left(r^2\frac{dR}{dr}\right)+\frac{2mr^2}{\hbar^2}\left[\varepsilon+\frac{q^2}{4\pi\epsilon_0 r}\right]=-\frac{1}{\Theta\sin\theta}\frac{d}{d\theta}\left(\sin\theta\frac{d\Theta}{d\theta}\right)+\frac{m^2}{\sin^2\theta}=l(l+1) \ .$$

$$(4.14 - 10)$$

The quantity $l(l + 1)$ on the extreme right is another separation constant; why it is written this way, and what the significance of l is, will soon be seen. The justification for setting the two leftmost expressions equal to this constant is the same as that used previously in connection with (4.14 - 6); there is no way that two functions of two different independent variables can be equal for all values of the respective variables unless each of them, individually, is equal to the same constant.

The two rightmost expressions above can be written as

$$\frac{1}{\sin\theta}\frac{d}{d\theta}\left(\sin\theta\frac{d\Theta}{d\theta}\right)-\frac{m^2\Theta}{\sin^2\theta}+l(l+1)\Theta(\theta)=0 \qquad (4.14 - 11)$$

This equation, known as Legendre's equation, arises frequently in mathematical physics, and it solutions have been analyzed in great detail. There is no point in reproducing this body of knowledge here, except to point out certain relevant facts. This equation is in many ways much like Hermite's equation. Solutions can be obtained by assuming that they can be written as power series, substituting these series solutions into the equation, and deriving recursion relations for the coefficients. Such solutions can be found for any real value of the separation constant l, but the solutions are not generally acceptable as wave functions, because (like the solutions of Hermite's equations) the normalization condition cannot be satisfied in view of divergences that arise. Like Hermite functions, however, the solutions reduce to *polynomials* in the functions $\cos\theta$ and $\sin\theta$ in certain cases, and these solutions are the only ones that can be accepted as wave functions. The polynomial solutions are found to exist only for the integer values of m defined by (4.14 - 9), and only when the parameter l is either zero or a positive integer. They can be defined by formulas somewhat similar to the definition of Hermite polynomials (4.12 - 9). If we denote the polynomial solutions as $\Theta(\theta) = P_l{}^m(\theta)$, these formulas can be written

$$P_l^m(\theta) = \sin^{|m|}\theta\frac{d^{|m|}}{d(\cos\theta)^{|m|}}P_l(\cos\theta) \ , \qquad (4.14 - 12)$$

where $P_l(\cos\theta) = P_l^0(\theta) = \frac{1}{2^n n!}\frac{d^l}{d(\cos\theta)^l}(\cos^2\theta-1)^l \ . \qquad (4.14 - 13)$

The functions $P_l(\cos\theta)$, which are the same as $P_l{}^0(\theta)$, are referred to as *Legendre polynomials*, and are defined by (4.14 - 13). The functions $P_l{}^m(\theta)$ are obtained by successive differentiation of $P_l{}^0(\theta)$ as shown in (4.14 - 12); they are referred to as *associated Legendre functions.* The angular fuctions obtained by multiplying $\Theta(\theta)$ as given by (4.14 - 12) by $\Phi(\varphi)$ as expressed by (4.14 - 8), are called *spherical harmonics*, and are usually denoted by $Y_{lm}(\theta, \varphi)$. Thus,

$$Y_{lm}(\theta,\varphi) = P_l^m(\theta)e^{im\varphi} \ . \tag{4.14-14}$$

Spherical harmonics arise not only as solutions to Schrödinger's equation, but also other linear partial differential equations of physics concerned with spherically symmetric potentials, fields, waves, and boundaries. Note that all associated Legendre functions for which $m > l$ are identically *zero*, since (4.14 - 13) vanishes when more than l derivatives are taken. This means that nonzero solutions exist *only* for

$$l = 0,1,2,3,...$$

and

$$m = 0,\pm1,\pm2,\pm3...\pm l \ . \tag{4.14-15}$$

The above definition of the associated Legendre functions generates a series of polynomial solutions $\Theta_{lm}(\theta)$ or $P_l{}^m(\theta)$ whose first several members are shown below. Their validity can be checked by substituting them directly into (4.14 - 11). Thus,

$$P_0^0(\theta) = 1$$

$$P_1^0(\theta) = \cos\theta \qquad\qquad P_1^1(\theta) = \sin\theta$$

$$P_2^0(\theta) = \tfrac{1}{2}(3\cos^2\theta - 1) \qquad\qquad P_2^1(\theta) = 3\sin\theta\cos\theta$$
$$P_2^2(\theta) = 3\sin^2\theta$$

$$P_3^0(\theta) = \tfrac{1}{2}(5\cos^3\theta - 3\cos\theta) \qquad\qquad P_3^1(\theta) = \tfrac{3}{2}(5\cos^2\theta - 1)$$
$$P_3^2(\theta) = 15\sin^2\theta\cos\theta$$
$$\text{(etc.)} \qquad\qquad P_3^3(\theta) = 15\sin^3\theta$$

Returning to (4.14 - 10), the radial functions $R(r)$ are solutions of the equation

$$\frac{1}{r^2}\frac{d}{dr}\left(r^2\frac{dR}{dr}\right) + \frac{2m}{\hbar^2}\left[\varepsilon + \frac{q^2}{4\pi\epsilon_0 r}\right]R(r) - \frac{l(l+1)R(r)}{r^2} = 0 \ . \tag{4.14-16}$$

In this equation, which is called the Laguerre equation, we know from our previous work that l must be zero or a positive integer. By now, it may not come as a surprise that solutions can be expressed as power series which diverge at $\pm\infty$, except in certain cases when they reduce to polynomials--polynomials that in this instance are multiplied by a decreasing exponential function of distance. These polynomials solutions can be obtained only when the energy has certain discrete values ε_n, such that

$$\varepsilon_n = \frac{\varepsilon_1}{n^2} \ , \qquad \text{where} \qquad \varepsilon_1 = -\frac{mq^4}{2(4\pi\epsilon_0)^2\hbar^2} = -13.62 \text{ eV}$$

$$\tag{4.14-17}$$

$$\text{and} \qquad n = 1,2,3,4,... \ .$$

This result agrees precisely with that obtained from the Bohr theory in Section 4.5. The polynomial solutions of (4.14 - 16) clearly involve the quantized parameters l and ε, which can equally well be expressed as l and n because of the above equation. If we denote these solutions as $R_{nl}(r)$, we can write the total wave function as

$$\psi_{nlm}(r,\theta,\varphi) = R_{nl}(r)\Theta_{lm}(\theta)\Phi_m(\varphi) = R_{nl}(r)P_l^m(\theta)e^{im\varphi} \ . \tag{4.14-18}$$

The radial functions R_{nl} are identically zero for $l > n - 1$. This fact, along with what we alrady know about possible values of l and m, as expressed by (4.14 - 15) leads us to conclude that the three quantum numbers n, l, and m are related as follows:

$$n = 1, 2, 3, 4 \ldots \ ,$$

$$l = 0, 1, 2, 3, \ldots n - 1 \ , \tag{4.14-19}$$

and

$$m = 0, \pm 1, \pm 2, \pm 3 \ldots \pm l \ .$$

In solving the radial wave equation (4.14 - 16) and writing out its solutions, it is advantageous to introduce a dimensionless distance variable ρ defined by

$$\rho = \frac{2r}{r_1} \ , \qquad \text{where} \qquad r_1 = \frac{4\pi\epsilon_0}{m}\frac{\hbar^2}{q^2} \ . \tag{4.14-20}$$

The parameter r_1 may be identified as the "first Bohr radius" originally encountered in (4.5 - 8). Explicit values for the wave functions can now be written, with the aid of (4.14 - 18), and are tabulated for the states of lowest energy in the table below. Explicit values for the radial wave functions R_{nl} are easily identified in this table. It is possible to verify the correctness of these expressions by direct substitution into the wave equation (4.14 - 3).

There are some important differences between this three-dimensional example and the one-dimensional problems worked previously. These differences can be largely attributed to the higher dimensionality of the problem itself. Most conspicuously, there are three quantized parameters instead of one, as expressed by the three quantum numbers n, l, and m. In this example, the energy depends *only* upon n, which is sometimes called the principal quantum number. The quantum numbers l and m, as we shall see directly, can be identified physically with the total angular momentum of the atom and its component along the polar z-axis, respectively. It is evident from the table that there can be many independent solutions of the wave equation all having the same quantum number n, though different values of l and m. Each of these solutions leads to a different electron density $\psi^*\psi$, and therefore represents a different electronic configuration of the atom. Each independent solution defined by a unique set of indices (n, l, m) defines a given *quantum state* of the system, while all quantum states having the same energy (in this example, all those having the same value of n) belong to a given energy state or *energy level* of the system. Thus, there can be many quantum states belonging to any given energy level. This phenomenon is referred to as *degeneracy*. One says that the energy levels of the hydrogen atom are degenerate, and that their degeneracy is given by $2n^2$, since there are $2n^2$ states in each energy level, as you can see from the table. This distinction between quantum states and energy levels is *very important*, and if not clearly understood can lead to endless confusion. The phenomenon of degeneracy is largely caused by dimensionality, and is not observed in systems that are strictly one-dimensional.

WAVE FUNCTIONS FOR THE HYDROGEN ATOM

$n = 1$ $l = 0$ $m = 0$ $\psi_{100} = Ae^{-\rho/2} = Ae^{-r/r_1}$ 1s
(1 state)

$n = 2$ $l = 0$ $m = 0$ $\psi_{200} = A(2 - \tfrac{1}{2}\rho)e^{-\rho/4}$ 2s
       $l = 1$ $m = 0$ $\psi_{210} = A\rho e^{-\rho/4}\cos\theta$
(4 states) $m = \pm 1$ $\psi_{21\pm1} = A\rho e^{-\rho/4}\sin\theta\, e^{\pm i\varphi}$ $2p^3$

$n = 3$ $l = 0$ $m = 0$ $\psi_{300} = A(\tfrac{1}{9}\rho^2 - 2\rho + 6)e^{-\rho/6}$ 3s
       $l = 1$ $m = 0$ $\psi_{310} = A\rho(4 - \tfrac{1}{3}\rho)e^{-\rho/6}\cos\theta$
               $m = \pm 1$ $\psi_{31\pm1} = A\rho(4 - \tfrac{1}{3}\rho)e^{-\rho/6}\sin\theta e^{\pm i\varphi}$ $3p^3$
       $l = 2$ $m = 0$ $\psi_{320} = A\rho^2 e^{-\rho/6}(3\cos^2\theta - 1)$
               $m = \pm 1$ $\psi_{32\pm1} = A\rho^2 e^{-\rho/6}\sin\theta\cos\theta e^{\pm i\varphi}$
(9 states) $m = \pm 2$ $\psi_{32\pm2} = A\rho^2 e^{-\rho/6}\sin^2\theta e^{\pm 2i\varphi}$ $3d^5$

$n = 4$ $l = 0$ $m = 0$ $\psi_{400} = A(24 - 9\rho + 3\rho^2 - \tfrac{1}{4}\rho^3)e^{-\rho/8}$ 4s
       $l = 1$ $m = 0$ $\psi_{410} = A\rho(20 - \tfrac{5}{2}\rho + \tfrac{1}{16}\rho^2)e^{-\rho/8}\cos\theta$
               $m = \pm 1$ $\psi_{41\pm1} = A\rho(20 - \tfrac{5}{2}\rho + \tfrac{1}{16}\rho^2)e^{-\rho/8}\sin\theta\, e^{\pm i\varphi}$ $4p^3$
       $l = 2$ $m = 0$ $\psi_{420} = A\rho^2(6 - \tfrac{1}{4}\rho)e^{-\rho/8}(3\cos^2\theta - 1)$
               $m = \pm 1$ $\psi_{42\pm1} = A\rho^2(6 - \tfrac{1}{4}\rho)e^{-\rho/8}\sin\theta\cos\theta\, e^{\pm i\varphi}$
               $m = \pm 2$ $\psi_{42\pm2} = A\rho^2(6 - \tfrac{1}{4}\rho)e^{-\rho/8}\sin^2\theta e^{\pm 2i\varphi}$ $4d^5$
       $l = 3$ $m = 0$ $\psi_{430} = A\rho^3 e^{-\rho/8}(\tfrac{5}{3}\cos^3\theta - \cos\theta)$
               $m = \pm 1$ $\psi_{43\pm1} = A\rho^3 e^{-\rho/8}(5\cos^2\theta - 1)\sin\theta e^{\pm i\varphi}$
               $m = \pm 2$ $\psi_{43\pm2} = A\rho^3 e^{-\rho/8}\sin^2\theta\cos\theta e^{\pm 2i\varphi}$
(16 states) $m = \pm 3$ $\psi_{43\pm3} = A\rho^3 e^{-\rho/8}\sin^3\theta\, e^{\pm 3i\varphi}$ $4f^7$
       etc.

In the above table, the symbol A represents a normalization constant chosen so as to satisfy (4.7 - 1). This constant is *not the same* for all states, but depends on the quantum numbers n, l, and m. It would have been more accurate to have used the notation A_{nlm}, but for simplicity, the subscripts have been omitted in the table. The states for which $l = 0, 1, 2, 3, \ldots$ are often referred to as $s, p, d, f, \ldots$ states, respectively. Thus, a state for which $n = 2$ and $l = 0$ is called a 2s-state, while one for which $n = 3$ and $l = 2$ is known as a 3d-state. The number of quantum states corresponding to each of these l-values is sometimes shown as a superscript. This notation is illustrated in the column on the right side of the table. The wave functions (4.14 - 18) are orthogonal, so that

$$\int_0^\infty \int_0^\pi \int_0^{2\pi} \psi_{nlm}^* \psi_{n'l'm'} r^2 \sin\theta\, dr d\theta\, d\varphi = 0 \ , \qquad (4.14 - 21)$$

unless *all* the indices satisfy the conditions $n = n'$, $l = l'$, and $m = m'$.

The wave functions shown above are in general complicated functions of the coördinates; a detailed analysis of their geometry would be time-consuming and is for our purposes unnecessary. It is nevertheless important to understand some of their more elementary properties. First of all, the state of lowest energy--the ground state of the atom--is $n = l = m = 0$, which is also referred to as a 1s state. Its wave function is a simple decreasing exponential function that depends only on the radial coördinate r. It has no angular dependence, and is thus spherically symmetric. The exponential decay distance is simply the first Bohr radius $r_1 = 0.528$Å described in Section 4.5. The probability density $\psi^*\psi$ is likewise exponential and spherically symmetric, with decay length $2r_1$. It will be noted that *all* the s-states ($l = 0$) are likewise spherically symmetric, though those of higher energy have more complex radial wave functions. The effect of the polynomials multiplying the exponential functions in these higher-order wave functions is to introduce a number of oscillations into the wave function and a corresponding series of maxima into the probability density. These features are illustrated in Figure 4.18. The larger the value of n, the more oscillations or maxima there can be.

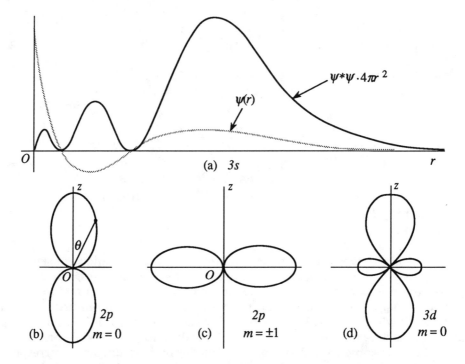

Figure 4.18 (a) Radial wave function and probability density for the 3s state $(nlm) = (300)$ of the hydrogen atom. (b), (c) Angular dependence of the wave functions $(nlm) = (210)$ and (21 ± 1) for the hydrogen atom. These plots are symmetric about the polar z-axis, and in three dimensions these figures should be visualized as being rotated about the polar axis. (c) Angular dependence of the wave function $(nlm) = (320)$ of the hydrogen atom.

For a spherically symmetric s-type wave function, the volume of a spherical shell of radius r and thickness dr is $4\pi r^2 dr$. Therefore, according to (4.7 - 1) the probability of finding the electron in a radial element of thickness dr at a distance r from the proton is given by $\psi^*\psi(4\pi r^2)$ rather than $\psi^*\psi$. For this reason, the former quantity is shown in Figure 4.18(a). The other plots in this figure show the angular dependence of wave functions for which $l > 0$. Note that these functions have lobes that closely resemble the polar radiation patterns of radio and microwave antennas. The larger the quantum number l, associated with the angular momentum of the electron, the greater the number of lobes and the complexity of the "radiation pattern". The angular patterns shown, for example at (b) and (c) for the $2p$ state, would seem to confer on the arbitrarily chosen z-axis the special status of an axis of symmetry. However, the $2p$ wave functions $(nlm) = (210, 211,$ and $21-1)$ all belong to the same energy level, and therefore all have exactly the same frequency of oscillation, as given by the Planck relation. This means that any linear combination of the three functions will still represent a time-independent state of the system. You can therefore construct a set of stationary-state eigenfunctions with a different symmetry axis by selecting certain linear superpositions of these three wave functions. The axis of symmetry can in fact be made to point in any direction by properly combining these three functions. You can do this because all these quantum states belong to the same energy level. One cannot, however, superpose quantum states of *different* energies and still obtain a time-independent wave function.

We have mentioned the fact that the quantum numbers l and m are associated with the angular momentum of the electron. To see why this is so, we must construct an operator to describe angular momentum in quantum mechanics. This can be done from its definintion in classical mechanics,

$$\mathbf{L} = \mathbf{r} \times \mathbf{p} , \qquad (4.14\text{-}22)$$

where $\mathbf{L}$ is the angular momentum, $\mathbf{p}$ the particle's linear momentum and $\mathbf{r}$ the dispacement vector locating the particle with respect to a fixed origin of coördinates. We can convert this into a vector operator by replacing the vectors on the right side of this equation by their operator equivalents in quantum mechanics, to obtain

$$\underline{\mathbf{L}} = \frac{\hbar}{i}\underline{\mathbf{r}} \times \nabla . \qquad (4.14\text{-}23)$$

The cartesian components of this operator can be obtained as

$$\underline{\mathbf{L_x}} = \frac{\hbar}{i}\left(y\frac{\partial}{\partial z} - z\frac{\partial}{\partial y}\right), \quad \underline{\mathbf{L_y}} = \frac{\hbar}{i}\left(z\frac{\partial}{\partial x} - x\frac{\partial}{\partial z}\right), \quad \underline{\mathbf{L_z}} = \frac{\hbar}{i}\left(x\frac{\partial}{\partial y} - y\frac{\partial}{\partial x}\right). \qquad (4.14\text{-}24)$$

These operators can be expressed in spherical coördinates by a straightforward though tedious process of coördinate transformation, whose details are for our purposes irrelevant. The result is,

$$\underline{\mathbf{L_x}} = \frac{\hbar}{i}\left(-\sin\varphi\frac{\partial}{\partial\theta} - \cot\theta\cos\varphi\frac{\partial}{\partial\varphi}\right) ,$$

$$\underline{\mathbf{L_y}} = \frac{\hbar}{i}\left(\cos\varphi\frac{\partial}{\partial\theta} - \cot\theta\sin\varphi\frac{\partial}{\partial\varphi}\right) , \qquad (4.14\text{-}25)$$

and $\quad \underline{L_z} = \dfrac{\hbar}{i}\dfrac{\partial}{\partial\varphi}$. $\hspace{6cm}$ (4.14 - 25)

The operator representing the square of the total angular momentum can now be written as

$$\underline{L}^2 = \underline{L}_x^2 + \underline{L}_y^2 + \underline{L}_z^2 = -\hbar^2\left[\frac{1}{\sin\theta}\frac{\partial}{\partial\theta}\left(\sin\theta\frac{\partial}{\partial\theta}\right)+\frac{1}{\sin^2\theta}\frac{\partial^2}{\partial\varphi^2}\right] . \hspace{2cm} (4.14\text{-}26)$$

We know that the wave functions ψ_{nlm} have the form (4.14 - 18); they are also, as we have seen above, eigenfunctions of the Hamiltonian operator. If the operator $\underline{L}_z$ operates on such a wave function, the functions R and Θ act as constants, since the operator contains only the variable φ. Since $\Phi_m(\varphi) = \exp(im\varphi)$, it is easy to see that

$$\underline{L}_z\psi_{nlm} = \frac{\hbar}{i}R_{nl}(r)\Theta_{lm}(\theta)\frac{\partial(e^{im\varphi})}{\partial\varphi} = \frac{\hbar}{i}R_{nl}(r)\Theta_{lm}(\theta)(im\Phi_m(\varphi)) = m\hbar\psi_{nlm} . \hspace{1cm} (4.14\text{-}27)$$

This shows that ψ_{nlm} are eigenfunctions of the $\underline{L}_z$ operator with eigenvalues $m\hbar$. They are also eigenfunctions of the Hamiltonian operator. In Section 4.13, however, we observed that an operator whose eigenfunctions are also eigenfunctions of the Hamiltonian represents a conserved quantity. So the z-component of the angular momentum is conserved in the hydrogen atom.

A similar result can be obtained for the operator $\underline{L}^2$. In this case, we note that since this operator does not depend upon r, we can write

$$\underline{L}^2\psi_{nlm} = -\hbar^2R_{nl}(r)\left[\frac{\Phi_m(\varphi)}{\sin\theta}\frac{\partial}{\partial\theta}\left(\sin\theta\frac{\partial\Theta_{lm}(\theta)}{\partial\theta}\right)+\frac{\Theta_{lm}(\theta)}{\sin^2\theta}\frac{\partial^2\Phi_m(\varphi)}{\partial\varphi^2}\right] . \hspace{1cm} (4.14\text{-}28)$$

However, since $\Phi_m(\varphi) = \exp(im\varphi)$, this can be stated as

$$\underline{L}^2\psi_{nlm} = -\hbar^2R_{nl}\Phi_m\left[\frac{1}{\sin\theta}\frac{\partial}{\partial\theta}\left(\sin\theta\frac{\partial\Theta_{lm}}{\partial\theta}\right)+\frac{m^2\Theta_{lm}}{\sin^2\theta}\right] = \hbar^2R_{nl}\Phi_m\cdot l(l+1)\Theta_{lm}(\theta)$$
$$= \hbar^2l(l+1)\psi_{nlm} . \hspace{3cm} (4.14\text{-}29)$$

Equation (4.14 - 11) has been used to obtain the final form of the above equation. From this, we see that the functions ψ_{nlm} are eigenfunctions of the Hamiltonian operator and also of the operator $\underline{L}^2$, whose eigenvalues are $l(l + 1)\hbar^2$. The square of the total angular momentum is therefore also a conserved quantity, which implies that the magnitude of the angular momentum itself is conserved. The components L_x and L_y are not separately conserved, though the sum $L_x{}^2 + L_y{}^2$ is conserved, because of the conservation of L^2 and L_z. The observable values of total angular momentum are therefore indexed by the quantum number l as

$$L = \sqrt{L^2} = \hbar\sqrt{l(l+1)} . \hspace{4cm} (4.14\text{-}30)$$

Likewise, the observable values of the z-component of angular momentum are indexed by the quantum number m such that

$$L_z = m\hbar \ .$$
(4.14 - 31)

It is important to note that the observable values of the square of the angular momentum are *not* $(l\hbar)^2$, as Bohr assumed in his model of the atom discussed in Section 4.5, but $l(l + 1)\hbar^2$. The possible orientations of the angular momentum vector with respect to the z-axis are quantized by the conditions (4.14 - 30) and (4.14 - 31). as shown in Figure 4.19.

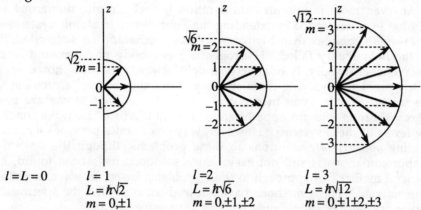

$$l = L = 0 \qquad \begin{array}{c} l = 1 \\ L = \hbar\sqrt{2} \\ m = 0, \pm 1 \end{array} \qquad \begin{array}{c} l = 2 \\ L = \hbar\sqrt{6} \\ m = 0, \pm 1, \pm 2 \end{array} \qquad \begin{array}{c} l = 3 \\ L = \hbar\sqrt{12} \\ m = 0, \pm 1 \pm 2, \pm 3 \end{array}$$

Figure 4.19 Possible orientations of the angular momentum vector of the hydrogen atom and possible values of its projection on the z-axis, for the cases $l = 0, 1, 2,$ and 3. The values of total and projected angular momentum are quantized according to the rules (4.14 - 30) and (4.14 - 31). The radii of the circles shown above and the projections of the angular momentum are given in units of $h/2\pi$.

States having the same value of n, but different values of l and m are degenerate in the normal hydrogen atom. When a magnetic field is applied, for example along the z-direction, this is no longer so, because associated with the atom's angular momentum is a magnetic dipole moment in the direction of its L vector--the kind of magnetic moment that arises from a circulating current. In the presence of an external field, this causes different energies to be associated with different orientations of the L-vector. Classically, the energy of the system will be smallest when the atomic magnetic moment is aligned parallel to the field, and greatest when moment and field are antiparallel. This is equally true in quantum mechanics, the result being that the different allowed orientations of the L-vector now correspond to somewhat different energies. The external influence removes the degeneracy of the states of the unperturbed atom, and "splits" the formerly degenerate single level into a number of closely-spaced but separate levels. This effect can be detected spectroscopically and is referred to as the *Zeeman effect*. The degeneracy of the energy levels of the atom can also be removed by other external perturbations, which also lead to spectroscopically observable phenomena.

We have already seen in (4.14 - 17) that wave mechanics predicts the same spectrum for the hydrogen atom as the much simpler Bohr theory. Why, then, do we go to such trouble to present all the details of this example? There are several answers to this question. First of all, it is clear that wave mechanics gives much more detailed information regarding the quantization of angular momentum and its z-component. Also, as we have already mentioned, the rule for quantization of angular momentum suggested by the Bohr theory is incorrect, because the quantized angular momenta depend upon $l(l + 1)$ rather than l^2. This does not introduce any error into the spectrum of hydrogen, but it does change the predicted spectra of more complex atoms. Moreover, the Bohr circular orbit theory suggests in (4.5 - 1) that there is a quantum of angular momentum $\hbar$ associated with the ground state of hydrogen, while wave mechanics--and a great deal of experimental evidence--indicates that the angular momentum of the ground state is zero.

An even more important consideration is that (despite numerous attempts) nobody has ever succeeded in extending the Bohr theory to atomic systems--like He, Li or Na--more complex than hydrogen. Wave mechanics has succeeded, however, where the Bohr theory failed. Hydrogen is a two-body problem, and its solution, even wave-mechanically, is relatively straightforward. Helium, however, presents us with a problem involving three strongly interacting bodies--a problem that cannot be solved exactly even in classical mechanics. Other atoms are even more complex. There is thus no hope of any exact solution for the wave functions and energy levels of these systems. However, wave mechanics provides a rational basis for finding *approximate* solutions to these problems, though the task of finding good approximations is still not easy. Such solutions have been found, however, and general methods of approach to these problems based on wave mechanics have been formulated. These methods have allowed us to predict the spectra and other properties of complex atomic systems with impressive accuracy.

Many-body problems in quantum mechanics must be dealt with by making reasonable approximations that permit the wave equation to be solved without undue difficulty. Unfortunately, it is frequently not clear whether such approximations are physically reasonable until the results of calculations are compared with experimental data. The approximations that are found to work well in practice are thus difficult to justify beforehand; you must become accustomed to trial and error methods based on hypotheses that are not obviously sound. When you get good answers, then--and only then--you know that your methods were correct!

4.15 SPIN, THE PAULI EXCLUSION PRINCIPLE AND THE PERIODIC TABLE

To view some of these problems in more detail, let us consider the case of helium, illustrated in Figure 4.20(a). Helium has a very heavy nucleus, of charge $+2q$, and two electrons, whose charges are $-q$. These three particles all exert strong forces on one another, but to simplify matters, let us suppose initially that the forces the two electrons exert on each other are negligible in comparison with those exerted by the nucleus on the electrons. This isn't such a good approximation, since the force between the electrons is not really small compared to the nuclear attractions, but if it were true, the two electrons would be entirely independent of one another The wave functions, quantum states and energy levels for each electron would then be *the same as those for hydrogen*. The only difference would be that, as explained in connection with equation (4.14 - 1), you would have to replace q^2 with $2q^2$ in all the results obtained for hydrogen. From (4.14 - 17), the ground state energy for each electron would then be –54.4eV. The quantum numbers, conserved quantities, quantization rules for angular momentum, wave functions, etc. for each electron, would be otherwise unaltered. The only difference is that there are now two electrons, which may or may not be in the same state, and there are now two sets of three coördinates each needed to describe their classical potential energy.

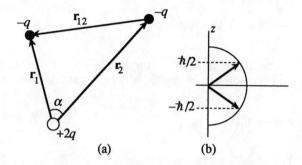

Figure 4.20 (a) Classical representation of the helium atom, a three-body system. (b) Spin angular momentum vector orientations for "spin 1/2" particle such as the electron, showing allowed projections of spin angular momentum along the polar axis. These two states are frequently referred to as "spin up" and "spin down".

When one introduces the interaction between electrons the most important physical effect is that the classical forces acting on the electrons are no longer purely radial, but include also a force directed along the line between the particles. The potential energy of the system is now

$$V = -\frac{2q^2}{4\pi\epsilon_0 r_1} - \frac{2q^2}{4\pi\epsilon_0 r_2} + \frac{q^2}{4\pi\epsilon_0 r_{12}} = \frac{q^2}{4\pi\epsilon_0}\left(-\frac{2}{r_1} - \frac{2}{r_2} + \frac{1}{|\mathbf{r}_1 - \mathbf{r}_2|}\right) , \qquad (4.15-1)$$

where the subscripts 1 and 2 refer to the coördinates of the two electrons, as illustrated. Since

$$r_1^2 = x_1^2 + y_1^2 + z_1^2 \quad \text{and} \quad r_2^2 = x_2^2 + y_2^2 + z_2^2 , \qquad (4.15-2)$$

the need for six position coördinates in this problem is evident. The term involving the interelectronic potential energy now present unfortunately imposes an insurmountable obstacle to obtaining an exact solution, just as it would in a classical three-body system. When this term is missing the potential energy has the form of two additive terms each involving the coordinates of a single electron. Now, whenever you can write the potential energy in the form

$$V = V_1(x_1, y_1, z_1) + V_2(x_2, y_2, z_2) , \qquad (4.15-3)$$

the Hamiltonian operator can be written as the sum of kinetic and potential energy terms

$$\underline{\mathbf{H}} = -\frac{\hbar^2}{2m_1}\nabla_1^2 - \frac{\hbar^2}{2m_2}\nabla_2^2 + V_1 + V_2 , \qquad (4.15-4)$$

where the subscripts on the ∇ operator indicate that partial derivatives are to be taken only with respect to the coordinates of that particular particle. You can then write the Schrödinger equation $\underline{H}\psi = \varepsilon\psi$ as

$$-\frac{\hbar^2}{2m_1}\nabla_1^2\psi - \frac{\hbar^2}{2m_2}\nabla_2^2\psi + V_1\psi + V_2\psi = \varepsilon\psi \ , \tag{4.15-5}$$

wherein the wave function ψ is now a function of all six of the space coördinates $(x_1,y_1,z_1,x_2,y_2,z_2)$. This equation can be regarded as the sum of two *separate* equations,

$$-\frac{\hbar^2}{2m_1}\nabla_1^2\psi + V_1\psi + = \varepsilon_1\psi \ , \tag{4.15-6}$$

and $\quad -\frac{\hbar^2}{2m_2}\nabla_2^2\psi + V_2\psi = \varepsilon_2\psi \ , \tag{4.15-7}$

in which
$$\varepsilon = \varepsilon_1 + \varepsilon_2 \ . \tag{4.15-8}$$

The benefit of being able to write the potential energy in the form (4.15 - 3) is that the two-electron equation (4.15 - 5) splits into two one-electron equations. Moreover, if two "one-electron" solutions $\psi_1(x_1,y_1,z_1)$ and $\psi_2(x_2,y_2,z_2)$ are known, the solution of (4.15 - 5) can be written as a *product* of these two wave functions,

$$\psi(x_1,y_1,z_1,x_2,y_2,z_2) = \psi_1(x_1,y_1,z_1)\,\psi_2(x_2,y_2,z_2) \ . \tag{4.15-9}$$

This can be verified by direct substitution into (4.15 - 5). These properties make any problem satisfying the condition (4.15 - 3) particularly simple. Under these circumstances the solutions of many-particle systems are simply the product of individual one-particle solutions. Though demonstrated in the context of two electrons, these same properties are associated with systems in which there are an arbitrary number of particles--and specifically with many-electron atoms.

Clearly, and unfortunately, the exact potential energy for helium (4.15 - 1) does not have this desirable property, due to the complex form of the electron-electron interaction term. One may now ask whether it is possible to make valid approximations that allow solutions of this kind to be found anyway. For example, if we could write the potential energy of the system as a sum of spherically symmetric terms, each of which depends *only* on the radial coordinate of one particular electron, the problem's complexity would be reduced drastically. Physically, this describes a system in which each electron experiences a central force due to the nucleus, plus another *purely radial* force that in some average sense expresses the net repulsion of all the other electrons in the atom. In the case of helium, only one "other" electron is involved. Since the electrons are in rapid motion, and since the tangential components of the forces they exert on one another are rapidly fluctuating quantities whose time-average magnitude is likely to be zero--or in any event small--this seems to be fairly reasonable, despite the crudeness of the arguments on which it is based. In any event, this assumption allows one to calculate energy eigenvalues and other quantities that can be determined experimentally. Moreover, when these predictions are compared with experimental observations, generally satisfactory agreement is obtained, giving one confidence in its general applicability.

The work entailed in writing suitable one-electron potentials for actual atomic systems is quite difficult and is not altogether relevant to our objectives in this discussion. The calculation is usually done by starting with an assumed potential function of the form suggested above for each electron in the system, based on an educated guess. From this one can calculate wave functions and probability densities. The electron density thus obtained can be viewed as an electrostatic source charge distribution, related to some corrected potential by Poisson's equation. The corrected potential is then used as the basis for a new quantum mechanical solution, which gives a new expression for the probability density. The procedure is then iterated until the quantum mechanically calculated probability density and the electrostatic charge density associated with the potential function are the same. Though numerical methods must be resorted to, convergence is usually rapid, and satisfactory results are obtained without undue difficulty. However, it is necessary to repeat this self-consistent iteration process for each quantum state of the system in order to obtain all possible eigenfunctions and energy eigenvalues. It is important to observe that since the assumed potentials are spherically symmetric, the *angular* equations (4.14 - 7) and (4.14 - 11) for each electron are the same as for the hydrogen atom. The difference shows up *only* in the radial equation (4.14 - 16), in which a "corrected" radial potential appears in place of the simple Coulomb potential $q^2/4\pi\varepsilon_0 r$.

Since the radial and azimuthal parts of the one-electron wave equations are the same as in the hydrogen atom, the angular momentum operators for each electron commute with the Hamiltonian operator just as they do for hydrogen, which means that the quantities L^2 and L_z are conserved, not only for the whole atom, but also for each of its electrons. Also, these observables are quantized for each electron in the same way as they are in hydrogen, according to (4.14 - 30) and (4.14 - 31). The quantum numbers l and m for each electron are thus valid quantum numbers for the atom as a whole. The fact that the energy of a hydrogenic state depends solely on a principal quantum number n is due to the simple form of the Coulomb potential; for the more complex radial potentials associated with many-electron atoms, this is no longer true. There is still a principal quantum number n, associated with the radial wave functions, but now the energy (though independent of m) will depend on l as well as n.

The picture of the atom that finally emerges is one in which each electron can be characterized by a one-electron wave function of generally hydrogenic character except for the fact that states of the same n and different l are no longer degenerate. The total wave function of the atom is given by the product of all the one-electron wave functions of each electron, and its total energy is the sum of all the energies associated with the one-electron wave functions. The one-electron wave functions are still indexed by hydrogenic quantum numbers, and the atom as a whole is characterized by the set of quantum numbers associated with every electron in the system. Thus, the state of the helium atom is characterized by six quantum numbers, n, l, and m for electron 1, and n, l, and m for electron 2. More concisely, it can be given, for the ground state as $1s1s$ (or $1s^2$) and for excited states by notation such as $1s2s$, $1s2p$, $2p^2$, etc. The energy levels of a "typical" many-electron atom are illustrated in Figure 4.21. The pattern illustrated shows the usual ordering of levels, though there are several elements for which this picture is not correct in all respects.

It is useful, nevertheless, in illustrating how the periodic table of elements can be understood on the basis of quantum theory.

If electrons automatically occupied the lowest energy quantum state of the system, an atom with Z electrons would have a ground state in which there were Z 1s electrons. Under these circumstances, all the electrons would have the same spherically symmetric wave function, and would be physically equivalent to one another in all respects. There would thus be Z valence electrons available to participate on an equal footing in chemical reactions and other atomic interactions. We know, however, that chemistry does not work this way. Actually, there are easily observed valence relationships in which periodic structures are discernable. It thus appears that the electrons do *not* all gravitate to the lowest energy quantum state, but instead fill up the lowest available energy states one by one, going to states of successively higher energy as states of lower energy become occupied. Indeed, you will *never* reconcile quantum theory and the periodic table of the elements unless you accept the fact that each hydrogenic quantum state of the atom, indexed by a given set of quantum numbers (n, l, m) will accept two--and only two--electrons. When it is occupied by two electrons, it is filled, and additional electrons can only be accommodated in other "unfilled" states. This is a specific example of a more general phenomenon known as the *Pauli exclusion principle.*

The Pauli exclusion principle is not a consequence of the laws of quantum mechanics as we have presented them so far. It is an additional postulate, that in its most general form requires the wave function of any many-body system to have certain symmetry properties. With regard to electronic systems, the Pauli exclusion principle states that *each distinct quantum state of a system can be occupied by at most a single electron.* Another way of putting it is that no two electrons of a many-electron system can have exactly the same set of quantum numbers. Still another way of looking at it is to observe that an energy level that is g-fold degenerate--that is, one that contains g distinct quantum states--can accommodate at most g electrons.

The apparent discrepancy involving a factor of two between the statements directly above and the remarks about many-electron atoms in the preceding paragraph can be attributed to the phenomenon of *electron spin*, an inherent property of the particle itself. Every electron has not only charge and mass, but also an inherent "spin" angular momentum of magnitude $\hbar\sqrt{3}/2$, whose projection along any given direction (for example, the polar axis) can have the two quantized values $\pm\hbar/2$ illustrated in Figure 4.20(b). It is therefore possible to assign to the electron a *spin quantum number* $s = 1/2$, which defines its spin angular momentum just as l defines the orbital angular momentum, according to (4.14 - 30) and (4.14 - 31). Thus, the total spin angular momentum L_s is obtained as

$$L_s = \hbar\sqrt{s(s+1)} = \tfrac{1}{2}\sqrt{3}\,\hbar \; . \tag{4.15-10}$$

The projection of the angular momentum vector on the z-axis would be such as to have two possible values related to a *spin projection quantum number* $m_s = \pm 1/2$, or,

$$L_{sz} = m_s\hbar = \pm\tfrac{1}{2}\hbar \; . \tag{4.15-11}$$

Although electrons obey the Pauli exclusion principle, certain other particles, for example photons (whose spin quantum number is $s = 1$), do not. In general, particles (like electrons) with half-integral spin ($s = 1/2, 3/2, 5/2, \ldots$) are subject to the Pauli exclusion principle, while those with integral intrinsic spin ($s = 0, 1, 2, \ldots$) are not. As we shall soon see, this introduces important differences into the statistical behavior of ensembles of these two kinds of particles. The two spin states of the

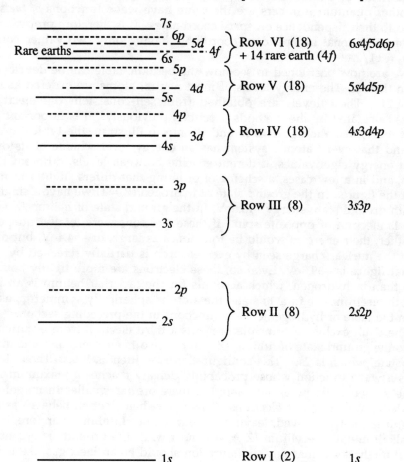

Figure 4.21 Ordering of energy levels in a "typical" many-electron atom, illustrating how the periodic table can be arrived at by populating successive energy levels with electrons, with due regard for spin and the Pauli exclusion principle. This diagram is not to scale with regard to the spacing between levels, and is not intended to represent accurately the energy level scheme for any specific element. There are, in fact, minor departures from this ordering scheme for certain elements.

electron are often designated "spin up" ($m_s = 1/2$) and "spin down" ($m_s = -1/2$). As a consequence of its charge and spin angular momentum, the electron also exhibits an inherent magnetic dipole moment.

If electron spin is taken into account, each electron with spin $s = 1/2$ can have two possible spin projections corresponding to $m_s = \pm 1/2$ and $L_{sz} = \pm \hbar/2$. The total set of quantum numbers describing each quantum state is thus actually (n, l, m, m_s), and since there are two possible values for m_s, there are really *two* quantum states for each state previously defined by given values of ($n. l, m$), one for which $m_s = 1/2$, (spin up), the other for which $m_s = -1/2$ (spin down). This accounts fully for the apparent discrepancy between the Pauli principle as introduced above for many-electron atoms and the later more general statements. In the absence of any external magnetic fields or similar perturbations, spin up and spin down quantum states whose other quantum numbers are the same have wave functions *of the same form* in regard to their dependence on space coördinates. It is therefore proper to think of spin as an additional independent coördinate having only two values corresponding to $m_s = \pm 1/2$.

We are now positioned to see how the periodic table can be developed using quantum theory. The energy levels of most neutral atoms are ordered as shown in Figure 4.21. These levels are obtained from self-consistent one-electron wave functions calculated by the methods described previously. It is important to recognize, however, that the figure is intended only to illustrate the typical ordering of levels, and that every atomic system has an energy level scheme of its own, with different energy eigenvalues, different spacing between levels, different ionization energies, and in a few cases, a scheme of ordering that differs slightly from the one given in the figure. In the ground state of hydrogen (Z = 1) we have a single 1s electron, with ground state energy –13.6eV. In the ground state of helium (Z = 2), there are two 1s electron of opposite spin. If these electrons were totally independent of one another, their energies would be four times as large, or –54.4eV, but due to the fact that the nuclear charge seen by each electron is partially screened by the other, the actual figure is –39.3eV. Even so, these electrons are more tightly bound to the nucleus than in hydrogen, which accounts for the fact that helium is an inert gas. Since both electrons are in a 1s state, the atom is spherically symmetric, as you can see from the table of hydrogenic wave functions in the preceding section.

The Pauli exclusion principle prevents a third electron from occupying the 1s states, so the ground state of lithium (Z = 3) has two 1s electrons and one in the next-highest state, which is 2s. This configuration is written as $1s^2 2s$. The outer 2s electron has a wave function whose probability density reaches a maximum rather far from the nucleus. Its potential energy is therefore far smaller in magnitude than that of the tightly bound 1s electrons. This outer-shell electron behaves as a valence electron; it is easily removed, leaving a positive ion. Lithium, therefore, is a monovalent alkali metal. Beryllium (Z = 4) is next, with the ground state configuration $1s^2 2s^2$. It might seem that this configuration should be an inert gas like helium, but in this case the two outer s electrons are so loosely bound that Be is metallic; helium is thus the only inert gas with two valence electrons. Boron (Z = 5), with the configuration $1s^2 2s^2 2p$ is next, followed by carbon, nitrogen, oxygen, and fluorine each successively having an additional p electron in the outer valence shell. Finally, with neon (Z = 10), we arrive at the configuration $1s^2 2s^2 2p^6$. As we go from lithium toward fluorine, the valence electrons become more tightly bound in each succeeding element, so that the elements become progressively less electronegative and less metallic in character. Indeed, nitrogen, oxygen, and fluorine tend to form ions and chemical compounds by accepting electrons rather than giving them up. When we reach neon, the 2s and 2p shells are filled, and we are back at a configuration that is not only spherically symmetric but so tightly bound that another inert gas is formed. All the succeeding inert gases are similarly charcterized by this same configuration of s and p electrons, the only difference being in the principal quantum number. The spherical symmetry of a closed p-shell can be inferred from the table of hydrogenic wave functions by summing the product $\psi^*\psi$ for all possible p-states, with due regard for normalization. The possibility of a spherically symmetric result follows from the form of the functions, and from $\cos^2\theta + \sin^2\theta = 1$. The details of this calculation are left as an exercise for the reader.

We have now completed Rows I and II of the periodic table. The filling of the 3s and 3p shells follows the same pattern as the 2s and 2p, giving Row III, which contains Na, Mg, Al, Si, P, S, Cl, and A (Z = 11–18), each of which bears a chemical similarity to the element in Row II having the same valence shell configuration. It seems as though the next group of levels to be populated should be the 3d group, giving a row of 10 elements having 1 to 10 outer d electrons. But, as you can see from Figure 4.21, nature isn't that simple, for the 4s state is *lower in energy* than the 3d!. So the 4s shell is filled first, giving K and Ca (Z = 19, 20), with one and two 4s valence electrons, respectively. At this point the 3d shell is populated, giving Sc, Ti, V, Cr, Mn, Fe, Co, Ni, Cu, Zn (Z = 21–30). Since the 4s shell is physically *exterior* to the 3d, however, the 4s electrons play the role of valence electrons and are the main participants in chemical reactions, while the interior unfilled 3d shell exerts a more subtle--though nevertheless perceptible--influence on the properties of these *transition elements*. Indeed, as you can see from the periodic table, there are no elements at all having d, or f, (or anything but s and p) valence electrons. There are some slight irregularities apparent in the filling of the d levels; in two cases (Cr and Cu), there is only one 4s valence electron rather than two, a situation arising presumably because of an unusually close spacing between the 4s and 3d levels in those elements. Now, the 4s and 3d shells being filled, the 4p levels, next higher in energy, are populated, giving the six elements Ga, Ge, As, Se, Br, and (at last) the inert gas Kr (Z = 31–36). We have now completed Row IV of the table, containing 18 elements, all of whose valence electrons belong to the 4s or 4p shells. Row V is an exact repeat of Row IV, containing the 18 elements from Rb to Xe (Z = 37–54), all having 5s or 5p valence electrons. It contains another group of 10 transition elements resulting from the filling of the interior 4d shell.

Row VI is similar, though there is now the added complexity of an interior 4f shell containing 14 states to be filled, as well as the expected 5d shell. This yields in addition to still another group of transition elements (Z = 57 and 72-80) a series of 14 *rare earth elements* (Z = 58–71), in which the interior 4f levels are partially filled. In all the Row VI elements, however, all of the outer valence electrons belong to the 6s or 6p shells. This row finally ends with still another inert gas, Rn, in which all levels up through 5d and 6p are filled. It contains a total of 32 elements from Cs (Z = 55) to Rn (Z = 86). We could go on to the next few naturally occurring elements, and the transuranium materials as well, but why bother? It should be obvious by now that quantum mechanics explains all the important features of the periodic system of elements, and most of the subtle details as well.

Quantum mechanics is surely a powerful tool, even if sometimes abstract and out of line with your intuitive feelings about how things should be. It is not easy to learn at a single pass. You will have to develop your understanding of it as an ongoing effort as you encounter problems in which it is needed. So feel free to revisit this chapter as required.

182

REFERENCES

1. R. G. Winter, *Quantum Physics*, Wadsworth, Belmont CA (1979). One of the best undergraduate-level texts available.

2. E. Merzbacher, *Quantum Mechanics*, John Wiley & Sons, New York (1961). A rigorous and authoritative, though readable, graduate-level text.

3. J. C. Slater, *Quantum Theory of Matter*, McGraw-Hill, New York (1951). A classic survey containing a great deal of valuable explanatory material offering excellent physical insight.

4. R. B. Leighton, *Principles of Modern Physics*. McGraw-Hill, New York (1959).

5. L. Pauling and E. B. Wilson, *Introduction to Quantum Mechanics*, McGraw-Hill, New York (1935). Reprinted by Dover Publications. An elderly text whose luster is undimmed by the passage of time.
6. R. A. Luboff, *Introductory Quantum Mechanics*, Holden-Day, San Francisco (1980). A comprehensive undergraduate text that offers a modern outlook on quantum theory.

7. F. Seitz, *Modern Theory of Solids*, McGraw-Hill, New York (1940). Another old, but eminently readable and useful text. Solid state has changed in the interim, but not the basic applications of quantum theory to the subject.

PROBLEMS

1. Express the frequency of a quantum of radiant energy in terms of Hz per electron volt. What quantum energy corresponds to a frequency of 1000 MHz?

2. Find the maximum spacing of quantized oscillator levels in a typical monatomic one-dimensional crystal lattice in which the long wavelength sound velocity is 3000 m/sec and the interatomic spacing is 2.6 Å. Use the Planck quantization rule.

3. Find the wavelength of maximum intensity for a Planck blackbody radiator of absolute temperature T. Show that this wavelength varies with temperature as $1/T$. What is the wavelength of maximum intensity for solar radiation, assuming that the sun can be considered a blackbody radiator of temperature 6000K?

4. A metal exhibits photoelectric emission for retarding grid potentials greater than –4.5 V. What is the work function of this material? What is the threshhold frequency and wavelength for this material? With what maximum initial kinetic energy are photoelectrons emitted when the substance is illuminated with ultraviolet light of wavelength 2000 Å?

5. Find the longest light wavelengths that can be used to ionize the lowest four energy levels of the hydrogen atom. What is the wavelength of the energy quantum emitted in a downward transition from the first excited state of the atom to the ground state?

6. Is the neglect of relativity in the Bohr theory valid for *all* possible circumstances in the treatment given in Section 4.5? Explain, using simple physical arguments.

7. Find the de Broglie wavelength associated with an electron of energy 1.0 eV. What is the wavelength of a proton of this energy? What is the wavelength of an atom of $_{92}U^{238}$?

8. A monoenergetic beam of electrons emitted by a heated filament is incident on the (111) planes of a crystal of fcc copper ($a = 3.62$ Å). How much voltage must be applied between the crystal

anode and a cathode at filament potential to observe first-order electron diffraction maxima at a Bragg angle of 20°? How many (111) reflections will be observed under these conditions?

9. A neutron of charge zero and mass 1.675×10^{-27} kg falls vertically from a height z onto a simple cubic crystal whose lattice spacing is 3.6 Å. The crystal is oriented so that the (100) planes are parallel to the earth's surface. What is the minimum value of z that will allow the neutron to undergo reflection instead of just falling through the crystal lattice?

10. Hydrogen atoms are prepared in a glass cell in an initial energy state for which $n = 5$. The glass walls of the cell absorb all light of wavelength shorter than 5000 Å. What are the energies of all the photons that escape from the cell as the hydrogen atoms return to the ground state ?

11. Show, for the potential well of finite depth treated in Section 4.11, that to satisfy the normalization condition (4.7 - 1) you must set

$$C_n^2 = \frac{2}{L} \frac{\frac{1}{2}k_n L}{\frac{1}{2}k_n L + \cot\frac{1}{2}k_n L} \quad ,$$

for even eigenfunctions, and for odd eigenfunctions,

$$B_n^2 = \frac{2}{L} \frac{\frac{1}{2}k_n L}{\frac{1}{2}k_n L - \tan\frac{1}{2}k_n L} \quad .$$

12. Find the transmission and reflection coefficients for the potential barrier illustrated in Figure 4.13 (b).

13. In the situation illustrated in Figure 4.13 (a), the barrier height is 2.5eV and the energy of incident electrons is 1.8eV. What is the exponential decay length of the wave function in the classically inaccessible region $x > 0$? What is the probability of finding an electron 5.0Å beyond the barrier in the inaccessible region, relative to the probability of finding it at the barrier?

14. Write the dispersion relation for photons in free space. What relation between photon energy and photon momentum is embodied in this dispersion relation?

15. Light of intensity I J/m^2-sec illuminates a surface of area A. If the light is normally incident and monochromatic, with wavelength λ, how many photons per unit area per unit time are incident on the surface?

16. Light of wavelength 6000Å from a monochromatic source is incident normally on a totally absorbing surface. If the intensity is 60 J/m^2-sec what is the force per unit area of surface due to "radiation pressure"? What would the result be if the surface were a perfect reflector?

17. Find the eigenfunctions and eigenvalues of the differential operator

$$\frac{d^4}{dx^4} + 2\alpha^2 \frac{d^2}{dx^2} \quad ,$$

acting on a function $\psi(x)$, where α is a constant, subject to the boundary conditions $\psi(0) = \psi(L)$.

18. Consider the case of a particle of mass m confined within a cubical enclosure of side L, but acted upon by no other forces. Find the allowed particle wavelengths and show that they can be related to an appropriately defined propagation vector **k**. Show that the allowed energies are given by

$$\varepsilon = \frac{h^2}{8mL^2}\left(n_x^2 + n_y^2 + n_z^2\right)$$

where n_x, n_y, and n_z are positive integers. What is the ground state energy of this system?

19. Compare the energy needed to excite an electron from the ground state to the first excited state of a hydrogen atom with the energy required to promote the same transition for an electron confined within a cubical enclosure whose side is twice the Bohr radius r_1. Does this appear to be a good model for the hydrogen atom?

20. A tiny dust particle of mass 10^{-15} g is trapped in a deep trench 0.8μ wide and 100μ long on the surface of a silicon chip. Find its minimum energy and velocity. How often does it collide with one of the walls of the trench? Use reasonable approximations.

21. Find the expectation values of momentum and kinetic energy for a particle in the n-th energy level of a square-well potential of infinite depth.

22. Derive equations (4.11 - 34) giving the transmission and reflection coefficients of a tunneling barrier of height V_0 and thickness L, for the case $\varepsilon < V_0$, as illustrated in Figure 4.12. *Hint*: Refer to the material preceding these equations, and solve the relevant simultaneous equations using determinants.

23. Derive equations (4.11 - 33) expressing the answers asked for in the preceding problem for the case $\varepsilon > V_0$.

24. A square well has a width of 2.5Å and a finite depth V_0. What is the minimum possible value of V_0 that will allow an electron in the well to have exactly five bound state energy levels? What is the minimum possible electronic ground state energy ε_1 for this five-level configuration? Don't be afraid of solving transcendental equations numerically!

25. Show, in a one-dimensional system, that the classical equations of motion are obeyed by the expectation values of quantum operators associated with the relevant classical dynamical variables.

26. An electron is incident on a potential barrier of the form shown in Figure 4.12. The electron's initial kinetic energy is 0.9 times the barrier height. Show that in order to obtain a transmission coefficient of 0.10, the thickness of the barrier must be

$$L = 7.864 \; \frac{\hbar}{\sqrt{2mV_0}} \; .$$

Find the required barrier thickness if the incident kinetic energy is 5.0eV. Would this barrier be very "transparent" to protons of the same incident kinetic energy?

27. Show, starting with Hermite's equation and using the results of Section 4.12, that

$$H_n^2(z) = 2zH_n(z)H_{n-1}(z) - 2(n-1)H_n(z)H_{n-2}(z) \; .$$

28. By imposing the normalization condition on the harmonic oscillator wave function given by (4.12 - 19), derive the expression (4.12 - 20) for the normalization constant. *Hint*: Begin by using the result derived in the preceding problem to find a relationship between the integral of the square of the weve function for state n and the corresponding integral for state $n - 1$. Also, utilize the orthogonality of the wave functions to show that some of the integrals that appear vanish.

29. Show, for a one-dimensional harmonic oscillator in any eigenstate, that the expectation values $<x>$ and $<p_x>$ are zero. If you're clever you can get these answers without doing any detailed calculations.

30. Find the expectation values $<x^2>$ and $<p_x^2>$ for any eigenstate of a one-dimensional harmonic oscillator. These results can be obtained only by detailed calculation.

31. Show, for a one-dimensional harmonic oscillator in any of its eigenstates, that the expectation values of the kinetic energy and potential energy are the same, and that each is equal to half the total energy of the oscillator.

32. Find the expectation value of the square of the amplitude of a one-dimensional harmonic oscillator in any of its eigenstates. What is the amplitude of the zero-point oscillation in the ground state of an atomic oscillator of mass 40amu and frequency 3.5×10^{-13} rad/sec?

33. A large number of identical one-dimensional harmonic oscillators are all in the same eigenstate initially. Measurements of position x or momentum p_x are made on these systems. Will the mesaured values of x or p_x all be the same, or will there be a "spread" of measured values? Describe in detail the character of the sets of observed values of x and p_x.

34. Write the classical Hamiltonian of a two-dimensional rigid body of mass m and moment of inertia I, rotating in the xy-plane about the origin O. Form the quantum mechanical operator corresponding to this classical expression and write the wave equation for this "rigid rotator". Find the energy eigenvalues and eigenfunctions of the system. Find the allowed values of angular momentum and show that angular momentum is a conserved quantity for the system. What is the form of the angular momentum operator for this system?

35. Consider a mass m constrained to move in the xy-plane, under the influence of a Hooke's law force described by a potential energy $m\omega^2 r^2/2 = m\omega^2(x^2 + y^2)/2$. Write Schrödinger's equation for this two-dimensional harmonic oscillator, and using the method of separation of variables, show that it reduces to two equations having the form of Hermite differential equations in the single variables x and y. Show, finally, that the total energy of the system must have the quantized form

$$\varepsilon = (n_x + n_y + 1)\hbar\omega \ , \quad \text{where } n_x \text{ and } n_y \text{ are positive integers.}$$

36. Find the degeneracy factor of a state of arbitrary energy ε for the system described in the preceding problem.

37. Find the components L_r, L_θ, and L_φ of the angular momentum oprator (4.14 - 23) in spherical coördinates. *Hint*: What form does the gradient operator take in spherical coördinates?

38. Using the results of the preceding problem, derive equation (4.14 - 25), which gives the cartesian components of the angular momentum operator in spherical coördinates. *Hint*: First find expressions for the cartesian unit vectors in terms of the unit vectors along the r-, θ-, and φ- directions in spherical coördinates.

39. Consider an f-state ($l = 3$) of the hydrogen atom. Find the total angular momentum L for such a state, and also the possible projections along the z-axis. What are the possible angles between the **L** vector and the polar axis?

40. What are the angles between the spin angular momentum vector of an electron and the polar z-axis in both of the allowed spin states?

41. Consider a particle (such as a photon) of spin 1. Find the total spin angular momentum, the possible projections of the spin angular momentum along the polar z-axis, and the angles between the spin angular momentum vector and the polar axis in all allowed spin states.

42. Work the preceding problem for a particle of spin 3/2.

43. Find the average force exerted by an electron in the potential well shown in Figure 4.7 on the constraining walls at $x = 0$ and $x = L$.

44. Suppose that the potential well illustrated in Figure 4.7 is occupied by exactly 8 electrons, and make the (somewhat dubious) assumptions that they can be viewed as independent, non-interacting particles. Neglecting any effect due to electron spin, describe the ground-state configuration of the system, and calculate the total energy of the electrons in the well. Also, find the energy of the electron

having the largest possible ground-state energy, and the average energy of an electron in the ground state configuration.

45. Find the answers asked for in the preceding problem for the first excited state of the system, again neglecting electron spin.

46. Calculate the answers to the questions in the two foregoing problems taking electron spin into account.

47. Does the effect of electron spin increase or decrease the pressure exerted by the electrons on the confining boundaries of the system considered in the three preceding problems?

48. A one-dimensional potential well is characterized by a harmonic oscillator potential energy $V = m\omega^2 x^2/2$ for $x > 0$, and a potential energy that is infinite for $x < 0$. The picture is that of a "half-oscillator" bounded at the origin by an infinitely high wall like that of the potential well of Section 4.10. What are the energy eigenvalues and stationary-state wave functions for this system?

49. Find the expectation values $<x>$ and $<p_x>$ for the ground state of the system described in the problem immediately above.

CHAPTER 5

STATISTICAL MECHANICS

5.1 INTRODUCTION

Most of the problems of condensed-matter physics concern systems having a large number of physically *identical* constituents--electrons, atoms, mass particles, harmonic oscillators, or other basic entities. In such problems, it is hopeless to try to trace the motion of each of these individual constituents. Instead, you must settle for knowing *averages* of relevant dynamical quantities over the entire range of possible system configurations. The macroscopic properties of the system can then be understood in terms of these average values. The questions that must be resolved are how to determine the probability that a given system configuration will occur, and what system configuration is of maximum probability. Also, it is important to understand how energy, velocity, and momentum are distributed among the system's particles or other constituents.

The area of physics that addresses these questions is referred to as *statistical mechanics* or *statistical physics*. Since quantum theory asserts that randomness is an inherent feature of microscopic physics, quantum mechanics and statistical physics are intimately related. On the other hand, the macroscopic behavior of systems whose internal dynamics is expressed by probabilistic methods can be related to the thermodynamic properties of the system, and therefore statistical physics is also closely associated with classical thermodynamics. Indeed, it can be thought of in some sense as a connecting link between the microworld of quantum theory and the macroscopic domain of classical mechanics and thermodynamics.

5.2 PHASE SPACE AND SYSTEM CONFIGURATIONS

To approach this subject one must think initially about how to describe the behavior of particles whose motion is completely unrestricted by any constraint or by any preassigned equation of motion. All you can say classically in these circumstances is that if you know a particle's initial position coördinates and momentum components, you can precisely determine its motion at all later times. The position coördinates and momentum components can therefore be thought of as quantities fundamental to a description of system dynamics. If particles are free from any and all constraints, what can you say about these quantities without any more detailed specification of the system and its dynamics? Well, only that any given set of position coördinates is as likely as any other, and that all conceivable sets of momentum (or velocity) components are of equal probability. One says, more precisely, that the *a priori* probability of all possible states of motion--as defined by position coördinates and momentum components--are the same. The words *a priori* in this context mean "in the absence of any dynamical constraints on the system or forces acting on its particles". This is the fundamental postulate of statistical mechanics.

This postulate suggests that very high particle velocities and kinetic energies are inherently as likely as those that are quite low. This seems counterintuitive, but you must remember that it refers to a system free of any constraint whatever. There is no "a priori" requirement that the system have a finite total energy, for example, or that it be a closed system having a finite mass and a finite and constant number of particles. So, under these circumstances, this odd conclusion may seem less strange. When constraints such as these are introduced, they change the probabilities associated with possible configurations of the system, so that they are no longer uniform. For example, when one imposes a requirement that the system have a fixed number of particles and a constant total energy, the effect is to change the probabilities so that low energy configurations are increased relative to those of very high energy. In such a system, it is clear that no single particle can have more energy than the fixed total energy assigned to the system as a whole. The probability of system configurations in which any particle possesses more than this preassigned energy is therefore *zero*. Clearly, probabilities have changed not in respose to the fundamental statistical principle stated above, but in response to constraints that have been introduced. The probabilities will change, in fact, precisely so that these constraints are satisfied.

It is convenient to describe the possible system configurations as points in an orthogonal multi-dimensional coördinate space referred to as *phase space*. In the simplest example, that of a one-dimensional system in which particles move only along the x-direction, the motion of a particle is completely determined when the quantities x and p_x are given as functions of time. The dynamical state of the system at any time is thus described by the coördinates of a point in a *phase plane* whose coördinate axes are x and p_x, and the motion of the particle can be completely specified by a curve in the phase plane whose points are indexed by these coördinates. For example, if the system is composed of independent (i.e., uncoupled) one-dimensional harmonic oscillators of mass m and frequency ω, we can write such an equation of motion (using energy conservation) as

$$\varepsilon = \frac{p_x^2}{2m} + \frac{1}{2} m \omega^2 x^2 \;, \tag{5.2-1}$$

where ε is the constant total energy. The simple harmonic motion is represented in the phase plane as an ellipse, since the above equation, regarded as a relationship between the relevant--or, in the jargon of theoretical physics, "canonical"--variables, has the form associated with an ellipse whose axes coincide with those of the coördinate system. Indeed, if you put the above equation into standard form by dividing both sides by ε, the semi-axes a and b of the ellipse can be expressed by

$$a = \sqrt{\frac{2\varepsilon}{m\omega^2}} \quad \text{and} \quad b = \sqrt{2m\varepsilon} \ . \tag{5.2-2}$$

This situation is illustrated in Figure 5.1. Statistical mechanics postulates that in the absence of constraints all states of motion have equal probability. The *a priori* probability that a point describing the state of the system will be in any area element $\Delta p_x \Delta x$ is therefore *the same for all area elements* in the phase plane. The number of possible system configurations in a given region of the phase plane is likewise directly proportional to the *area* of that region.

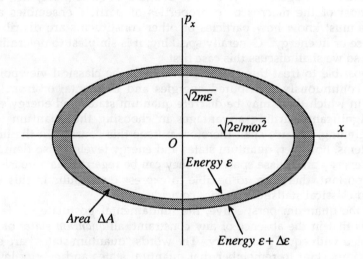

Figure 5.1 Phase space trajectory for a one-dimensional harmonic oscillator of constant energy ε.
A slightly larger trajectory is shown for an oscillator of somewhat larger energy. The area between the two curves is proportional to the number of possible states of the system in this energy interval.

In this example, of course, the equation of motion (5.1 - 1) must be viewed as a constraint restricting the motion to an elliptical path, around which the phase point circulates as time elapses. This constraint, physically, is imposed by forces that act on the particle and cause it to behave as an oscillator rather than a free particle. In the phase plane, it confines the particle to system configurations described by points on the ellipse. Now, all system configurations are not of equal probability. Indeed, such states have probability *zero* unless they lie on the curve, in which case their probability is determined by how fast the phase point travels along the ellipse. If you relax the constraint of constant total energy ε, however, the ellipse can be of arbitrary size, and the particle can be in any area element with equal probability. The probability that it will be in the region between the two elliptical curves shown in Figure 5.1 is now directly proportional to the phase plane area enclosed between them. For systems whose constituents can move in three dimensions, three position coördinates and three momentum components are needed to define the state of motion, and the phase space is a six-dimensional orthogonal space whose points are indexed by coördinates (x, y, z, p_x, p_y, p_z). This restricts our ability to visualize its geometry, but in no way limits its usefulness as a tool for the further development of statistical mechanics. The basic postulate of statistical mechanics can now be understood as stating that every volume element of this six-dimensional space has, in the absence of any constraint, equal probability for any constituent of the system.

5.3 THE DISTRIBUTION FUNCTION AND THE DENSITY OF STATES

In order to calculate the number of persons in the USA under 30 years of age, you need to know the age distribution of the population--that is, what fraction of the entire population is of age 0 to 1 years, 1 to 2, 2 to 3, . . . n to $n + 1$, etc. Likewise, to determine most of the macroscopic properties of particle ensembles and similar systems, one must know how particles or other constituents are distributed, either in phase space or in energy. Generally speaking, it is simplest to determine averages over energy, so we shall discuss this case first.

It is possible to treat this subject either from the classical viewpoint of particles having continuously distributed energies and momenta, or from a quantum perspective, in which there may be discrete quantum states and energy eigenvalues. There are significant learning advantages in choosing the quantum formulation from the beginning, and we shall therefore pursue this course. In the limit of macroscopic systems, however, quantum states and energy levels are so dense and closely spaced in energy and phase space that they can be regarded as a quasi-continuum. It is also important, therefore, to be able to express our results in this limit where quantum and classical statistical physics coincide.

From the quantum perspective, the fundamental postulate of statistical mechanics states that in the absence of any constraint, all *quantum states* of the system can be occupied with equal probability. The words "quantum states" are emphasized because it is important to remember that quantum states and energy levels are not the same when degeneracy is present. Under these circumstances there can be many different independent solutions of the wave equation, each defining a distinct quantum state with a unique probability density, all belonging to the same energy eigenvalue. It is the quantum states, not the energy levels, that are occupied with equal *a priori* probability.

As mentioned previously, when the usual constraints are introduced, this *a priori* probability will be modified in some as yet unspecified fashion. If we now define a quantity $f(\varepsilon)$ as the average number of particles occupying a single quantum state at energy ε, and if we let $g(\varepsilon)d\varepsilon$ be the number of quantum states of the system in an energy range $d\varepsilon$ about energy ε, the number $N(\varepsilon)d\varepsilon$ of particles (or other constituents) in this energy range will be the product of these two factors, or

$$N(\varepsilon)d\varepsilon = f(\varepsilon)g(\varepsilon)d\varepsilon . \qquad (5.3-1)$$

The function $f(\varepsilon)$ as defined above is referred to as the *distribution function*. The distribution function expresses the statistical average of the number of particles in a quantum state of given energy. For the present, the Pauli exclusion principle will not be imposed, so this number can be very small, of the order of unity, or very large. One of our objectives is to calculate this function, using the laws of probability. We shall find that it is essentially a statistical quantity, independent of the kind of particles or other constituents that comprise the system, of interactions between these entities, and of system dynamics in general. The density of states function, on the other hand, is a reflection of how energy levels are spaced, and of how many quantum states are allocated to them. These quantities are determined ultimately from Schrödinger's equation and the boundary conditions, and thus depend *only* on the dynamical properties of the system. The density of states is therefore a dynamical quantity, and is independent of any probabilistic phenomena.

Equation (5.3 - 1) is written in the context of the classical limit, where there is a quasi-continuum of energies, in which, though energy levels are discrete, there are always many quantum states in any experimentally resolvable energy range $d\varepsilon$. A similar equation can be written, however, for the case of discrete and widely separated energy levels. In this case, we consider the n-th energy level, of energy ε_n, to which there belong g_n distinct quantum states; the number g_n is referred to as the degeneracy factor of the level. The average number of particles N_n occupying this level can now be written (recalling the definition of the distribution function) as

$$N_n = g_n f(\varepsilon_n) \; , \tag{5.3-2}$$

It is clear from the two above expressions that the degeneracy factor and the density of states function are essentially similar quantities.

If we know the distribution function and the density of states or the degeneracy factor, we can calculate the average of any energy-dependent parameter ξ, as

$$\langle \xi \rangle = \frac{\int \xi(\varepsilon) N(\varepsilon) d\varepsilon}{\int N(\varepsilon) d\varepsilon} = \frac{1}{N} \int \xi(\varepsilon) N(\varepsilon) d\varepsilon \; , \tag{5.3-3}$$

where N, the total number of particles or other constituents in the system, can be expressed as the integral of $N(\varepsilon)$ over the range of energies accessible to system constituents. This is simply the standard procedure for averaging over a distribution; you take an energy range, figure the number of particles in it, multiply that number by the value of ξ at that energy, sum over energies, and divide by the total number of particles. It differs nevertheless from the prescription for finding an expectation value in quantum theory; in the equation above, ξ is presumably already an expectation value. A similar calculation is appropriate for widely spaced discrete energy levels, but in this case the integral can be represented as a discrete sum over the allowed energies, so that

$$\langle \xi \rangle = \frac{\sum_j \xi(\varepsilon_j) N_j}{\sum_j N_j} = \frac{1}{N} \sum_j \xi(\varepsilon_j) N_j \; , \tag{5.3-4}$$

where N_j is given by (5.3 - 2).

It is also possible to compute averages such as these by integrating or summing over the phase space coördinates. We have mentioned in the preceding section that the possible states of motion--defined by the possible values of the position and momentum components--are uniformly distributed in phase space. According to quantum theory, allowed quantum states are also uniformly distributed in phase space, for essentially the same reasons. This means that the density of states factor is *constant* in phase space. The formula for averaging over phase space coördinates is thus written

$$\langle \xi \rangle = \frac{\iint \xi(p_i, q_i) f(p_i, q_i) d\mathbf{p}\, d\mathbf{q}}{\iint f(p_i, q_i) d\mathbf{p}\, d\mathbf{q}} \quad , \tag{5.3-5}$$

where f is the distribution function expressed in terms of phase space coördinates. and p_i, q_i, $d\mathbf{p}$, and $d\mathbf{q}$ merely abbreviations for (p_x, p_y, p_z), (x, y, z), (dp_x, dp_y, dp_z), and (dx, dy, dz), respectively. The density of states factor, being constant in both numerator and denominator, cancels. Several examples of these averaging procedures will be presented in subsequent sections.

We must now turn our attention to the problem of calculating the distribution function and the density of states function. We shall start with the density of states, since it is simpler, and show how it is obtained for a system of independent free particles. As indicated previously, the density of states can be calculated from the solutions of Schrödinger's equation under appropriate boundary conditions. We shall assume that our "free" particles are confined by a rectangular container whose sides extend from the origin to distances L_x, L_y, and L_z along the respective axes, the container being treated simply as a three-dimensional potential well of infinite depth. Under these circumstances, within the well, the potential energy is zero, which allows us to write Schrödinger's equation for any particle inside as

$$\nabla^2 \psi + k^2 \psi = 0 \quad , \tag{5.3-6}$$

where

$$k^2 = \frac{2m\varepsilon}{\hbar^2} \quad . \tag{5.3-7}$$

The solutions to this equation are, as one can verify by direct substitution,

$$\psi(x,y,z) = A e^{ik_x x} e^{ik_y y} e^{ik_z z} = A e^{i(\mathbf{k}\cdot\mathbf{r})} \quad , \tag{5.3-8}$$

where k_x, k_y, k_z behave as components of a propagation vector $\mathbf{k}$, and satisfy the relation

$$k_x^2 + k_y^2 + k_z^2 = k^2 = \frac{2m\varepsilon}{\hbar^2} \quad . \tag{5.3-9}$$

As in the mathematically similar case of acoustic waves in crystal lattices, we shall require these solutions to obey periodic boundary conditions, in which values of the wave function on opposite parallel faces of the enclosure are equal at all times. This is not strictly a proper boundary condition for a wave function in a rigid rectangular enclosure; we should actually require the wave function to be zero on all boundaries to preserve its continuity. As in the case of sound waves, however, the imposition of periodic boundary conditions suggests that a "topological transformation" has been made, in which all opposite faces are placed in contact with one another. In one dimension, we have seen that this ampounts to bending a line into a ring. In a two-dimensional system, it can be accomplished by bending and joining opposite sides of a square to form first a cylinder, and subsequently bending and stretching the free edges until a toroid is formed. In three dimensions, it's geometrically impossible, though we shall use its consequences anyway. We have seen in Chapter 3 that such transformations have essentially no effect on the number of allowed states or on their disposition in frequency or energy. For this reason, the use of these boundary conditions is standard practice in solid-state theory; we shall use them not only here, but elsewhere, as a matter of course. In this case, we shall set

$$\psi(0,y,z) = \psi(L_x,y,z) \ ,$$
$$\psi(x,0,z) = \psi(x,L_y,z) \ ,$$
and $\quad \psi(x,y,0) = \psi(x,y,L_z) \ .$ \hfill (5.3-10)

If this set of boundary conditions is substituted into (5.3 - 8), it will be seen that they can be satisfied only if k_x, k_y, and k_z have certain sets of discrete values, given by

$$k_x = 2\pi n_x/L_x \ , \qquad (n_x = 0,\pm1,\pm2,...) \ ,$$
$$k_y = 2\pi n_y/L_y \ , \qquad (n_y = 0,\pm1,\pm2,...) \ ,$$
$$k_z = 2\pi n_z/L_z \ , \qquad (n_z = 0,\pm1,\pm2,...) \ .$$ \hfill (5.3-11)

Since **p** and **k** are related by de Broglie's relation, this equation in effect defines a set of quantum states associated with the momentum eigenvalues,

$$p_x = h n_x/L_x \ , \qquad (n_x = 0,\pm1,\pm2,...) \ ,$$
$$p_y = h n_y/L_y \ , \qquad (n_y = 0,\pm1,\pm2,...) \ ,$$
$$p_z = h n_z/L_z \ , \qquad (n_z = 0,\pm1,\pm2,...) \ .$$ \hfill (5.3-12)

It will be observed that, as mentioned previously, these quantum states are uniformly distributed throughout phase space. There is also a set of energy eigenvalues, which we can obtain from (5.3 - 9) with the aid of (5.3 - 11); they can be written as

$$\varepsilon(n_x,n_y,n_z) = \frac{h^2}{2m}\left[\frac{n_x^2}{L_x^2} + \frac{n_y^2}{L_y^2} + \frac{n_z^2}{L_z^2}\right] \ .$$ \hfill (5.3-13)

Using de Broglie's relation, we can write (5.3 - 9) as an energy-momentum relation of the form

$$p^2 = p_x^2 + p_y^2 + p_z^2 = 2m\varepsilon \ .$$ \hfill (5.3-14)

In this three-dimensional problem, phase space has six coördinates, x, y, z, p_x, p_y, p_z. Since the above equations are independent of the coördinates x, y, and z, we can plot our results in a three-dimensional orthogonal momentum space (p_x, p_y, p_z) without loss of generality. In such a space, the above equation defines a spherical surface of radius p or $(2m\varepsilon)^{1/2}$ for a free particle of constant energy ε, as illustrated in Figure 5.2. For a slightly greater energy $\varepsilon + d\varepsilon$, corresponding to a larger momentum $p + dp$, the constant-energy sphere will increase in radius by an amount dp, as shown. From (5.2 - 14), it is clear that the relationship between dp and $d\varepsilon$ is,

$$p\,dp = m\,d\varepsilon \ . \tag{5.3-15}$$

The allowed momentum eigenvalues given by (5.3 - 12) can be plotted in this diagram as a rectangular orthogonal lattice of points corresponding to all possible integral values of the quantum numbers n_x, n_y, and n_z. In such a lattice, the "unit cell" is a rectangular volume as illustrated in the figure. Each side of the cell corresponds to a unit difference between quantum numbers in the respective coördinate directions. The lengths of these sides are thus as labeled in the diagram, according to (5.3 - 12). Note that the side lengths involve Planck's constant--a very small number on the scale of macroscopic units--divided by a macroscopic length. The cells are therefore *very* small for macroscopic systems, far smaller than any experimentally resolvable energy difference. For this reason it is possible to determine how many quantum states there are in any energy range $d\varepsilon$--which is, by definition, the density

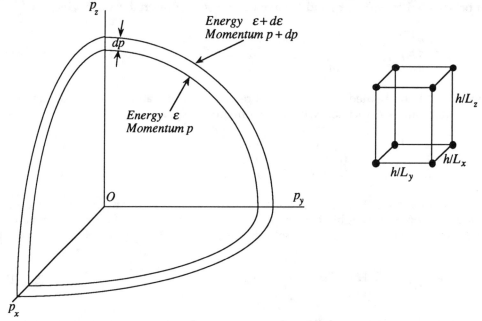

Figure 5.2 Spherical surfaces of constant energy in momentum space. The allowed momentum states are arranged in a rectangular orthogonal lattice of closely spaced points whose "unit cell" is shown at the right. In reality, this cell is far smaller than any experimentally resolvable energy difference $d\varepsilon$. The sides of the unit cells are as labeled in this diagram. It must be noted that the black dots at the corners of this cell do not represent atoms, but simply allowed momentum eigenvalues. The free particles themselves are distributed randomly in real space throughout the volume of the container. Only a single octant of the spherical surfaces is illustrated for simplicity, but in reality the surfaces are complete spheres.

of states--simply by calculating the phase space volume between the two spherical shells shown in the diagram and dividing by the volume allotted to each quantum state as given by the volume of the above unit cell. The volume of momentum space dV_p enclosed by the shells is

$$dV_p = 4\pi p^2\, dp = 4\pi p \cdot m d\varepsilon = 4\pi m \sqrt{2m\varepsilon}\, d\varepsilon \ . \tag{5.3-16}$$

If we divide this by the cell volume $h^3/(L_x L_y L_z) = h^3/V$, where V is the volume of the container, we obtain the quantity previously defined as $g(\varepsilon)d\varepsilon$, whose form in this case is

$$g(\varepsilon)d\varepsilon = \frac{4\sqrt{2}\,\pi V}{h^3} m^{3/2}\sqrt{\varepsilon}\, d\varepsilon \ . \tag{5.3-17}$$

Note that the container *localizes* particles within a region whose dimensions in *coördinate* space are $(\Delta x, \Delta y, \Delta z) = (L_x, L_y, L_z)$. The volume of *momentum* space per quantum state, however, is $\Delta p_x \Delta p_y \Delta p_z = h^3/(L_x L_y L_z)$ This can now be recognized as a relationship stemming from the Heisenberg uncertainty principle, of the form

$$(\Delta p_x\, \Delta x)(\Delta p_y\, \Delta y)(\Delta p_z\, \Delta z) = h^3 \ . \tag{5.3-18}$$

The left side of this expression can be interpreted as the *volume of phase space per quantum state*, and the uncertainty principle requires it to be constant, in this case equal to h^3. The Heisenberg principle is obeyed, of course, irrespective of the dynamical properties of the system, or of the mechanisms that localize its constituents in coördinate or momentum space. Its effect is to guarantee that quantum states are distributed uniformly in phase space, in the sense that the same phase space volume is associated with each quantum state.

If the particles, like electrons, have spin $s = 1/2$, the quantum states will have spin degeneracy, in which two states of opposite spin ($m_s = \pm 1/2$) appear for every quantum state identified in the absence of spin. The density of states is now multiplied by a factor of two, the result being

$$g(\varepsilon)d\varepsilon = \frac{8\sqrt{2}\,\pi V}{h^3} m^{3/2}\sqrt{\varepsilon}\, d\varepsilon \ . \tag{5.3-19}$$

The above derivation assumes a rectilinear container, but the fact that only the total volume appears in the density of states suggests that $g(\varepsilon)$ is independent of the shape of the enclosure, a conjecture verifiable by detailed calculation. If the particles exert forces on one another, the eigenfunctions and energy eigenvalues are altered, which in turn changes the density of states function. If the system constituents are entities (such as harmonic oscillators) having dynamical properties different from those of free particles, the eigenfunctions and energy eigenvalues will also differ, leading to an altered density of states, even when the constituents are totally independent of one another. In all cases, however, the density of states function can be calculated by a procedure similar to the one given above.

In condensed-matter physics, the harmonic oscillator plays an important part in many different situations. It is thus important to know the density of states function for an assembly of harmonic oscillators. For simplicity, we assume initially that there is no coupling between oscillators, thus that they are entirely independent of one another. For a system of one-dimensional oscillators, the energy levels are equally spaced and non-degenerate, so the number of quantum states in an interval $d\varepsilon$ is proportional to $d\varepsilon$ so long as $d\varepsilon$ is much larger than the spacing $\hbar\omega$ between levels. In fact. we may conclude from this that $g(\varepsilon)d\varepsilon$ must have the value $d\varepsilon/\hbar\omega$.

Alternatively, since all states are allotted equal amounts of phase space, you can find the shaded area between the two constant energy contours in Figure 5.1, and divide by the area per quantum state to find the number of states in $d\varepsilon$. In this one-dimensional system, the Heisenberg uncertainty principle has the form--in analogy to (5.3 - 18), $\Delta x \Delta p_x = h$, so one must divide by h rather than h^3. Since the area of an ellipse is πab, where a and b are the semi-axes, from (5.2 - 2), we can write

$$A = \pi ab = \pi\sqrt{\frac{2\varepsilon}{m\omega^2} \cdot 2m\varepsilon} = \frac{2\pi\varepsilon}{\omega} \quad . \tag{5.3-20}$$

Then,

$$dA = \frac{dA}{d\varepsilon}\, d\varepsilon = \frac{2\pi}{\omega}\, d\varepsilon \ , \quad \text{and} \quad \frac{dA}{h} = \frac{2\pi}{h\omega}\, d\varepsilon = \frac{d\varepsilon}{\hbar\omega} \ ,$$

and $\quad g(\varepsilon)\, d\varepsilon = \dfrac{d\varepsilon}{\hbar\omega} \ . \tag{5.3-21}$

For a system of three-dimensional oscillators, the above method works, but requires the calculation of areas and included volumes of six-dimensional figures in phase space. To avoid this mind-boggling exercise, a direct extension of the method so useful for free particles can be used. First, we must note that the potential energy of an isotropic harmonic oscillator in three dimensions can be written as

$$V(x,y,z) = \tfrac{1}{2}m\omega^2(x^2+y^2+z^2) = \tfrac{1}{2}m\omega^2 r^2 \quad . \tag{5.3-22}$$

The Hamiltonian operator for this system thus has the form

$$\mathbf{H} = \frac{\mathbf{p}^2}{2m} + \mathbf{V}(x,y,z) = \left(-\frac{h^2}{2m}\frac{\partial^2}{\partial x^2} + \tfrac{1}{2}m\omega^2 x^2\right) + \left(-\frac{h^2}{2m}\frac{\partial^2}{\partial y^2} + \tfrac{1}{2}m\omega^2 y^2\right)$$
$$+ \left(-\frac{h^2}{2m}\frac{\partial^2}{\partial z^2} + \tfrac{1}{2}m\omega^2 z^2\right) = \mathbf{H}_x(x) + \mathbf{H}_y(y) + \mathbf{H}_z(z) \quad . \tag{5.3-23}$$

This Hamiltonian splits nicely into three parts, each of which has the form of a one-dimensional oscillator Hamiltonian depending on one and only one coördinate. Each of the parts, therefore, has eigenfunctions ψ_x, ψ_y, and ψ_z, of the form (4.12 - 19), that likewise depend on only one coördinate, and that satisfy one-dimensional wave equations of the form

$$\mathbf{H}_x\, \psi_x(x) = \left(n_x + \tfrac{1}{2}\right)\hbar\omega \cdot \psi_x(x) \ ,$$
$$\mathbf{H}_y\, \psi_y(y) = \left(n_y + \tfrac{1}{2}\right)\hbar\omega \cdot \psi_y(y) \ ,$$
and $\quad \mathbf{H}_z\, \psi_z(z) = \left(n_z + \tfrac{1}{2}\right)\hbar\omega \cdot \psi_z(z) \ . \tag{5.3-24}$

Now, consider the product wave function $\psi(x, y, z) = \psi_x(x)\psi_y(y)\psi_z(z)$, and let the full Hamiltonian (5.3 - 23) operate on it. In each part of the resulting expression, two of these three factors are regarded as constants by the operators H_x, H_y, and H_{z}, and with the aid of (5.3 - 24) one may finally obtain,

$$(H_x + H_y + H_z)\, \psi_x(x)\, \psi_y(y)\, \psi_z(z) = \varepsilon(n_x, n_y, n_z)\, \psi_x(x)\, \psi_y(y)\, \psi_z(z) \;, \qquad (5.3\text{-}25)$$

where

$$\varepsilon(n_x, n_y, n_z) = \left(n_x + n_y + n_z + \tfrac{3}{2}\right)\hbar\omega \qquad (n_x, n_y, n_z = 0,1,2,3,\dots) \;. \qquad (5.3\text{-}26)$$

The wave functions are products of functions of x, y, and z, having the form (4.12 - 19), and the energy eigenvalues can be written as the sum of those of three one-dimensional oscillators with the three independent quantum numbers n_x, n_y, and n_z, each of which can be zero or a positive integer. This result--and the algebraic form of the Hamiltonian--suggests, correctly in most cases, that the three-dimensional oscillator can be viewed as three independent one-dimensional oscillators.

There is no way of plotting quantum states of this system in real coördinate space or in momentum space as we did for free particles, since neither position or momentum is a conserved quantity. Nevertheless, the three independent quantum numbers, n_x, n_y, and n_z, provide the basis for a similar geometric argument. If these three quantum numbers are envisioned as the coördinates of an orthogonal three-dimensional system, and if the energy ε is constant, the surface defined in this space by the above equation is a plane, as illustrated in Figure 5.3. For a slightly greater energy, the surface is a parallel plane as shown. If we assume that the energy levels

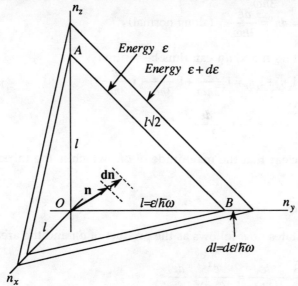

Figure 5.3 Planar surfaces of constant energy in an orthogonal space whose coördinates are the three quantum numbers of the isotropic three-dimensional harmonic oscillator. The density of states follows from calculating the volume between these planes and dividing by the unit cell volume, which in this case is unity.

are so closely spaced as to form a quasi-continuum, an assumption necessary for the density of states concept to be meaningful, the quantity 3/2 in (5.3 - 26) can be neglected, and the equation of the constant-energy surface written as

$$n_x + n_y + n_z = \frac{\varepsilon}{\hbar\omega} \; , \tag{5.3-27}$$

where ε is constant. The intercepts of this plane on all three axes axes are at a distance $l = \varepsilon/\hbar\omega$ from the origin. The equation of the second plane is

$$(n_x + dn_x) + (n_y + dn_y) + (n_z + dn_z) = \frac{\varepsilon + d\varepsilon}{\hbar\omega} \; , \tag{5.3-28}$$

and its intercepts are thus as indicated in the diagram. The quantum states plotted in the this system form a simple cubic lattice of points, spaced at distances $\Delta n = 1$ along all three axes. They therefore form a lattice of cells having *unit* volume, so that the density of states is given directly by the volume dV_n included between the two surfaces in the figure. Since the quantum numbers are all positive or zero, only the first octant, as illustrated, is relevant. The area of the planar surface at energy ε is that of an equilateral triangle whose side, from the figure, is $l\sqrt{2}$. The area of an equilateral triangle of side s is $s^2\sqrt{3}/4$, and for side $l\sqrt{2}$, therefore, $l^2\sqrt{3}/2$. The volume dV_n is found as the product of this area and the thickness of the element, which must be measured along the *normal* to the planes, not along the axes. Along the normal, the numbers n_x, n_y, and n_z are all equal, their common value being, from (5.3-27),

$$n_x = n_y = n_z = \frac{\varepsilon}{3\hbar\omega} \; ;$$

also, $\quad dn_x = dn_y = dn_z = \dfrac{d\varepsilon}{3\hbar\omega} \quad$ (along normal) . $\tag{5.3-29}$

The normal vectors $\mathbf{n}$ and $d\mathbf{n}$ can thus be written

$$\mathbf{n} = \mathbf{i}_x n_x + \mathbf{i}_y n_y + \mathbf{i}_z n_z = \mathbf{i}_x \frac{\varepsilon}{3\hbar\omega} + \mathbf{i}_y \frac{\varepsilon}{3\hbar\omega} + \mathbf{i}_z \frac{\varepsilon}{3\hbar\omega} \; ,$$

and $\quad d\mathbf{n} = \mathbf{i}_x \dfrac{d\varepsilon}{3\hbar\omega} + \mathbf{i}_y \dfrac{d\varepsilon}{3\hbar\omega} + \mathbf{i}_z \dfrac{d\varepsilon}{3\hbar\omega} \quad . \tag{5.3-30}$

From this, it is clear that the magnitude of $d\mathbf{n}$, which is the thickness of the volume element, is

$$dn = \frac{d\varepsilon}{\sqrt{3}\,\hbar\omega} \quad . \tag{5.3-31}$$

The density of states now follows as the product of dn and the area calculated above;

$$dV_n = \frac{l^2\sqrt{3}}{2} \cdot \frac{d\varepsilon}{\sqrt{3}\,\hbar\omega} = \frac{\varepsilon^2}{2(\hbar\omega)^2} \cdot \frac{d\varepsilon}{\hbar\omega} \; ,$$

or, $\quad g(\varepsilon)d\varepsilon = \dfrac{\varepsilon^2 d\varepsilon}{2(\hbar\omega)^3} \quad . \tag{5.3-32}$

This expression is useful in studying the thermal properties of crystals, particularly their specific heats, and also in certain other contexts. Similar methods can be used to find density of states functions for more complex systems. The reader should review Section 3.8 (Chapter 3) for still another example of this type of problem.

5.4 THE MAXWELL-BOLTZMANN DISTRIBUTION FUNCTION

The problem yet unsolved is that of determining the distribution function $f(\varepsilon)$. As noted previously, if there are no constraints like those imposed by a closed system with a constant number of particles and constant total energy, the probability associated with all quantum states is the same, and the average number of particles per quantum state--and thus the distribution function--is constant and independent of energy. This case is really too simple to be of much practical value, and it is more realistic to consider a thermally isolated system with a fixed number of particles or other constituents, and a fixed total energy. In this case, it is found that the distribution function is no longer constant, but decreases exponentially with energy.

We shall proceed initially along classical lines, envisioning a system of N identical particles that can (like billiard balls) be distinguished from one another by an assigned number or other identifier. However, the framework of quantum states and energy levels will be used from the beginning, though we shall refrain from imposing the Pauli exclusion principle until later. We shall thus assume an isolated system of N identical (but identifiable) particles, with constant total energy U. These particles populate n energy levels with energies $\varepsilon_1, \varepsilon_2, \varepsilon_3, \ldots \varepsilon_n$. There will be a statistical distribution of particles among energies so that the number of particles in each level is given by $N_1, N_2, N_3, \ldots N_n$. The laws of probability indicate that some of these possible distributions of particles among energies can be arrived at by many different and independent chains of events, while some can be formed statistically by only a few independent paths, and are thus far less probable.

The situation can easily be understood by considering a simultaneous toss of 5 identical coins. Intuitively, it is obvious that a distribution of 3 heads and 2 tails occurs much oftener than 5 heads. But why? Well, the distribution 5 heads requires that, independently, *each coin* turn up heads. The configuration 3 heads, 2 tails, however can happen in several different ways. There is, for example, no requirement that coin No. 1 turn up heads. If it does not, coin No. 2 need not turn up heads, either, necessarily. All that is needed is for *any three* of the five to fall heads up, and there are *ten* independent ways for this to occur: 123, 124, 125, 134, 135, 145, 234, 235, 245, and 345, to be exact. So there are ten ways to obtain the outcome 3 heads, 2 tails, while 5 heads can occur in only one way. The probability of the first distribution is therefore ten times greater than that of the second. The distribution of particles among energy levels is governed by similar considerations, though the number of "coins" and "possible end results" is vastly greater. Finally, one must ask what distribution of particles among levels has *maximum* probability, and also whether one may assume that this distribution satisfactorily represents the thermal equilibrium state of the system.

The calculation of the number of ways of distributing identifiable particles among energy levels is equivalent to calculating the number of ways of distributing numbered objects among a set of numbered boxes. Adopting this simple model, we shall ask how many independent ways there are of distributing N identifiable objects among n boxes so that there are finally N_1 objects in the first box, N_2 in the second, $\ldots N_i$ in the i-th, $\ldots N_n$ in the n-th. The probability that this final distribution will ultimately occur is, as in the previous example concerning the toss of five coins, proportional to this number.

First let us assume that there are only two boxes, as shown in Figure 5.4. Then, in general, there can be N_1 objects in box 1 and N_2 in box 2, where

$$N_1 + N_2 = N \ . \tag{5.4-1}$$

Let us now denote by $Q(N_1, N_2)$ the number of independent ways of arriving at a configuration in which there are N_1 objects in box 1 and N_2 in box 2. If N_1 is zero, there is only one such way--to have all the objects in box 2. Thus, $Q(0, N_2) = 1$, as illustrated in Figure 5.4(a).

For $N_2 = 1$, there are N ways of choosing which particle to put into box 1, as shown at (b) in the figure, so $Q(1, N_2) = N$. For $N_2 = 2$, there are N ways of choosing the first particle and $N - 1$ ways of selecting the second, which leads to $N(N - 1)$ ways of arriving at this configuration. But some of these choices lead to the same final state, in which the same two particles turn up in box 1. The duplication can be eliminated, as illustrated at (c) in the figure, by dividing by the number of ways of permuting the two particles in box 1 among themselves; this number is 2--or, more

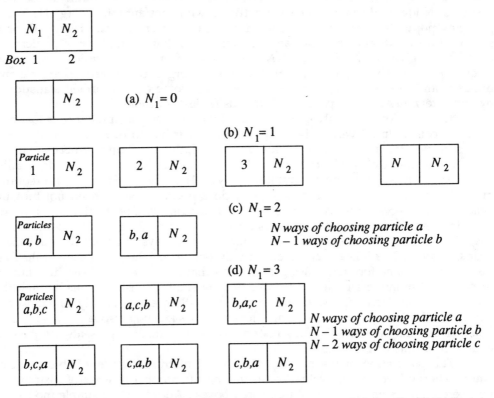

Figure 5.4 Configurations in which there are (a) zero, (b) one, (c) two, and (d) three identifiable objects in the first of two containers which hold a total of N such objects. As illustrated, configurations which differ only in that the same particles are interchanged within a given container are not distinguishable physically, and therefore do not count as different configurations.

precisely, 2!. The answer is therefore $Q(2, N_2) = N(N - 1)/2!$. When $N_2 = 3$, the first particle in box 1 can be selected in N ways, the second in $N - 1$ ways, and the third in

$N - 2$ ways. But the three particles in box 1 can be permuted among themselves in $3! = 6$ ways, as shown at (d) in the figure. As a result, $Q(3, N_2) = N(N - 1)(N - 2)/3!$. Clearly, when there are N_1 particles in the first box. we shall find

$$Q(N_1, N_2) = \frac{N(N - 1)(N - 2) \cdots (N - N_1 + 1)}{N_1!} = \frac{N!}{(N - N_1)!N_1!} = \frac{N!}{N_1!N_2!} , \qquad (5.4\text{-}2)$$

the final form of this result being obtained with the aid of (5.4 - 1).

Now suppose that the second box is divided by an internal partition into two compartments, as illustrated in Figure 5.5, and let the quantity N_2 be partitioned into two parts v_1 and v_2 representing the number of particles in each compartment. According to (5.4 - 2), the number of ways of realizing the distribution (v_1, v_2) in these internal compartments is

$$Q(v_1, v_2) = \frac{N_2!}{v_1!v_2!} . \qquad (5.4\text{-}3)$$

But now, we can view the system as having *three* distinct containers, and designate the number of ways of arriving at a distribution in which there are N_1 particles in box 1, v_1 in the first compartment of box 2, and v_2 in the second as $Q(N_1, v_1, v_2)$.

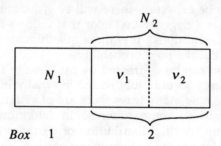

Figure 5.5 A system in which the second box is divided into two compartments by an internal partition.

The number of ways of arriving at the original distribution (N_1, N_2) between the original boxes is still given by (5.4 - 2). For *each* of these, there are $Q(v_1, v_2)$ ways of arranging N_2 particles among the internal subdivisions of box 2, as given by (5.4 - 3). The total number of ways of realizing the distribution (N_1, v_1, v_2) among three distinct containers is clearly the product of these two expressions, so that

$$Q(N_1, v_1, v_2) = \frac{N!}{N_1!N_2!} \cdot \frac{N_2!}{v_1!v_2!} = \frac{N!}{N_1!v_1!v_2!} . \qquad (5.4\text{-}4)$$

We may now simply relabel the three compartments, writing v_1 as N_2 and v_2 as N_3, and writing, for three separate containers, the expression

$$Q(N_1, N_2, N_3) = \frac{N!}{N_1!N_2!N_3!} . \qquad (5.4\text{-}5)$$

It is easy to see, moreover, that this process of subdivision can be iterated as often as desired, and that it will lead ultimately to a result of the form

$$Q(N_1, N_2, N_3 \cdots N_n) = \frac{N!}{N_1! N_2! N_3! \cdots N_n!} = \frac{N!}{\prod_{i=1}^{n} N_i!} \; , \tag{5.4-6}$$

as the number of ways of realizing a distribution $(N_1, N_2, N_3, \ldots N_n)$ in a system of N objects distributed among n boxes. The Π-notation above is used for products in the same way as the Σ-notation for sums. The actual probability of this distribution is obtained by dividing by the number of ways of assigning N objects to n boxes without regard for what final arrangement is obtained, which is equal to n^N. In our work, there is no urgent need for doing this, so we shall simply work with the quantity $Q(N_1, N_2, N_3, \ldots N_n)$ as written above. There is, however, a more important modification to (5.4 - 6) that must be made before it can be applied to our problems.

We wish ultimately to associate the "objects" in the boxes with the particles or other constituents of our physical system, and the boxes themselves with the energy levels of the system. If there were no such thing as quantum degeneracy, there would be no problem, since then there would be one quantum state associated with each box. In the presence of degeneracy--and in three-dimensional systems, you will recall, degeneracy is to be expected--there will be g_i quantum states associated with the i-th level, where g_i is a degeneracy factor that follows from Schrödinger's equation and the boundary conditions. It is these quantum states, not the energy levels, that are occupied with equal *a prori* probability.

This complication can be addressed by the already familiar approach of supposing that the i-th energy level is subdivided internally into g_i compartments. It is now necessary to know how many ways there are of assigning the N_i particles in the energy level to these various compartments. In determining this number, there is no requirement that any specific distribution of particles among compartments be realized, nor any limit (as yet) as to how many particles can be placed in any given compartment. The first particle can be assigned with equal probability to any of the g_i compartments, as can the second, the third, etc. The total number of possibilities is thus g_i multiplied by itself N_i times, or $g_i^{N_i}$. There is a factor of this form for every energy level, so a product of all these factors over all levels must be included in the final expression for $Q(N_1, N_2, N_3, \ldots N_n)$, which now becomes

$$Q(N_1, N_2, N_3 \cdots N_n) = \frac{N!}{\prod_{i=1}^{n} N_i!} \prod_{i=1}^{n} g_i^{N_i} \; , \tag{5.4-7}$$

We shall assume that the thermal equilibrium distribution corresponds to that which is most probable, in other words to the one which--among all possible configurations--can be achieved in the maximum number of statistically independent ways. The problem is now a purely mathematical exercise of maximizing the above expression for Q with respect to the parameters $N_1, N_2, N_3, \ldots N_n$, that is, finding what set of values for these parameters will make Q as large as possible, subject to the *constraints* of a constant number of particles and constant total energy. These constraints can be stated algebraically as

$$\sum_{i=1}^{n} N_i = N = \text{const.} \tag{5.4-8}$$

and
$$\sum_{i=1}^{n} \varepsilon_i N_i = U = \text{const.} \tag{5.4-9}$$

If there were no constraints, the problem could be solved by setting $\partial Q / \partial N_i = 0$ ($i = 1, 2, 3, \ldots n$) and solving the resulting equations for the set of values $\{N_i\}$. The fact that the parameters must be maximized only within the subset of values for which the equations of constraint are obeyed introduces an added complexity which is most easily resolved by the method of *Lagrangean multipliers*. Consider a function f of several variables $(x_1, x_2, \ldots x_n)$, which is to be maximized subject to a constraint requiring that a given function $\varphi(x_1, x_2, \ldots x_n)$ remain constant. For f to be a maximum, df must be zero, and if φ is held constant, $d\varphi$ must also vanish. Under these circumstances it is clear that

$$df + \alpha \, d\varphi = 0 \ , \tag{5.4-10}$$

where α is an arbitrary, and as yet undetermined, multiplier. This can also be written as

$$\left(\frac{\partial f}{\partial x_1} + \alpha \frac{\partial \varphi}{\partial x_1}\right) dx_1 + \left(\frac{\partial f}{\partial x_2} + \alpha \frac{\partial \varphi}{\partial x_2}\right) dx_2 + \cdots + \left(\frac{\partial f}{\partial x_n} + \alpha \frac{\partial \varphi}{\partial x_n}\right) dx_n = 0 \ . \tag{5.4-11}$$

This equation will clearly be satisfied if all the terms in parentheses above are zero, so that

$$\frac{\partial f}{\partial x_i} + \alpha \frac{\partial \varphi}{\partial x_i} = 0 \ , \qquad (i = 1, 2, 3, \ldots n) \ . \tag{5.4-12}$$

In this problem, there are n unknown values of the variables x_i, as well as the undetermined multiplier α, for a total of $n + 1$ unknowns. Equation (5.4 - 12) defines n relationships between these quantities, and the equation of constraint

$$\varphi(x_1, x_2, \ldots x_n) = \text{const.} \tag{5.4-13}$$

provides another, giving $n + 1$ equations which can be solved for the $n + 1$ required answers. The quantity α is referred to as a Lagrangean multiplier.

Consider as an example the case where $f(x, y, z) = x^2 + y^2 + z^2$ is to be a maximum subject to the constraint that $\varphi(x, y, z) = x^4 + y^4 + z^4 = 256$. Now, the set of equations (5.4 - 12) with $x_i = x, y$, and z yield

$$\begin{array}{lcl} 2x + 4\alpha x^3 = 0 & & 4\alpha x^2 = -2 \\ 2y + 4\alpha y^3 = 0 & \text{or,} & 4\alpha y^2 = -2 \\ 2z + 4\alpha z^3 = 0 & & 4\alpha z^2 = -2 \end{array}$$

$$\text{while} \qquad x^4 + y^4 + z^4 = 256 \ .$$

The first three of the four equations above require that

$$x^2 = y^2 = z^2 = -2/\alpha \ .$$

Substituting this into the last equation gives $12/\alpha^2 = 256$, an equation that can lead to either a positive or negative value for α. If the positive value is chosen, the values of x, y, and z as given by the equation immediately above will be imaginary, so you must take the negative value. One then obtains

$$\alpha = -\frac{\sqrt{3}}{8} \ , \quad \text{and} \quad x^2 = y^2 = z^2 = \frac{16}{\sqrt{3}} \ .$$

It is easily seen that the above answers satisfy the conditions of the problem as initially stated. It is also apparent that they are correct, since f can be interpreted as the square of the distance from the origin in an (x, y, z) coördinate system, and the equation of constraint restricts the points (x, y, z) to lie on a surface which when plotted looks like a cube with rounded edges and somewhat convex sides. The points furthest from the origin are, in view of the cubic symmetry of this surface, those on the "cube" diagonal, which is exactly what is found above. Though this discussion has been presented in the context of maximizing a certain function, it is clearly applicable also to problems in which minimization is sought.

In the specific problem of finding the most probable distribution of particles among the allowed energies of a system we must satisfy not one but two equations of constraint, (5.4 - 8) and (5.4 - 9). This is easily accomplished by introducing two multipliers instead of one. Thus, if there are two equations of constraint, in which two functions, $\varphi(x_1, x_2, \ldots x_n)$ and $\psi(x_1, x_2, \ldots x_n)$, are held constant, under the stated conditions df, $d\varphi$ and $d\psi$ must all be zero, and one can write

$$df + \alpha\, d\varphi + \beta d\psi = 0 \ , \tag{5.4-14}$$

If this is expanded in the same way as (5.4 - 12), n equations of the form

$$\frac{\partial f}{\partial x_i} + \alpha \frac{\partial \varphi}{\partial x_i} + \beta \frac{\partial \psi}{\partial x_i} = 0 \ , \quad (i = 1, 2, 3, \ldots n) \ , \tag{5.4-15}$$

can be written, which with the two equations of constraint,

$$\varphi(x_1, x_2, \ldots x_n) = N = \sum_{i=1}^{n} N_i = \text{const.} \tag{5.4-16}$$

and

$$\psi(x_1, x_2, \ldots x_n) = U = \sum_{i=1}^{n} \varepsilon_i N_i = \text{const.} \tag{5.4-17}$$

provide $n + 2$ relations solvable for the $n + 2$ unknowns $(x_1, x_2, \ldots x_n)$, α and β.

Returning now to the problem at hand, we must find the values of the independent variables $(N_1, N_2, N_3, \ldots N_n)$ that maximize Q in (5.4 - 7), subject to the two constraints (5.4 - 8) and (5.4 - 9). The problem is made much simpler if we settle for maximizing the logarithm of Q rather than Q itself. Then, since the logarithm of a product is the sum of the logarithm of the factors, the products will be converted to sums, which are much easier to handle mathematically. The procedure is valid because a set of independent variables that maximizes any quantity also maximizes its logarithm, or any other function of it monotonic with respect to all variables.

If we take the natural logarithm of both sides of (5.4 - 7), we obtain

$$\ln Q(N_1, N_2, \ldots N_n) = \ln N! + \sum_{i=1}^{n} N_i \ln g_i - \sum_{i=1}^{n} \ln N_i! \ . \tag{5.4-18}$$

It will be necessary to find derivatives of the quantities $N_i!$ in the above expression to carry out the maximization procedure outlined above. In order to do this, it is convenient to use the Stirling series expansion for the factorial function, which expresses the logarithm of the factorial of a number z as

$$\ln(z!) = \ln \sqrt{2\pi} + \left(z + \tfrac{1}{2}\right)\ln z - z + \frac{1}{12z} - \frac{1}{360z^3} + \frac{1}{1260z^5} - \cdots \ . \tag{5.4-19}$$

This can be differentiated term by term to get

$$\frac{d}{dz}\ln z! = \ln z + \frac{1}{2z} - \frac{1}{12z^2} + \frac{1}{120z^4} - \frac{1}{252z^6} + \cdots \ . \tag{5.4-20}$$

The series expansion (5.4 - 19) is not easy to obtain, but there is nothing particularly illuminating about the difficult but fairly standard mathematical work involved in getting it. We shall therefore not attempt to derive it here.

It is assumed in these calculations that there is an extremely large number of particles in the system, so many that the number N_i in any given energy level, or in any resolvable energy interval is also very large. In (5.4 - 20), all terms in the series except the first approach zero under these circumstances, which suggests that they may be neglected. We shall therefore retain only the first term in (5.4 - 20). We must now find the derivatives called for in (5.4 - 15). In doing this, it is important to note that the quantities N_i are independent variables, and that if you differentiate a function of N_i with respect to the variable N_j, you will get *zero* unless i and j are the same. Therefore, in (5.4 - 18), for example, in differentiating with respect to N_j, there is no contribution to the result from any summation term other than those for which $i = j$. Also, it is important to recall that the degeneracy factors g_i are constant. Remembering these facts, and using only the first term in the series in (5.4 - 20), one finds,

$$\frac{\partial \ln Q}{\partial N_j} = \sum_i \frac{\partial}{\partial N_j}(N_i \ln g_i) - \sum_i \frac{\partial}{\partial N_j}(\ln N_i!) = \ln g_j - \ln N_j \ . \tag{5.4-21}$$

Also, from (5.4 - 16) and (5.4 - 17), it follows that

$$\frac{\partial \varphi}{\partial N_j} = \frac{\partial}{\partial N_j} \sum_{i=1}^{n} N_i = 1 \text{ and } \frac{\partial \psi}{\partial N_j} = \frac{\partial}{\partial N_j} \sum_{i=1}^{n} \varepsilon_i N_i = \varepsilon_j \ . \tag{5.4-22}$$

Substituting all these results into (5.4 - 15), we get

$$\ln g_j - \ln N_j + \alpha + \beta \varepsilon_j = 0 \ . \tag{5.4-23}$$

The quantity N_j in this expression is the most probable number of particles to be found in the j-th energy level, which we identify with the average number there in the thermal equilibrium state. The number g_j is the number of quantum states associated with the j-th energy level. It follows that N_j/g_j is the average number of particles per quantum state at that energy, which is by definition the distribution function $f(\varepsilon_j)$. If we remove the first two terms above to the right side of the equation and exponentialize both sides, we can write the distribution function explicitly as

$$\frac{N_j}{g_j} = f(\varepsilon_j) = e^\alpha e^{\beta \varepsilon_j} \ . \tag{5.4-24}$$

In this expression, the multipliers α and β are still undetermined. They can be evaluated from the equations of constraint (5.4 - 16) and (5.4 - 17), as we shall soon see. The distribution function is an exponential function of energy, and since β is negative, it decreases exponentially with energy. We shall show in the next section that

$$\beta = -\frac{1}{kT} \ , \tag{5.4-25}$$

where T is the absolute temperature and k is Boltzmann's constant, equal to the ideal gas constant per particle. The distribution function (5.4 - 24), calculated under the assumption of identifiable particles and without reference to the Pauli exclusion principle, is referred to as the *Maxwell-Boltzmann* distribution function.

From (5.4 - 24) and (5.4 - 25), it is evident that N_j can be written as

$$N_j = g_j e^\alpha e^{-\varepsilon_j/kT} \ . \tag{5.4-26}$$

From (5.4 - 16) and the above equation, however, we can write

$$N = \sum_j N_j = e^\alpha \sum_j g_j e^{-\varepsilon_j/kT} \ , \tag{5.4-27}$$

which can be solved for the quantity $\exp\alpha$ to obtain

$$e^\alpha = \frac{N}{\sum_j g_j e^{-\varepsilon_j/kT}} \tag{5.4-28}$$

and

$$N_j = g_j e^\alpha e^{-\varepsilon_j/kT} = \frac{N g_j e^{-\varepsilon_j/kT}}{\sum_j g_j e^{-\varepsilon_j/kT}} \ . \tag{5.4-29}$$

For systems having a quasi-continuum of energy levels, the degeneracy factor g_j will be be replaced by the density of states function $g(\varepsilon)d\varepsilon$, the population factors N_j are replaced by the function $N(\varepsilon)d\varepsilon$ and the summations by integrations over the range of allowed energies. This allows the four expressions above to be written as

$$N(\varepsilon)\,d\varepsilon = f(\varepsilon)g(\varepsilon)d\varepsilon = e^{\alpha}e^{-\varepsilon/kT}g(\varepsilon)d\varepsilon\ ,\tag{5.4-30}$$

$$N = \int N(\varepsilon)\,d\varepsilon = e^{\alpha}\int g(\varepsilon)e^{-\varepsilon/kT}d\varepsilon\ ,\tag{5.4-31}$$

$$e^{\alpha} = \frac{N}{\displaystyle\int g(\varepsilon)e^{-\varepsilon/kT}d\varepsilon}\ ,\tag{5.4-32}$$

and

$$N(\varepsilon)\,d\varepsilon = \frac{N\,e^{-\varepsilon/kT}g(\varepsilon)d\varepsilon}{\displaystyle\int g(\varepsilon)e^{-\varepsilon/kT}d\varepsilon}\ .\tag{5.4-33}$$

The quantity $Q(N_1, N_2, N_3, \ldots N_n)$ is closely related to the thermodynamic entropy of the system. You will recall that entropy is a measure of the randomness or disorder in a thermodynamic system. The parameter Q has similar properties. When the quantities $(N_1, N_2, N_3, \ldots N_n)$ describe a highly ordered state, for example, one in which all the particles are in a single energy level, there are relatively few ways of realizing such a distribution, and Q is therefore small. The distributions of high probability, conversely, are random configurations that can be realized in many independent ways, and for which Q is relatively large. The equilibrium state--a state toward which a closed system tends to evolve over time--is a distribution of maximum probability, for which Q has the largest possible value. This is also a property associated with the entropy. Indeed, it can be shown (though we shall not bother to do so here) that the relationship between these two quantities can be written as

$$S = k\ln\frac{Q}{n^{N}}\ ,\tag{5.4-34}$$

where S is the thermodynamic entropy.

5.5 MAXWELL-BOLTZMANN STATISTICS OF AN IDEAL GAS

We shall now apply the results derived in the preceding section to a monatomic ideal gas. We envision such a gas as a system of free particles--particles that may undergo elastic collisions with one another, but between which there are no long-range forces. In such a system, the potential energy of interaction is zero, and the entire energy of the system resides in the kinetic energy of the particles. The quantum states and energy levels of this system have been described in Section 5.3, and the density of states function has already been exhibited as equation (5.3 - 17) for particles with no spin degeneracy, which is what we shall assume for the present.

Substituting this density of states function into (5.4 - 32), we can express the parameter expα as

$$e^{\alpha} = \frac{N}{\dfrac{4\sqrt{2}\pi V m^{3/2}}{h^3} \displaystyle\int_0^\infty \sqrt{\varepsilon}\, e^{-\varepsilon/kT}\, d\varepsilon} \quad . \tag{5.5-1}$$

The lowest energy a particle in this system can have is zero, when it is at rest. The range of allowed energies, which defines the integration limits, is thus as shown above. The above integral may now be transformed by the substitution

$$x = \varepsilon/kT \quad , \tag{5.5-2}$$

to the form

$$e^{\alpha} = \frac{N}{4\sqrt{2}\pi V \left(\dfrac{mkT}{h^2}\right)^{3/2} \displaystyle\int_0^\infty \sqrt{x}\, e^{-x}\, dx} \quad . \tag{5.5-3}$$

The integral in this equation can be expressed as a Γ-function, which is a generalization of the factorial function to numbers that need not be integers. The Stirling series (5.4 - 19) and (5.4 - 20) are actually expansions of this function. The Γ-function and its relationship to the factorial function, however, is most simply defined by

$$\Gamma(n) = (n-1)! = \int_0^\infty x^{n-1} e^{-x}\, dx \quad . \tag{5.5-4}$$

From this, it is apparent that the above integral is $\Gamma(3/2)$, which can be shown to have the value $\sqrt{\pi}/2$. Subsituting this value into (5.5 - 3), we can write

$$e^{\alpha} = \frac{N}{V} \left(\frac{h^2}{2\pi mkT}\right)^{3/2} . \tag{5.5-5}$$

The Maxwell-Boltzmann distribution function for this system can now be written

$$f(\varepsilon) = e^{\alpha} = \frac{N}{V} \left(\frac{h^2}{2\pi mkT}\right)^{3/2} e^{-\varepsilon/kT} \quad . \tag{5.5-6}$$

It is important to note that the value of expα is temperature-dependent. Also, one must observe that these expressions are applicable only to free-particle systems whose density of states is given by (5.3 - 17), and do not apply to systems whose density of states functions differs from this form. A plot of the Boltzmann distribution (5.5 - 6) for several temperatures is shown in Figure 5.6. The distribution of particle densities in energy can be written as

$$N(\varepsilon)\, d\varepsilon = f(\varepsilon) g(\varepsilon)\, d\varepsilon = \frac{2\pi N}{(\pi kT)^{3/2}} \sqrt{\varepsilon}\, e^{-\varepsilon/kT}\, d\varepsilon \quad . \tag{5.5-7}$$

The total energy U, which represents the thermodynamic internal energy of the system, and the specific heat, can also be calculated quite simply. The internal energy is clearly expressable as

$$U = \int_0^\infty \varepsilon N(\varepsilon)\,d\varepsilon = \frac{2NkT}{\sqrt{\pi}} \int_0^\infty x^{3/2} e^{-x}\,dx \ ,$$

(5.5-8)

where, as in (5.5 - 3), $x = \varepsilon/kT$. The integral can be identified from (5.5 - 4) as $\Gamma(5/2)$, or $(3/2)!$, which must equal $(3/2)(1/2)!$. Since we have seen above that $(1/2)!$ has the value $\sqrt{\pi}/2$, the above integral must be equal to $3\sqrt{\pi}/4$, which allows us to write a result that may already be familiar,

$$U = \tfrac{3}{2} NkT \ .$$

(5.5-9)

The internal energy per particle is thus $3kT/2$. The heat capacity C_v (at constant volume) is defined as the increment of internal energy needed to produce unit temperature rise. This can be written as

$$C_v = \left(\frac{\partial U}{\partial T}\right)_v = \tfrac{3}{2} Nk \ .$$

(5.5-10)

The specific heat c_v is simply the heat capacity per unit mass, per mole, per particle, or other unit quantity. Per particle, the specific heat is clearly $3k/2$. In a mole of substance, the number of atoms is Avogadro's number, N_a, so that the molar specific heat is

$$c_v = \tfrac{3}{2} N_a k \ .$$

(5.5-11)

This result indicates that the specific heat of an ideal gas should be independent of temperature, a result that is in agreement with experiment, as is also the predicted magnitude of c_v.

It is also important to know how particles are distributed in velocity or momentum, as well as in energy. The distribution (5.5 - 7) can be converted to a velocity distribution by recalling that

$$\varepsilon = \tfrac{1}{2} m(v_x^2 + v_y^2 + v_z^2) = \tfrac{1}{2} mv^2 \ , \qquad \text{and} \quad d\varepsilon = mv\,dv \ .$$

(5.5-12)

Making these substitutions in (5.5 - 7) yields

$$N(v)\,dv = 4\pi N \left(\frac{m}{2\pi kT}\right)^{3/2} v^2 e^{-mv^2/2kT}\,dv \ .$$

(5.5-13)

The quantity $N(v)\,dv$ can be interpreted as the number of particles in a velocity interval dv about the velocity v. Since only the magnitude of the velocity appears, it is really a distribution of particle speeds, though the term "velocity distribution" has become ingrained by usage. Another interpretation is that it expresses the number of particles in a spherical shell of radius v and thickness dv in a three-dimensional orthogonal velocity or momentum space.

Finally, it is sometimes useful to know how the cartesian components of velocity are distributed. It is easy to write the distribution function (5.5 - 6) in terms of these velocity components as

$$f(v_x, v_y, v_z) = \frac{N}{V} \left(\frac{h^2}{2\pi m kT} \right)^{3/2} e^{-m(v_x^2 + v_y^2 + v_z^2)/2kT} \ .$$

(5.5 - 14)

Also, according to (5.4 - 30), we can write

$$N(v_x, v_y, v_z) dv_x dv_y dv_z = f(v_x, v_y, v_z) g(v_x, v_y, v_z) \, dv_x dv_y dv_z \ ,$$

(5.5 - 15)

where $g(v_x, v_y, v_z) \, dv_x dv_y dv_z$ represents the number of quantum states in a rectangular volume element. However, velocity and momentum differ only by a factor m, and since from Figure 5.2 it is evident that each quantum state occupies a volume of momentum space h^3/V, the volume of velocity space per quantum state is

$$dv_x dv_y dv_z = \frac{dp_x dp_y dp_z}{m^3} = \frac{h^3}{m^3 V} \ .$$

(5.5 - 16)

This means that the number of quantum states per unit volume of velocity space is $m^3 V / h^3$, and that

$$g(v_x, v_y, v_z) \, dv_x dv_y dv_z = \frac{m^3 V}{h^3} \, dv_x dv_y dv_z \ .$$

(5.5 - 17)

Substituting (5.5 - 14) and (5.5 - 17) into (5.5 - 15), we obtain finally

$$N(v_x, v_y, v_z) dv_x dv_y dv = N \left(\frac{m}{2\pi kT} \right)^{3/2} e^{-m(v_x^2 + v_y^2 + v_z^2)/2kT} \, dv_x dv_y dv_z \ .$$

(5.5 - 18)

It is also of interest to inquire about the distribution in velocity space of each cartesian component of velocity. This distribution may be obtained merely by integrating the above distribution over two of the three velocity components. Thus, if we integrate (5.5 - 18) over v_y and v_z, from $-\infty$ to $+\infty$, we obtain an expression for $N(v_x)dv_x$, the number of particles whose x-velocity components are in an interval dx about the velocity v_x. Using the table below to evaluate the required integrals, we find

$$N(v_x)dv_x = \int_{-\infty}^{\infty} \int_{-\infty}^{\infty} \left[N(v_x, v_y, v_z) dv_x \right] dv_y dv_z = N \sqrt{\frac{m}{2\pi kT}} \, e^{-mv_x^2/2kT} dv_x \ .$$

(5.5 - 19)

The Boltzmann distribution function and the free-particle velocity distributions (5.5 - 13) and (5.5 - 19) are plotted for several temperatures in Figure 5.6. It is easily observed from the figure that the most probable value of v_x (and the other cartesian components as well) is zero, while the *least* probable particle speed v is zero. This seemingly paradoxical result can be explained by recalling that for a particle to be at rest it isn't sufficient that its x-component of velocity be zero; what is required is that *all three* cartesian components be zero simultaneously. This is a far less probable event, and despite the high relative probability that a single component vanishes, the probability that all of them are zero simultaneously is very low. The situation can also be understood with reference to the density of states function $g(\varepsilon)$, which goes to zero as ε approaches zero, for similar reasons.

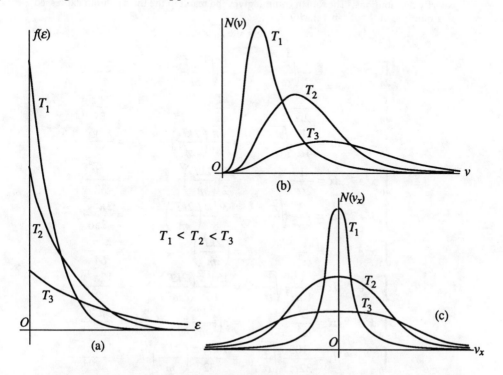

Figure 5.6 (a) The Maxwell-Boltzmann distribution of energies at three different temperatures for a monatomic ideal gas. (b) The distribution of molecular speeds and (c) the distribution of velocity components along one of the cartesian axes for this system.

When the distribution function and the velocity distributions that follow from it are known, it is possible to calculate average values of many quantities of interest over the distributions, using the basic rules (5.2 - 3, 4, and 5). For example, the average thermal speed $<v>$ for a particle in an ideal Maxwell-Boltzmann distribution can be calculated from (5.5 - 13) as

$$\langle v \rangle = \frac{\int_0^\infty vN(v)\,dv}{\int_0^\infty N(v)\,dv} = \frac{1}{N} \cdot 4\pi N \left(\frac{m}{2\pi kT}\right)^{3/2} \int_0^\infty v^3 e^{-mv^2/2kT} \quad ,$$

or $\quad \langle v \rangle = \bar{v} = \sqrt{\frac{8kT}{\pi m}} \quad .$ (5.5 - 20)

Table 5.1 is helpful in evaluating the definite integral. Both bracket and "v-bar" notation are frequently used in reference to this quantity. For helium, this formula yields an average velocity of 1260m/sec at 300K. The root mean square velocity can

TABLE 5.1   MAXWELL-BOLTZMANN INTEGRALS

The second column below gives the value of the integral in the first column. In the third column are listed values of the integral when α has the value $m/2kT$, as is usual in the velocity distributions. The fourth column gives the result in the third column expressed as a multiple of the mean velocity,

$$\bar{v} = \sqrt{8kT / \pi m}.$$

$$\int_0^\infty e^{-\alpha x^2} dx = \frac{1}{2}\sqrt{\frac{\pi}{\alpha}} \quad = \frac{1}{2}\sqrt{\frac{2\pi kT}{m}} \quad = \frac{\pi \bar{v}}{4}$$

$$\int_0^\infty x e^{-\alpha x^2} dx = \frac{1}{2\alpha} \quad = \frac{kT}{m} \quad = \frac{\pi \bar{v}^{-2}}{8}$$

$$\int_0^\infty x^2 e^{-\alpha x^2} dx = \frac{1}{4\alpha}\sqrt{\frac{\pi}{\alpha}} \quad = \frac{\sqrt{\pi}}{4}\left(\frac{2kT}{m}\right)^{3/2} \quad = \frac{\pi^2 \bar{v}^{-3}}{32}$$

$$\int_0^\infty x^3 e^{-\alpha x^2} dx = \frac{1}{2\alpha^2} \quad = \frac{1}{2}\left(\frac{2kT}{m}\right)^2 \quad = \frac{\pi^2 \bar{v}^{-4}}{32}$$

$$\int_0^\infty x^4 e^{-\alpha x^2} dx = \frac{3}{8\alpha^2}\sqrt{\frac{\pi}{\alpha}} \quad = \frac{3\sqrt{\pi}}{8}\left(\frac{2kT}{m}\right)^{5/2} \quad = \frac{3\pi^3 \bar{v}^{-5}}{256}$$

$$\int_0^\infty x^5 e^{-\alpha x^2} dx = \frac{1}{\alpha^3} \quad = \left(\frac{2kT}{m}\right)^3 \quad = \frac{\pi^3 \bar{v}^{-6}}{64}$$

$$\int_0^\infty x^6 e^{-\alpha x^2} dx = \frac{15}{16\alpha^3}\sqrt{\frac{\pi}{\alpha}} \quad = \frac{15\sqrt{\pi}}{16}\left(\frac{2kT}{m}\right)^{7/2} \quad = \frac{15\pi^4 \bar{v}^{-7}}{2^{11}}$$

$$\int_0^\infty x^7 e^{-\alpha x^2} dx = \frac{3}{\alpha^4} \quad = 3\left(\frac{2kT}{m}\right)^4 \quad = \frac{3\pi^4 \bar{v}^{-8}}{256}$$

$$\int_0^\infty x^8 e^{-\alpha x^2} dx = \frac{105}{32\alpha^4}\sqrt{\frac{\pi}{\alpha}} \quad = \frac{105\sqrt{\pi}}{32}\left(\frac{2kT}{m}\right)^{9/2} \quad = \frac{105\pi^5 \bar{v}^{-9}}{2^{14}}$$

also be calculated in this manner. In this case, however, it is simpler merely to observe that, as we have seen in (5.5 - 9), the average kinetic energy per particle is $U/N = 3kT/2$. Therefore,

$$\left\langle \tfrac{1}{2}mv^2 \right\rangle = \tfrac{1}{2}m\left\langle v^2 \right\rangle = \tfrac{3}{2}kT \quad , \qquad \text{or} \qquad \left\langle v^2 \right\rangle = v_{rms}^2 = \frac{3kT}{m} \quad . \tag{5.5 - 21}$$

The two average velocities defined by (5.5 - 20) and (5.5 - 21) differ by only 8%.

It is now possible to find the equation of state of this system. Consider particles that strike a unit area of the wall of the container, as shown in Figure 5.7. We shall assume that these particles make elastic collisions--that is, collisions in which energy as well as momentum is conserved--with the rigid container wall. In such collisions the velocity component v_x directed toward the wall is changed to a component $-v_x$ directed away from the wall. Conservation of momentum requires that there be momentum $2mv_x$ transferred to the wall, per collision.

Consider at first only the group of particles whose x-velocity is in a range dv_x about v_x. The number of particles of this set that will collide with the wall within time dt is the number within the volume shown in the figure, which is $v_x dt$ times $N(v_x)dv_x/V$. The momentum transferred to the wall in this time interval is thus,

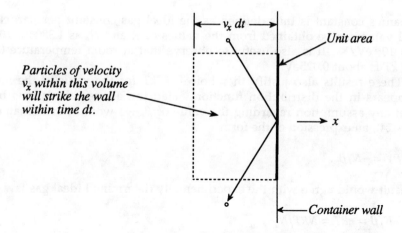

Figure 5.7 Elastic collision of a free particle with a given x-component of velocity with the wall of a rigid container.

$$(dp_x)_{v_x} = 2mv_x \cdot \frac{v_x dt \cdot N(v_x) dv_x}{V} \quad ,$$

or, $\qquad \left(\frac{dp_x}{dt} \right)_{v_x} = \frac{2m}{V} v_x^2 N(v_x) dv_x \quad .$ \hfill (5.5 - 22)

The total rate of momentum transfer is now found by integrating over the distribution of x-velocities (5.5 - 19), which gives, with the help of the table,

$$\left(\frac{dp_x}{dt} \right) = \frac{2m}{V} N \sqrt{\frac{m}{2\pi kT}} \int_0^\infty v_x^2 e^{-mv_x^2/2kT} dv_x = \frac{NkT}{V} \quad . \tag{5.5 - 23}$$

The integral above is taken only over positive values of v_x, since particles with negative x-velocities will not collide with the wall during the given time interval. The momentum transfer dp_x/dt can now be identified as the normal force exerted on a unit area of the container wall, that is, the pressure P. The above expression can now be recognized as the ideal gas law,

$$PV = NkT \quad . \tag{5.5 - 24}$$

In this equation, N is the total number of particles and k is Boltzmann's constant. This equation can also be written in a form more familiar from chemistry,

$$PV = nRT \quad , \tag{5.5 - 25}$$

where n is the number of moles of gas and R the ideal gas constant, whose value is 8.314 J/mole-K. If $n = 1$, the total number of particles is Avogadro's number, N_a, equal to 6.022×10^{23} mole^{-1}. One may now infer from the two above equations that

$$N_a k = R \quad , \quad \text{or} \quad k = R/N_a \quad . \tag{5.5 - 26}$$

Boltzmann's constant is thus defined as the ideal gas constant per particle. Its numerical value can be obtained from the values of R and N_a as 1.3806×10^{-23} J/K, or 8.615×10^{-5} eV/K. It is also useful to observe that at room temperature (300K), the energy kT is about 0.025eV.

These results also justify the choice $-1/kT$ for the value of the multiplier β that appears in the distribution function. Had the above calculations been made without any assumption regarding the value of β, we would have obtained instead of (5.5 - 24), an expression of the form

$$PV = -N/\beta \ . \tag{5.5-27}$$

This result would agree with the experimentally determined ideal gas law only if

$$-N/\beta = nRT = NRT/N_a \ ,$$

or, $\quad \beta = -N_a/RT = -1/kT \ . \tag{5.5-28}$

5.6 FERMI-DIRAC STATISTICS

In deriving the Maxwell-Boltzmann distribution function, though the formalism of quantum states and energy levels is adopted from the beginning, the rest of the development is based on a purely classical view of the system whose properties are of interest. Though there are many instances in which this classical view of the system is valid, some of the assumptions on which it is founded are not always in harmony with the requirements of quantum mechanics. Two points in particular can be questioned. The first pertains to the Pauli exclusion principle, which must be obeyed by particles, like electrons, with spin 1/2. The second has to do with the assumption that on the atomic level particles can be distinguished from one another, like billiard balls with numbers or other identifiers. This is sometimes possible, but for systems wherein elementary particles like electrons or photons are the constituents, there is no way of making any such identification. Under these circumstances, quantum theory takes the point of view that particles are *inherently indistinguishable*, and that ways of forming distributions which differ only in regard to differences in classical identifiers assigned to the particles, and which are treated classically as different, must now be regarded as identical. In the case of tossing five coins, this means that the five different classical ways of realizing a distribution of 4 heads, 1 tail (which differ only in that the one that comes up tails bears five different identifying numbers) must somehow collapse into one. This viewpoint is admittedly strange, but it has been consistently upheld by experimental evidence. If both these additional requirements are imposed, a new distribution function is obtained, the distribution now being referred to as a *Fermi-Dirac* distribution.

If the particles of the system cannot be distinguished by number, all the ways of arriving at the distribution (N_1, N_2) in the two-level system shown in Figure 5.4(b) are the same, and the number of ways of realizing it shown in the third row of the diagram reduce to a single statistical possibility. The same is true of the situations shown at (c) and (d) in the same figure, for the only difference between all the ways of realizing the final distribution resides in the numbering of particles. As a result, the expression on the right side of (5.4 - 6) reduces to unity. In (5.4 - 7) this also happens, leaving only the ways of distributing particles among quantum states of the multiply degenerate levels to contibute to the number of ways of realizing a given final distribution of particles among energy levels. It is nevertheless still possible to permute these particles in many ways, each representing a statistically independent way of forming the given distribution. The situation is shown schematically for the g_i quantum states and N_i particles in the i-th level of the system in Figure 5.8.

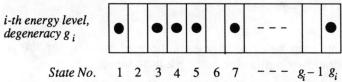

State No.   1   2   3   4   5   6   7   - - - $g_i - 1$ g_i

Figure 5.8 A possible distribution of particles among quantum states in an energy level of a system in which the Pauli exclusion principle is obeyed.

In the diagram, it is clear that due to the Pauli principle, each quantum state accommodates at most a single particle, and that there is no way of distinguishing one particle from another. It is assumed as usual that there is a given distribution of $(N_1, N_2, N_3, \ldots N_n)$ particles in the energy levels, and that in the i-th level, which is illustrated, there are N_i. There are g_i quantum states to accommodate a particle initially; when one particle is present, there are only $g_i - 1$ states available for the next, and then only $g_i - 2$ for the next, and so on. The number of ways of realizing a distribution of N_i particles like the one shown is thus $g_i(g_i - 1)(g_i - 2) \ldots (g_i - N_i + 1)$. However, since the particles are indistinguishable, the $N_i!$ permutations of the particles among themselves cannot be counted as separate configurations, so we must divide this number by $N_i!$ to obtain

$$\frac{1}{N_i!} \cdot g_i(g_i - 1)(g_i - 2) \cdots (g_i - N_i + 1) , \quad \text{or} \quad \frac{g_i!}{N_i!(g_i - N_i)!}$$

The total number of ways of realizing the distribution $(N_1, N_2, N_3, \ldots N_n)$, which we shall call Q_f, is then the product of factors of this form over the n energy levels, or

$$Q_f(N_1, N_2, \ldots N_n) = \prod_{i=1}^{n} \frac{g_i!}{N_i!(g_i - N_i)!} . \tag{5.6-1}$$

Taking the logarithm of this quantity as in our previous calculation, we find

$$\ln Q_f = \sum_i \ln g_i! - \sum_i \ln N_i! - \sum_i (g_i - N_i)! . \tag{5.6-2}$$

Finally, using Stirling's series (5.4 - 20) as before, noting that g_i are constants, and recalling that partial derivatives of functions of N_i with respect to N_j are zero unless $i = j$, we can write

$$\frac{\partial \ln Q_f}{\partial N_j} = -\ln N_j + \ln(g_j - N_j) \ , \tag{5.6-3}$$

the sign reversal in the last term following from the operation $\partial / \partial (g_j - N_j)$ needed in the chain of derivatives that is required. Equations (5.4 - 22) are still valid, and in the maximization condition (5.4 - 15), the constraints of constant number of particles N and total energy U lead to the terms $\alpha + \beta \varepsilon_j$ exactly as before. Equations (5.4 - 15) and (5.6 - 3) now give

$$\ln\left(\frac{g_j}{N_j} - 1\right) = -\alpha - \beta \varepsilon_j \ . \tag{5.6-4}$$

Exponentializing both sides of this equation and solving for the quantity N_j / g_j, which defines the distribution function, we now obtain

$$\frac{N_j}{g_j} = f(\varepsilon_j) = \frac{1}{1 + e^{-\alpha} e^{-\beta \varepsilon_j}} \ . \tag{5.6-5}$$

This is the Fermi-Dirac distribution function.

As before, we shall assume the value $-1/kT$ for β, a choice which will be justified later. In the Fermi distribution it is usual to express the parameter α in terms of a quantity ε_f referred to as the *Fermi energy* or *Fermi level*, and defined by

$$\alpha = \frac{\varepsilon_f}{kT} \ . \tag{5.6-6}$$

Equation (5.6 - 5) then becomes

$$N_j = \frac{g_j}{1 + e^{(\varepsilon_j - \varepsilon_f)/kT}} \ , \tag{5.6-7}$$

or, for a quasi-continuum of levels in which the degeneracy is represented by a density of states function,

$$N(\varepsilon) d\varepsilon = f(\varepsilon) g(\varepsilon) d\varepsilon = \frac{g(\varepsilon) d\varepsilon}{1 + e^{(\varepsilon - \varepsilon_f)/kT}} \ . \tag{5.6-8}$$

The free electrons in metals can often be considered as a dense free-particle Fermi-Dirac gas. The free-particle density of states function (5.3 - 19), which includes the effect of spin degeneracy, is applicable under these circumstances.

Like the parameter $\exp \alpha$ in the Maxwell-Boltzmann distribution (as described by (5.5 - 5) for a free-particle gas), the Fermi energy is a function of temperature, whose exact form depends on the density of states function appropriate for the system. The Fermi energy can be determined, much like the parameter $\exp \alpha$, by the condition that the sum of N_i or the integral of $N(\varepsilon) d\varepsilon$ must equal the total number of particles N. Its value is thus determined for a quasi-continuum of levels, by

$$N = \text{const.} = \int f(\varepsilon)g(\varepsilon)d\varepsilon = \int \frac{g(\varepsilon)d\varepsilon}{1+e^{(\varepsilon-\varepsilon_f)/kT}} . \tag{5.6-9}$$

The integral is evaluated over all attainable energies. For a three-dimensional free-particle Fermi gas, $g(\varepsilon)$ is given by (5.3 - 19), and the Fermi energy is determined by

$$N = \frac{8\sqrt{2}\pi Vm^{3/2}}{h^3} \int_0^\infty \frac{\sqrt{\varepsilon}\,d\varepsilon}{1+e^{(\varepsilon-\varepsilon_f)/kT}} . \tag{5.6-10}$$

One would now hope to evaluate the integral and solve the resulting equation for ε_f in terms of N (and T), just as in evaluating $\exp\alpha$ for the Maxwell-Boltzmann ideal gas. It is impossible to carry out this procedure explicitly, because the above integral cannot be evaluated in closed form. There is therefore no "simple formula" for the Fermi energy of a three-dimensional free-particle Fermi gas, and to get anywhere at all one must resort to algebraically complex approximate methods, which yield their answers only after much detailed calculation.

For a *two-dimensional* free-particle system, however, the same methods used to derive (5.3 - 19) lead to an energy-independent density of states function of the form

$$g(\varepsilon)d\varepsilon = \frac{4\pi mA}{h^2}d\varepsilon . \tag{5.6-11}$$

In this expression. A is the area of the two-dimensional "container" within which the gas is confined. For this system, equation (5.6 - 9) takes the form

$$N = \frac{4\pi mA}{h^2} \int_0^\infty \frac{d\varepsilon}{1+e^{(\varepsilon-\varepsilon_f)/kT}} . \tag{5.6-12}$$

If you multiply the integrand above and below by $\exp(-\varepsilon/kT)$, you will find that the numerator is (apart from a constant factor $-kT$) the differential of the denominator. This allows one to determine that its integral is $-kT \ln[\exp(-\varepsilon/kT) + \exp(-\varepsilon_f/kT)]$. The fact that this integral can be evaluated in closed form makes this system an excellent example for illustrating the results of calculations very difficult to carry out in the three-dimensional case, but which are quite similar to those found for three dimensions. There are, moreover, some important systems in which a two-dimensional gas of this sort is actually present, for example, the electron gases encountered in thin metallic films. In the present example, evaluating the above integral in the manner suggested, we find

$$N = -\frac{4\pi mAkT}{h^2}\left[\ln\left(e^{-\varepsilon/kT} + e^{-\varepsilon_f/kT}\right)\right]_0^\infty = \frac{4\pi mAkT}{h^2}\ln\left(1 + e^{\varepsilon_f/kT}\right) . \tag{5.6-13}$$

Thus,

$$1 + e^{\varepsilon_f/kT} = e^{\frac{Nh^2}{4\pi mAkT}} ,$$

or

$$\varepsilon_f = kT\ln\left(e^{\frac{Nh^2}{4\pi mAkT}} - 1\right) . \tag{5.6-14}$$

218

This expression gives the Fermi energy explicitly. Its value clearly depends on the temperature as well as on the number of particles. If T approaches zero, the exponential factor in the above equation becomes very large, and in this limit one may simply neglect the term -1 that follows it in the parentheses. Taking the logarithm of the surviving exponential factor, we can express the Fermi energy at absolute zero as

$$\varepsilon_f(0) = \frac{nh^2}{4\pi m A} \, ,$$
(5.6 - 15)

which allows us finally to express the temperature-dependent Fermi energy (5.6 - 14) as

$$\varepsilon_f(T) = kT \ln\left(e^{\varepsilon_f(0)/kT} - 1\right) ,$$
(5.6 - 16)

with $\varepsilon_f(0)$ given by (5.6 - 15).

The temperature dependence of the Fermi energy for this system is illustrated in Figure 5.9. It will be observed that the Fermi energy decreases monotonically with increasing temperature from the zero-temperature value (5.6 - 15), and at sufficiently high temperatures becomes negative, eventually attaining arbitrarily large negative values. For three-dimensional free-particle systems, the behavior is qualitatively similar, except that the low-temperature part of the curve is approximately parabolic in form, and thus differs slightly from the logarithmic behavior observed in two dimensions. It should be noted that though free particles must have positive energies, the Fermi energy is not defined any specific particle energy, and it is therefore possible for the Fermi energy to be negative even when all particle energies are positive.

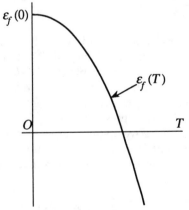

Figure 5.9 Schematic representation of the variation of the Fermi energy with termperature in a two-dimension free particle Fermi-Dirac gas, according to (5.6 -16).

The Fermi distribution proper, as given by

$$f(\varepsilon) = \frac{1}{1 + e^{(\varepsilon - \varepsilon_f)/kT}} \, ,$$
(5.6 - 17)

is plotted in Figure 5.10 for several values of temperature. At temperature $T = 0$, this function is seen to become a step function of the form

$$f(\varepsilon) = 1 \qquad (\varepsilon < \varepsilon_f)$$

$$= 0 \qquad (\varepsilon > \varepsilon_f) . \qquad (5.6\text{-}18)$$

As the temperature increases, the edges of the step function becomes slightly rounded, and the function spreads out slightly, varying rapidly from nearly unity to nearly zero over an energy range of a few times kT, as shown. As the temperature increases further, the effect becomes more pronounced, until at very high temperatures the distribution becomes very diffuse and spread-out. As this occurs, the Fermi energy moves downward, very slowly at first, then more rapidly. When $\varepsilon = \varepsilon_f$, $f(\varepsilon)$ has the vaue $1/2$, according to (5.6 - 17), which allows its position to be clearly observed in the figure.

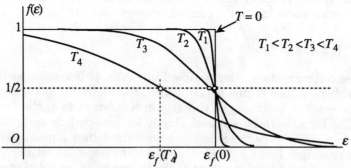

Figure 5.10 The form of the Fermi distribution function for several temperatures. The variation of the Fermi energy as illustrated is typical of a three-dimensional free-particle gas, but in general depends on the density of states function for the system at hand.

Since at most one particle can occupy a quantum state when the Pauli principle is applicable, the value of $f(\varepsilon)$ for the Fermi distribution gives directly the probability that a quantum state at energy ε is occupied. At the Fermi energy, this probability is exactly one-half.

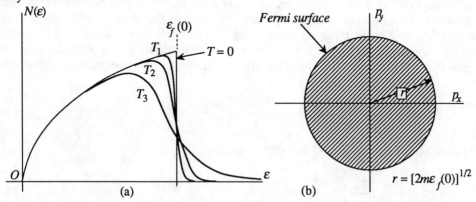

Figure 5.11 (a) Schematic representation of particle density *versus* energy for a three-dimensional Fermi free-particle gas (b) Representation of the distribution of occupied states in a three-dimensional Fermi free particle gas at a temperature of absolute zero as a sphere in momentum space. The z-direction in momentum space is normal to the page. States in the shaded region are completely filled at T = 0. The spherical exterior boundary of this region is called the *Fermi surface*.

Figure 5.11(a) shows the number distribution of particles for a three-dimensional Fermi free-particle gas. At zero temperature, the distribution again has a steplike form, the parabolic shape below the Fermi energy being accounted for by the form of the density of states function. Again, as the temperature rises, the distribution becomes less sharply steplike, and at very high temperatures becomes very spread-out. as illustrated. At low temperatures, when the Fermi distribution is steplike, the distributions shown above are said to be highly *degenerate*.

It is also possible to visualize the Fermi distribution, at least in the low temperature limit, in momentum space, as shown in Figure 5.11(b). At absolute zero, all states of energy less than the Fermi energy are occupied, while those of greater energy are empty. In the case of a free-particle gas, the surfaces of constant energy in momentum space are spherical, as indicated by (5.3 - 14). Accordingly, the equation of a sphere corresponding to the constant energy $\varepsilon_f(0)$ will be

$$p_x^2 + p_y^2 + p_z^2 = 2m\varepsilon_f(0) \ . \tag{5.6-19}$$

Thus, at zero temperature, the occupied quantum states reside as illustrated above, within a sphere whose radius is $[2m\varepsilon_f(0)]^{1/2}$, shown by the shaded region in the diagram. The exterior boundary of this region is referred to as the *Fermi surface* of the system. The Fermi surface is spherical only for free-particle systems. More complex systems, in which the particles interact with the lattice ions (or with one another), have non-spherical Fermi surfaces whose form depends on the symmetry of the crystal lattice and the precise nature of the interparticle potential energy.

At temperatures far above absolute zero, many states at energies above that of the Fermi surface will be occupied, and there will also be empty states in the range of energies below the Fermi energy. The surface then becomes fuzzy and ill-resolved, the concept of a sharply defined Fermi surface losing some of its usefulness under these circumstances. Fortunately, in most substances this occurs to a significant extent only at temperatures far above room temperature.

Though except in the case treated above, it is difficult to find the Fermi energy as an explicit function of temperature, it is a simple matter to calculate this quantity at zero Kelvin because of the step-function form of the distribution function at that temperature. Under these circumstances, the integral (5.6 - 10) for the three-dimensional free-particle system, for example, can be evaluated by using (5.6 - 18) rather than (5.7 - 17) to represent the distribution function. The integral then becomes

$$\frac{N}{V} = \frac{8\sqrt{2}\pi m^{3/2}}{h^3} \int_0^{\varepsilon_f(0)} \sqrt{\varepsilon} \, d\varepsilon = \frac{16\sqrt{2}\pi m^{3/2}\left[\varepsilon_f(0)\right]^{3/2}}{3h^3} \ . \tag{5.6-20}$$

This equation can be solved for $\varepsilon_f(0)$ to obtain

$$\varepsilon_f(0) = \frac{h^2}{8m}\left(\frac{3N}{\pi V}\right)^{2/3} \ . \tag{5.6-21}$$

In a similar way, the internal energy U, which involves the integral of $\varepsilon N(\varepsilon)$ over the step function form of the distribution can be evaluated as

$$\frac{U(0)}{N} = \tfrac{3}{5}\varepsilon_f(0) \; . \tag{5.6-22}$$

The reader is asked as an exercise to verify this result.

For particles of energy much larger than the Fermi energy ε_f, the exponential factor in the denominator of the distribution function (5.6 - 17) is much greater than unity, and for such energies the distribution function can be approximated by

$$f(\varepsilon) \cong e^{\varepsilon_f/kT} \cdot e^{-\varepsilon/kT} = e^{\alpha} \cdot e^{-\varepsilon/kT} \; . \tag{5.6-23}$$

This expression has the form of the Maxwell-Boltzmann distribution, so that the high-energy exponential "tail" of a Fermi-Dirac distribution is of Maxwellian form. If *all* energies available to particles of the system satisfy the condition

$$\varepsilon - \varepsilon_f \gg kT \; , \tag{5.6-24}$$

that is, if ε_f is several kT units below the *least* energy a particle belonging to the system can have, (5.6 - 24) is a good approximation for all particles, and the Fermi distribution is Maxwellian for the system as a whole. In the free-particle systems treated above, the lowest possible particle energy is zero for a particle at rest with no kinetic energy. Thus, in order that the Fermi distribution have Maxwellian form for all particles, the Fermi energy must be *less than zero* by several kT units. We have already seen from (5.6 - 16) and Figure 5.9 that this can actually happen in the two-dimensional gas, and have observed that the three-dimensional case is similar. One can now conclude that when the Fermi energy is greater than zero by many kT units, the distribution function has a more or less steplike form, while if it is negative to a similar extent, the distribution resembles a Maxwell-Boltzmann decreasing exponential. This being the case, it is clear that the the transition between these two extremes of behavior must occur when the Fermi energy is roughly zero.

If you now set the Fermi energy $\varepsilon_f(T)$ equal to zero in (5.6 - 16), you can solve the resulting equation for the temperature. The right side of this equation can be zero only when the argument of the logarithm in it attains the value unity, which leads to

$$e^{\varepsilon_f(0)/kT} = 2 \; ,$$

or $\quad kT \ln 2 = \varepsilon_f(0) \; , \qquad kT = \dfrac{\varepsilon_f(0)}{\ln 2} = 1.4427 \cdot \varepsilon_f(0) \; , \tag{5.6-25}$

where $\varepsilon_f(0)$ is defined by (5.6 - 15). This, in effect, defines the intercept of the curve in Figure 5.9 on the temperature axis. It is clear that the temperature so defined is of the order of $\varepsilon_f(0)/k$. for this two-dimensional system. The same calculation can be carried out for the three-dimensional gas, and an exact answer is obtainable even though an explicit formula for the Fermi energy as a function of temperature isn't available. In this case, as above, we set the Fermi energy equal to zero in (5.6 - 10), and make the substitution $x = \varepsilon/kT$, as in (5.5 - 2). We then arrive at

$$\frac{N}{V} = 8\sqrt{2}\,\pi\left(\frac{mkT}{h^2}\right)^{3/2} \int_0^{\infty} \frac{\sqrt{x}\,dx}{1+e^x} \; . \tag{5.6-26}$$

In this equation, the integral is merely a definite integral over the range $(0 < x < \infty)$. It is not easy to evaluate in closed form, but is, after all, only a number. One can evaluate it by numerical integration, if not by methods more elegant, and find that its value is 0.67810. Using this result, and some rather fancy algebra to express the final answer in terms of $\varepsilon_f(0)$ as given by (5.6 - 21), it can finally be shown that

$$kT = 0.9887 \cdot \varepsilon_f(0) \; . \tag{5.6-27}$$

Thus, though we cannot easily draw a curve like the one in Figure 5.9 showing the Fermi energy *versus* temperature for this system, we do now know where it intersects the temperature axis. Again, the temperature where the Fermi energy is zero is very close to $\varepsilon_f(0)/k$. Indeed, if you define a "Fermi temperature" T_f such that

$$kT_f = \varepsilon_f(0) \; , \tag{5.6-28}$$

you will find that it is usually a good indicator of where the Fermi energy goes negative, and therefore gives a good idea of where the transition between the steplike low-temperature behavior of the Fermi distribution and its Maxwellian high-temperature régime is to be found. More specifically, if the temperature of the system is much lower than T_f, the step function is a good approximation, while if the reverse is true, the distribution function is approximately Maxwellian. In between, unfortunately, things are complicated.

Physically, it is not hard to understand why the Fermi distribution is of Maxwellian form at high temperatures. Because of the Pauli principle, each state can accommodate only one particle, so when the lowest energy level is fully occupied, particles must go into the one of next lowest energy, and so on. In the quantum "ground state", therefore, particles fill up the levels of lowest possible energy like water in a jug, resulting in the steplike distribution function that prevails at zero temperature. At higher temperatures, particle energies need not have the smallest possible values; states of higher energy are available to them, and states at energies below the Fermi energy also need not all be filled. In the limit of very high temperatures, the distribution becomes very "spread-out" in energy, and the average energy of the particles may greatly exceed the Fermi energy, which means that there are far more quantum states accessible to them than at low temperatures. Now the probability that a given quantum state of any energy is occupied becomes quite small, and the probability that *two* particles might wish to be there simultaneously is negligible. The Pauli principle therefore ceases to have any noticeable effect, and the conditions under which the Maxwell-Boltzmann distribution is to be expected prevail.

The arbitrary assignment $\beta = -1/kT$ can now be justified by observing that had some other choice been made, the Fermi distribution would not in the high-temperature limit approach a Maxwell-Boltzmann distribution for which the PV product has the value expected from the ideal gas law.

The most familiar examples of systems in which Fermi-Dirac statistics are applicable are "electron gases", that is, independent-particle systems whose constituents are free electrons. The most important gas of this sort is the ensemble of free valence electrons in metallic conductors, though thermionically excited electronic charge distributions in vacuum tubes, the electrons in gas-discharge plasmas, charge carrier distributions in semiconductors, and electron beams in cathode-ray tubes and similar devices are other examples. The "gas" of free valence electrons in metals is, of course, responsible for the high electrical and thermal conductivities of these materials, as well as their optical properties. It differs from more familiar gaseous systems in that its particle density is extremely high, the particle mass is very small, and particle velocities and kinetic energies can be comparatively high. In a mole of an ordinary ideal gas at room temperature, 6.023×10^{23} molecules occupy a volume of $24,600\text{cm}^3$, while in a typical metal, the same number of free electrons occupy less than 10cm^3. Moreover, the electron mass is smaller than that of a typical gas molecule by a factor of nearly 10^5. These differences are responsible for the fact that the free electron gases in metals are Fermi-Dirac gases whose distribution functions at all realizable temperatures differ only slightly from the step function that prevails at absolute zero. This is easily shown by finding the Fermi temperature from (5.6 - 28) and (5.6 - 21). For copper, assuming one valence electron per atom, the number of free electrons per unit volume is about $7.5 \times 10^{22}\text{cm}^{-3}$, or $7.5 \times 10^{28}\text{m}^{-3}$. Therefore,

$$T_f = \frac{\varepsilon_f(0)}{k} = \frac{h^2}{8mk}\left(\frac{3N}{\pi V}\right)^{2/3} = \frac{(6.626\times10^{-34})^2}{(8)(9.11\times10^{-31})(1.381\times10^{-23})}\cdot\left(\frac{3}{\pi}\cdot 7.5\times10^{28}\right)^{2/3} = 75,200\text{K}.$$

The Fermi temperature is in this case astronomical--far above room temperature, and far above the melting point or boiling point of solid copper. This means simply that at any realizable temperature, the Fermi distribution differs from a step function only slightly, like the curve labeled T_1 in Figure 5.10. The Fermi energy likewise differs little from the zero-temperature value at any practically attainable temperature; you are always on the part of the curve close to the origin of the temperature scale in Figure 5.9. The Fermi energy itself, according to the above calculation, is about 6.48eV, much larger than the room-temperature value of kT, which is about 0.025eV. Since the width of the region in which the Fermi function decreases from near unity to almost zero is only a few times kT, this reiterates the picture of a steplike distribution function. Moreover, it suggests that because of the Pauli exclusion principle, the particles in this distribution have much higher kinetic energies, and velocities than those of a Maxwellian gas at the same temperature. This can be seen more clearly by noting that the average kinetic energy per particle in a Maxwellian gas, according to (5.5 - 9), is $3kT/2$, or 0.0375eV at 300K, while for the Fermi free electron gas in copper, this average kinetic energy would be given by (5.6 - 22) as $0.6\varepsilon_f(0)$, or 3.89eV. This translates to an average electron velocity of $1.17 \times 10^6\text{m/sec}$. This very high (though thankfully still non-relativistic) speed should be contrasted with average molecular speeds of about 1000m/sec in typical Maxwellian ideal gases at similar temperatures.

It should not be concluded from this example that all the Fermi distributions associated with physically realizable electron gases are steplike. In the electron and hole distributions found in typical semiconductor crystals, for example, the particle density N/V is typically smaller by a factor of at least 10^6 than in normal metallic substances like copper. This is also true of the electron space charge distributions in vacuum tubes and gas-discharge plasmas. In the above example, if one reduces N/V by a factor of 10^6, the Fermi temperature comes down by a factor of 10^4, and the Fermi temperature calculated above is reduced to 7.5K. Now, normal room temperature, indeed, even the boiling temperature of liquid nitrogen (77K), is far *above* the Fermi temperature of the system, and the Fermi distribution is hardly distinguishable from a Maxwell-Boltzmann distribution. You are now far to the right of the temperature-axis intercept of the curve in Figure 5,9, and the Fermi energy at these temperatures is now *large and negative*. It is now quite safe to use the mathematically much simpler Maxwell-Boltzmann distribution function. Similar conclusions follow for systems whose particles are massive atoms or molecules rather than electrons, because of the factor m in the denominator of the above expression for T_f.

It should also be noted that the above derivation for the Fermi distribution function is subject to criticism when the quantities $g_i - N_i$ in equations (5.6 - 1) and (5.6 - 2) are not large numbers. This can happen when the quantum states belonging to a given energy level are almost totally occupied, an occurance not uncommon in Fermi-Dirac systems. Under these circumstances, neglecting terms beyond the first in Stirling's expansion (5.4 - 20), as we have done in our calculations, is no longer strictly justified. We shall merely state, to dispel any doubts regarding the matter, that is possible--though with considerable difficulty--to obtain the Fermi-Dirac distribution function in exactly the form given above as (5.6 - 7), without employing this approximation at all.

Finally it is useful to observe that the expressions (5.6 - 21) and (5.6 - 28), which define $\varepsilon_f(0)$ and T_f, can be used to rewrite the expression (5.3 - 19) giving the density of states function for the three-dimensional free electron gas, as

$$g(\varepsilon)\,d\varepsilon = \frac{3N}{\left(2kT_f\right)^{3/2}}\sqrt{\varepsilon}\,d\varepsilon \ . \tag{5.6 - 29}$$

This form of the density of states function simplifies the algebra required in working with certain problems related to free-electron gases. The details of deriving it are assigned as an exercise for the reader.

5.7 BOSE-EINSTEIN STATISTICS

As pointed out in the preceding chapter, only elementary particles of half-integral spin ($s = 1/2, 3/2, 5/2, \ldots$) obey the Pauli exclusion principle. Particles of integral spin, whose spin quantum number has the form ($s = 0, 1, 2, 3, \ldots$) are not subject to the Pauli principle, and any number of particles such as these can occupy any quantum state. These particles, however, still have the property of indistinguishability, and must therefore be treated statistically in a way that differs somewhat from either classical Maxwell-Boltzmann or Fermi-Dirac statistics. The photon, for which $s = 1$, is the most common example of such a particle, which is referred to as a Bose particle, or boson. The distribution function appropriate for Bose particles is called the Bose-Einstein distribution. As in the Fermi-Dirac case, the lack of any identifier associated with individual particles makes the first factor on the right side of (5.4 - 7) reduce to unity, and we are left with only the second, which accounts for permuting N_i particles among g_i quantum states in the typical i-th energy level of the system, though there is now no restriction regarding the number of particles that can occupy any quantum state.

The picture shown in Figure 5.8 is no longer valid, but it can be fixed up by pulling out the $g_i - 1$ partitions that divide the energy level into separate quantum states, and rearranging them so that there can be different--and arbitrary--numbers of particles between each of them, as shown below in Figure 5.12.

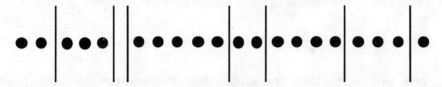

Figure 5.12 A row of indistinguishable particles divided into groups corresponding to quantum states of the i-th energy level of a system in which the Pauli exclusion principle is not obeyed.

In the diagram are shown the N_i particles and the $g_i - 1$ partitions needed to divide them into g_i groups, which represent quantum state occupancies. There are $N_i + 1$ ways of choosing where to put a first partition; it can be put into any of the $N_i - 1$ spaces between the particles, or on either end, beyond the first or last particle. These last two choices leave a blank space on one end or the other, corresponding to an empty first or last state, which is clearly a possibility that one must account for. The second partition can be located in $N_i + 2$ ways, because there are now a total of $N_i + 1$ objects--particles plus partitions--in the row. The third partition can be located likewise in $N_i + 3$ ways, and so on. For $g_i - 1$ partitions, the total number of possible arrangements is the product of these numbers, or

$$(N_i+1)(N_i+2)(N_i+3) \cdots (N_i+g_i-1) = \frac{(N_i+g_i-1)!}{N_i!} \; .$$

Clearly, however, permuting the different partitions among themselves leads to no difference in the picture of particles and quantum states, so this number must be divided by the $(g_i - 1)!$ ways of permuting partitions among themselves to get the number of ways of realizing any distribution of N_i particles among g_i states. The total number of ways of realizing a given distribution $(N_1, N_2, N_3, \ldots N_n)$ particles among the n energy levels of the system, $Q_b(N_1, N_2, N_3, \ldots N_n)$, is now written as the product

$$Q_b(N_1, N_2, \cdots N_n) = \prod_{i=1}^{n} \frac{(N_i+g_i-1)!}{N_i!(g_i-1)!} \; . \tag{5.7-1}$$

One can now maximize Q_b as given above, under the constraints (5.4 - 8) and (5.4 - 9) expressing the constancy of the total number of particles and their total energy, using the method of Lagrangean multipliers, as in previous work. The details will not be presented here, but are instead assigned as an exercise. The result is,

$$f(\varepsilon_j) = \frac{N_j}{g_j} = \frac{1}{e^{-\alpha} e^{-\beta \varepsilon_j} - 1} \; . \tag{5.7-2}$$

This is the Bose-Einstein distribution function. As usual, we can express β in terms of the temperature as

$$\beta = -1/kT \; , \tag{5.7-3}$$

while $\exp\alpha$ can be determined in terms of the total number of particles, as in previous work. For the case of a quasi-continuum of closely spaced levels, the degeneracy factor is replaced by the density of states and N_j by $N(\varepsilon)d\varepsilon$ to give,

$$f(\varepsilon) = \frac{N(\varepsilon)d\varepsilon}{g(\varepsilon)d\varepsilon} = \frac{1}{e^{-\alpha}e^{\varepsilon/kT}-1} \quad . \qquad (5.7-4)$$

In this case, as in Fermi-Dirac statistics, at high temperatures the exponential term in the denominator of the distribution function becomes much larger than unity and the distribution function then approaches the form of the Maxwell-Boltzmann distribution. For three-dimensional independent particle Bose-Einstein systems, the parameter α becomes small as the temperature appproaches zero, and in this limit all particles condense into the lowest energy state of the system at a low but well-defined nonzero temperature, a phenomenon referred to as the Bose condensation.

Bose-Einstein systems are often composed of particles--like photons--that are easily created and annihilated. In systems such as these, the total number of particles need not remain constant, and the constraint (5.4 - 8) that imposes this restriction is no longer valid. It is clear that this constraint can be discarded in the Lagrangean multiplier procedure simply by setting α equal to zero. Under these circumstances, the Bose-Einstein distribution function reduces to the simple form

$$f(\varepsilon) = \frac{1}{e^{\varepsilon/kT}-1} \quad . \qquad (5.7-5)$$

REFERENCES

1. W. Band, *An introduction to Quantum Statistics*, van Nostrand, Princeton NJ (1955).

2. J. E. Mayer and M. Göppert-Mayer, *Statistical Mechanicss*, Wiley & Sons, New York (1950).

3. D. ter Haar, *Elements of Statistical Mechanics*, Holt, Rinehart and Winston, New York (1954).

4. R. B. Lindsay, *Introduction to Physical Statistics*, Wiley & Sons, New York (1941).

5. R. C. Tolman, *Principles of Statistical Mechanics*, Oxford University Press, London (1938).

6. A. H. Wilson, *Thermodynamics and Statistical Mechanics*, Cambridge University Press, Cambridge/London (1960).

7. E. S. R. Gopal, *Statistical Mechanics and Properties of Matter*, Ellis Horwood Ltd., Chichester (1974); (USA) Wiley & Sons, New York (1974).

8. E. A. Desloge, *Statistical Physics*, Holt, Rinehart and Winston, New York (1966).

9. H. Eyring, D. Henderson, B. J. Stover, and E. M. Eyring, *Statistical Mechanics and Dynamics*, Wiley & Sons, New York (1974)

PROBLEMS

1. From the value $k = 1.381 \times 10^{-28}$J/K, find Boltzmann's constant in units of eV/K. Express the energy kT in eV for $T = 4$K, 30K, 77K, 100K, 300K, 1000K, and 3000K.

2. Two identical but identifiable dice are tossed simultaneously. Find the probability associated with all possible total scores (2 through 12).

3. What are the answers to the preceding problem when three identical but identifiable dice are rolled?

4. Calculate the density of states function (5.6 - 11) for a two-dimensional gas of independent particles, using the methods developed in Section 5.3 for the three-dimensional case. Assume that the gas is confined by a rectangular container of area A whose sides are L_x and L_y.

5. Calculate the density of states function in the classical limit for a system of independent particles confined by a one-dimensional potential well of infinite depth and length L. *Hint*: consider the particles as "oscillators" and draw a phase-plane diagram like Figure 5.1, in which the area between two curves of constant but slightly different energy can be related to the number of allowed quantum states. Are these "oscillators" harmonic?

6. Calculate the density of states function for a system consisting of a large number of independent two-dimensional simple harmonic oscillators. Use an adaptation of the methods developed in Section 5.3 for the three-dimensional case.

7. Consider a system consisting of a large number of independent one-dimensional simple harmonic oscillators whose total energies are distributed according to the Maxwell-Boltzmann law. Show (starting with (5.3 - 5)) that the average kinetic energy of an oscillator in this system is $kT/2$. Show also that the average potential energy of such an oscillator is also $kT/2$. This result suggests that the ensemble averages calculated above are equal to averages over time, since it is a well-known result of elementary classical mechanics that the time averages of these quantities for a simple harmonic oscillator are the same as these ensemble averages.

8. Show (using (5.3 -3) and (5.3 - 21)) that the average total energy of one of the oscillators in the preceding problem is kT, in agreement with the previous calculations.

9. Show that the average total energy of an oscillator in a system of three-dimensional oscillators of the type described in Problem 7 is $3kT$.

10. Find the area and dimensions of the rectangle of maximum area that can be inscribed in an ellipse of semiaxes a and b. Use the method of Lagrangean multipliers.

11. Find the most probable molecular speed in a Maxwell-Boltzmann free-particle gas.

12. The particle flux or particle current density is defined as the number of particles per unit area per unit time that cross a planar surface whose normal is oriented in some given direction. Show that the flux of particles having positive x-velocities across a surface normal to the x-axis in an ideal Maxwell-Boltzmann gas is $N<v>/4V$.

13. Show that in the low-temperature limit the internal energy per unit volume of a three-dimensional free-electron gas is $3N\varepsilon_f(0)/5V$. Show for a two-dimensional free-electron gas that the low-temperature internal energy per unit area is $N\varepsilon_f(0)/2A$.

14. Show that if the quantity $Q(N_1. N_2, \ldots N_n)$ is given by (5.8 - 1), the distribution function corresponding to the most probable values of $N_1. N_2, \ldots N_n$ is the Bose-Einstein distribution (5.7 - 2). Use the method of Lagrangean multipliers.

15. Show for a two-dimensional Bose-Einstein gas of free particles that the parameter α is given by

$$\alpha = \ln\left(1 - e^{-Nh^2/(2\pi mAkT)}\right) .$$

16. Consider a system containing N free electrons whose density of states function has the constant value G for energies less than some maximum value ε_m, and is zero for energies larger than this. Show that the Fermi energy at zero temperature has the value N/G. Show that at higher temperatures the Fermi energy can be written as

$$\varepsilon_f(T) = kT \ln\left(\frac{e^{\varepsilon_f(0)/kT} - 1}{1 - e^{(\varepsilon_m - \varepsilon_f(0))/kT}}\right) .$$

17. Find the range of energy $\Delta\varepsilon$ over which the probability of occupation of a quantum state of a system obeying Fermi-Dirac statistics drops from 0.9 to 0.1. What does this answer become if the occupation probability limits are 0.99 to 0.01?

18. Prove that the normalization parameter α for any free-particle system obeying Bose-Einstein statistics must be negative.

19. Consider a container holding a volume of one cubic micron of helium. Assuming that the behavior is that of an ideal free-particle gas, estimate roughly the spacing between energy levels at the lowest possible energies. Also, estimate roughly the number of quantum states between energy zero and energy 1.0×10^{-6} eV. How do these quantities change if the container volume increases?

20. Find the analogs of equations (5.5 - 6, 7, 13, 14, and 19) for a two-dimensional Maxwell-Boltzmann free-particle gas (no spin).

21. Show that the distribution $N(v_x, v_y, v_z)\, dv_x dv_y dv_z$ (similar to that shown in (5.5 - 18) for a Maxwell-Boltzmann gas) for a three-dimensional Fermi-Dirac free-particle gas has the form

$$N(v_x, v_y, v_z)\, dv_x dv_y dv_z = \frac{3\sqrt{\pi} N}{4}\left(\frac{m}{2\pi kT_f}\right)^{3/2} \frac{dv_x dv_y dv_z}{1 + e^{mv_x^2/2kT}\, e^{mv_y^2/2kT}\, e^{mv_z^2/2kT}} .$$

22. Starting with the result of the preceding problem, show (in analogy to (5.5 - 19)) that for a three-dimensional free-particle Fermi-Dirac gas, the distribution $N(v_z)\, dv_z$ can be written as

$$N(v_z)\, dv_z = \frac{3N}{4V} \cdot \frac{T}{T_f} \ln\left(1 + e^{(\varepsilon_f - \frac{1}{2}mv_z^2)/kT}\right) dv_z ,$$

where the Fermi velocity v_f is defined by

$$\varepsilon_f(0) = \tfrac{1}{2} mv_f^2 = kT_f .$$

23. Show that the equation of state of a monatomic three-dimensional free-particle gas can be written as $PV = 2U/3$, where U is the equilibrium internal energy, and show that this result is valid for either Boltzmann or Fermi-Dirac gases. *Hint*: Start with (5.5 - 22).

24. Use the result of the preceding problem to show that a Fermi-Dirac free-particle gas can have a large pressure even at a temperature of absolute zero. Write an expression for this pressure at zero temperature, and show for the case of the electron gas in a typical metal such as Cu, that the

pressure is nearly 300,000 atmospheres! Sketch roughly the form of the pressure-temperature relation such an electron gas must have, and compare it with the result for a Maxwell-Boltzmann gas.

25. Show that the density of states factor $g(\varepsilon)d\varepsilon$ for a three-dimensional Fermi-Dirac free electron gas can be expressed as

$$g(\varepsilon)d\varepsilon = \frac{3N}{\left(2kT_f\right)^{3/2}}\sqrt{\varepsilon}\,d\varepsilon \ .$$

26. Find the most probable particle speed, the mean particle speed, and the rms average particle speed for a three-dimensional Fermi-Dirac free-electron gas at temperatures small in comparison with the Fermi temperature. What are the numerical magnitudes of these velocities in Cu, assuming one free electron per atom?

27. Show that the molar specific heat of a two-dimensional Maxwell-Boltzmann free-particle gas (at constant volume) is R $(=N_a k)$.

CHAPTER 6

LATTICE VIBRATIONS
AND THERMAL PROPERTIES

6.1 INTRODUCTION

The treatment of quantum mechanics and statistical physics needed for the further development of condensed matter physics is now finished. It has been a long excursion from the main path, but it will be of lasting usefulness.

The first and most immediate application of this work concerns the thermal properties of nonmetallic crystalline substances. The specific heat of crystals is easy to measure, and--in the absence of any understanding of quantum theory and statistical mechanics--difficult to understand. Historically, this subject was one of those loose ends of unexplained phenomena that resulted in the collapse of the structure of classical physics in the early years of the 20th century. The story has already been related in Chapter 4 (Section 4.4); the reader should revisit this subject if its impact has faded.

In this chapter we shall use our knowledge of quantum physics and statistical mechanics to develop an understanding of the specific heat of nonmetallic crystals and to obtain a somewhat less rigorous command of related subjects such as thermal expansion and lattice thermal conductivity. In all this material, the vibrational excitations of the crystal lattice provide the physical constituents needed to construct a theory of these phenomena.

6.2 THE CLASSICAL THEORY OF LATTICE SPECIFIC HEAT

Students of elementary chemistry are often introduced to the Law of Dulong and Petit as a rough guide to the assignment of atomic masses and atomic numbers. Its physical origins, however, are not ordinarily explored, a logical gap we shall now fill. The Law of Dulong and Petit is an empirical finding that the specific heat of most solid substances at and above room temperature is independent of temperature, and is the same for all materials when expressed in molar or molecular units. This common value is 5.96cal/mole-K, 24.94J/mole-K, or 2.585×10^{-4}eV per molecule per Kelvin. At temperatures far below room temperature the behavior is very different, in that the specific heat decreases rapidly and approaches zero at absolute zero, as shown in Figure 4.4. This can be traced to the failure of classical physics and the onset of quantum behavior, as explained in Section 4.4. This low-temperature anomaly will soon be explained, but first the Law of Dulong and Petit itself, which is a purely classical phenomenon, must be treated.

As one increases the temperature of an ideal nonmetallic crystal, its internal energy increases This additional internal energy appears as vibrational kinetic and potential energy of the atoms, molecules, or ions of the crystal lattice. In the simplest possible model (one that is oversimplified in some respects) the lattice can be visualized as N independent three-dimensional simple harmonic oscillators of frequency $\omega = (\beta/m)^{1/2}$, where β is the interatomic force constant. We have seen, however, in connection with equation (5.3 - 26) that we can treat N independent three-dimensional harmonic oscillators as $3N$ one-dimensional oscillators. In so doing, we simplify considerably any subsequent calculations. Adopting this picture of $3N$ uncoupled harmonic oscillators all having the same oscillator frequency, we can now calculate the total internal vibrational energy. In the spirit of classical physics, it is assumed in this exercise that the energy distribution of the oscillators is adequately described by Maxwell-Boltzmann statistics.

The total vibrational internal energy per oscillator for a system of N one-dimensional oscillators whose density of states is given by (5.3 - 21), can be written as

$$\frac{U}{N} = \frac{\int_0^\infty \varepsilon N(\varepsilon)\,d\varepsilon}{\int_0^\infty N(\varepsilon)\,d\varepsilon} = \frac{\int_0^\infty \varepsilon f(\varepsilon)g(\varepsilon)\,d\varepsilon}{\int_0^\infty f(\varepsilon)g(\varepsilon)\,d\varepsilon} = \frac{e^\alpha \int_0^\infty \varepsilon\, e^{-\varepsilon/kT}\,\dfrac{d\varepsilon}{\hbar\omega}}{e^\alpha \int_0^\infty e^{-\varepsilon/kT}\,\dfrac{d\varepsilon}{\hbar\omega}} = \frac{\int_0^\infty \varepsilon\, e^{-\varepsilon/kT}\,d\varepsilon}{\int_0^\infty e^{-\varepsilon/kT}\,d\varepsilon} = kT \ ,$$

or, $U = NkT$. $\hspace{4cm}$ (6.2-1)

Replacing N by $3N$, this becomes

$\hspace{2cm} U = 3NkT$. $\hspace{4cm}$ (6.2-2)

The specific heat at constant volume is obtained as $\partial U/\partial T$, the result being

$$c_v = \left(\frac{\partial U}{\partial T}\right)_v = 3Nk \ . \hspace{3cm} (6.2\text{-}3)$$

This leads to a calculated specific heat per particle of 2.585×10^{-4} eV/molecule-K, and for a mole one obtains $c_v = 3N_a kT = 3R = 5.96$ cal/mole-K, in good agreement with experiment for most substances at and above room temperature.

This result can also be found by integrating over phase space coördinates. In this case the energy must be expressed in terms of position and momentum; for a one-dimensional oscillator it is given by (5.2 - 1). The energy U is then expressed as the sum of kinetic and potential energies U_k and U_p, as follows:

$$\frac{U_k}{N} = \frac{\int_{-\infty}^{\infty}\int_{-\infty}^{\infty} \frac{p_x^2}{2m} e^{-p_x^2/2mkT} e^{-m\omega^2 x^2/2kT} \, dp_x dx}{\int_{-\infty}^{\infty}\int_{-\infty}^{\infty} e^{-p_x^2/2mkT} e^{-m\omega^2 x^2/2kT} \, dp_x dx} = \tfrac{1}{2}kT$$

and

$$\frac{U_p}{N} = \frac{\int_{-\infty}^{\infty}\int_{-\infty}^{\infty} \tfrac{1}{2}m\omega^2 x^2 e^{-p_x^2/2mkT} e^{-m\omega^2 x^2/2kT} \, dp_x dx}{\int_{-\infty}^{\infty}\int_{-\infty}^{\infty} e^{-p_x^2/2mkT} e^{-m\omega^2 x^2/2kT} \, dp_x dx} = \tfrac{1}{2}kT \ .$$

(6.2 - 4)

Therefore,

$$\frac{U_k}{N} + \frac{U_p}{N} = \frac{U}{N} = kT \ ,$$

(6.2 - 5)

as above. It is evident from this that the averages of kinetic and potential energy over the Maxwell-Boltzmann distribution are the same and are equal to one-half the total oscillator energy. This is reminiscent of a theorem in classical mechanics which states that the *time averages* of the potential and kinetic energies of a simple harmonic oscillator are each equal to half the total energy, and suggests that in statistical physics it is legitimate to substitute ensemble averages for time averages. In any event, both methods of ensemble averaging used above give the same answer. Also, if you are not convinced of the validity of replacing N three-dimensional oscillators by $3N$ one-dimensional oscillators, you should repeat the calculation shown in (6.2 - 1) using the three-dimensional density of states function (5.3 - 32) to get the result $U = 3NkT$ directly. In doing so, feel free to use tables (or the relation (5.5 - 4) defining the Γ-function) to evaluate the required integrals.

As mentioned in Section 4.4, this classical calculation of lattice specific heat is badly out of line with experimental evidence at low temperatures. On the other hand, it can be regarded as working quite well when one considers how many unwarranted assumptions go into it. Not only are quantum effects completely ignored, but the oscillators are assumed to vibrate with a single frequency, which we have shown in Chapter 3 to be incorrect; indeed, the effects of coupling between oscillators--which are known to be important in many instances--are entirely neglected in this theory. Even so, it exhibits the physical basis of the Law of Dulong and Petit, and gives a satisfactory account of the high-temperature molar specific heat for most materials.

6.3 THE EINSTEIN THEORY OF SPECIFIC HEAT

The discrepancies between classical theory and experiment in the specific heat of solids at low temperatures were resolved by Albert Einstein in 1911. Einstein suggested that the observed decrease of specific heat is a quantum effect, and applied the ideas of this new and controversial theory to explain the phenomenon. Einstein used the picture of $3N$ uncoupled one-dimensional harmonic oscillators vibrating independently at a single frequency, but he suggested that their energies are restricted to the discrete values given by quantum theory, that is,

$$\varepsilon = \varepsilon_n = (n+\tfrac{1}{2})\hbar\omega , \qquad (n = 0,1,2,3,...) . \qquad (6.3\text{-}1)$$

When the temperature approaches absolute zero, the energy kT also becomes small, eventually becoming much smaller than the spacing between the oscillator levels. The discreteness of allowed oscillator energies then becomes important, and it is no longer true that there are many allowed energies of the system in any attainable energy interval. Energy supplied in increments of size kT or thereabouts now no longer suffices to excite atomic oscillators to a higher allowed state. We must thus replace the picture of an energy continuum and a density of states function with that of widely spaced discrete levels having degeneracy factors g_n. The integrals that appear in former calculations are now replaced by summations like those in (5.3 - 4), and the average total energy of an oscillator in an ensemble where energies are distributed by the Maxwell-Boltzmann law can be written, using (5.3 - 2) and (5.3 - 4), as

$$\langle\varepsilon\rangle = \frac{\displaystyle\sum_{n=0}^{\infty} \varepsilon_n g_n e^{\alpha} e^{-\varepsilon_n/kT}}{\displaystyle\sum_{n=0}^{\infty} g_n e^{\alpha} e^{-\varepsilon_n/kT}} = \hbar\omega \cdot \frac{\displaystyle\sum_{n=0}^{\infty} (n+\tfrac{1}{2}) e^{(n+\frac{1}{2})x}}{\displaystyle\sum_{n=0}^{\infty} e^{(n+\frac{1}{2})x}} , \qquad (6.3\text{-}2)$$

where

$$x = -\hbar\omega/kT . \qquad (6.3\text{-}3)$$

Since the levels of the one-dimensional harmonic oscillator are all singly degenerate, $g_n = 1$ for all n. Also, the normalizing factors $\exp\alpha$ are independent of n and cancel above and below. The use of Maxwell-Boltzmann statistics in these circumstances may seem surprising, but is perfectly proper even in quantum theory under the conditions of this problem, which involve oscillator levels not restricted by the Pauli principle, and vibrating atoms regarded as physically distinguishable systems located at distinct and identifiable lattice sites, as required in Section 5.3 of the preceding chapter. Equation (6.3 - 2) can now be transformed algebraically as follows:

$$\langle\varepsilon\rangle = \hbar\omega \cdot \frac{\tfrac{1}{2}e^{\frac{1}{2}x} + \tfrac{3}{2}e^{\frac{3}{2}x} + \tfrac{5}{2}e^{\frac{5}{2}x} + \cdots}{e^{\frac{1}{2}x} + e^{\frac{3}{2}x} + e^{\frac{5}{2}x} + \cdots} = \hbar\omega \cdot \frac{d}{dx}\ln\left[e^{\frac{1}{2}x}\left(1 + e^x + e^{2x} + \cdots\right)\right]$$

$$= \hbar\omega \frac{d}{dx}\left[\tfrac{1}{2}x - \ln(1 - e^x)\right] = \hbar\omega\left[\frac{1}{2} + \frac{1}{e^{\hbar\omega/kT} - 1}\right] . \qquad (6.3\text{-}4)$$

The internal energy is now obtained by multiplying by the number of oscillators, as

$$U = 3N\langle\varepsilon\rangle = \frac{3N\hbar\omega}{2} + \frac{3N\hbar\omega}{e^{\hbar\omega/kT} - 1} , \qquad (6.3\text{-}5)$$

and $\quad C_v = \left(\dfrac{\partial U}{\partial T}\right)_v = 3Nk\left(\dfrac{\hbar\omega}{kT}\right)^2 \dfrac{e^{\hbar\omega/kT}}{(e^{\hbar\omega/kT} - 1)^2} . \qquad (6.3\text{-}6)$

The first term in (6.3 - 5) is simply the total zero-point energy of the $3N$ oscillators. Since it is temperature-independent it contributes nothing to the lattice specific heat.

The result can be more simply expressed by defining an *Einstein Temperature* Θ_E, such that

$$\hbar\omega = k\Theta_E \ . \tag{6.3-7}$$

Substituting this into (6.3 - 6), we can express the heat capacity C_v finally as

$$C_v = 3Nk\left(\frac{\Theta_E}{T}\right)^2 \frac{e^{\Theta_E/T}}{(e^{\Theta_E/T}-1)^2} \ . \tag{6.3-8}$$

This expression, plotted as a function of temperature, is generally similar in appearance to the experimental curve shown in Figure 4.4. In the above expression, when T approaches zero, the exponential term in the denominator becomes infinite and the specific heat approaches zero. When T is much larger than Θ_E, the expression is indeterminate, but if you expand the exponential in the denominator (which is small in this limit) retaining only the first two terms, you will see that the whole expression approaches the classical limit $3Nk$.

At the Einstein temperature, $\Theta_E/T = 1$, and the expression reduces to 0.921 times $3Nk$. Above Θ_E, therefore, the classical answer is relatively accurate, while below this temperature quantum effects become increasingly significant. In Figure 4.4, it is evident that Θ_E is about 200K, which is typical of most crystalline substances. In Einstein's theory, the oscillator frequency ω, so far unspecified, is related to the temperature Θ_E by (6.3 - 7). If one substitutes the value 200K into this equation, the oscillator frequency ω can be evaluated as 2.5×10^{13} rad/sec. In reality, we know that there is no single oscillator frequency, but instead a range of frequencies defined by the dispersion relation, from zero to a maximum frequency ω_m, calculated in Section 3.6 in a similar instance to be about 3.3×10^{13} rad/sec. It is apparent that the frequency implied by the Einstein temperature is consistent with what has been calculated previously in a different way. Indeed, the frequency suggested by the Einstein theory is close to what one might find as a mean oscillator frequency within the spectrum of allowed acoustical frequencies. Einstein's theory in any event gives a far more satisfactory picture of the specific heat of crystalline materials than the classical theory, and is of historical interest in that it provided an early and most convincing demonstration of the validity of quantum theory.

The Einstein theory, though in comparison with experiment far better than the classical result, is still not satisfactory in all ways. In particular, detailed experimental studies in the low-temperature region show clearly that the lattice specific heat of crystalline substances varies with temperature as T^3, in contrast with the exponential temperature variation predicted by the Einstein theory in this régime. The discrepanciy is not surprising, because the theory still employs the relatively crude picture of independent oscillators and a common vibrational frequency. A more realistic theory of specific heats must incorporate the vibrational frequency spectrum given by the dispersion relation as well as the quantization of oscillator energies. Such a theory, which quickly became the basis for many subsequent refinements, was worked out in 1912 by P. P. Debye. This theory is discussed in detail in the next section.

6.4 THE DEBYE THEORY OF SPECIFIC HEAT

Debye's theory regards the atoms of the crystal lattice as harmonic oscillators coupled together by Hooke's law interatomic forces, which propagate acoustic waves over a range of frequencies from zero to a maximum value given by the dispersion relation. In a one-dimensional lattice, this relation has the form (3.6 - 6), but in three dimensions it is much more complex. Certain approximations are therefore still required. The Debye theory, though not exact, agrees with experiment satisfactorily over a wide range of temperatures, and has become the standard description of lattice specific heat in solids.

Since atoms of the lattice no longer vibrate independently, it is easier to work with the allowed normal modes of oscillation rather than the individual atomic oscillators. We have already observed (in Chapter 3) that a one-dimensional linear crystal has essentially N independent vibrational modes, provided that the number of atoms N is large. In a three-dimensional lattice, the number of vibrational modes is $3N$, since boundary conditions allow independent oscillations along all three cartesian axes. Since any configuration of vibrating atoms can be expressed as a superposition of normal mode oscillations, we can treat the lattice as a system of $3N$ independent normal-mode motions, whose energies are given by (6.3 - 1), and whose average energy is expressed by (6.3 - 4), assuming that oscillator energies are distributed according to the Maxwell-Boltzmann law. The beauty of this approach is that though the atomic oscillators are now coupled together, the normal modes are independent of one another. We can now find the internal energy associated with the normal modes having frequencies in a range $d\omega$ about any given frequency ω, and integrate over frequency to obtain the total vibrational energy of the lattice.

Accordingly, the differential energy for waves of frequency ω can be written as

$$dU = \langle \varepsilon(\omega) \rangle g(\omega) d\omega \ , \tag{6.4-1}$$

where $<\varepsilon(\omega)>$ is obtained from (6.3 - 4), and where $g(\omega)d\omega$ is the number of normal modes in a frequency range $d\omega$ about ω. The "density of modes" factor $g(\omega)$ has been calculated for a one-dimensional lattice in Chapter 3, as (3.8 - 14). It is easier in practice to calculate the number of modes $g(k)dk$ in an interval dk about a given value of the propagation constant k than the number $g(\omega)d\omega$, but, since as illustrated in Section 3.8 the two quantities are equal, (6.4 - 1) can be written as

$$dU = \langle \varepsilon(\omega) \rangle g(k) \frac{dk}{d\omega} d\omega \ . \tag{6.4-2}$$

The quantity $g(k)dk$ can be evaluated by a method that should by now be familiar. Assuming a rectangular crystal of dimensions L_x, L_y, L_z, with volume V, the allowed components of the propagation vector $\mathbf{k}$, under periodic boundary conditions requiring that the wave amplitudes on opposite faces of the crystal be equal, are

$$k_x = 2\pi n_x/L_x \ , \qquad k_y = 2\pi n_y/L_y \ , \qquad k_z = 2\pi n_z/L_z \ , \tag{6.4-3}$$

where n_x, n_y, n_z are positive or negative integers. The procedure is the same as that used to derive the free particle density of states function in Section 5.3, except that

236

acoustical waves rather than Schrödinger wave functions are involved. One plots the allowed values of the vector components in (6.4 - 3) in an orthogonal k-space as shown in Figure 6.1. The surface on which the magnitude of the propagation vector has the constant value k is a sphere whose equation is

$$k_x^2 + k_y^2 + k_z^2 = k^2 \ , \tag{6.4-4}$$

as shown in the diagram. A "unit cell" corresponding to a single normal mode is also illustrated. It is evident from this diagram that the volume of k-space occupied by a single mode is $8\pi^3/(L_x L_y L_z)$, or $8\pi^3/V$.

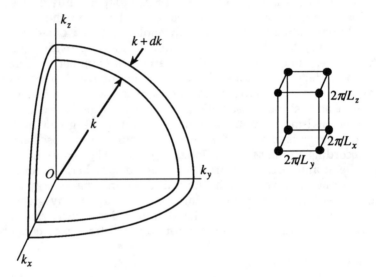

Figure 6.1 Spherical surfaces corresponding to constant vaues k and $k + dk$ of the propagation vector magnitude for acoustic waves in a crystal lattice, plotted in an orthogonal space whose axes describe the components of the propagation vector. Also shown is the "unit cell" volume occupied by a single vibrational mode of the lattice.

The volume of k-space included between the two spheres shown above is $4\pi k^2 dk$. If this is divided by the volume corresponding to a single mode, one obtains $g(k)dk$ as $k^2 V dk/2\pi^2$. However, this takes no account of the fact that there are two transverse modes and a single longitudinal mode of oscillation having the same set of indices n_x, n_y, n_z. This suggests that there should be three vibrational modes rather than one assigned to the unit cell, which increases $g(k)dk$ by a factor of three, so that

$$g(k)dk = \frac{3k^2 V}{2\pi^2} dk \ . \tag{6.4-5}$$

We now have all the ingredients in the prescription (6.4 - 2) except $dk/d\omega$, which can be recognized as the reciprocal of the group velocity. If the dispersion relation is known, this is a simple quantity to calculate, but one which even in a one-dimensional lattice leads to an integral very difficult to evaluate. In lattices of higher dimensionality, the dispersion relation is not easily expressed in closed form, and the problem is even more intractible mathematically. Therefore, some simplifying assumption must be found at this point if any further progress is to be made. Debye assumed a dispersion relation of linear form, in which ω and k are related by a constant sound velocity like that of a continuous homogeneous medium. He also assumed, however, that the spectrum of allowed frequencies extends from zero to a cutoff frequency ω_m, corresponding to a maximum value of k equal to k_m. These assumptions make the calculation of the specific heat possible, while taking into account the discrete lattice structure of the crystal more realistically than previous theories. In using the approximations, however, it is necessary to choose the cutoff value k_m in such a way that the total number of normal modes having frequencies and k-values below this cutoff value is the same as the actual number of allowed normal modes of oscillation for the crystal, which is known to be $3N$. This is accomplished by choosing k_m to be the radius of a sphere (like that in Figure 6.1) which encloses *exactly* $3N$ modes.

The Debye approximation, therefore, embraces the assumptions

$$\omega = v_0 k , \qquad (k < k_m) ,$$
(6.4-6)

where v_0 is the acoustical mode long-wave sonic group velocity, and where

$$\tfrac{4}{3}\pi k_m^3 = 3N \cdot \frac{8\pi^3}{3V} , \quad \text{or} \quad k_m = \left(6\pi^2 \frac{N}{V}\right)^{1/3} .$$
(6.4-7)

Now, substituting (6.3 - 4), (6.4 - 5) and the relation $dk/d\omega = 1/v_0$ from (6.4 - 6) into (6.4 - 2), expressing k as ω/v_0, and integrating from $\omega = 0$ to $\omega = \omega_m = v_0 k_m$ we find

$$U = \frac{3\hbar V}{2\pi^2 v_0^3}\int_0^{\omega_m}\left[\frac{\omega^3}{2} + \frac{\omega^3}{e^{\hbar\omega/kT}-1}\right]d\omega = \frac{9}{8}N\hbar\omega_m + \frac{9N\hbar}{\omega_m^3}\int_0^{\omega_m}\frac{\omega^3 d\omega}{e^{\hbar\omega/kT}-1} .$$
(6.4-8)

The final form of this equation is obtained by using (6.4 - 7) to eliminate V from the expression. It is also useful to express these results in still another form, letting

$$x = \frac{\hbar\omega}{kT} , \qquad x_m = \frac{\hbar\omega_m}{kT} , \quad \text{and} \quad \Theta = \frac{\hbar\omega_m}{k} = \frac{\hbar v_0}{k}\left(\frac{6N\pi^2}{V}\right)^{1/3} .$$
(6.4-9)

In the expressions above, Boltzmann's constant has been written as the unitalicized symbol k to differentiate it from the propagation constant, which is written in italics as k. The quantity Θ defined in (6.4 - 9) has the dimensions of temperature, and is referred to as the *Debye Temperature*. It is useful to remember that $\hbar\omega_m = k\Theta$. The Debye temperature is seen to play a role similar to that of the Einstein temperature in the preceding section. Using these definitions, (6.4 -8) can be written as

$$U = \frac{9}{8}Nk\Theta + 9NkT\left(\frac{T}{\Theta}\right)^3\int_0^{\Theta/T}\frac{x^3 dx}{e^x-1} .$$
(6.4-10)

We may now find the specific heat by differentiating the internal vibrational energy U with respect to temperature. This is most simply accomplished by working with the form given in (6.4 - 8), in which the limits of integration are independent of T. Differentiating this expression with respect to temperature under the integral, we find, with the aid of (6.4 - 8),

$$C_v = 9Nk\left(\frac{T}{\Theta}\right)^3 \int_0^{\Theta/T} \frac{x^4 e^x dx}{(e^x-1)^2} .$$

(6.4 - 11)

The integral above cannot be worked analytically, but since its value depends only on the value of Θ/T, it is not difficult to evaluate numerically. As you can see from Figure 6.2, it looks very much like the experimental curve of Figure 4.4. You should

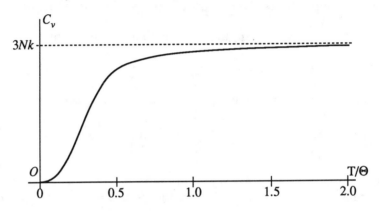

Figure 6.2 The heat capacity of a monatomic nonmetallic crystal as given by the Debye theory, plotted against the reduced temperature variable Θ/T.

observe that the Debye temperature Θ as defined above is temperature-independent, since both the sound velocity and N/V are practically independent of T. When $T = \Theta$, the limits of the integral above are 0 to 1, and the result reduces to 0.952 times the limiting classical value $3Nk$. Below this temperature the specific heat falls off rapidly, and in the low-temperature limit approaches zero as shown. Moreover, when T is much less than Θ, the upper limit of the integral becomes infinite. It is then possible to show that the definite integral attains the value $4\pi^4/15$, the specific heat (6.4 - 11) becoming

$$C_v = \frac{12\pi^4}{5} Nk \left(\frac{T}{\Theta}\right)^3 .$$

(6.4 - 12)

This indicates that the theory agrees with the previously mentioned experimental finding that the specific heat is proportional to T^3 in the low-temperature limit. Indeed, the Debye theory is in good agreement with experimental determinations of the lattice specific heat at all attainable temperatures for many substances. The problem of showing that the Debye expression reduces to the classical value $3Nk$ at high temperatures is assigned as an excercise for the reader.

The above discussion is framed in the context of a monatomic nonmetallic crystal lattice. The difference in the group velocities of longitudinal and transverse modes has also been ignored, the common sound velocity v_0 having been used for both. This can be corrected simply by regarding v_0 as a *mean* velocity defined in terms of the longitudinal and transverse velocities v_l and v_t, by

$$\frac{3}{v_0^3} = \frac{1}{v_l^3} + \frac{2}{v_t^3} \; . \tag{6.4-13}$$

If the factor $3/v_0^3$ in (6.4 - 8) is replaced by this expression, it will be observed that the internal energy of the single longitudinal mode and the two transverse modes is now separately--and correctly--represented. One must remember, however, that the expressions for ω_m and k_m based on (6.4 - 6) and (6.4 - 7) do not give the true allowed maximum values for ω and k, but are merely effective values which serve only to regenerate the known number of modes ($3N$) from the approximate dispersion relation that has been introduced. Fortunately, the use of these values introduces no physically significant error into the final results.

The Debye theory considers only the contribution of lattice vibrations to the specific heat of crystalline materials. Since there is a dense Fermi-Dirac electron gas also to be accounted for in metallic substances, it would seem that its specific heat might also contribute significantly to the observed specific heat of metals. A Maxwell-Boltzmann gas, as shown in the preceding chapter, contributes $(3/2)NkT$ to the internal energy, and $(3/2)Nk$ to the heat capacity; at high temperature, this is half the Debye lattice contribution, and is even larger, proportionally, at low temperatures. However, experiment shows that in copper, for example, the Debye theory alone predicts the observed specific heat almost perfectly. The resolution of this paradox lies in the Pauli exclusion principle and Fermi statistics, which are applicable to the electron gas, but not to the atomic oscillators of the crystal lattice. At energies well below the Fermi energy, the Pauli principle prevents electrons from undergoing excitations of energy kT or thereabouts, since there are very few unoccupied states for them to enter. This leaves only the small fraction of the electron population near the surface of the Fermi sphere, where unoccupied states are readily available, to be excited thermally into higher energy states and thus to increase the internal energy of the distribution. As a result, the specific heat of the electron gas at realizable temperatures can amount to no more than a small fraction of the total. A more detailed account of electronic specific heats will be given in the next chapter.

It is possible to calculate the Debye temperature from observed material parameters, using (6.4 - 9). For Cu, a typical example, the density is 8.96g/cm^3, and the atomic mass is 63.55 amu, which leads to $N/V = 8.49 \times 10^{28} \text{m}^{-3}$. In this material the sound velocities are $v_l = 5010 \text{m/sec}$ and $v_t = 2270 \text{m/sec}$. For these material parameters, (6.4 - 9) yields $\Theta = 335$K, as compared with the value 343K which is the best fit to experimental data. Clearly, the Debye theory agrees well with experimental data in this case. The Debye temperature as given by (6.4 - 9) depends primarily on the sound velocity and (less critically because of the cube root) on the volume per atom. The sound velocity (as discussed in Section 3.4) varies directly as Young's modulus and inversely as the density. Materials with a large elastic modulus, which are thus very stiff, hard, and strong, and yet of low density, therefore, have high Debye temperatures, while weak and easily deformable substances of high density have low Debye temperatures. Carbon in the form of diamond is the most conspicuous example of the first category, with a Debye temperature of around 2000K, while lead, with a Debye temperature of 95K is typical of the other extreme. Most other elements have Debye temperatures in the range 100-400K. Since when $T = \Theta$, the specific heat has already attained 95% if its limiting classical value $3Nk$, this means that essentially all the solid elements obey the law of Dulong and Petit rather well at room temperature. The single anomaly is carbon in the form of diamond, an oddity that had always puzzled people until the Debye theory came along.

TABLE 6.1 DEBYE TEMPERATURE OF CRYSTALLINE SOLIDS

Substance	Debye Θ	Substance	Debye Θ
Al	396K	Fe	460K
Cu	343	Pt	220
Ag	220	Ge	378
Cd	164	Si	650
Pb	95	C (diamond)	2000

Despite the rather large observed range of Debye temperatures, the specific heat versus temperature curve is always the same when the temperature is scaled to the Debye temperature by using the reduced temperature variable T/Θ. The Debye specific heat curve as plotted in Figure 6.2 is therefore a *universal* relationship exhibited by nearly all solid substances. The Debye theory has been successfully extended to embrace more complex crystalline materials such as ionic crystals, intermetallic compounds, and organic substances. By now, however, it should be clear that the exotic concepts such as sonic dispersion, cutoff frequencies, density of states, and quantized energy levels introduced in the preceding chapters is not merely abstract speculation.

6.5 PHONONS

In quantum mechanics, we have observed that transitions of a system from one energy level to another are often accompanied by the emission or absorption of a quantum of electromagnetic energy of frequency $\hbar \Delta \omega$, equal to the difference in energy between the final and initial quantum states. These quanta, which are called photons, have been shown frequently to behave like discrete particles rather than continuous electromagnetic waves. Though conservation of energy requires that energy of some kind be emitted or absorbed in these transitions, there is nothing in quantum theory that requires that it be electromagnetic in character. In the case of the atomic vibrations in crystal lattices, which are described in terms of quantum harmonic oscillators, these discrete quanta are most often not electromagnetic quanta, but instead quanta of acoustical energy referred to as *phonons*. Phonons exhibit many of the same properties associated with electromagnetic quanta, including the now familiar wave-particle duality and the Heisenberg uncertainty relation. Like photons, phonons can interact with other quanta and with particles like electrons, *via* scattering processes resembling particle interactions that conserve momentum and energy. These scattering processes play a major part in explaining electrical and thermal conductivity and certain other properties of crystalline solids. Phonons differ from photons, however, in that their group velocity depends on wavelength, as expressed by the dispersion relation of the lattice, and also in that their maximum frequency is limited by the cutoff frequency associated with lattice vibrations.

Transitions in which the harmonic oscillator goes from one energy state to another ordinarily proceed so that there is unit change in the quantum number n, that is, in which

$$\Delta n = \pm 1 , \quad \text{and} \quad \Delta \varepsilon = \pm \hbar \omega . \tag{6.5-1}$$

Processes in which n changes by two or more steps are under normal circumstances so infrequent as to be termed *forbidden*. Actually, they're not forbidden, just highly improbable. The above equation, which expresses this fact, is referred to as a *selection rule*. Similar selection rules can be shown to apply to some of the transitions of atomic systems from one quantum state to another. The derivation of these selection rules is neither simple nor particularly relevant to our objectives, and therefore will not be undertaken here.

If phonons can behave like particles, it makes sense to ask whether one can consider effects caused by lattice vibrations as properties associated with a gas of free phonons, somewhat like the gas of free electrons that describes the behavior of these particles in metals. This question can be answered affirmatively, provided certain precautions are observed. In particular, phonons (unlike the oscillating atoms that emit and absorb them) resemble photons in being indistinguishable particles. Moreover, since they do not have half-integral spin (nor any spin at all in the present context), they are not subject to the Pauli exclusion principle. This means that Bose-Einstein statistics must be used to describe how they are distributed in energy. This fact is also suggested by the form of (6.3 - 4) and later expressions that follow from it.

The number of phonons in a frequency range $d\omega$ about ω can now be written as

$$N(\omega)d\omega = f(\omega)g(\omega)d\omega = \frac{g(\omega)d\omega}{e^{\hbar\omega/kT}-1} , \tag{6.5-2}$$

where $g(\omega)d\omega$ is the density of vibrational states, given by (6.4 - 5) and (6.4 - 6) in the Debye approximation as

$$g(\omega)d\omega = g(k)\frac{dk}{d\omega}d\omega = \frac{3\omega^2 V}{2\pi^2 v_0^3}d\omega . \tag{6.5-3}$$

Substituting this into (6.5 - 2), we find

$$N(\omega)d\omega = \frac{3V}{2\pi^2 v_0^3} \frac{\omega^2 d\omega}{e^{\hbar\omega/kT}-1} . \tag{6.5-4}$$

The contribution to the internal energy from phonons of frequency in the range $d\omega$ about ω is

$$dU = \varepsilon(\omega)N(\omega)d\omega = \hbar\omega \cdot N(\omega)d\omega = \frac{3\hbar V}{2\pi^2 v_0^3} \frac{\omega^3 d\omega}{e^{\hbar\omega/kT}-1} . \tag{6.5-5}$$

Integrating this over the range of possible phonon frequencies ($0 < \omega < \omega_m$), we obtain the second term of the Debye expression (6.4 - 8) for the internal energy. The heat capacity or specific heat follows as before by differentiating with respect to temperature. The first term in (6.4 - 8) is not obtained from this calculation, since the internal energy of the phonon gas arises solely from excitation energies, and thus includes no zero-point energy. With this slight difference, the same result is found from a calculation involving classical identifiable atomic oscillators using Maxwell-Boltzmann statistics, and from the picture of a gas of particle-like (but indistinguishable) excitation quanta obeying Bose-Einstein statistics. It should be noted also, that because of the differences in longitudinal and transverse acoustical wave propagation, there are longitudinal and transverse phonons which have different velocities and in general obey different dispersion relations.

If you substitute $\omega = 2\pi c / \lambda$, $d\omega = -2\pi c \, d\lambda / \lambda^2$ into the above expression and replace the sound velocity with the speed of light, you will obtain an expression identical (except for a constant factor) to Planck's radiation formula (4.2 - 4). This illustrates the similarity between the idea of a phonon gas in equilibrium with the crystal lattice and the concept (based on Planck's ideas) of blackbody radiation as a gas of photons in an enclosure in which it is in equilibrium with atomic oscillators in the cavity walls. The only difference is that phonons have a maximum frequency ω_m, while photons can have arbitrarily large frequencies. As an exercise, the reader is asked to clarify this equivalence, and to show rigorously that these two formulas are identical in all respects except the cutoff frequency.

6.6 ANHARMONICITY AND THERMAL EXPANSION

In gases, thermal expansion is a fairly large and easily observed phenomenon. For example, the volume of an ideal gas at a constant pressure of one atmosphere and room temperature (300K) expands by about one part in 300 per degree change in temperature. In crystalline solids, on the other hand, thermal expansion, though measurable, is a far smaller effect, amounting under similar conditions to a volume change of only about one part in 20,000 for most substances. The reason is, of course, that the atoms of the crystal are held in place by relatively strong forces, while gas atoms are essentially free particles.

So far, we have been able to calculate most of the properties of crystalline substances in terms of a model in which atoms are bound to equilibrium sites by harmonic forces--the kind of forces exerted by Hooke's law springs. When you try to describe the thermal expansion of a crystal considering only these forces, however, the calculated thermal expansion coefficient is *zero*. Since the thermal expansion of a solid is admittedly a small effect, this answer isn't absolutely ridiculous, but since there is a measurable expansion, it is clear that it must be caused by the departure of interatomic forces from the form given by Hooke's law. This departure is often referred to as *anharmonicity*.

The validity of this assertion can be illustrated by a simple one-dimensional calculation. In it, we assume an interatomic potential energy qualitatively of a form similar to that introduced in Chapter 3 in discussing the binding energy of ionic substances. This potential energy $V(x)$ is illustrated in Figure 6.3. In this picture, the atom vibrates back and forth in a potential well of the form illustrated, with kinetic energy that increases with rising temperature. We shall treat the system classically in this first approach, assuming a continuum of allowed energies, and neglecting zero-point energy. At zero temperature the atom is at rest at the bottom of the well, and the equilibrium interatomic separation is a, as illustrated.

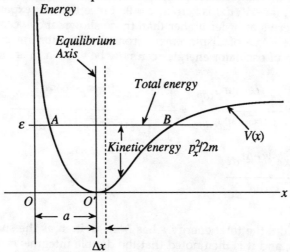

Figure 6.3 Potential well for an atom in a linear one dimensional crystal whose equilibrium lattice spacing is a. If the atom has thermal kinetic energy it will vibrate about the equilibrium point, the maximum excursions of its motion being defined by the points A and B. The asymmetry of the potential energy curve causes point B to be further from the equilibrium point than A, resulting in an average distance between atoms that is larger than a by a temperature-dependent amount Δx.

If the interatomic forces obeyed Hooke's law exactly, the potential well in the figure would be parabolic and its vertical symmetry axis would coincide with the equilibrium axis. In such a symmetric well, the atom would execute harmonic oscillations whose maximum excursions from equilibrium at points A and B. would be equidistant from the equilibrium axis. The probability associated with a given positive value of displacement from equilibrium and an equal negative value is now the same, and the *average* distance between atoms is the equilibrium distance a, independent of the vibration amplitude or the total particle energy.

When the interatomic potential energy is not parabolic, but has the form shown above, the points A and B are no longer equidistant from the equilibrium axis. This suggests, correctly, that the time required to go from equilibrium to B and back is greater than the time elapsed during the journey to A and back. The mean interatomic distance is now slightly larger than the equilibrium spacing, and moreover will increase with increasing particle energy. The lattice now exhibits the phenomenon of *thermal expansion*, an effect that clearly must depend on the extent to which interatomic forces *depart* from Hooke's law.

This effect can be treated quantitatively by writing the interatomic potential energy as a power series expansion about the equilibrium point. Such a series can be written as

$$V(x) = \tfrac{1}{2}\beta x^2 - bx^3 - cx^4 + \cdots .$$

(6.6-1)

In this expression, the coördinate x is measured from an origin at the equilibrium point O' rather than the point O in the figure. The quantity β is the usual harmonic force constant, while b and c are the usual Taylor's series coefficients involving third and fourth derivatives of $V(x)$ evaluated at $x = 0$. The constant term in this series is zero because of the choice of origin, while the coefficient of the first power of x vanishes because F_x ($= -dV/dx$) is zero at $x = 0$. Since thermal expansion is known to be a small effect, terms of order higher than those shown above can safely be neglected. The mean value $\langle \Delta x \rangle$ of displacement from the equilibrium point over a Maxwellian distribution of oscillator energies can now be written in analogy with (5.3 - 5) as

$$\langle \Delta x \rangle = \frac{\iint x e^{-\varepsilon(x,p_x)/kT} dx\, dp_x}{\iint e^{-\varepsilon(x,p_x)/kT} dx\, dp_x} = \frac{\int_{-\infty}^{\infty}\int_{-\infty}^{\infty} x e^{-p_x^2/2mkT} e^{-V(x)/kT} dx\, dp_x}{\int_{-\infty}^{\infty}\int_{-\infty}^{\infty} e^{-p_x^2/2mkT} e^{-V(x)/kT} dx\, dp_x} \quad ,$$

or, $$\langle \Delta x \rangle = \frac{\int_{-\infty}^{\infty} x e^{-V(x)/kT} dx}{\int_{-\infty}^{\infty} e^{-V(x)/kT} dx} \quad . \tag{6.6-2}$$

In this expression, the total energy ε has been written as the sum of kinetic and potential energies, and it is then noted that the double integrals can be expressed as the product of two single integrals over dx and dp_x. The integrals over the momentum variable are now seen to cancel above and below, leading to the final result.

Because thermal expansion is such a small effect, the cubic and quartic terms in (6.6 - 1) will be much smaller than the leading harmonic term. This permits us to expand the exponential term containing those coefficients in (6.6 - 2) as follows:

$$\int_{-\infty}^{\infty} x e^{-V(x)/kT} dx = \int_{-\infty}^{\infty} x e^{-\beta x^2/2kT} \left(e^{(bx^3+cx^4)/kT} \right) dx = \int_{-\infty}^{\infty} x e^{-\beta x^2/2kT} \left(1 + \frac{bx^3}{kT} + \frac{cx^4}{kT} \right) dx \ .$$

$$\tag{6.6-3}$$

In this expression, the first and third terms in the series in parentheses lead to integrals of odd functions of x, whose values are zero. The only term to survive is the cubic term, which with the help of the table of integrals in Section 5.5 yields,

$$\int_{-\infty}^{\infty} x e^{-V(x)/kT} dx = \frac{3\sqrt{\pi}}{4} \left(\frac{2kT}{\beta} \right)^{5/2} \frac{b}{kT} \quad . \tag{6.6-4}$$

The other integral is treated in a similar way, giving

$$\int_{-\infty}^{\infty} e^{-V(x)/kT} dx = \int_{-\infty}^{\infty} e^{-\beta x^2/2kT} \left(1 + \frac{bx^3}{kT} + \frac{cx^4}{kT} \right) dx = \sqrt{\pi} \left(\frac{2kT}{\beta} \right)^{1/2} \quad . \tag{6.6-5}$$

In this expression the cubic term leads to an integral of an odd function, which is zero, while the contribution of the quartic term has been neglected in comparison to that of the leading term. When these results are substituted into (6.6 - 2), one obtains finally,

$$\langle \Delta x \rangle = \frac{3bkT}{\beta^2} \, , \qquad \text{and} \qquad \frac{d\langle \Delta x \rangle}{dT} = \frac{3bk}{\beta^2} \, . \qquad (6.6\text{-}6)$$

For a crystal of length L, the coefficient of linear expansion a is defined as

$$\alpha = \frac{1}{L}\frac{\Delta L}{\Delta T} \, , \qquad \text{or} \qquad \alpha = \frac{1}{Na} \cdot \frac{Nd\langle \Delta x \rangle}{dT} = \frac{3bk}{a\beta^2} \, . \qquad (6.6\text{-}7)$$

This theory predicts a lattice expansion which is a linear function of temperature, with an expansion coefficient that depends on the *cubic* term in the potential energy expansion. This is in good agreement with experiment at and above normal room temperature, but as in the case of specific heat (and for similar reasons) the expansion coefficient falls off drastically at low temperatures. Indeed, as we shall see in a later section, the coefficient of expansion is proportional to the specific heat, a fact suggested by the factor $3k$ in the above expressions. The cubic anharmonicity as expressed by the factor b is very difficult to measure or calculate directly; the above relations, however, allow it to be determined experimentally from measured expansion coefficients.

6.7 THE GIBBS AND HELMHOLTZ THERMODYNAMIC FUNCTIONS

Thermodynamics can be as useful in treating solid-state problems as it is in discussing the properties of gases and liquids. If the thermodymamics you've been exposed to in elementary physics or engineering couses has faded away, this section will furnish a good excuse for refreshing your memory. In particular, you should review the definitions of heat, temperature, pressure, internal energy, enthalpy. and entropy. You should also understand the concept of thermodynamic equilibrium, and the distinction between well-defined physical quantities like pressure, temperature, volume, internal energy, and entropy, which depend only on the thermodynamic state of the system, and quantities like heat and work which depend not only on changes of the thermodynamic state, but also on the specific processes that bring about these changes. Examples of such processes include isothermal, adiabatic, isobaric and isovolumetric processes, and the processes that define various thermodynamic cycles--Carnot, Otto, Benz, Diesel, etc. In particular, you should recall that the first set of quantities undergo no net change during any reversible cyclic process in which the system returns to its initial equilibrium state, while net work is usually done and net heat absorbed or given up in these processes. The Carnot cycle affords a good example of the changes these variables undergo in a cyclic process. You should also understand the difference between reversible and irreversible processes. Finally, you should review the first and second laws of thermodynamics, and understand them from several different perspectives.

The second law of thermodynamics as applied to a closed system that does not exchange energy with its surroundings, states that the condition of thermal equilibrium corresponds to that of maximum entropy, and that any *spontaneous* change in the state of the system when it is not initially at equilibrium must be such as to increase its entropy, and thus make it resemble more closely the equilibrium state. This statement is also true when the word *disorder* is substituted for entropy.

In reality, however, we deal more frequently with systems that can exchange heat or work with their surroundings, so this rather restricted statement is of limited usefulness. For these more general circumstances, the statement of the second law we shall find most useful is as follows: in reversible processes that carry the system from an initial equilibrium state to a final equilibrium state, *the entropy of the system plus that of its surroundings* is unchanged, but when irreversible processes connect these same initial and final states, the entropy of system plus surroundings increases. You must consider not only the entropy change of the system, but the total entropy change of system and surroundings. For system and surroundings as a whole, a final thermal equilibrium state of the entire domain is attained when the entropy of the system plus that of its surroundings is maximized.

Reversible processes are those that never compel the state of a system to be much different from one of thermal equilibrium. In this limit, the state is thus always adequately described as an equilibrium state, having a well-defined temperature and pressure. Changes of state in such processes are made very slowly, with very low pressure and temperature gradients. Heat fluxes, and the rates at which volume is changed and work is done are likewise infinitesimal. It is necessary, obviously, that in carrying out such processes, one must have *absolute control* over these gradients, fluxes and rates of change. Any two equilibrium states can in principle be connected by such processes. It is an inherent property of these processes that the system can always be returned to its original condition *without the performance of any net external work*, simply by retracing the thermodynamic path followed originally. The slow melting or freezing of a crystal of ice by a gradual positive or negative heat flux is a good example of a reversible process. Naturally, since any process is truly reversible only in the limit of infinitesimally small rates of change of the relevant variables, reversible processes are (like the concept of an ideal gas) never quite attainable in practice. Nevertheless, they are useful in that they provide an approach to the understanding of thermodynamic processes in general.

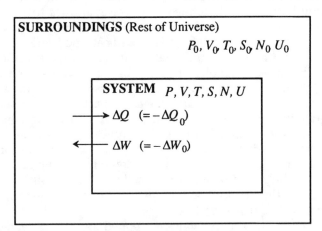

Figure 6.4 Schematic illustration of a thermodynamic system that can exchange heat with and do work on its surroundings. The arrows suggest that heat is being absorbed by the system, and that the system does work on the surroundings. An equivalent amount of heat is therefore given up by the surroundings, and an equal amount of work of opposite sign is done by the surroundings on the sysatem.

Irreversible processes, on the other hand, are those in which there is no way of controlling the rates of change of thermodynamic variables. These processes are "spontaneous" changes in which rates are inherent in the process itself, and cannot be controlled externally. In irreversible processes there can be sharp gradients, turbulent irreglarities, and temporal fluctuations of temperature and pressure that make it difficult even to discuss temperature and pressure with any precision, since these quantities are ordinarily defined with reference to an equilibrium state. Irreversible processes are inherently dissipative in nature, and they are inevitably associated with an increase in the disorder of the system. They therefore can be said to create entropy. It is inherent in an irreversible process that *external work* must be supplied to return the system to its initial state. If a hot body is placed in thermal contact with a cold one, heat flows spontaneously from hot to cold until the temperatures are equalized. The heat flows at a rate determined by the system itself, a rate not subject to external control. When a gas confined in a cylinder is released into a surrounding vacuum by opening a valve, gas escapes at a rate determined (for a given orifice size) by the internal kinetics of the system until pressure is equalized. Such processes are irreversible. To restore the system to its initial state, external work must be done. In the first instance, you must put one object in an oven and the other in a refrigerator; work must be done to operate both appliances. In the second case, the gas must be recompressed into its original volume, an operation that cannot be accomplished without the aid of external work.

The interplay of system and surroundings is illustrated in Figure 6.4, where the system and surroundings interchange work dW and heat dQ. The sign convention is that work done by a system is positive, work done on it is negative, while heat absorbed by a system is positive and heat given up is negative. In the diagram, and in the rest of this development, quantities associated with the system have no subscripts, while those related to the surroundings have the subscript zero. The figure suggests that positive heat dQ is absorbed by the system and positive work dW is done by it, while heat and work equal in magnitude but opposite in sign is given up by (and done upon) the surroundings. Assuming that the process is reversible, the entropy change of the system is by definition $dS = dQ/T$, while the entropy change of the surroundings is $dS_0 = dQ_0/T_0 = -dQ/T$. For system plus surroundings, however, the entropy change in any reversible process is zero, so that

$$dS + dS_0 = \frac{dQ}{T} - \frac{dQ}{T_0} = 0 , \qquad \text{from which} \qquad T = T_0 . \qquad (6.7\text{-}1)$$

We conclude from this that a truly reversible process can be carried out only when there is no temperature difference between system and surroundings. In practice, no heat will flow unless there is a temperature gradient, so the process cannot really occur as ideally envisioned; nevertheless it can be approached under circumstances in which the temperature difference is arbitrarily small. The equilibrium state of the system and surroundings is defined as a state of maximum entropy, for which $d(S + S_0) = 0$, which leads similarly to the result $T = T_0$, and thus to the conclusion that system and surroundings must have the same uniform temperature in thermal equilibrium.

Though the entropy of the entire domain is a maximum in thermal equilibrium, it is not possible to make the same statement about either S or S_0. In other words, though at equilibrium $d(S + S_0) = 0$, this does not mean that $dS = 0$ or $dS_0 = 0$. Moreover, it is sometimes not easy to determine the entropy of the surroundings. It therefore makes sense to find properties of the system alone that attain maximum or minimum values in equilibrium, if only to define the condition of thermal equilibrium itself. For reversible processes that exchange heat and work in systems of constant volume and temperature one can show that the quantity $F = U - TS$, called the Helmholtz function or the Helmholtz free energy, plays such a role. In a system such as the one in Figure 6.4, when the volume V is held constant in thermal equilibrium, both dF and dF_0 are zero. Likewise, in a system held at constant pressure and temperature, one can show that the function $G = U - TS + PV = F + PV$ behaves similarly. The function G is called the Gibbs function, or the Gibbs free energy. In both cases (and in contrast with the entropy) the value of these functions is a *minimum* in the thermal equilibrium condition. In view of the above definitions, it is clear that these quantities (like temperature, pressure, internal energy, enthalpy and entropy) depend only on the thermodynamic state of the system itself, and that the changes they undergo when the state of the system changes depend only on its initial and final states, and are therefore process-independent.

The validity of these statements can be understood from Figure 6.4. In the diagram, heat ΔQ is absorbed by the system, increasing its internal energy by an amount ΔU, and causing it to do work ΔW. We shall assume that this process takes place at constant volume and temperature. In any event, the second law requires that

$$\Delta S + \Delta S_0 \geq 0 \; , \tag{6.7-2}$$

However, we know that $\Delta S_0 = \Delta Q_0 / T = -\Delta Q / T$, so that this can also be written as

$$\Delta S - \frac{\Delta Q}{T} \geq 0 \quad \text{or} \quad T(S_f - S_i) \geq \Delta Q \; . \tag{6.7-3}$$

In these equations, the subscripts f and i refer to final and initial states; for reversible processes the equals sign is applicable, while for irreversible processes there is an inequality related to the increase in entropy. The first law of thermodynamics, which is merely a statement that energy is conserved, can be written,

$$\Delta Q = \Delta U + \Delta W \; , \qquad \text{or} \qquad \Delta W = \Delta Q - \Delta U \; . \tag{6.7-4}$$

If we now substitute the larger quantity $T\Delta S$ in (6.7 - 3) for ΔQ, the right side of the above expression becomes larger than the left, and we obtain

$$\Delta W \leq T(S_f - S_i) - (U_f - U_i) \; . \tag{6.7-5}$$

Now consider the quantity $F = U - TS$. At constant temperature we can write

$$\Delta F = F_f - F_i = U_f - U_i - T(S_f - S_i) \; , \tag{6.7-6}$$

or,

$$\Delta W = -\Delta F \quad \text{for a reversible process,}$$

$$\tag{6.7-7}$$

and $\quad \Delta W < -\Delta F \quad$ for an irreversible process.

In the context of this discussion, $-\Delta F$ is a *positive* quantity. Therefore, $-\Delta F$ represents the maximum work that can be performed by a system in a process that takes place at constant volume and temperature. This maximum is obtained when the process is reversible; otherwise less work is performed. The condition of thermal equilibrium, moreover, corresponds to that of maximum total entropy, in which

$$d(S + S_0) = dS - \frac{dQ}{T} = 0 \ . \tag{6.7-8}$$

Using the first law of thermodynamics, this can be transformed as follows;

$$dQ = TdS = dU + PdV = d(F + TS) + PdV,$$

$$TdS = dF + TdS + SdT + PdV \ ,$$

$$0 = dF + SdT + PdV \ . \tag{6.7-9}$$

However, in a system at constant volume and temperature, dV and dT are zero, and

$$dF = 0 \ . \tag{6.7-10}$$

This condition implies an extremal value for F at equilibrium, which can be shown always to be a minimum. It is useful in that it defines the thermal equilibrium state of a system held at constant volume and temperature.

A similar argument based upon a system maintained at constant *pressure* and temperature, shows for the Gibbs function defined by

$$G = F + PV = U - TS + PV \ , \tag{6.7-11}$$

that at thermal equilibrium

$$0 = dG + SdT - VdP \ . \tag{6.7-12}$$

For a system at constant pressure and temperature, dV and dT are zero, giving for a system in thermal equilibrium

$$dG = 0 \ , \tag{6.7-13}$$

corresponding to a minimum of the Gibbs function for equlibrium under constant pressure and temperature. It also follows that $-\Delta G$ represents the maximum work that can be obtained from a system in a process carried out at constant temperature and pressure. As above, this maximum occurs when the process is reversible; when it is not, a smaller amount of work is done by the system. The proof of these assertions is assigned as an exercise for the reader.

It is possible, using the Gibbs and Helmholtz functions, to derive certain important relations between thermodynamic quantities. In the case of the Helmholtz function, from (6.7 - 9) we can write,

$$dF = \left(\frac{\partial F}{\partial V}\right)_T dV + \left(\frac{\partial F}{\partial T}\right)_V dT = -SdT - PdV \ . \tag{6.7-14}$$

Since T and V are independent variables, one can equate the coefficients of their respective differentials on both sides of this equation to obtain

$$\left(\frac{\partial F}{\partial V}\right)_T = -P \ , \tag{6.7-15}$$

and

$$\left(\frac{\partial F}{\partial T}\right)_V = -S \ . \tag{6.7-16}$$

In a similar way, one can show from (6.7 - 12) that the Gibbs function yields the relations

$$\left(\frac{\partial G}{\partial P}\right)_T = V \quad \text{and} \quad \left(\frac{\partial G}{\partial T}\right)_P = -S \ . \tag{6.7-17}$$

Finally, it is evident from (6.7 - 16) and (6.7 - 17) that.

$$\left(\frac{\partial F}{\partial T}\right)_V = \left(\frac{\partial G}{\partial T}\right)_P . \tag{6.7-18}$$

These relationships are useful in investigating the equation of state of a crystalline substance, as we shall soon see.

6.8 THE DEBYE–GRÜNEISEN EQUATION OF STATE

The Debye theory is useful not only in explaining lattice specific heat, but also in discussing other thermodynamic properties of crystals, in particular, their equations of state. One reason for its utility is that the Debye temperature can easily be related to the volume changes a crystal exhibits under pressure. Experimental studies show that in most simple crystalline materials the lattice specific heat predicted by the Debye theory agrees closely with measurements over a very wide temperature range. In such substances, experimentally determined points can (by choosing the right value for Θ) be made to coincide closely with the Debye curve shown in Figure 6.2, from the lowest temperatures attainable to temperatures near the melting point. Moreover, the experimentally determined "right value" for Θ usually agrees rather well with that given by the theoretical expression (6.4 - 9).

This information can be interpreted as establishing the fact that the parameter Θ is practically *independent of temperature*. It is clear from (6.4 - 9), however, that Θ depends explicitly on the volume, and also can have an implicit volume dependence through the sound velocity, which changes as a result of changes in the density and elastic moduli as the volume of the crystal changes. Since the thermodynamic state of the crystal can be described by the two independent thermodynamic quantities V and T, and since Θ is independent of T, it is clear that volume changes can be directly related to changes in the Debye Temperature. There are, of course, some substances for which this general statement is not true, but they are usually materials exhibiting phase changes and other transitions whose effects are clearly evident, and which are obviously not considered in Debye's theory of specific heat.

Debye's theory allows us to calculate the vibrational part of the lattice internal energy of a crystal explicitly, as shown in (6.4 - 10). To find the total thermodynamic internal energy, we must add to this the *cohesive energy* of the lattice, which is the potential energy of interaction between atoms in the absence of lattice vibrations. This cohesive energy can be regarded as the interaction potential energy of the lattice at a temperature of absolute zero. This allows us to write the internal energy as

$$U = U_0 + U_L , \qquad (6.8-1)$$

where U_0 is the zero-temperature cohesive energy and U_L the Debye vibrational energy, which includes the zero-point term in (6.4 - 10). Since U and F are the same at absolute zero, the Helmholtz function can be written as

$$F = U_0 + F_L = U_0 + (U_L - TS_L) . \qquad (6.8-2)$$

The pressure follows from (6.7 - 15) once F is known, leading directly to an equation of state. The quantity U_L can be expressed with the help of (6.7 - 16) as

$$U_L = F_L + TS_L = F_L - T\left(\frac{\partial F_L}{\partial T}\right)_V = \left(\frac{\partial (F_L/T)}{\partial (1/T)}\right)_V . \qquad (6.8-3)$$

The final form of this result can be verified by direct differentiation, as follows;

$$\left(\frac{\partial (F_L/T)}{\partial (1/T)}\right)_V = \frac{\partial (F_L/T)}{\partial T} \cdot \frac{\partial T}{\partial (1/T)} = -T^2 \frac{\partial (F_L/T)}{\partial T} = F_L - T\left(\frac{\partial F_L}{\partial T}\right)_V . \qquad (6.8-4)$$

If the zero-point vibrational energy in (6.4 - 10) is written as $(9/8)NkT \cdot (\Theta/T)$, it is clear that the internal energy (6.8 - 3) has the functional form

$$U_L = Tf(\Theta/T) . \qquad (6.8-5)$$

The change in entropy between any two equilibrium states is determined only by the initial and final thermodynamic states, independent of the process that takes the system from one to the other. In a reversible constant-volume process, it is easy to calculate entropy changes, for then $dQ = TdS = C_v dT$, and $dS = C_v dT/T$. However, since

$$\frac{dT}{T} = -\frac{d(\Theta/T)}{\Theta/T} , \qquad (6.8-6)$$

we can write, noting that in (6.4 - 11) C_v depends only on (Θ/T),

$$TS_L = T\int_0^T C_v \frac{dT}{T} = -T\int_\infty^{\Theta/T} C_v\left(\frac{\Theta}{T}\right) \cdot \left(\frac{\Theta}{T}\right)^{-1} d\left(\frac{\Theta}{T}\right) = T \cdot S_L(\Theta/T) . \qquad (6.8-7)$$

Therefore, the Helmholtz function can be written

$$F_L = U_L - TS_L = Tf(\Theta/T) - TS_L(\Theta/T) = T\varphi(\Theta/T) . \qquad (6.8-8)$$

Also, it follows that

$$\frac{\partial(F_L/T)}{\partial(1/T)} = \frac{\partial\varphi(\Theta/T)}{\partial(1/T)} = \frac{\partial\varphi(\Theta/T)}{\partial(\Theta/T)} \cdot \frac{\partial(\Theta/T)}{\partial(1/T)} = \Theta \cdot \frac{d\varphi(\Theta/T)}{d(\Theta/T)} = \Theta\varphi' , \qquad (6.8\text{-}9)$$

where the prime denotes differentiation with respect to the argument (Θ/T). Moreover, from (6.8 - 8), observing that Θ and T are independent of one another,

$$\frac{\partial F_L}{\partial\Theta} = T\frac{\partial\varphi(\Theta/T)}{\partial\Theta} = T\frac{\partial\varphi(\Theta/T)}{\partial(\Theta/T)} \cdot \frac{\partial(\Theta/T)}{\partial\Theta} = \varphi' . \qquad (6.8\text{-}10)$$

This allows us to write

$$U_L = \Theta\varphi' = \Theta\frac{\partial F_L}{\partial\Theta} = F_L - T\left(\frac{\partial F_L}{\partial T}\right)_V . \qquad (6.8\text{-}11)$$

From (6.7 - 15) and (6.8 - 2), and from the fact that Θ depends only on V, it is now possible to express the pressure as

$$P = -\left(\frac{\partial F}{\partial V}\right)_T = -\left(\frac{\partial F_L}{\partial\Theta}\right)_T\left(\frac{\partial\Theta}{\partial V}\right) - \frac{\partial U_0}{\partial V} . \qquad (6.8\text{-}12)$$

Using (6.8 - 10) and (6.8 - 11) this can be put in the form

$$P = -\frac{\partial U_0}{\partial V} - \varphi'\frac{\partial\Theta}{\partial V} = -\frac{\partial U_0}{\partial V} - \frac{U_L}{\Theta}\frac{\partial\Theta}{\partial V} . \qquad (6.8\text{-}13)$$

Finally, multiplying both sides by V, this becomes

$$PV = -U_0 \cdot \frac{V}{U_0}\frac{\partial U_0}{\partial V} - U_L \cdot \frac{V}{\Theta}\frac{\partial\Theta}{\partial V} = \gamma_0 U_0 + \gamma U_L , \qquad (6.8\text{-}14)$$

where

$$\gamma = -\frac{V}{\Theta}\frac{\partial\Theta}{\partial V} = -\frac{\partial(\ln\Theta)}{\partial(\ln V)} \quad \text{and} \quad \gamma_0 = -\frac{V}{U_0}\frac{\partial U_0}{\partial V} = -\frac{\partial(\ln U_0)}{\partial(\ln V)} . \qquad (6.8\text{-}15)$$

The quantity γ is referred to as the Grüneisen parameter. Both γ and γ_0, though seemingly complicated functions of volume, can usually be treated as constants. This can be understood by noting that a power-law relationship of the form $\Theta \cong V^{-n}$ between Debye temperature and volume is usually valid when fractional volume changes are not too large. Under these circumstances, according to (6.8 - 15) γ has the constant value n. Similar remarks are valid for the functional relationship between U_0 and γ_0. For example, in materials for which the Born-Madelung theory of Chapter 3 is appropriate, U_0 is given by (3.2 - 14) as

$$U_0 = -\frac{N\alpha e^2}{r}\left(1 - \frac{1}{n}\right) , \qquad (6.8\text{-}16)$$

where r is the interatomic spacing, α the Madelung constant and n the repulsive exponent. Since V/N, the volume per atom, is equal to r^3, we have $r = (V/N)^{1/3}$. Substituting this into the above equation, and using the resulting expression to calculate γ_0 according to the definition in (6.8 - 15), one obtains $\gamma_0 = 1/3$. In crystals that are not ionic, but in which other electromagnetic interactions (Van der Waals forces, for example) hold the atoms together, the binding energy will be different, though still roughly dependent on an inverse power of interatomic distance, leading as above to a constant value for γ_0. The Grüneisen constant γ is listed below for a number of solid substances. Since Θ is practically independent of T, the Grüneisen constant is also temperature-independent.

TABLE 6.2 THE GRÜNEISEN CONSTANT

Substance	Grüneisen γ
Cu	1.96
Ag	2.40
Al	2.17
Fe	1.60
Ni	1.88
Co	1.87
Na	1.25
K	1.35
NaCl	1.63
KCl	1.60

The equation of state of an ideal gas can be written as $PV = 2U/3$, where the internal energy U is $3NkT/2$. The Debye-Grüneisen equation of state (6.8 - 14), whose temperature dependence is the same as that of U_L, has a somewhat similar form. It differs, however, in that the low-temperature limit of the PV product is not zero, but has a value related to the zero-temperature cohesive energy and the zero-point vibrational energy. Moreover, its temperature dependence is more complex than that of an ideal gas, having the form of the *integral* of the specific heat curve in Figure 6.3. The second term in (6.8 - 15) can be viewed as the equation of state of the phonon gas in the Debye theory. The temperature dependence of the PV product given by the Debye-Grüneisen theory for a solid, is shown in comparison with that of the ideal gas in Figure 6.5. It is important to note that the schematic curves in the figure are *not* drawn to the same scale.

If we differentiate (6.8 - 14), holding volume constant and noting that U_0 is temperature-independent, we find

$$\left(\frac{\partial P}{\partial T}\right)_v = \frac{\gamma}{V}\left(\frac{\partial U_L}{\partial T}\right)_v = \frac{\gamma C_v}{V} \ . \tag{6.8-17}$$

The temperature derivative shown above can be related to the volume coefficient of expansion 3α, by the use of a purely mathematical relationship

$$\left(\frac{\partial P}{\partial T}\right)_v\left(\frac{\partial T}{\partial V}\right)_P\left(\frac{\partial V}{\partial P}\right)_T = -1 \ , \tag{6.8-18}$$

254

whose derivation is assigned as an exercise for the reader. This equation can be rearranged to read

$$\left(\frac{\partial P}{\partial T}\right)_v = -\left[\left(\frac{\partial T}{\partial V}\right)_P\left(\frac{\partial V}{\partial P}\right)_T\right]^{-1} = -\left(\frac{\partial V}{\partial T}\right)_P\bigg/\left(\frac{\partial V}{\partial P}\right)_T . \tag{6.8-19}$$

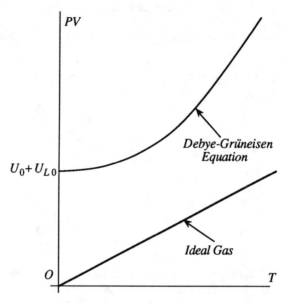

Figure 6.5 Schematic diagram illustrating the difference between the PV product of an ideal gas and a crystal obeying the Debye-Grüneisen equation of state. The two curves shown above are *not* drawn to the same scale.

If the right side of (6.8 - 19) is multiplied above and below by $1/V$, this result can be expressed as a relationship between the volume coefficient of expansion and the isothermal compressibility, having the form

$$\left(\frac{\partial P}{\partial T}\right)_v = \frac{\alpha_v}{K_i} = \frac{3\alpha}{K_i} , \tag{6.8-20}$$

where the volume expansion coefficient α_v and the isothermal compressibility K_i are defined by

$$\alpha_v = 3\alpha = \frac{1}{V}\left(\frac{\partial V}{\partial T}\right)_P \quad \text{and} \quad K_i = -\frac{1}{V}\left(\frac{\partial V}{\partial P}\right)_T . \tag{6.8-21}$$

Substituting (6.8 - 20) into (6.8 - 17) and solving for α, we can finally write

$$\alpha = \frac{\gamma K_i C_v}{3V} . \tag{6.8-22}$$

This can be compared with the expression obtained by a rather different route in Section 6.6 as (6.6 - 7). The two results are compatible, though it must be recalled that (6.6 - 7) is valid only at high temperatures, where the specific heat equals the constant $3Nk$. The factor $3k$ in this equation can thus be identified as C_v/N. We are now being nudged in the odd direction of associating the cubic anharmonicity parameter b in (6.6 - 7) with the Grüneisen constant γ. Equation (6.8 - 17) impels us even more strongly in this direction, because we have already seen that when b is zero there is no anharmonicity, and also no thermal expansion. Suppose one has a crystal whose thermal expansion is zero. If it is enclosed in a perfectly rigid container and heated, it will not expand and therefore cannot increase the pressure exerted on the confining vessel. Then, the right side of (6.8 - 17) must clearly be zero. But this can come about only if γ is zero, since neither the specific heat nor the volume of a crystal having purely harmonic interatomic forces is zero. There is thus no way to avoid the conclusion that b and γ are directly proportional, and that γ is a measure of the cubic anharmonicity of the interatomic potential energy.

Equation (6.8 - 15) indicates that γ depends only on the Debye temperature Θ and upon the rate at which Θ changes in response to volume changes brought about by thermal expansion, mechanical compression or other means. In a crystal having perfectly harmonic interatomic forces, γ is zero, which implies that $\partial\Theta/\partial V = 0$, and that Θ is now independent not only of temperature, but also of volume. It is thus only when anharmonicity is present that Θ varies with V. Moreover, in a crystal whose atoms are bound by totally harmonic forces, the equation of state (6.8 - 14) implies that the product PV equals $\gamma_0 U_0$ a quantity independent of temperature. The upper curve in Figure 6.5 then becomes a horizontal straight line.

There is nothing in Debye's original theory of specific heat--based, you will recall, on the assumption that vibrating atoms are ideal harmonic oscillators--to indicate that Θ has to be independent of volume as well as temperature in such a system. Indeed, from (6.4 - 9) one might think otherwise. But the arguments given above indicate it must be so, and suggest that the Grüneisen constant provides a useful indicator not only of the extent to which Θ varies with V, but also of the extent to which cubic anharmonicity has infiltrated the lattice.

6.9 LATTICE THERMAL CONDUCTIVITY

So far we have discussed only equilibrium thermal properties of crystalline materials. Thermal conductivity is an example of a property that pertains to a state which is not one of thermal equilibrium. When you put two identical blocks of copper initially at different temperatures in contact, heat flows because of the temperature gradient until a final state is reached in which the temperature attains some constant intermediate value everywhere. Though the final state is one of equilibrium, during the preceding stages of the heat conduction process, time-dependent changes in temperature and internal energy are in progress, and the condition of the system differs from that of equilibrium. Even a system in which heat flow is time-independent is not in thermal equilibrium in view of the thermal current or energy flux that exists. Since the energy distribution functions developed so far have been derived in the context of equilibrium, they are not generally applicable to non-equilibrium states. In such instances, the best general approach is to find distribution functions that are valid for non-equilibrium conditions. When the departure from thermal equilibrium is small, it is not too difficult to calculate approximately the extent to which the distribution function deviates from its equilibrium form. We shall see how to do this in the next chapter. It is also possible to use kinetic arguments to treat systems in which steady state fluxes of matter or energy are present. This is how we shall treat the case of lattice thermal conductivity.

When heat flows through a crystalline solid, it is usually observed that the flow of heat per unit time is directly proportional to the temperature gradient and the cross-sectional area through which heat energy flows. The constant of proportionality relating these variables is a material parameter K_t known as the thermal conductivity. In metals, the free electron distribution is primarily responsible for the very high thermal conductivities that are observed, but in nonmetallic substances the lattice alone determines the conductivity. We shall limit this discussion to lattice thermal conductivity; free-electron conductivity will be treated separately in a later chapter. In a one-dimensional situation, in which heat flows in the x-direction between parallel isothermal boundaries, as illustrated in Figure 6.6, we can express the observed relationships as

$$\frac{\Delta Q}{\Delta t} = -K_t A \cdot \frac{\Delta T}{\Delta x} , \qquad (6.9\text{-}1)$$

where K_t is the thermal conductivity and A the area, as shown below. The minus sign in this expression is needed since a positive slope $\Delta T / \Delta x$ causes a heat flow in the negative x-direction. If heat ΔQ_1 enters at the left and heat ΔQ_2 leaves at the right

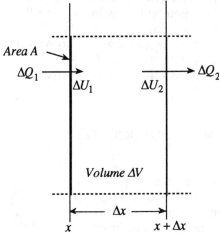

Figure 6.6 Heat flow between two isothermal planes a distance Δx apart in a sample in which heat flow is along the x-direction. There is a temperature difference ΔT between the two planar isothermals.

during a time interval Δt, there will be a change of internal energy $\Delta U_1 - \Delta U_2$ within the region shown during this time interval. From the first law of thermodynamics,

$$\frac{\Delta U}{\Delta t} = \frac{\Delta U_1}{\Delta t} - \frac{\Delta U_2}{\Delta t} = \frac{\Delta Q_1}{\Delta t} - \frac{\Delta Q_2}{\Delta t} , \qquad (6.9\text{-}2)$$

assuming conditions of constant volume, so that ΔV is zero. This assumption is a good one, since thermal expansion is so small an effect in solids. If we define the internal energy per unit volume as u, and recall the definition of the second partial derivative, we may now write (6.9 - 1) in the form

$$\frac{\Delta U}{\Delta t} = \frac{\Delta u}{\Delta t} \cdot \Delta V = K_t A \frac{\left[\left(\frac{\partial T}{\partial x}\right)_{x+\Delta x} - \left(\frac{\partial T}{\partial x}\right)_x\right]}{\Delta x} \cdot \Delta x = K_t A \frac{\partial^2 T}{\partial x^2} \cdot \Delta x \ . \qquad (6.9\text{-}3)$$

In this expression, the volume ΔV is equal to $A\Delta x$; cancelling these terms and writing the limit of the quotient of finite differences as a partial derivative, we find

$$\frac{\partial u}{\partial t} = K_t \frac{\partial^2 T}{\partial x^2} \ . \qquad (6.9\text{-}4)$$

Finally, noting that in a constant-volume process $du = C_v dT$, where C_v is the specific heat, we obtain

$$\frac{K_t}{C_v} \frac{\partial^2 T}{\partial x^2} = \frac{\partial T}{\partial t} \ . \qquad (6.9\text{-}5)$$

This is the familiar partial differential equation for the temperature distribution in a uniform material through which heat flows; an equation of the same form describes the concentration distribution of a solute that diffuses into a homogeneous solid or liquid solvent. It is important to note that it is *not* a wave equation, since its solutions are not of the form $\exp[i(kx - \omega t)]$, but have instead a real exponential time dependence.

Equation (6.9 - 5) is derived from an empirical relation (6.9 - 1) which stems from experimental observations regarding heat flow through actual solid substances. This is a macroscopic relationship having little or no connection with any fundamental theory on the level of atoms and molecules. It is nevertheless a good description of what is observed in the real world.

When one attempts to approach the phenomenon of thermal conductivity from the picture of harmonically vibrating atoms in a crystal lattice, a curious paradox arises. It seems obvious on this level that thermal energy must be transmitted through the crystal as sound waves. This leads to the conclusion that the crystal acts as an acoustical waveguide, and delivers energy from one end to the other at the speed of sound, just as microwaves travel through an electromagnetic waveguide at roughly the speed of light. Such a picture is in sharp disagreement with experiment since (6.9 - 5), which sums up experimental evidence, does not have the form of a wave equation. Nevertheless, a detailed study of the acoustic waveguide model, flawed though it may be, will lead us to a resolution of the problem.

Let us then consider phonons travelling at the sound velocity v_0 through a segment of crystal of length L and area A in which a temperature gradient exists, as illustrated in Figure 6.7. We shall use the Debye approximation of sound velocity independent of frequency up to an effective cutoff frequency ω_m defined as in

Section 6.4. The path of a typical phonon entering the leftmost end of the crystal, where the temperature is T_2, and travelling down the "waveguide" at some arbitrary

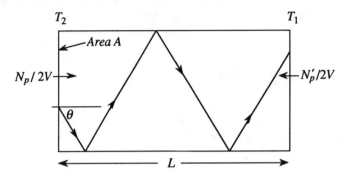

Figure 6.7 A crystal of length L and area A acting as an acoustic waveguide for phonons. The path of a typical phonon entering at an arbitrary angle to the normal is illustrated.

angle θ to the normal is illustrated. Each of these phonons contributes to a kinetic energy flux, defined as energy per unit area per unit time crossing area A, equal to $\varepsilon_{av} v_x$ or $\varepsilon_{av} v_0 \cos\theta$, where ε_{av} is the average phonon energy. The temperature gradient is assumed to be constant, with the left end of the region at temperature T_2 and the right end at a lower temperature T_1. There is a similar energy flux from right to left that carries thermal kinetic energy in the direction *opposite* that shown in the figure. If there were no temperature gradient, the number of phonons per unit volume would be the same at both ends, and these two fluxes would be equal and opposite, resulting in no net energy transport. As it is, however, due to the lower temperature at the right end, there are fewer phonons per unit volume there, and the leftward energy flux is smaller than that going to the right.

The number of phonons per unit volume, N_p/V, can be found by integrating equation (6.5 - 4) from $\omega = 0$ to $\omega = \omega_m$. Using the relation $\hbar\omega_m = k\Theta$, the result can be expressed in the classical high-temperature limit, in which $T \gg \Theta$. as

$$\frac{N_p}{V} = \frac{9N}{2V} \cdot \frac{T}{\Theta} \ , \qquad\qquad (6.9\text{-}6)$$

where N is the number of oscillators. It is clear from this that N and N_p are different quantities, a fact that should not be forgotten. The actual calculation is not difficult, and is assigned as an exercise. The density of phonons at either end can be obtained by substituting T_1 or T_2 into this relation. It is also important to note that only *half* the phonon population at either end contributes to the energy fluxes within the sample, since half the phonons are moving away from rather than toward the "waveguide". This introduces a factor of $1/2$ into the equation we shall write for the energy flux. The average phonon energy also follows from this if it is recalled that the vibrational internal energy in the high-temperature limit is $3NkT$. Thus,

$$\varepsilon_{av} = \frac{3NkT}{\frac{9}{2}N(T/\Theta)} = \tfrac{2}{3}k\Theta = \tfrac{2}{3}\hbar\omega_m \ . \qquad\qquad (6.9\text{-}7)$$

Now, noting that $C_v = 3Nk$, we can write an expression for the energy flux in the following way;

$$\frac{N_p}{2V} \cdot \varepsilon_{av} v_0 \langle \cos\theta \rangle = \frac{9N}{4V} \cdot \frac{T_2}{\Theta} \cdot \frac{2k\Theta}{3} \cdot v_0 \langle \cos\theta \rangle = \frac{3NkT_2}{2V} v_0 \langle \cos\theta \rangle$$

$$= \tfrac{1}{2} v_0 C_v \langle \cos\theta \rangle \cdot T_2 \ , \tag{6.9-8}$$

where the brackets indicate that $\cos\theta$ has been somehow averaged over all possible angles of incidence. The factor of one-half mentioned above also appears in this expression, the effective number of phonons per unit volume being written as $N_p/2V$.

The details of the required averaging process are complicated by the need for the inclusion of a number of weighting factors. One of them is required because the rate at which phonons cross the plane of incidence at temperature T_2 depends on the x-component of their velocity, and is therefore proportional to $\cos\theta$. Also, though the phonon velocity vectors are distributed isotropically in space, the fraction of incident vectors in the range of angle $d\theta$ about angle θ depends on angle, introducing a factor of the form $\sin\theta \, d\theta$ into the calculation. This is clear from Figure 6.8, wherein the ends of all phonon velocity vectors are uniformly distributed over a sphere of radius v_0 in velocity space. The fraction incident in a range $d\theta$ about θ is the ratio of the *area* of the ring element dA to that of the hemisphere ($0 < \theta < \pi/2$) containing all incident velocity vectors of phonons that enter the region. The latter range also defines the limits of integration. The fraction of total phonon population in the given range of incidence is thus

$$\frac{2\pi v_0^2 \sin\theta \, d\theta}{2\pi v_0^2} = \sin\theta \, d\theta \ . \tag{6.9-9}$$

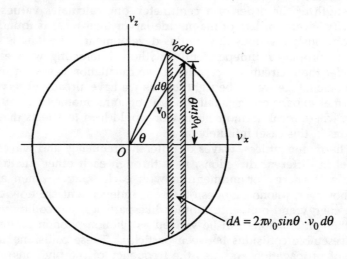

Figure 6.8 Fraction of incident velocity vectors with angles of incidence in a range $d\theta$ about θ, as illustrated by shaded area element in velocity space.

The averaging over angles must be carried out as shown below, leading to

$$\langle \cos \theta \rangle = \frac{\int_0^{\pi/2} (\cos \theta) \cdot \cos \theta \sin \theta d\theta}{\int_0^{\pi/2} \cos \theta \sin \theta d\theta} = \frac{2}{3} \ . \tag{6.9-10}$$

Substituting this value into (6.9 - 8) we obtain finally

$$\frac{N_p}{2V} \cdot \varepsilon_{av} v_0 \langle \cos \theta \rangle = \tfrac{1}{3} v_0 C_v T_2 \ . \tag{6.9-11}$$

A similar calculation for the oppositely directed energy flux from the cold end at temperature T_1 yields a result of the same form in which T_1 appears in place of T_2. The net energy flux is the difference between the two expressions, and can be identified as the heat flow dQ/dt per unit area. We may therefore write

$$\frac{1}{A} \frac{dQ}{dt} = \tfrac{1}{3} v_0 C_v (T_2 - T_1) = \tfrac{1}{3} v_0 C_v L \cdot \frac{(T_2 - T_1)}{L} = K_t \frac{(T_2 - T_1)}{L} \ , \tag{6.9-12}$$

recalling the definition of the thermal conductivity K_t. The thermal conductivity now follows as

$$K_t = \tfrac{1}{3} v_0 C_v L \ . \tag{6.9-13}$$

This result is odd in that it predicts that the thermal conductivity is proportional to the length L of the sample. The conductivity could be made as large as desired simply by making the sample longer and longer. This is clearly not in agreement with what is observed experimentally. Moreover, if one assumes a reasonable sample length of the order of a centimeter, one calculates values for the thermal conductivity several orders of magnitude larger than what is found experimentally. There is obviously a serious flaw in this development. The flaw is that phonons are assumed to propagate independently, without interacting with each other in any way. Under these circumstances, the above calculation based on wave propagation in a harmonic lattice would be right, but as we have already observed in connection with thermal expansion, a small amount of anharmonicity is often important in situations where ideal harmonic behavior would lead to effects that are vanishingly small, or (as in this case) infinitely large.

In harmonic lattices, waves of different frequency and wavelength, or waves that travel in different directions, pass through each other unaltered, and do not exchange any energy or momentum with each other. When anharmonicity is present, however, phonon modes otherwise independent are now coupled, and can exchange energy and momentum much like particles that collide with one another. Indeed, their interactions can be viewed as phonon-phonon scattering events that strongly resemble collisions between particles. These collisions act to change the direction of propagation and also the frequency of the phonons that carry energy through the substance; their effect is, on the average, to reduce the flux of heat carried by a phonon in the x-direction to *zero*, and hence to restore the condition of thermal equilibrium after the event.

If there are no collisions, the phonons carrying the energy flux travel unimpeded the entire length of the "waveguide". When phonon-phonon scattering is present, however, they are scattered after having covered, on the average, a much shorter distance λ along the x-direction, a distance referred to as the scattering *mean free path*. The effect of the scattering process is to return the distribution of phonons to an *equilibrium state* characterized--once again on the average--by a slightly lower intermediate temperature. The effective length of the waveguide is reduced from L to λ by this mechanism. The whole energy transport process must now begin again, indeed, must occur over and over again, until energy incident at the left end of the sample arrives at the other end. The scattering processes may occasionally even reverse the direction of the energy flux, the net result being a random multistage diffusive transport process in which many changes of course and speed occur from beginning to end. Its effect can be seen, as suggested above, as reducing the effective waveguide length from L to λ. However, since λ is a parameter of the *material*, independent of sample configuration, the observed thermal conductivity no longer depends on the sample geometry. We may thus substitute λ for L in (6.9 - 13), to obtain,

$$K_t = \tfrac{1}{3} v_0 C_v \lambda \ . \tag{6.9-14}$$

Even the small anharmonicity associated with most crystalline materials at room temperature suffices to produce a phonon mean free path of the order of 10^{-6} to 10^{-7}cm, corresponding to a free time λ/v_0 of about 10^{-11} to 10^{-12}sec. The mean free path is usually very much smaller than any physical dimension of even the smallest sample that can be made. The problem of calculating the mean free path from first principles from the cubic anharmonicity term in the interatomic potenial energy is quite difficult and will not be pursued further.

The problem was first treated in detail in 1929 by R. Peierls, who showed that at high temperatures, the mean free path is proportional to $1/T$, in agreement with what is observed experimentally for many substances. In the low-temperature limit, Peierls showed that the phonon mean free path is proprtional to $\exp(\Theta/2T)$. At sufficiently low temperatures in very pure materials, therefore, the mean free path can become much longer than it is at room temperature--so long that in some cases it may be of the order of the size of very small macroscopic samples, permitting the odd "size effect" suggested by (6.9 - 13) actually to be observed. The mean free path can also be influenced by the presence of impurities and lattice imperfections. In general, the theory developed by Peierls and his successors has been quite successful in describing the observed lattice thermal conductivity of many substances, as well as its dependence on temperature and other relevant parameters.

The phonon-phonon interactions responsible for the phenomenon of lattice thermal conductivity are of two general types, which are illustrated in Figure 6.9. In both processes it is assumed that phonon momentum can be represented as $\hbar k$, as suggested by the de Broglie relation, and that overall, both total phonon energy and momentum are conserved. The diagrams illustrate phonon propagation vectors for interactions in which two incoming phonons interact to form a single outgoing phonon. The vectors $\mathbf{k}_1$ and $\mathbf{k}_2$ illustrate the momentum of the incoming phonons, while $\mathbf{k}_3$ exhibits the final momentum of the outgoing phonon. The x-components of these vectors are proportional to the x-component of the phonon momenta. The figure illustrates the reciprocal space of a two-dimensional square crystal lattice in which the interatomic spacing is a. This choice of a two-dimensional lattice is made primarily for convenience in drawing the diagrams; the extension of the forthcoming results to three dimensions is straightforward and easily visualized.

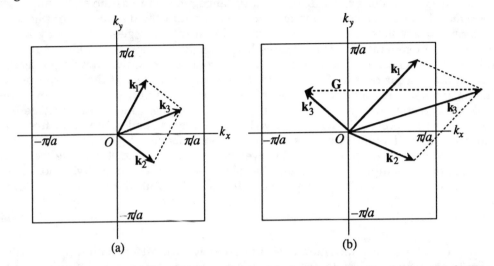

Figure 6.9 Schematic diagram illustrating initial and final propagation vectors of phonons in phonon-phonon scattering processes typical of (a) normal processes, and (b) Umklapp-processes. Square regions correspond to the first Brillouin zone in the reciprocal lattice of a two-dimensional square lattice with interatomic spacing a.

The square region shown above is the first "Brillouin zone" of this lattice, which accommodates all propagation vectors whose cartesian momentum components satisfy the requirements $(-\pi/a < k_x < \pi/a)$ and $(-\pi/a < k_y < \pi/a)$, in analogy to the one-dimensional zones discussed in Chapter 3. If both energy and momentum of phonons are conserved in these interactions, one can write the following equations:

$$\hbar\omega_1 + \hbar\omega_2 = \hbar\omega_3 \qquad (6.9\text{-}15)$$

and

$$\hbar\mathbf{k}_1 + \hbar\mathbf{k}_2 = \hbar\mathbf{k}_3 \quad . \qquad (6.9\text{-}16)$$

Thermal kinetic carried by phonons is propagated with a group velocity derivable from the lattice dispersion relation. This group velocity, in two- or three-dimensional systems is difficult to calculate exactly, and moreover, isn't necessarily in the same direction as the phonon propagation vector $\mathbf{k}$. Therefore, one must be very cautious about identifying momentum components such as $\hbar k_x$ as being strictly proportional to the corresponding cartesian phonon group velocity component v_x. We have seen, however, that the Debye approximation offers a way of circumventing difficulties of this kind that is not only in good agreement with experiment in the case of specific heat, but is equally successful in treating certain other phenomena like thermal expansion and the equation of state. It is therefore reasonable to suppose that it could be useful also in this context. Assuming that it is, we shall use the approximate dispersion relation (6.4 - 6), the implicit assumption that phase and group velocities are the same, and that vibrational energy is propagated with wave velocity v_0 in the direction of the propagation vector $\mathbf{k}$. The conclusions we shall draw from doing so are correct, but it should be noted that a more detailed treatment is needed to establish these conclusions rigorously.

In Figure 6.9(a) we see what is referred to as a *normal* process, in which initial k-vectors k_1 and k_2, representing the momenta of the incoming phonons add to give a final vector k_3 giving the momentum of a single outgoing phonon, both components of which reside within the first Brillouin zone. Such a process does not change the sum of the x-components of the k-vectors--and thus the total sum of x-momenta, before and after the interaction. As a result, the flux of heat energy carried by these constituents, which is proportional to v_x, is the same before and after the collision. Since these processes do not alter the energy flux, they have no effect at all in defining the effective mean free path or the thermal conductivity. If they were the only allowed interactions, one would be driven to conclude that the effective mean free path is infinite, and that the "acoustic waveguide" expression (6.9-13) is in fact valid.

The interaction shown at (b) in the figure depicts a process in which the vector sum of k_1 and k_2 is a vector extending across the boundary of the first Brillouin zone into the second. Thus, at least one of the components of the vector is larger than π/a, and the wavelength of the phonon it represents, (as given by $2\pi/k_3$) is *smaller* than twice the interatomic spacing. We have seen in Section 3.6 that any point outside the first zone is physically equivalent to a point within the first zone, and that the spacing between these points along the k_x- or k_y-directions are integral multiples of the zone length $2\pi/a$. This means that the vector k_3 can be replaced with a vector *within* the first zone by (in this case) adding to it a vector G of length $2\pi/a$, which can be regarded as 2π times the lattice vector a^* of the reciprocal lattice. To make any physical sense of this situation, we are *compelled* to make such a transformation, because we know that all the physical results of lattice dynamics can be described within the first zone, and that trying to visualize it outside that region is difficult and may even be misleading. So in this interaction, which is known as an *Umklapp* process, we are led to replace (6.9 - 16) with the physically equivalent relation

$$\hbar k_1 + \hbar k_2 = \hbar k_3 + G = \hbar k_3' \ , \tag{6.9-17}$$

where G is 2π times a lattice vector of the reciprocal lattice. The vector G in this above process is shown as the dotted vector in Figure 6.9(b), and the equivalent first-zone outgoing k-vector is therefore k_3'.

Now, however, the x-component of k_3' is *negative*, while the x-components of both incoming k-vectors are positive. The energy flux, which is related to the x-component of the final propagation vector k_3', is therefore *opposite* in direction to what it was before the interaction. The effect of the Umklapp process has been to change--in this case to reverse--the energy flux. In general, one can demonstrate that Umklapp processes, on the average, have the effect of reducing the energy flux to zero, or more generally, and in an average sense, to *restoring the condition of thermal equilibrium* after any such collision. As Peierls showed, one can express the mean free path λ as a properly averaged distance between interactions of this type, and hence calculate the thermal conductivity in terms of fundamental thermal and material parameters. This is the key to formulating an adequate physical theory of lattice thermal conductivity. We shall study phenomena involving Brillouin zones in two-and three-dimensional structures in more detail in Chapter 8.

REFERENCES

C. Kittel, *Introduction to Solid State Physics* 2nd Edition, J. Wiley & Sons, New York (1956), Chapter 6.

P. G. Klemens, *Thermal Conductivity and Lattice Vibrational Modes*, in *Solid State Physics, Advances in Research and Applications*, Vol 2, Academic Press, New York, (1956).

R. B. Peierls, *Quantum Theory of Solids*, Clarendon Press, Oxford (1955).

J. S. Blakemore, *Solid State Physics*, 2nd Edition, W. B. Saunders Co., Philadelphia (1974), Chapter 2.

F. W. Sears and G. L. Salinger, *Thermodynamics, Kinetic Theory, and Statistical Mechanics*, 3rd Edition, Addison-Wesley, Reading Mass. (1975).

PROBLEMS

1. Derive the Dulong-Petit expression for the classical specific heat of an ideal crystal by assuming that there are N three-dimensional harmonic oscillators, and employing the density of states function for the three-dimensional oscillator in the calculation shown in (6.2 - 1).

2. Find expressions for the Einstein specific heat (6.3 - 8) in the limit of (a) very low temperatures, (b) very high temperatures.

3. Show explicitly that the Debye expression for the lattice specific heat approaches the value $3Nk$ in the high-temperature limit.

4. Calculate using the Debye theory the internal energy and specific heat of a two-dimensional periodic crystal lattice containing N identical atoms. Show that at low temperatures the specific heat varies with temperature as T^2. Find also the specific heat in the high-temperature limit.

5. Show using the quantum dispersion relation that the mass of a free particle such as an electron can be expressed as

$$m = \frac{\hbar^2}{\left(\dfrac{\partial^2 \varepsilon}{\partial k^2}\right)} \ .$$

Use this expression in conjunction with the phonon dispersion relation to show that one can define an effective mass for the phonon and show that in the limit of high temperatures this mass is several hundred times the electron mass.

6 Consider an assembly of N identical and independent atomic systems each having just two discrete energy levels at energies zero and ε_0. Assume that the systems are identifiable and that there is a single quantum state associated with each level. Find (a) the internal energy of the system, (b) the heat capacity of the system, and (c) approximate expressions for the heat capacity in the high and low-temperature limits. Plot the heat capacity as a function of temperature.

7. For the assembly of systems described in the preceding problem, show that the heat capacity reaches a maximum value at a temperature T_0 defined by

$$x \tanh x = 1 \qquad \text{where} \qquad x = \varepsilon_0 / 2kT \ .$$

Also, show that the heat capacity at this temperature can be written as

$$C_v = Nk(x_0^2 - 1) \qquad \text{where} \qquad x_0 = \varepsilon_0/2kT_0 \ .$$

Thermal effects arising from systems of this kind are often found at low temperatures in paramagnetic materials, and are referred to as *Schottky anomalies*.

8. By integrating (6.5 - 4) over all frequencies from 0 to ω_m, derive equation (6.9 - 6), which gives the number of available phonons as a function of temperature at temperatures large compared with the Debye temperature Θ.

9. Show by making the substitutions outlined in the last paragraph of Section 6.5 that Planck's blackbody radiation formula radiation follows from (6.5 - 5).

10. In a Fermi-Dirac free-electron system, calculate the fraction of quantum states that are at energies less than kT below the Fermi surface. Assume that the temperature is much smaller than the Fermi temperature.

11. The long-wave sound velocity in aluminum is about 5200m/sec, and the measured linear coefficient of thermal expansion α is 2.4×10^{-5} K^{-1}. Show that the coefficient of cubic anharmonicity b in the potential energy expansion (6.6 - 1) can be expressed as

$$b = \frac{(mv_0^2)^2}{3a^3 k} \ ,$$

where m is the atomic mass, a the lattice spacing, v_0 the long-wave sound velocity and k Boltzmann's constant. Then calculate the ratio of the cubic anharmonicity energy term in (6.6 - 1) to the leading harmonic term (assuming $x = a/2$), and show that the ratio is small even under these rather extreme conditions.

12. Use the data given in the preceding problem to calculate the Grüneisen constant γ for aluminum. (*Hint:* Observe that the given coefficient of linear expansion is the room-temperature value.)

13. Show using the first law of thermodynamics, that for any substance

$$\left(\frac{\partial P}{\partial T}\right)_V = \frac{\alpha_V}{K_i} \ .$$

14. Derive the relationship

$$\left(\frac{\partial P}{\partial T}\right)_V \left(\frac{\partial T}{\partial V}\right)_P \left(\frac{\partial V}{\partial P}\right)_T = -1$$

between the thermodynamic variables P, V, and T. Note that this is a purely mathematical exercise; the only thermodynamics that enters is the fact that the three variables are related by an equation of state.

15. Show that the heat absorbed or given off by a system during a process taking place at constant pressure is given by $\Delta Q = \Delta H = H_f - H_i$, where H is the *enthalpy*, defined by

$$H = U + pV \ .$$

16. Using the results of the preceding problem, show that in an adiabatic process (one in which $dQ = dS = 0$),

$$\left(\frac{\partial H}{\partial P}\right)_S = V \qquad \text{and} \qquad \left(\frac{\partial H}{\partial S}\right)_P = T \ .$$

17. Show that in a system at constant temperature and pressure, equilibrium is attained when $dG = 0$, where G is the Gibbs function defined by $G = U - TS + PV$. Show also that the maximum work that can be performed by a system under these conditions is $-\Delta G$, obtained when the process is reversible, and that if the process is irreversible the work performed by the system must be less than this.

18. Show, using the laws of thermodynamics, that the difference between the specific heats of any substance measured at constant pressure and constant volume can be expressed as

$$c_p - c_v = \frac{(3\alpha)^2 VT}{K_i} \ .$$

It is clear from this that c_p has to be larger than c_v. Explain in physical terms why is this always so.

19. Show, using the results of the preceding problem that for a crystalline material obeying the Grüneisen equation of state,

$$\frac{c_p}{c_v} = c_v(1 + 3\alpha\gamma T) \ ,$$

where γ is the Grüneisen constant. Find the above ratio of specific heats for aluminum, using the value $2.4 \times 10^{-5} \ K^{-1}$ for the linear expansion coefficient.

20. Use the results of problem 18 to find the ratio of specific heats for an ideal monatomic gas.

21. Calculate the Grüneisen constant γ for copper, assuming a linear expansion coefficient equal to $1{,}7 \times 10^{-5} \ K^{-1}$.

22. Show that solutions of the heat flow equation (6.9 - 5) cannot have the form of undamped propagating plane waves.

23. Calculate the lattice thermal conductivity of a planar sample of crystalline silicon 1.0cm thick at 300K, using the "acoustic waveguide" result (6.9 - 13), and compare the result with the measured value of 150W/m⁻¹K⁻¹. (The sound velocity in Si is 9000m/s, and $3Nk$ is close enough for the molar specific heat.)

24. What is the mean free path for phonon-phonon scattering suggested by the data given in the preceding problem for crystalline silicon at 300K?

25. Roughly how thin does a film of crystalline silicon have to be to exhibit a thickness-dependent lattice thermal conductivity at room temperature (300K)?

26. Consider a one-dimensional lattice of coupled harmonically oscillating atoms of mass m and interatomic spacing a. Using the exact density of states function (3.8 - 14) plus the quantum expression (6.3-4) for the average oscillator energy, calculate expressions in the form of definite integrals for the lattice internal energy and specific heat of this system *without using the Debye approximation*. Why isn't it easy to extend this calculation to two and three-dimensional systems?

CHAPTER 7

CLASSICAL FREE ELECTRON THEORY OF METALS

7.1 INTRODUCTION

We have already seen the usefulness of regarding metallic crystals as containers or potential wells within which free-particle electron gases are confined. From today's perspective, this is an obvious picture that leads to an easily understood and reasonably accurate explanation for the high electrical and thermal conductivity of these materials, as well as for certain other properties. Before the discovery of the electron in 1897, it was far less obvious, though even then most scientists believed that these properties must be associated with the presence of some kind of a mobile free charge distribution. Indeed, even the earliest investigators of electrostatic phenomena, for example, Coulomb, Gilbert, Humboldt, Benjamin Franklin, Galvani, Volta, etc., believed that there was some kind of "subtle fluid" that permeated metals and other conducting substances. This early idea may seem naïve in the light of current understanding, but our present view of metallic conductors has developed directly from this ancient concept, the "subtle fluid" of the early investigators being what we now refer to as a Fermi gas of free electrons. The concept has already been used in Section 4.3 to explain the photoelectric effect, and is illustrated in Figure 4.3, where we can now identify the highest occupied electron energy level as the Fermi energy of the electron gas.

During the 19th century, quantitative understanding of steady-state current flow in conducting circuits followed on the development of the electrochemical cell by Alessandro Volta. One aspect of this understanding lay in the area of electromagnetism, discovered by Oersted in 1819, and further developed by Ampère, Faraday, and Henry. Another, which is of more interest in our context, had to do with the properties of conducting materials themselves, which were investigated by Ohm, Joule, and Wiedemann and Franz, before the discovery of the electron. These investigations uncovered much experimental evidence that pointed in the direction of a gas of free charges, and also some whose relationship to this model was far less obvious. Thomson's discovery of the electron provided a firm foundation for the free-electron gas model, and by 1909 a fairly comprehensive quantitative theory of the electrical properties of metallic conductors based on this concept had been worked out by P. Drude and H. A. Lorentz. The Drude-Lorentz theory provided answers to many of the more obvious problems concerning this subject, but also left many important questions unanswered. These were ultimately resolved, but only after the introduction of quantum theory and Fermi-Dirac statistics.

In this chapter we shall study the classical free-electron model, though many later results obtained by introducing Fermi-Dirac statistics will also be presented. This study involves several levels of sophistication, which we shall introduce one by one. First there is the simple picture of free electrons that takes no account of their thermal energy distribution or collisions. Then the effect of collisions and the equilibrium distribution of energies and mean free paths are considered. Finally energy distributions for systems not at equilibrium, and effects arising from Fermi-Dirac statistics and the Pauli exclusion principle are introduced. The quantum-mechanical aspects of this problem stemming from the interaction of free electrons with the periodic potential of the lattice, however, are treated in the next chapter.

7.2 KINETIC THEORY, MEAN FREE PATH, AND MEAN FREE TIME

The most obvious properties exhibited by metallic substances are extremely high electrical and thermal conductivities. The electrical conductivity of most metals is described accurately, under most conditions attainable experimentally, by Ohm's law, which states that the current density is directly proportional to the electric field within the material. The constant of proportionality σ is referred to as the electrical conductivity, and its reciprocal ρ is called the resistivity of the material. For such materials, we can write Ohm's law as

$$\mathbf{J} = \sigma \mathbf{E} = \mathbf{E}/\rho \ , \tag{7.2-1}$$

where $\mathbf{J}$ is the current density (amp/m^2) and $\mathbf{E}$ the electric field (V/m). In a system in which the x-axis is oriented in the direction of current flow, this becomes

$$J_x = \sigma E_x = E_x/\rho \ . \tag{7.2-2}$$

Ohm's law is a statement of experimental reality, not a necessary consequence of any fundamental physical principle. Nevertheless, it describes quite accurately how real conducting materials behave under most attainable conditions of temperature, electric field strength, and other relevant parameters. Therefore, any free-electron model, if it is to believed at all, has to lead to Ohm's law. If you take the trouble to determine experimentally what happens when the electric field is much higher than usual, you will find Ohm's law no longer valid. In most normal metals it is very hard to attain these fields without blowing your sample to kingdom come. It would be helpful, nevertheless, if your theoretical model would also yield some understanding of why Ohm's law breaks down under these extreme conditions.

In a good metallic conductor, such as silver, the electrical conductivity at room temperature is of the order of 10^8 ohm^{-1}m^{-1}, while the best insulators under similar conditions have a conductivity of about 10^{-16} ohm^{-1}m^{-1}. The conductivity of metallic substances can thus exceed that of insulators by a factor of 10^{24}. This enormous ratio is observed, presumably, because there is a free electron gas in metals, a gas whose density corresponds roughly to the number of valence electrons per unit volume, while in insulators very few (if any) free electrons are around. The further question of why this gas is found in metals but not insulators can be answered by observing that the electrons are tightly bound to the atoms of the lattice in insulators, while in metals they are essentially free particles. The more probing question of why electrons are bound so tightly to atoms in some crystalline substances but not in others is one that cannot be answered by classical free-electron theory, and is only resolved within the framework of quantum theory. The explanation of this phenomenon is in fact one of the more important examples of the usefulness of quantum mechanics in solid-state physics. As suggested above, however, we shall postpone a detailed discussion of this subject until the next chapter, accepting for the present the less comprehensive explanations of classical physics.

When free charges are acted upon by an electric field, they experience a force that accelerates them, giving them a *drift velocity* in the field direction--or in the opposite direction if the charge is negative. There arises in either case a *current* flow in the direction of the field. In addition to the drift velocity caused by the action of the applied electric field, the charges that constitute an electron gas have thermal kinetic energy, and as a consequence, a random *thermal velocity* distribution. Since in the absence of a field there can be no net current, it is clear that the average thermal velocity over the equilibrium distribution must be zero. More precisely, all three of the cartesian components of the vector velocity, averaged over the equilibrium velocity distribution, according to (5.5 - 19) or Figure 5.6(c), are zero. One may therefore neglect the thermal distribution of velocities, at least as a first approximation, and consider initially only the drift velocity associated with the field. If we assume that there are n free charges per unit volume, each with charge q, the charge density is nq. The current density $\mathbf{J}$ is defined as charge density times drift velocity, so that

$$\mathbf{J} = nq\mathbf{v} \ , \tag{7.2-3}$$

where $\mathbf{v}$ is the average drift velocity. Let us assume for simplicity that the charges are at rest initially, which is certainly true in an average sense at least. Then, since the force on each charge is by definition $q\mathbf{E}$, we can write Newton's law for its drift motion as

$$\mathbf{F} = q\mathbf{E} = m\frac{d\mathbf{v}}{dt} \ , \qquad \text{from which} \qquad d\mathbf{v} = \frac{q\mathbf{E}}{m}dt \ . \tag{7.2-4}$$

This can now be integrated using the initial condition just mentioned, to give

$$\mathbf{v} = q\mathbf{E}t/m \ . \tag{7.2-5}$$

The current density can now be written as

$$\mathbf{J} = nq\mathbf{v} = \frac{nq^2\mathbf{E}}{m} \cdot t \quad . \tag{7.2-6}$$

There's nothing at all wrong with this reasoning, but the above result *isn't* Ohm's law, which tells us that we should find a constant current density $\mathbf{J}$ associated with a constant field $\mathbf{E}$. When you put an ammeter in series with a battery and an ohmic resistance and close the circuit, the pointer immediately rises to some constant indicated current and remains there as long as the field is present. The above equation predicts that the current increases linearly with time, and becomes as large as desired after a sufficient time interval. Not only is this not Ohm's law, it is not what happens in the real world.

This disagreeable result doesn't spell the end of the free-electron theory, but it does suggest that the above development is oversimplified and that something important has been omitted. What is missing is the effect of *collisions* that act now and then to end the continual acceleration of the electron and alter its drift velocity. On the average, the effect of these collisions is to *reduce the drift velocity to zero*, which, in effect, returns the electron after some short time interval to the equilibrium thermal distribution. The energy it has acquired from the field thus appears as heat, a phenomenon known as Joule heating, which is exactly what one observes. If we assume that there is some average time τ that defines the mean time between these collisions, the average value of velocity during the interval $(0 < t < \tau)$ will be one-half the maximum velocity given by (7.2 - 5) at the final time τ, or

$$\langle \mathbf{v} \rangle = q\mathbf{E}\tau/2m \quad , \tag{7.2-7}$$

The current density now follows as before from (7.2 - 3) as

$$\mathbf{J} = \frac{nq^2\tau}{2m} \cdot \mathbf{E} = \sigma\mathbf{E} \quad , \tag{7.2-8}$$

where the conductivity now has a constant value given by

$$\sigma = \frac{nq^2\tau}{2m} \quad . \tag{7.2-9}$$

This repair work has saved the free-electron model, and allowed us to understand not only Ohm's law, but also the Joule heating that invariably accompanies ohmic conduction. Indeed, one can show by further elaboration of the above calculation that the heat produced per unit time is

$$dQ/dt = \mathbf{J} \cdot \mathbf{E} = J^2\rho \quad , \tag{7.2-10}$$

in agreement with experimental evidence. The details are assigned as an exercise.

The collisions that destroy the drift velocity of the electrons are not electron-electron collisions. The components of the current density vector associated with a charged particle are proportional to its velocity components. The components of its momentum vector are also proportional to the velocity components. Thus, any electron-electron interaction that conserves overall momentum will *also* conserve the combined current density of the interacting particles, and therefore cannot act to alter the vector sum of their drift velocities. Electron-electron interactions thus do not change the sum of electron drift velocities or current densities. The collisions effective in changing these quantities are primarily interactions between electrons and phonons and between electrons and impurity atoms or lattice imperfections. In pure crystalline materials, electron-phonon collisions are most probable. Since phonons have no charge, momentum conservation no longer necessarily conserves current density. An electron can recoil from a collision with a phonon, for example, and end up going in the opposite direction. The current is reversed, despite the fact that momentum is conserved, for the phonon carries no current at all. The other interactions mentioned above act in essentially the same way. Because the number of available phonons increases as the temperature rises, electron-phonon collisions are most frequent at high temperatures. This means that the average time τ between electron-phonon collisions decreases with rising temperature, and accounts for the fact that the electrical conductivity of normal metals decreases as the temperature rises. It is clear from all this that the free-electron picture, with due allowance for collisions, accounts not only for Ohm's law but for many other observations concerning electrical conductivity in metals.

From (7.2 - 7), it is obvious that the average drift velocity is directly proportional to the field, and that the proportionality constant is $q\tau/2m$. This proportionality factor is referred to as the *mobility* of the free charge and can be regarded as the average drift velocity per unit field. The mobility is a material parameter directly related to the mean free time τ. If we write the mobility as μ, (7.2 - 7) becomes

$$\langle \mathbf{v} \rangle = \mu E = \frac{q\tau}{2m} \cdot E \ . \tag{7.2-11}$$

From (7.2 - 9), it is clear that the conductivity can be expressed in terms of the mobility as

$$\sigma = nq\mu \ . \tag{7.2-12}$$

It is also important to understand that the collisions responsible for Ohm's-Law behavior are very, very, frequent on the scale of measurable time intervals. If this were not so, there would be an observable time interval during which a constantly increasing current as predicted by (7.2 - 6) would be perceived as free electrons start from rest and "get up to speed", while a similar period of decreasing current flow would be observed after the accelerating field is turned off as electrons "coast along" before being brought to rest by collisions. These effects have never been observed, even with the fastest available detectors. We are thus led to conclude that the mean time τ is so small as to be undetectable in this manner, and to assume that it must be less than about 10^{-10} seconds. If one substitutes a value $10^8 \mathrm{ohm^{-1}m^{-1}}$ for σ, corresponding to typical observed metallic conductivities, into (7.2 - 9), along with a value for n that corresponds to one free electron per atom and the observed charge and mass of the electron, one can derive a value of about 10^{-13} seconds for τ. So it is clear that the mean time between collisions is much too small to observe directly.

We must now examine more closely the concept of mean free time, and the related mean free path. In the above development it is assumed that each particle undergoes collision interactions from time to time, and that the duration of these collisions is very small compared to the "free" time between interactions, when the particle, though perhaps acted upon by known external forces, behaves otherwise as a free particle. Let us focus our attention on a subgroup of n_0 particles at time $t = 0$, all having the *same* kinetic energy. As time elapses, collisions occur whose effect is to change the kinetic energy of the colliding particle, and thus remove it from this particular subclass of the distribution. The surviving population of the group therefore is a decreasing function of time, which we shall write as $n(t)$. In the simplest possible situation, the probability of collision for any particle in a time interval dt is independent of time, and depends only on the length of the free time interval. The number of collisions per unit time is thus directly proportional to the population $n(t)$ and to dt. The change in population during this time interval can therefore be written

$$dn = -\frac{1}{\tau} \cdot n(t)\, dt \ . \tag{7.2-13}$$

In this expression the constant of proportionality has been written $1/\tau$, in anticipation of the end result. The equation is easily integrated, using the initial condition $n(0) = n_0$, to obtain

$$n(t) = n_0 e^{-t/\tau} \ . \tag{7.2-14}$$

The population of surviving particles is an exponentially decreasing function of time with the time constant τ. The average time of survival can be evaluated as

$$t_{av} = \frac{\displaystyle\int_0^\infty t n(t)\, dt}{\displaystyle\int_0^\infty n(t)\, dt} = \frac{\displaystyle\int_0^\infty t e^{t/\tau}\, dt}{\displaystyle\int_0^\infty e^{t/\tau}\, dt} = \tau \ . \tag{7.2-15}$$

The time constant τ, which has been referred to previously as the mean free time, is also known as the *relaxation time*. If you divide both sides of (7.2-13) by $n(t)\, dt$, you will see that the reciprocal of τ can be regarded as the number of collisions per particle per unit time, or the *collision frequency* per particle.

It is important to observe that the above development concerns only a subclass of the distribution whose members all have the same kinetic energy and therefore the same particle speed v. In the simplest possible case, the collision frequency is independent of particle speed, and therefore the relaxation time itself is independent of velocity. Under these conditions, the relaxation time of the whole distribution is the common relaxation time of all velocity subgroups. This simple state of affairs is rarely encountered in the real world, however, and ordinarily the collision frequency is energy-dependent. The reason for this is simply that collision probabilities calculated from realistic dynamical collision models usually depend on incident particle energy. For example Rutherford scattering of charged particles by coulomb forces deflects slow, low-energy particles, through larger angles than fast ones whose energies are very high. The reason for this is that slow particles spend more time in the region where forces are strongest, which allows them to impart more transverse momentum. Ordinarily, therefore, the relaxation time is a function of velocity or energy, and its velocity dependence must be accounted for in calculating properties, such as electrical conductivity, that depend on it. The simple calculations leading to

(7.2 - 8) and (7.2 - 9) do not take this velocity dependence into account. A more rigorous treatment that incorporates this refinement into the theory is therefore needed, and will be presented in the next section.

The discussion of particle kinetics given above can be framed in the context of free paths, rather than free times, between collisions. If we let x denote the *distance* between collisions, then for a subclass of particles with constant speed v, it is clear that $x = vt$, and $dx = v \, dt$. Multiplying the right side of (7.2 - 13) above and below by v, and defining the mean free path λ for the subgroup having this speed as

$$\lambda = v\tau , \tag{7.2-16}$$

we obtain, integrating over x rather than t,

$$n(x) = n_0 e^{-x/\lambda} . \tag{7.2-17}$$

The surviving particle population decreases exponentially with distance as well as time; also, a repetition of the calculation (7.2 - 15) integrating over x instead of t reveals that $x_{av} = \lambda$. It is apparent also that λ as well as τ can be a function of energy or particle speed when all velocity subgroups are considered, so that (7.2 - 16) could more precisely have been written

$$\lambda (v) = v\tau (v) . \tag{7.2-18}$$

It is clear from this that the mean free path and the relaxation time have inherently different velocity dependences. If the mean free path is independent of v, for example, the mean free time must be velocity dependent, and *vice-versa*. The case of a mean free path that is at least approximately velocity-independent is one fairly often encountered in real materials, since the simplest type of electron-phonon scattering behaves roughly in this way.

7.3 THE BOLTZMANN TRANSPORT EQUATION AND OHM'S LAW

Cases involving the transport of particles or of energy are not situations of thermodynamic equilibrium, and cannot properly be described by the equilibrium distribution functions derived in Chapter 5. The case of electrical current flow is in this category even when the current is constant, because the kinetic energy of electrons is continually converted into heat by the randomizing effect of collisions. This production of heat can also be considered as a continuous creation of *entropy*, since $dQ = T \, dS$. From the thermodynamic point of view, entropy is continually increasing and has therefore not attained its maximum value. From the statistical viewpoint, the system is becoming more and more disordered; chemical energy is taken from an electrochemical cell somewhere and is turned into random thermal energy. So it is incorrect to assume that the distribution of particle energies is the same as in the equilibrium state. Indeed, if this were so, there could be no current, due to the symmetry of equilibrium velocity distributions like (5.5 - 18) or (5.5 - 19) about the origin in velocity space. Similar remarks apply to a system in which heat flows steadily from a high temperature reservoir to one at a lower temperature.

It is desirable in discussing situations such as these to be able to determine an energy distribution for systems not in equilibrium. The Boltzmann transport equation, which is a differential equation describing such distribution functions, is frequently used to treat such problems. To derive this equation, consider a volume element of phase space about a point (x, y, z, p_x, p_y, p_z). The distribution function depends on these variables, and expresses the number of particles in a volume element about such a point. Let the element have dimensions $(dx, dy, dz, dp_x, dp_y, dp_z)$. During a time interval dt, particles leave this element and are replaced by particles that were in a region of phase space at $(x - v_x dt, y - v_y dt, z - v_z dt, p_x - F_x dt, p_y - F_y dt, p_z - F_z dt)$ at a time dt earlier. In this expression F_x, F_y, F_z are the components of the resultant *external* forces that act on the particle, where it is observed from Newton's laws that $dp_x = F_x dt$, etc. The effect of *internal* forces, forces exerted by particles *on each other* (during collisions, for example), are so far neglected, and will be accounted for later. The net change in the distribution function during this time interval can now be expressed as

$$df = f(x - v_x dt, y - v_y dt, z - v_z dt, p_x - F_x dt, p_y - F_y dt, p_z - F_z dt) - f(x, y, z, p_x, p_y, p_z) \ .$$
$$(7.3\text{-}1)$$

The first term above can be expanded in a Taylors' series, in which only terms to first order in the differentials need be retained. The above expression then reduces to

$$df = \left(-v_x \frac{\partial f}{\partial x} - v_y \frac{\partial f}{\partial y} - v_z \frac{\partial f}{\partial z} - F_x \frac{\partial f}{\partial p_x} - F_y \frac{\partial f}{\partial p_y} - F_z \frac{\partial f}{\partial p_z} \right) dt \ , \qquad (7.3\text{-}2)$$

or,

$$\frac{df}{dt} = -\mathbf{v} \cdot \nabla f - \mathbf{F} \cdot \nabla_p f \ . \qquad (7.3\text{-}3)$$

In this expression, the symbol ∇_p refers to the gradient operator in the momentum space (p_x, p_y, p_z).

So far, the effect of collisions in altering the distribution function has been neglected. To describe their effect rigorously, one must introduce a suitable dynamical model of particle interactions, in which interparticle forces are written explicitly and their effect in scattering particles from one region of phase space to another is accounted for in detail. This is usually an extremely complex mathematical problem, one that we should at this level prefer to avoid. We have already shown that the net effect of collisions is to randomize the distribution, and to ultimately return it to its equilibrium form. We have also seen that if certain simple yet fairly realistic assumptions are made, the distribution relaxes exponentially to equilibrium with a relaxation time τ whose average value is identified as a mean free time between scattering interactions. This suggests that a collision term of the form

$$\left(\frac{\partial f}{\partial t} \right)_{\text{coll}} = -\frac{f - f_0}{\tau} \ , \qquad (7.3\text{-}4)$$

in which f_0 represents the equilibrium form of the distribution function, be added to the right side of (7.3 - 3). The reasoning is as follows; consider a situation such as that of a uniform metallic conductor in which there is a steady current. When current flows, a steady state exists in which the distribution function f is different from f_0, but is the same everywhere in the material; that this is true can be seen from the fact that heat is generated at the same rate at all points. Under these circumstances, ∇f is zero. If the field is now suddenly removed, the quantity $\mathbf{F}$ also becomes zero, and the distribution relaxes to equilibrium. Now the *entire* change in the distribution function comes from (7.3 - 4) and we may write

$$\frac{df}{dt} = \left(\frac{\partial f}{\partial t}\right)_{\text{coll}} = -\frac{f - f_0}{\tau} , \qquad (7.3 - 5)$$

which in view of the fact that f_0 is time-independent, can be solved to obtain

$$f - f_0 = A e^{-t/\tau} , \qquad (7.3 - 6)$$

as suggested by (7.2 - 12). The relaxation time has been regarded as a constant in this discussion, but no problem arises when it is assumed to depend on velocity. In this case an equation of form (7.3 - 5) can be written for every velocity subgroup, and the relaxation to equilibrium is exponential for every such subgroup, though with a different time constant for each, as in the preceding section. The expression given in (7.3 - 4) is referred to as the *relaxation time approximation*. It assumes that the probability of scattering is isotropic and time-independent during the intervals between collisions. If it is adopted, the Boltzmann transport equation has the form

$$\frac{df}{dt} = -\mathbf{v} \cdot \nabla f - \mathbf{F} \cdot \nabla_p f - \frac{f - f_0}{\tau} . \qquad (7.3 - 7)$$

There are situations for which this approximation is not valid, but it is generally applicable when the state of the system does not differ too greatly from that which prevails at equilibrium.

One may now proceed by solving the Boltzmann transport equation for the nonequilibrium distribution f. It will usually be found that the distribution function for the nonequilibrium state is related to the *equilibrium* distribution function f_0 in a fairly simple way. This means that relevant physical quantities, expressed as averages over the nonequilibrium distribution, can ultimately be expressed in terms of properly defined averages involving *only* the equilibrium distribution function. The consequences of this situation will be observed in the examples that follow.

We may now use the Boltzmann equation as the starting point for a discussion of electrical conductivity in free-electron conductors. Consider the case of a uniform isotropic metallic conductor in which the valence electrons are regarded as a gas of free particles confined only by the surfaces of the crystal. We shall assume that a steady current density J associated with a constant field E has been established, and that the z-axis is oriented in the direction of the electric field. It is further assumed that the temperature is constant throughout the substance. The equilibrium distribution function f_0 is the Fermi-Dirac distribution function (5.7 - 17). Since the system is in a state of steady, time-independent current flow, df/dt is zero, and since the temperature is uniform, it is reasonable to expect the distribution to be the same at all points, which means that ∇f is also zero. Assuming that collisions can be adequately described by the relaxation time approximation, we can write (7.3 - 7) as

$$q\mathbf{E} \cdot \nabla_p f = \frac{qE}{m}\frac{\partial f}{\partial v_z} = -\frac{f - f_0}{\tau(v)} \; . \tag{7.3-8}$$

In writing this equation, we have made use of the fact that $\mathbf{E}$ has only a z-component, and that $dp_z = m\, dv_z$. It is noted explicitly that the relaxation time may depend on the particle speed v. If the system is not too far from equilibrium, f and f_0 will not be very different. The only thing that keeps the right side of the above equation from being identically zero is precisely the difference between f and f_0; there is therefore no room for making any further simplification here. On the left, however, if these two quantities are nearly the same, a sensible approximation is to replace $\partial f/\partial v_z$ by $\partial f_0/\partial v_z$. At equilibrium, the distribution function f_0 will be the Fermi-Dirac distribution given by (5.7 - 17). For this distribution function,

$$\frac{\partial f_0}{\partial \varepsilon} = \frac{\partial}{\partial \varepsilon}\left(\frac{1}{1 + e^{\varepsilon - \varepsilon_f/kT}}\right) = -\frac{1}{kT}\cdot\frac{e^{\varepsilon - \varepsilon_f/kT}}{(1 + e^{\varepsilon - \varepsilon_f/kT})^2} = -\frac{1}{kT}f_0(1 - f_0) \; . \tag{7.3-9}$$

Then, since for free particles, $\varepsilon = m(v_x^2 + v_y^2 + v_z^2)/2$, we can write

$$\frac{\partial f_0}{\partial v_z} = \frac{\partial f_0}{\partial \varepsilon}\cdot\frac{\partial \varepsilon}{\partial v_z} = -\frac{mv_z}{kT}\cdot f_0(1 - f_0)q\mathbf{E} \; . \tag{7.3-10}$$

Finally, substituting this expression into (7.3 - 8), and solving for f, we obtain

$$f(\varepsilon) = f_0(\varepsilon) - \frac{\tau(v)\cdot v\cos\theta}{kT}\cdot f_0(1 - f_0)q\mathbf{E} \; . \tag{7.3-11}$$

This is the distribution function for a situation wherein a steady current flows in a free-electron conductor. It is important to note that though the situation is not one of equilibrium, the nonequilibrium distribution function can be expressed in terms of the equilibrium function f_0. Therefore, any averages that are sought will involve ultimately only the equilibrium distribution function. The above distribution function f reduces, as expected, to the equilibrium distribution when the field is zero. If the field is not too large, the second term is only a small perturbation and the distribution function clearly differs very little from the equilibrium form. The current density J_z, given by (7.2 - 6), depends on the value of v_z, averaged over the distribution function (7.3 - 11) in some way. In general, this average may be written

$$\bar{v}_z = \frac{\int v_z f(\mathbf{v})d\mathbf{v}}{\int f(\mathbf{v})d\mathbf{v}} \; , \tag{7.3-12}$$

where the boldface symbol $\mathbf{v}$ implies velocity space spherical coördinates v, θ, φ, and $d\mathbf{v}$ represents the volume element $v^2\sin\theta\, dv\, d\theta\, d\varphi$. The integral is actually a triple integral taken over all velocity space, $0 < v < \infty$; $0 < \theta < \pi$; $0 < \varphi < 2\pi$. There is no need to include a density of states factor, since the density of states in velocity space is constant and cancels out of numerator and denominator. First of all, it is important to observe that,

$$\int f(\mathbf{v})\,d\mathbf{v} = \int\int\left[f_0(v) - \frac{\tau(v)\cdot v\cos\theta}{kT}\cdot f_0(1-f_0)qE\right]\cdot v^2\sin\theta\, dv\, d\theta\, d\varphi \ . \tag{7.3-13}$$

The second term in this integrand depends on angle only through the factor $\cos\theta$, since the equilibrium distribution function f_0 and the relaxation time are both isotropic and depend only on the particle speed v or, if you prefer, the kinetic energy ε. The angular dependence of this term is given by $\sin\theta\cos\theta = \sin(2\theta)/2$, which when integrated over the interval zero to π, gives zero. We see therefore that

$$\int f(\mathbf{v})\,d\mathbf{v} = \int f_0(v)\,d\mathbf{v} \ . \tag{7.3-14}$$

Making use of this relationship and (7.3 - 13), we can write (7.3 - 12) as

$$\bar{v}_z = \frac{\int v_z f_0(v)\,d\mathbf{v}}{\int f_0(v)\,d\mathbf{v}} - \frac{qE}{kT}\frac{\int v^2\tau(v)\cdot f_0(1-f_0)\cdot v^2\cos^2\theta\sin\theta\, dv\, d\theta\, d\varphi}{\int f_0(v)\,d\mathbf{v}} \ . \tag{7.3-15}$$

In this expression the first term represents the average value of v_z over the equilibrium velocity distribution, which is zero since the components v_z and $-v_z$ are of equal probability in the equilibrium state. We are now left with

$$\bar{v}_z = -\frac{qE}{kT}\frac{\int v^2\tau(v)\cdot f_0(1-f_0)\cdot v^2\cos^2\theta\sin\theta\, dv\, d\theta\, d\varphi}{\int f_0(v)\cdot v^2\sin\theta\, dv\, d\theta\, d\varphi} \ . \tag{7.3-16}$$

This may now be integrated over the angular variables θ and φ. The relaxation time is assumed to depend only on the speed v, so it can be treated as as a constant in this integration. The integrands are independent of the azimuthal angle φ. The integral over this angle therefore simply yields factors of 2π above and below, which cancel. The integration over θ on $(0 < \theta < \pi)$ gives a factor of $2/3$ in the numerator and 2 in the denominator, leading to

$$\bar{v}_z = -\frac{qE}{3kT}\frac{\int v^2\tau(v)\cdot f_0(1-f_0)\cdot v^2\,dv}{\int f_0(v)\cdot v^2\,dv} \ . \tag{7.3-17}$$

The factor $3kT$ is an energy, identical dimensionally to mv^2. The above equation can thus be regarded as qE/m times an expression having dimensions of *time*. Equation (7.2 - 11) suggests that this time factor is one-half the mean free time $\tau(v)$. We may therefore write this expression as qE/m times a factor that can be viewed as *defining* how an average of the relaxation time over the nonequilibrium distribution must be written. We are thus persuaded to write,

$$\bar{v}_z = -\frac{qE}{3kT} \frac{\int v^2 \tau(v) \cdot f_0(1-f_0) \cdot v^2 dv}{\int f_0(v) \cdot v^2 dv} = -\frac{qE\bar{\tau}}{m} \quad, \tag{7.3-18}$$

where

$$\bar{\tau} = \frac{m}{3kT} \frac{\int v^2 \tau(v) \cdot f_0(1-f_0) \cdot v^2 dv}{\int f_0(v) \cdot v^2 dv} \quad. \tag{7.3-19}$$

It is important to note that the average given above is not a "straight" average of τ over the equilibrium distribution, but contains weighting factors that can be traced to the Boltzmann transport equation. It is therefore an average that expresses the perturbing effect of the field. Moreover, though not a simple average over the equilibrium distribution of velocities, it is an average involving only the equilibrium distribution function. There remains, however, the slightly disturbing matter of our neglect of the factor of $1/2$ appearing in (7.2 - 11). The presence of this factor in that expression is due to a subtle oversimplification connected with the picture of collisions used in its derivation. In this earlier calculation, if you had taken a snapshot of the distribution at some given instant of time, the average particle would be halfway between collisions. It has thus already drifted for a time $\tau/2$ on the average before the calculation has even begun, and has another $\tau/2$ seconds to go before colliding. The time τ appearing in (7.2 - 11) is therefore too small by a factor of two.

The expression above, moreover, may be regarded in a more general sense, as the proper way of averaging *any* function of velocity--not merely τ--over a distribution function perturbed as described by (7.3 - 11). Thus, if $\alpha(v)$ is a function of v (independent of the angular variables in velocity space) we can equally well write,

$$\bar{\alpha} = \frac{m}{3kT} \frac{\int v^2 \alpha(v) \cdot f_0(1-f_0) \cdot v^2 dv}{\int f_0(v) \cdot v^2 dv} = \frac{2}{3kT} \frac{\int \varepsilon^{3/2} \alpha(\varepsilon) \cdot f_0(1-f_0) \cdot d\varepsilon}{\int \varepsilon^{1/2} f_0(\varepsilon) d\varepsilon} \quad. \tag{7.3-20}$$

The second form of this result follows from the relations $\varepsilon = mv^2/2$ and $d\varepsilon = mv\,dv$. The notation we adopt is that quantities in brackets, like $<\tau>$, are averages over the equilibrium distribution, while quantities over which a bar is written, like $\bar{\tau}$, are averages over a nonequilibrium distribution function derived from the Boltzmann equation.

In the above derivation it is assumed that f_0 represents the Fermi-Dirac distribution function (5.7 - 17). The results derived are therefore of general applicability. However, it is difficult to evaluate the above integrals when the general Fermi function (5.7 - 17) is employed. Fortunately, there are two important limiting cases in which these integrals are easily evaluated. The first concerns a situation in which the number of particles is small in comparison to the number of available quantum states. As shown in Chapter 5, the Fermi distribution then closely resembles a Maxwell-Boltzmann distribution. Such circumstances arise, as we shall see more clearly later, in semiconductors like silicon and germanium, in which the density of the gas of free charges is ordinarily much lower than in metals. The other easily soluble case is that of a normal metal at temperatures far below the Fermi temperature, which as we have already shown, is in these materials of the order of tens of thousands of degrees Kelvin. Under these conditions the Fermi function resembles a step function with slightly rounded edges.

In the Maxwellian case, the Fermi energy is large and negative. At the positive energies accessible to free particles f_0 is now much smaller than unity and is very nearly equal to $A\exp(\varepsilon/kT)$, while $1 - f_0$ is essentially unity. This permits us to write

$$f_0 \cong f_0(1 - f_0) = A e^{-\varepsilon/kT} , \qquad (7.3\text{-}21)$$

where A is a factor independent of particle energy or velocity. In the averaging calculation (7.3 - 20), the factor $1 - f_0$ is now very close to unity, and the expression reduces to an average of the quantity $v^2\alpha(v)$ over an equilibrium Maxwell-Boltzmann distribution function, of the form

$$\bar{\alpha} = \frac{m}{3kT} \frac{\int v^2\alpha(v) \cdot f_0(v) \cdot v^2\, dv}{\int f_0(v) \cdot v^2\, dv} = \frac{m}{3kT} \left\langle v^2\alpha(v) \right\rangle . \qquad (7.3\text{-}22)$$

In a Boltzmann free-particle gas the average kinetic energy of a particle is $3kT/2$. so that

$$\tfrac{1}{2}mv^2 = \tfrac{3}{2}kT \quad \text{or} \quad \left\langle v^2 \right\rangle = 3kT/m . \qquad (7.3\text{-}23)$$

This allows us to write (7.3 - 22) as

$$\bar{\alpha} = \frac{\left\langle v^2\alpha(v) \right\rangle}{\left\langle v^2 \right\rangle} . \qquad (7.3\text{-}24)$$

Again, we observe that though this expression involves only the equilibrium distribution function, it is not a simple average of α over the distribution, but contains the weighting factor v^2. The nonequilibrium character of the distribution function defined by the Boltzmann transport equation is responsible for this fact.

The mean free time, averaged over velocity, can be written by substituting τ for α, as

$$\bar{\tau} = \frac{\left\langle v^2\tau(v) \right\rangle}{\left\langle v^2 \right\rangle} . \qquad (7.3\text{-}25)$$

It now follows from (7.3 - 18) that the average drift velocity is

$$\bar{v}_z = -\frac{q\bar{\tau}}{m} \cdot E \ .$$

(7.3 - 26)

Since the mobility μ has been defined as the drift velocity per unit field, it follows that

$$\mu = \frac{q\bar{\tau}}{m} \ .$$

(7.3 - 27)

The current density can now be written as

$$J = -nq\bar{v}_z = \frac{nq^2\bar{\tau}}{m} \cdot E = \sigma E \ ,$$

(7.3 - 28)

from which it is clear that Ohm's law has been derived, and that the conductivity is given by

$$\sigma = \frac{nq^2\bar{\tau}}{m} \ .$$

(7.3 - 29)

Physically, the picture differs from the crude model of the preceding section only in that the character of the nonequilibrium distribution function is now understood, and that proper procedures for averaging physical parameters over this distribution are now established. The functional dependence of the relaxation time τ on velocity, however, cannot be exhibited unless a detailed dynamical model of the collision interaction is introduced. The calculation of the scattering probability as a function of velocity for Rutherford scattering of charged particles by coulomb forces associated with a fixed source charge affords a good example of the type of calculation that must be undertaken. Such calculations are somewhat beyond the scope of this text, and will not be attempted here, though, on occasion, their results will be quoted and used. In any event, it is clear that if τ is a constant, independent of velocity, (7.3 - 25) yields simply $\bar{\tau} = \tau$. If the mean free path $\lambda = v\tau(v)$ is independent of velocity, a condition often approximately valid for electron-phonon scattering, then $\tau(v) = \lambda/v$, and (7.3 - 25) yields

$$\bar{\tau} = \frac{\langle v^2 \tau(v) \rangle}{\langle v^2 \rangle} = \frac{\lambda \langle v \rangle}{\langle v^2 \rangle} = \frac{\lambda}{3}\sqrt{\frac{8m}{\pi kT}} \ .$$

(7.3 - 30)

The algebraic details involved in writing this expression in the final form shown above are assigned as an exercise. The fact that the conductivity is proportional to the relaxation time, and that the other factors in (7.3 - 29) are independent of temperature suggests a conductivity proportional to $T^{-1/2}$. This is correct if the *number* of scatterers is independent of temperature. In pure metals electrons are scattered primarily by phonons, however, and the number of phonons is (at high temperatures) proportional to $1/T$. This endows the mean free path with a similar temperature dependence, resulting in an overall $T^{-3/2}$ temperature dependence for the conductivity. Experimentally, the conductivity of most metals is found to be proportional to

$1/T$, a discrepancy that can be resolved only by remembering that Fermi-Dirac statistics must be used in discussing the behavior of electrons in normal metallic substances. In semiconductors, where Boltzmann statistics are applicable, however, the $T^{-3/2}$ law can often be observed.

In metallic conductors, because of the very high density of free electrons, the Fermi-Dirac distribution is nearly a step function, as illustrated in Figure 7.1(a). The function $1 - f_0$, which is also illustrated, is also of this form, though reversed left to right. The product $f_0(1 - f_0)$ is very small except in the immediate neighborhood of the Fermi energy, since f_0 becomes small very rapidly above that point, and $1 - f_0$ falls of rapidly below. This product can be regarded as behaving much like the Dirac δ-function $\delta(x - x_0)$, an idealized function whose value is identically zero everywhere except at $x = x_0$, where there is an infinite singularity. This singularity causes the integral of $\delta(x - x_0)$ over any interval that includes the point x_0 to have the value unity. Its integral over any interval that does not include this point is obviously zero. This function can be visualized as a "spike" of infinite height and zero width at the singular point x_0, as shown. The product function at (a) is, for clarity, not drawn to the same scale as the curves f_0 and $1 - f_0$. Also its width is somewhat exaggerated; under normal circumstances it would be much narrower and spiked than the curve in the figure, for normal metals at room temperature.

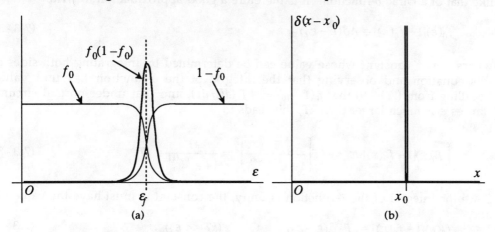

Figure 7.1 (a) Fermi-Dirac functions f_0 and $1 - f_0$ and their product. For clarity the height of the curve representing the product function has been exaggerated, while at normal temperatures its width would ordinarily be significantly smaller than that illustrated above. (b) A schematic representation of the Dirac delta function.

As suggested above, the δ-function, whose form is shown schematically in Figure 7.1(b), is defined in such a way that

$$\int_a^b \delta(x - x_0)\,dx = 1 \qquad \text{for} \qquad (a < x_0 < b)$$
$$= 0 \qquad \text{(otherwise)} . \qquad\qquad (7.3\text{-}31)$$

The δ-function has another property that makes it an extremely useful device in certain cases, including this one. This property concerns the integral of an arbitrary function $f(x)$ times the δ-function. Suppose that one multiplies the first equation above on both sides by the constant quantity $f(x_0)$, which gives the numerical value of $f(x)$ at the singular point of the δ-function. Since this is merely a constant, it can be written inside the integral, giving

$$\int_a^b f(x_0)\delta(x - x_0)dx = f(x_0) \quad \text{for} \quad (a < x_0 < b) \tag{7.3-32}$$

Now consider the effect of replacing $f(x_0)$ with $f(x)$ inside this integral. Since the δ-function is identically zero everywhere except at the singular point there can be no contribution to the integral *except* at the point $x = x_0$. Values of $f(x)$ elsewhere simply do not count. Therefore, replacing $f(x_0)$ with $f(x)$ within the integral has no effect on its value, and we can write

$$\int_a^b f(x)\delta(x - x_0)dx = f(x_0) \quad \text{when } (a < x_0 < b)$$
$$= 0 \quad \text{(otherwise)} \tag{7.3-33}$$

Returning now to the problem of Fermi-Dirac statistics, Figure 7.1(a) suggests that the product $f_0(1 - f_0)$, though having a small but finite width, has a form much like that of a Dirac δ-function. It is therefore a good approximation to write

$$f_0(\varepsilon)[1 - f_0(\varepsilon)] \cong A\delta(\varepsilon - \varepsilon_f) , \tag{7.3-34}$$

where A is a constant whose value can be determined by integrating both sides of this equation and observing that the integral of the δ-function has unit value. Recalling from (7.3 - 9) that $f_0(1 - f_0) = -kT (df_0/d\varepsilon)$, and that under normal circumstances ε_f is much larger than kT, this leads to

$$\int_0^\infty f_0(\varepsilon)[1 - f_0(\varepsilon)]d\varepsilon = -kT\left[\frac{1}{1 + e^{\varepsilon - \varepsilon_f/kT}}\right]_0^\infty = \frac{kT}{1 + e^{-\varepsilon_f/kT}} \cong kT . \tag{7.3-35}$$

Since the integral of the δ-function is unity, the constant A must have the value kT, and

$$f_0(\varepsilon)[1 - f_0(\varepsilon)] \cong kT \cdot \delta(\varepsilon - \varepsilon_f) \qquad (kT \ll \varepsilon_f) . \tag{7.3-36}$$

Substituting this in the numerator of the averaging formula (7.3 - 20), evaluating the resulting integral with the aid of (7.3 - 33), and using in the denominator the step-function approximation that $f_0 = 1$ below the Fermi energy and zero above, we obtain

$$\bar{\alpha} = \frac{2}{3kT} \frac{\displaystyle\int_0^\infty \varepsilon^{3/2}\alpha(\varepsilon) \cdot kT\delta(\varepsilon - \varepsilon_f)d\varepsilon}{\displaystyle\int_0^{\varepsilon_f} \varepsilon^{1/2}d\varepsilon} = \alpha(\varepsilon_f) . \tag{7.3-37}$$

This tells us that for a steplike Fermi distribution the properly avaraged value of a physical parameter that depends on the energy or particle speed can be expressed simply as its value at the Fermi energy. For the relaxation time $\tau(\varepsilon)$, this gives

$$\bar{\tau} = \tau(\varepsilon_f) \ . \tag{7.3-38}$$

The previously derived results (7.3 - 27, 28, 29) that follow directly from knowing the properly averaged relaxation time are still valid, provided that one remembers that a different prescription for evaluating this average is used in the two cases we have examined in detail. In the case of a dense Fermi gas at temperatures much less than the Fermi temperature, that prescription is given by the above equation, while for a much less dense Boltzmann gas, it is given by (7.3 - 25). If α is expressed in terms of velocity, it is clear that (7.3 - 37) also implies that

$$\bar{\alpha} = \alpha(v_f) \ , \quad \text{where} \quad v_f^2 = 2\varepsilon_f/m \ . \tag{7.3-39}$$

The free path λ, for any velocity subgroup can be written as $\tau(v) = \lambda(v)/v$. If the free path has the same value λ for all velocities, from (7.3 - 39) it is apparent that

$$\sigma = \frac{nq^2\bar{\tau}}{m} = \frac{nq^2\lambda}{mv_f} \ . \tag{7.3-40}$$

For a fixed number of scatterers, all quantities in this expression are constant. One could then expect the conductivity to be temperature-independent. However, when electrons are scattered by phonons, the number of scatterers, at temperatures above the Debye temperature, is proportional to T, which makes the mean free path λ, and thus the conductivity, vary with temperature as $1/T$. This is the explanation of the well-known fact that the resistance of most pure metallic conductors is (at room temperature and above) directly proportional to the absolute temperature.

Though the two special cases discussed above are useful in many cases, there are a number of important problems in which they are of little or no value, and which require the use of more accurate methods in handling averages arising from equation (7.3 - 20). It is frequently necessary in these problems also to know, approximately at least, how the Fermi energy varies with temperature. These topics will be discussed in later sections.

We have assumed in the preceding development that the field perturbs the distribution function only very slightly, which allows us to replace derivatives of the equilibrium distribution function with those of the nonequilibrium distribution function. We shall now establish the range of validity of this assumption, and also show some numerical calculations that illustrate the magnitude of the effects we are studying.

Let us consider the case of a metal like copper, which has a high conductivity and an extremely dense free electron gas. We have already observed that the conductivity of such substances implies a relaxation time of roughly 10^{-13}sec. We shall begin by assuming a relaxation time of this magnitude, and a molar volume of 8cm³ or 8×10^{-6}m³, which is roughly that of copper. The drift velocity v_z, corresponding to a field $E = 1.0\text{V/m} = 0.01\text{V/cm}$, is then

$$\bar{v}_z = \frac{q\bar{\tau}}{m}E = \frac{(1.602 \times 10^{-19})(10^{-13})}{9.11 \times 10^{-31}}(1.0) = 0.0176\text{m / sec} = 1.76\text{cm / sec}.$$

This leads to a current density J having the value,

$$J = nq\bar{v}_z = \frac{(6.022 \times 10^{23})}{8 \times 10^{-6}}(1.602 \times 10^{-19})(0.0176) = 2.12 \times 10^8 \text{amp} / \text{m}^2 = 212 \text{amp} / \text{mm}^2,$$

where Avogadro's number has been used for the number of free electrons per mole, which implies a density of one free electron per atom. The conductivity now follows from

$$\sigma = J / E = 2.12 \times 10^8 \text{ohm}^{-1}\text{m}^{-1} = 2.12 \times 10^6 \text{ohm}^{-1}\text{cm}^{-1},$$

which leads to a resistivity of 0.471×10^{-6}ohm–cm. The mobility μ is the velocity per unit field, which is seen from above to be 0.0176m^{2}V^{-1}sec^{-1}, or 176cm^{2}V^{-1}sec^{-1}. The small-field approximation will be valid when the average drift velocity is very small compared to the average thermal velocity of an electron. In a Fermi distribution, the average electron energy is, according to (5.7 - 22), $3\varepsilon_f(0)/5$, so that

$$\tfrac{1}{2}m\langle v^2 \rangle = \tfrac{3}{5}\varepsilon_f(0) , \quad \text{or} \quad \langle v^2 \rangle = \tfrac{6}{5}\varepsilon_f(0)/m .$$

A Fermi temperature $T_f = 75,000$K, which we calculated in Section 5.7 to be about right for copper, leads to a value $\varepsilon_f(0) = kT_f = 6.25$eV for the Fermi energy. Thus,

$$\langle v \rangle_{rms} = \sqrt{\langle v^2 \rangle} = \left[(1.20)\frac{(6.25)(1.602 \times 10^{-19})}{9.11 \times 10^{-31}} \right]^{1/2} = 1.148 \times 10^6 \text{m} / \text{sec} .$$

These figures indicate, first of all, that only a very small field suffices to generate quite a large current density in a good metallic conductor, a fact that anyone who has done much experimental work can verify. Even so, the drift velocity of the electrons is quite small. The calculated conductivity is in agreement with the value of 10^8ohm^{-1}m^{-1} mentioned earlier in this chapter. The average *thermal* speed of the electrons, on the other hand, is over 1100km/sec, almost 0.5% of the speed of light! The assumption that the drift velocity is very much less than the average thermal speed is therefore one that would be hard to violate under any practical set of circumstances.

It is interesting to repeat these calculations for the case of a semiconductor in which the electron gas is of such low density that Boltzmann statistics can be used. In semiconductor devices based on silicon or germanium, an electron (or hole) density of about 10^{15}cm^{-3} or 10^{21}m^{-3} is typical. In these materials, the relaxation time is longer than in metals by roughly a factor of 10, so it is realistic to assume a value of 10^{12}sec for this parameter. The same set of calculations, assuming, as before, a field of 1.0V/m, now yields a drift velocity of 0.176m/sec or 17.6cm/sec and a current density of 28.2amp/m^2 or 0.00282amp/cm^2. The reduced current density is caused by the far smaller density of current carriers in the Boltzmann gas. The conductivity can be found as before, the result being 28.2 ohm^{-1}m^{-1}, which corresponds to a resistivity of 3.55 ohm–cm. The mobility, defined as drift velocity per unit field is now found to be 0.176m^{2}V^{-1}sec^{-1}, or 1760cm^{2}V^{-1}sec^{-1}. In a Maxwellian distribution the rms average particle velocity, according to (7.3 - 23), is $(3kT/m)^{1/2}$, and since $kT = 0.025$ eV at 300K, we find

$$\langle v \rangle_{rms} = \sqrt{\frac{3kT}{m}} = \left[\frac{(3)(0.025)(1.602 \times 10^{-19})}{9.11 \times 10^{-31}} \right]^{1/2} = 114,800\text{m / sec} = 1.147 \times 10^7 \text{cm / sec} .$$

Despite the higher calculated drift velocity and lower thermal speed, the drift velocity is still far smaller than the thermal velocity. It is clear from the figures that this would be true even if the field were thousands of times larger.

One can show that when the drift velocity is small, the field has essentially no effect on the distribution function other than to introduce a small drift velocity in the field direction. If one adopts a coördinate system that moves with the average drift velocity in the direction of current flow, the distribution function given by the Boltzmann transport equation expressed in this reference frame corresponds closely to an equilibrium distribution function, so long as the small-field condition is satisfied. When the drift velocity becomes comparable to the mean thermal velocity, however, the distribution function will differ significantly from the equilibrium distribution, even in the moving reference system. The reader is asked as an exercise to demonstrate this fact for a Maxwellian velocity distribution.

This discussion confirms the usefulness of the Boltzmann transport equation and shows how the equilibrium distribution function is modified by external forces that perturb the equilibrium state. The results obtained are in agreement with what is expected from the simple picture of the free-electron gas described in the preceding section. They also illustrate explicitly how the problem of averaging over nonequilibrium distributions is approached. Despite the fact that nothing new or unusual has been revealed, the foundation needed for investigating situations that are more interesting physically, and in which less obvious effects are to be found, is now in place.

7.4 AVERAGES OVER THE FERMI DISTRIBUTION AND THE VARIATION OF THE FERMI ENERGY WITH TEMPERATURE

Though integrals that arise from the averaging prescription (7.3 - 20) when Fermi-Dirac statistics must be used cannot be calculated exactly, it is possible to find approximate expressions for them that are more generally applicable than those obtained in the preceding section. This is fortunate, for as we shall soon see, there are many important problems in which these simpler procedures are not very useful. In these problems, it is usually necessary to determine averages of powers of the particle energy ε, which in turn requires the evaluation of integrals of the form

$$I = \int_0^\infty \frac{\varepsilon^n d\varepsilon}{1 + e^{\beta(\varepsilon - \varepsilon_f)}} , \qquad \text{where} \qquad \beta = \frac{1}{kT} , \qquad (7.4-1)$$

and where n is some arbitrary exponent. This exponent need not be an integer; for example, the general problems of finding the Femi energy and the internal energy of a Fermi-Dirac free-particle gas discussed in Section 5.6 lead to integrals in which the exponent has the values $1/2$ and $3/2$, respectively.

286

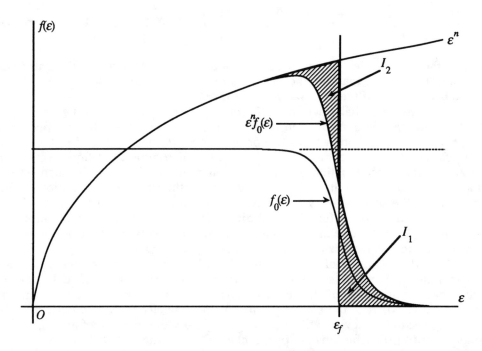

Figure 7.2 Graphs showing the equilibrium Fermi-Dirac distribution and the function that is generated by multiplying it by some arbitrary power of energy. The integral of this function can be thought of as the area under the curve ε^n from zero to the Fermi energy plus the shaded area I_1 minus the area I_2. The figure above is drawn for the case $n = 1/2$.

The situation is illustrated graphically in Figure 7.2, in which we see curves representing the equilibrium function f_0 and the multiplier ε^n. The integral I defined above can clearly be written in terms of of three separate integrals,

$$I = I_0 + I_1 - I_2 \; , \tag{7.4-2}$$

where I_0 is the integral of $\varepsilon^n \, d\varepsilon$ from zero to the Fermi energy, and where I_1 and I_2 are integrals that express the shaded areas so labeled in the diagram. Thus, as indicated above, the area under the curve $\varepsilon^n f_0(\varepsilon)$ is given by I_0 plus I_1 minus I_2, where

$$I_0 = \int_0^{\varepsilon_f} \varepsilon^n d\varepsilon = \frac{\varepsilon_f^{n+1}}{n+1} \; , \tag{7.4-3}$$

$$I_1 = \int_{\varepsilon_f}^{\infty} \varepsilon^n f_0(\varepsilon) d\varepsilon = \int_{\varepsilon_f}^{\infty} \frac{\varepsilon^n d\varepsilon}{1 + e^{\beta(\varepsilon - \varepsilon_f)}} \; , \tag{7.4-4}$$

and $\quad I_2 = \int_0^{\varepsilon_f} \varepsilon^n [1 - f_0(\varepsilon)] d\varepsilon = \int_0^{\varepsilon_f} \frac{\varepsilon^n d\varepsilon}{1 + e^{\beta(\varepsilon_f - \varepsilon)}} \; . \tag{7.4-5}$

We shall assume, as in previous work, that T is much smaller than T_f, or $kT \ll \varepsilon_f$. Now, however, we shall systematically *retain* correction terms up to the order of $(kT/\varepsilon_f)^2$, while neglecting terms of higher order in this ratio. This apparently trivial refinement is crucial in a number of important problems, as we shall see later.

We begin by expressing the function ε^n in (7.4 - 4) and (7.4 - 5) by its Taylor expansion about $\varepsilon = \varepsilon_f$,

$$\varepsilon^n = \varepsilon_f^n + n\varepsilon_f^{n-1}(\varepsilon - \varepsilon_f) + \frac{n(n-1)}{2!} \cdot \varepsilon_f^{n-2}(\varepsilon - \varepsilon_f)^2 + \frac{n(n-1)(n-2)}{3!} \cdot \varepsilon_f^{n-3}(\varepsilon - \varepsilon_f)^3 + \cdots.$$

(7.4-6)

If this is substituted into (7.4 - 4) a series of integrals that can be evaluated is obtained. The terms in the series contain successively higher powers of kT/ε_f; moreover, as we shall soon see, terms in which odd powers of this quantity appear cancel when the sum in (7.4 - 2) is evaluated. It is necessary to retain only the first two terms in the above series to obtain accuracy of order $(kT/\varepsilon_f)^2$. If all terms shown above are included, terms of order $(kT/\varepsilon_f)^4$ will appear in the answer. One can then show that these terms are so small under all realizable conditions that there is no need to consider them at all. The first two terms above yield

$$I_1 = \int_{\varepsilon_f}^{\infty} \varepsilon^n f_0(\varepsilon) d\varepsilon = \varepsilon_f^n \int_{\varepsilon_f}^{\infty} \frac{d\varepsilon}{1 + e^{\beta(\varepsilon - \varepsilon_f)}} + n\varepsilon_f^{n-1} \int_{\varepsilon_f}^{\infty} \frac{(\varepsilon - \varepsilon_f) d\varepsilon}{1 + e^{\beta(\varepsilon - \varepsilon_f)}} .$$

(7.4-7)

If we now make the substitution

$$x = \varepsilon - \varepsilon_f, \quad d\varepsilon = dx ,$$

(7.4-8)

we find

$$I_1 = \varepsilon_f^n \int_0^{\infty} \frac{dx}{1 + e^{\beta x}} + n\varepsilon_f^{n-1} \int_0^{\infty} \frac{x \, dx}{1 + e^{\beta x}} .$$

(7.4-9)

These definite integrals can be evaluated by standard techniques, and are given in most integral tables. Indeed, the first has been worked out in Section 5.6. Its value is $(\ln 2)/\beta$; the second has the value $\pi^2/12\beta^2$. Using these results, we can write

$$I_1 = \varepsilon_f^{n+1}\left(\frac{kT}{\varepsilon_f} \ln 2 + \frac{n\pi^2}{12}\left(\frac{kT}{\varepsilon_f} \right)^2 \right) .$$

(7.4-10)

Integral I_2 can be evaluated in essentially the same way. Now, however, instead of (7.4 - 8) one must use the substitution

$$y = \varepsilon_f - \varepsilon, \quad d\varepsilon = -dy ,$$

(7.4-11)

which leads to an integral of the form

$$I_2 = -\varepsilon_f^n \int_{\varepsilon_f}^0 \frac{dy}{1 + e^{\beta y}} + n\varepsilon_f^{n-1} \int_{\varepsilon_f}^0 \frac{y \, dy}{1 + e^{\beta y}} .$$

(7.4-12)

It is now useful to interchange the limits of integration, which also changes the algebraic signs of the integrals. Also, since the Fermi energy ε_f is assumed to be much larger than kT, the quantity $\exp(\beta y)$ is very large when $\varepsilon = \varepsilon_f$, and there is thus no appreciable contribution to either integral for energies larger than the Fermi energy. We can thus change the upper limits from ε_f to ∞ without significantly altering their values. Using previously quoted values for the resulting definite integrals, we find

$$I_2 = \varepsilon_f^{n+1}\left(\frac{kT}{\varepsilon_f}\ln 2 - \frac{n\pi^2}{12}\left(\frac{kT}{\varepsilon_f}\right)^2\right) .$$ (7.4-13)

We may now substitute the values of the three relevant integrals into (7.4 - 2). In so doing, the terms in $(kT\ln 2)/\varepsilon_f$ will cancel, leaving the quadratic terms as the only meaningful correction term in the final answer. If you chart the path of the cubic term in the series through this calculation, you will see that it also cancels in the expressions for I_1 and I_2; it is then clear that *all* odd powers in the expansions for these integrals are zero, leaving only even powers of kT/ε_f. If this quantity has the value 0.1, corresponding to a temperature of $0.1T_f$, or several thousand Kelvins for typical metals, the fourth-power term can clearly be no more than about one percent of the above quadratic term, and is negligible even in the most extreme circumstances.

Substituting the values given by (7.4 - 3, 10, and 13) into (7.4 - 2), we obtain finally.

$$I = \varepsilon_f^{n+1}\left(\frac{1}{n+1} + \frac{n\pi^2}{6}\left(\frac{kT}{\varepsilon_f}\right)^2\right) .$$ (7.4-14)

We shall find this result to be of great importance, for it is not only the key to understanding how the Fermi energy changes with temperature, but is also the starting point for determining the specific heat of the Fermi free electron gas, and many of its other thermal and electrical properties as well. Indeed, it allows us in most practical cases, to circumvent the awkwardness of not being able to evaluate Fermi-Dirac integrals in closed form.

This is apparent if we return to the unsolved general problem of finding the Fermi energy for a three-dimensional free-electron gas, given by equation (5.6 - 10). The problem is simplified by observing that (5.6 - 21) allows us to write (5.6 - 10) as

$$\int_0^\infty \frac{\sqrt{\varepsilon}\,d\varepsilon}{1 + e^{\beta(\varepsilon - \varepsilon_f)}} = \frac{N}{V}\left(\frac{h^3}{8\sqrt{2}\pi m^{3/2}}\right) = \frac{2}{3}\varepsilon_f^{3/2}(0) .$$ (7.4-15)

The integral on the left is a special case of (7.4 - 1) for which $n = 1/2$. Its approximate value is easily obtained by setting n equal to $1/2$ in (7.4 - 14), which leads to

$$I = \frac{2}{3}\varepsilon_f^{3/2}(0) = \frac{2}{3}\varepsilon_f^{3/2}\left(1 + \frac{\pi^2}{8}\left(\frac{kT}{\varepsilon_f}\right)^2\right) ,$$ (7.4-16)

and
$$\frac{\varepsilon_f}{\varepsilon_f(0)} = \left(1 + \frac{\pi^2}{8}\left(\frac{kT}{\varepsilon_f}\right)^2\right)^{-2/3} . \tag{7.4-17}$$

In this expression the second term in parentheses is much smaller than the first; under these circumstances, we may note from the binomial theorem that for small values of z, $(1 + z)^n \cong 1 + nz$, which enables us to write this as

$$\frac{\varepsilon_f}{\varepsilon_f(0)} = \left(1 - \frac{\pi^2}{12}\left(\frac{kT}{\varepsilon_f}\right)^2\right) \cong \left(1 - \frac{\pi^2}{12}\left(\frac{kT}{\varepsilon_f(0)}\right)^2\right) . \tag{7.4-18}$$

In the final form of this result, we have replaced ε_f by $\varepsilon_f(0)$. Since the second term in parentheses is far less than unity, no significant error is introduced by this substitution. We have previously been careful to preserve the distinction between ε_f and $\varepsilon_f(0)$, so that no problems involving such a replacement could arise earlier. One can show that the the above result is valid up to fourth order in the ratio $kT/\varepsilon_f(0)$. As has been suggested in Section 5.6, the Fermi energy of ordinary metallic systems is now seen to decrease quadratically with temperature for all attainable temperatures.

The next unsolved problem has to do with the internal energy and specific heat of the Fermi free-electron gas in three dimensions. The internal energy of particles in a range $d\varepsilon$ is given by $dU = \varepsilon N(\varepsilon)\, d\varepsilon$, and the total internal energy will be

$$U = \frac{8\sqrt{2}\,\pi V m^{3/2}}{h^3} \int_0^\infty \frac{\varepsilon^{3/2}\, d\varepsilon}{1 + e^{\beta(\varepsilon - \varepsilon_f)}} . \tag{7.4-19}$$

The integral in this equation will be recognized as a special case of (7.4 - 1) for which $n = 3/2$. Denoting this integral by I', we can write, with the aid of (7.4 - 15),

$$I' = \frac{U}{V} \cdot \frac{h^3}{8\sqrt{2}\pi m^{3/2}} = \frac{U}{N} \cdot \frac{N}{V}\left(\frac{h^3}{8\sqrt{2}\pi m^{3/2}}\right) = \frac{U}{N} \cdot \frac{2}{3}\varepsilon_f^{3/2}(0) . \tag{7.4-20}$$

Substituting $n = 3/2$ into (7.4 - 14) to get I', and using the binomial theorem as above, we can now write this equation as

$$\frac{U}{N} \cdot \frac{3}{5}\varepsilon_f^{3/2}(0) = \frac{3}{5}\varepsilon_f^{5/2}\left(1 + \frac{5\pi^2}{8}\left(\frac{kT}{\varepsilon_f}\right)^2\right) . \tag{7.4-21}$$

Now, however, we know the temperature-dependence of the Fermi energy from (7.4 - 17). This allows us to write ε_f in the above equation as an explicit function of temperature, and to obtain

$$\frac{U}{N} = \frac{3}{5}\varepsilon_f(0)\left(1 - \frac{\pi^2}{12}\left(\frac{kT}{\varepsilon_f}\right)^2\right)^{5/2}\left(1 + \frac{5\pi^2}{8}\left(\frac{kT}{\varepsilon_f}\right)^2\right) ,$$

or, $\quad \dfrac{U}{N} = \dfrac{3}{5}\varepsilon_f(0)\left(1 - \dfrac{5\pi^2}{24}\left(\dfrac{kT}{\varepsilon_f}\right)^2\right) \cdot \left(1 + \dfrac{5\pi^2}{8}\left(\dfrac{kT}{\varepsilon_f}\right)^2\right)$, $\quad$ and finally,

$$\dfrac{U}{N} = \dfrac{3}{5}\varepsilon_f(0)\left(1 + \dfrac{5\pi^2}{12}\left(\dfrac{kT}{\varepsilon_f}\right)^2\right) .$$

(7.4 - 22)

In this work, the binomial theorem has been employed as usual, and a fourth-order term has been discarded in writing the product of the two expressions in parentheses. It is clear from (7.4 - 22) that (as suggested also in (5.6 - 22)) the quantity $3\varepsilon_f(0)/5$ expresses the internal energy per particle in the low-temperature limit. Writing this quantity as U_0/N, and expressing $\varepsilon_f(0)$ as kT_f, we find at last,

$$U = U_0 + \dfrac{\pi^2}{4}Nk \cdot \dfrac{T^2}{T_f} .$$

(7.4 - 23)

The specific heat follows immediately by differentiating with respect to temperature, as

$$C_v = \dfrac{\pi^2}{2}Nk \cdot \dfrac{T}{T_f} .$$

(7.4 - 24)

This expression shows that the specific heat of the free electron gas in metallic substances, because of the factor T/T_f, is much smaller than the value $3Nk/2$ associated with a Maxwellian free-particle gas or the amount $3Nk$ associated with the vibrational modes of the crystal lattice. For a Fermi Temperature of 75,000K this reduces the electronic component of the specific heat to less than one percent of the lattice specific heat at and above room temperature. The reason for this surprising result is the effect of the Pauli exclusion principle, which prevents electrons whose energy is appreciably less than the Fermi energy from being excited through energies of a few times kT to quantum states higher in energy, since practically all such final states are already occupied. The only electrons that can make such transitions are those whose energies are within a few kT of the Fermi energy, which comprises only a small fraction of the total electron population. The measured specific heat of metals thus differs very little from the lattice specific heat at and above the Debye temperature.

At low temperatures, however, the Debye lattice specific heat falls off as T^3, which is more rapid than the first-power law given by (7.4 - 24). At sufficiently low temperatures (in practice less than about 10K), the lattice specific heat may thus become smaller than that associated with the electron gas, and the electronic component may become dominant in this temperature range, announcing its presence by the linear temperature variation just mentioned. The fact that this effect is observed experimentally in many metallic substances confirms the reality of the Fermi-Dirac distribution as well as the validity of the above theoretical development.

7.5 THERMAL CONDUCTIVITY, THERMOELECTRIC EFFECTS, AND THE WIEDEMANN–FRANZ RATIO

One of the earliest experimental observations associated with the mobile free charges in metals was made in 1853 by Weidemann and Franz, who found that the ratio

$$\Sigma = \frac{\sigma_t}{T\sigma_e} ,$$

(7.5-1)

where σ_t and σ_e are the thermal and electrical conductivities and T is the absolute temperature, is the same for nearly all metals. Some experimental data that illustrate this effect are shown in Figure 7.3.

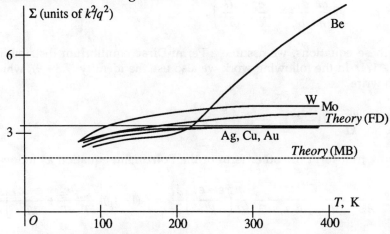

Figure 7.3 Comparison of experimental data on the Wiedemann-Franz ratio with theory. The horizontal line marked (MB) shows the prediction of theory using Maxwell-Boltzmann statistics, while the line labeled (FD) is the corresponding prediction when Fermi-Dirac statistics are employed.

It is clear from these data that the Wiedemann-Franz law is obeyed by many typical metallic elements, though clearly there are some anomalies, such as beryllium. The predictions of theory are also shown, though detailed comment on them will be reserved until later. The Wiedemann-Franz law was puzzling when first discovered, since there is nothing in the qualitative physical picture of a metallic free-electron conductor that suggests why it should be obeyed. The effect was not explained until the quantitative theory of Drude and Lorentz was formulated in the first decade of the 20th century, and reasonable quantitative agreement with the data was not obtained until Fermi-Dirac statistics were introduced about 1928. The subject of thermoelectricity, also investigated experimentally during the 19th century, posed similar problems that were not clearly resolved until the free-electron theory of metals was formulated.

All these effects concern situations wherein a temperature gradient is present; in the case of thermoelectricity there is also an electric field. In writing the Boltzmann transport equation under these conditions, both of these external factors must be included. If we assume that both electric field and temperature gradient are in the z-direction, the steady-state Boltzmann equation (7.3 - 7) can be written, using the relaxation time approximation, as

$$\frac{df}{dt} = 0 = -v_z \frac{\partial f_0}{\partial z} - \frac{qE}{m} \frac{\partial f_0}{\partial v_z} - \frac{f - f_0}{\tau(v)} \ . \tag{7.5-2}$$

In this expression, we have replaced the derivatives of the actual distribution function f with the corresponding derivatives of the equilibrium distribution function, for reasons already discussed in Section 7.3. The derivative of f_0 with respect to z exists only because of the temperature gradient; we can therefore relate this derivative to a temperature derivative, and solving for f, write

$$f = f_0 - \tau(v) \left(\frac{qE}{m} \frac{\partial f_0}{\partial v_z} + v_z \frac{\partial f_0}{\partial T} \cdot \frac{\partial T}{\partial z} \right) \ . \tag{7.5-3}$$

In these equations, we assume a Fermi-Dirac equilibrium distribution of the form (5.7 - 17). In the following work we also use the identity (7.3 - 9), which allows us now to write

$$\frac{\partial f_0}{\partial v_z} = -\frac{mv_z}{kT} f_0(1 - f_0) \ . \tag{7.5-4}$$

We can now transform the other term in the Boltzmann equation as follows:

$$\frac{\partial f_0}{\partial T} \cdot \frac{\partial T}{\partial z} = -\frac{e^{-(\varepsilon - \varepsilon_f)/kT}}{\left(1 + e^{-(\varepsilon - \varepsilon_f)/kT}\right)^2} \frac{\partial}{\partial T} \left(\frac{\varepsilon - \varepsilon_f}{kT} \right) \frac{\partial T}{\partial z} = f_0(1 - f_0) \left[\frac{1}{kT} \frac{\partial \varepsilon_f}{\partial T} + \frac{\varepsilon - \varepsilon_f}{kT^2} \right] \frac{\partial T}{\partial z}$$

$$= \frac{f_0(1 - f_0)}{kT} \left[\frac{\partial \varepsilon_f}{\partial T} - \frac{\varepsilon_f}{T} + \frac{\varepsilon}{T} \right] \frac{\partial T}{\partial z} = \frac{f_0(1 - f_0)}{kT} \left[T \frac{\partial (\varepsilon_f/T)}{\partial T} + \frac{\varepsilon}{T} \right] \frac{\partial T}{\partial z} \ . \tag{7.5-5}$$

Substituting these results into (7.5 - 3) and noting that $v_z = v\cos\theta$, we can write the distribution function as

$$f = f_0 + \frac{\tau(v) \cdot v\cos\theta}{kT} f_0(1 - f_0) \left[qE - \left(T \frac{\partial (\varepsilon_f/T)}{\partial T} + \frac{\varepsilon}{T} \right) \frac{\partial T}{\partial z} \right] \ . \tag{7.5-6}$$

The current density then follows as in Section 7.7 from

$$J_z = nq\bar{v}_z = nq \frac{\displaystyle\int \frac{\tau(v) \cdot v\cos\theta}{kT} f_0(1 - f_0) \left[qE - \left(T \frac{\partial (\varepsilon_f/T)}{\partial T} + \frac{\varepsilon}{T} \right) \frac{\partial T}{\partial z} \right] v^2 \sin\theta \, dv \, d\theta \, d\varphi}{\displaystyle\int f_0 \cdot v^2 \sin\theta \, dv \, d\theta \, d\varphi} \ . \tag{7.5-7}$$

As before, we may now integrate over the angular coördinates, obtaining a factor of $1/3$, which leaves

$$J_z = \frac{nq}{m} \cdot \frac{m}{3kT} \frac{\int v^2 \tau(v) f_0 (1-f_0) \left[qE - \left(T \frac{\partial (\varepsilon_f/T)}{\partial T} + \frac{\varepsilon}{T} \right) \frac{\partial T}{\partial z} \right] v^2 dv}{\int f_0 \cdot v^2 dv} . \tag{7.5-8}$$

In the numerator, the first two terms in the bracketed expression are merely constants with regard to the integral over velocity; they therefore simply multiply an average of the relaxation time τ as defined by (7.3 - 19) or (7.3 - 20). The third term contains a factor of ε $(=mv^2/2)$ which changes this term to an average of the quantity $\varepsilon\tau$ over velocity, as defined by those equations. We may therefore write

$$J_z = \frac{nq}{m} \left[\left(qE - T \frac{\partial (\varepsilon_f/T)}{\partial T} \frac{\partial T}{\partial z} \right) \cdot \bar{\tau} - \frac{1}{T} \frac{\partial T}{\partial z} \cdot \overline{\varepsilon\tau} \right] , \tag{7.5-9}$$

the averages being defined by (7.3 - 20).

The thermal flux associated with a particle is defined as the particle's kinetic energy ε times the component of velocity v_z along the direction of the temperature gradient. Another way of arriving at it is to replace the charge q with the kinetic energy ε in the definition of current density nqv_z to obtain an expression for the flux of energy instead of charge. In any event, this product must be properly averaged over the energy distribution to obtain the total flux carried by all particles. It is important to note, in this connection, that all particles have the same charge, but not the same kinetic energy. We must therefore write the heat flux K_z as

$$K_z = \varepsilon v_z , \quad \text{(single particle)}$$

$$\text{or,} \quad K_z = n(\overline{\varepsilon v_z}) \quad \text{(whole system)} . \tag{7.5-10}$$

The averaging calculation shown in (7.5 - 7) and (7.5 - 8) is now repeated, using the above expression for the heat flux. The only effect of this is to introduce an additional factor of ε into every term in these equations, leading to an expression for the heat flux in which slightly different averages appear. as follows;

$$K_z = \frac{n}{m} \left[\left(qE - T \frac{\partial (\varepsilon_f/T)}{\partial T} \frac{\partial T}{\partial z} \right) \cdot \overline{\varepsilon\tau} - \frac{1}{T} \frac{\partial T}{\partial z} \cdot \overline{\varepsilon^2\tau} \right] . \tag{7.5-11}$$

As in the previous case the averages must be calculated using (7.3 - 20).

If there is no electric current, then J_x can be set equal to zero in (7.5 - 9). When one does this, it is observed that there is an electric field present, despite the absence of a current. Solving for this electric field, which we shall refer to as E_0, we find

$$E_0 = \frac{1}{q} \left[T \frac{\partial (\varepsilon_f/T)}{\partial T} + \frac{1}{T} \cdot \frac{\overline{\varepsilon\tau}}{\bar{\tau}} \right] \cdot \frac{\partial T}{\partial z} . \tag{7.5-12}$$

The field is directly proportional to the temperature gradient, which suggests that it is thermally generated. When there is a temperature gradient, the average kinetic energy of electrons decreases from the hot end to the cold end of a conductor. This means that electrons going "downstream" from hot to cold are on the average going slightly faster than those going in the opposite direction. Temporarily, then, more charge flows downstream than up, causing a slight accumulation of excess charge at the cold end and a slight deficiency at the hot end. This tiny imbalance of charge creates the above electric field, and builds up, impelling electrons in the opposite direction until a dynamic equilibrium is reached in which the current is reduced once more to zero. The field has now reached the value given above, and on the open ends of the conducting sample there resides a small net surface charge density that can be regarded as the source of this thermoelectric field.

If the conductor is a closed loop, this field and the associated charge asymmetry remain, but the potential difference between hot and cold ends of the loop is clearly the same in both halves of the circuit, and the total change in potential (as measured by the integral of $-E_0 \cdot dl$ around the loop) will be zero. There is therefore no emf in the circuit and no steady current will flow, as anyone who has tried to make a thermocouple from a single species of metallic conductor will admit. When the two branches are dissimilar, though, the field may not be equal in each branch, since the relaxation time and Fermi energy may differ in the two substances. There is now a *difference* in the integral of $-E_0 \cdot dl$ in the two halves of the circuit, and this integral evaluated around the loop is no longer zero, but is equal to the difference between the integrals in the respective branches. A thermocouple emf given by this difference is now present. This emf is referred to as a *Seebeck emf*, and the phenomenon of thermoelectrically generated voltages is known as the *Seebeck effect*.

If we now substitute the field given by (7.5 - 12) into the heat flow expression (7.5 - 11), the terms containing $\partial(\varepsilon_f/T)/\partial T$ will be found to cancel, leaving

$$K_z = -\frac{n}{mT}\left(\frac{\bar{\tau}(\overline{\varepsilon^2 \tau}) - (\overline{\varepsilon \tau})^2}{\bar{\tau}}\right)\frac{\partial T}{\partial z} = -\sigma_t \frac{\partial T}{\partial z} \; , \tag{7.5-13}$$

where

$$\sigma_t = -\frac{n}{mT} \cdot \frac{\bar{\tau}(\overline{\varepsilon^2 \tau}) - (\overline{\varepsilon \tau})^2}{\bar{\tau}} \tag{7.5-14}$$

can be identified as the thermal conductivity. Since the electrical conductivity σ_e is given by (7.3 - 30) as $nq^2\bar{\tau}/m$, the Wiedemann-Franz ratio can be written as

$$\Sigma = \frac{\sigma_t}{T\sigma_e} = \frac{1}{q^2 T^2} \cdot \frac{\bar{\tau}(\overline{\varepsilon^2 \tau}) - (\overline{\varepsilon \tau})^2}{\bar{\tau}^2} \; . \tag{7.5-15}$$

The problem is now reduced to one of finding the averages that appear in the expressions above. The relaxation time depends on energy (or particle speed, depending on how you express it), but exactly how is not revealed by the Boltzmann equation when the relaxation time approximation is used. We must therefore make reasonable guesses and comparisons with experimental data. One thus relies on experiment to determine whether or not this picture of the electron distribution is reasonable, and also to show how the relaxation time depends on energy.

It is customary to assume a power law to describe how the relaxation time depends upon energy. Such a variation is often obtained from calculations based upon actual collision dynamics. More practically, power-law assumptions have also had good success in explaining experimental data. We therefore proceed by assuming that

$$\tau(\varepsilon) = C \cdot \varepsilon^n ,$$

(7.5-16)

where C is a constant. The evaluation of averages now involves only finding averages of powers of ε. According to our avaraging prescription (7.3 - 20),

$$\overline{\varepsilon^n} = \frac{2}{3kT} \frac{\int_0^\infty \varepsilon^{n+\frac{3}{2}} f_0(1-f_0)\,d\varepsilon}{\int_0^\infty \varepsilon^{1/2} f_0\,d\varepsilon} .$$

(7.5-17)

However, as suggested by (7.3 - 9), $f_0(1 - f_0) = -kT(df_0/d\varepsilon)$. Therefore, we can write, for an arbitrary power p,

$$\int_0^\infty \varepsilon^p f_0(1-f_0)\,d\varepsilon = -kT \int_0^\infty \varepsilon^p \cdot \frac{df_0}{d\varepsilon}\,d\varepsilon$$

$$= -kT\left(\left[\varepsilon^p f_0\right]_0^\infty - p\int_0^\infty \varepsilon^{p-1} f_0\,d\varepsilon\right) = p \cdot kT \int_0^\infty \varepsilon^{p-1} f_0\,d\varepsilon .$$

(7.5-18)

In this calculation an integration by parts, in which $u = \varepsilon^p$ and $dv = (df_0/d\varepsilon)\,d\varepsilon = df_0$, has been performed. The term uv, evaluated as shown, vanishes because ε^p is zero for $\varepsilon = 0$ (if p is positive), while f_0 is zero in the limit of large ε. When p is negative, however, this argument breaks down. If we assign p the value $n + (3/2)$, we obtain the integral in the numerator of (7.5 - 17), which then can be written

$$\overline{\varepsilon^n} = \tfrac{2}{3}\left(n+\tfrac{3}{2}\right) \cdot \frac{\int_0^\infty \varepsilon^{n+\frac{1}{2}} f_0\,d\varepsilon}{\int_0^\infty \varepsilon^{1/2} f_0\,d\varepsilon} .$$

(7.5-19)

Both integrals above are of the form (7.4 - 1), whose value, as shown in the preceding section, is given by (7.4 - 14). Using this result to evaluate them, we now find

$$\overline{\varepsilon^n} = \varepsilon_f^n \cdot \frac{1+\frac{\pi^2}{6}\left(n+\frac{1}{2}\right)\left(n+\frac{3}{2}\right)\left(\frac{kT}{\varepsilon_f}\right)^2}{1+\frac{\pi^2}{8}\left(\frac{kT}{\varepsilon_f}\right)^2} = \varepsilon_f^n \cdot \left[1+\frac{\pi^2}{6}\left(n+\frac{1}{2}\right)\left(n+\frac{3}{2}\right)\left(\frac{kT}{\varepsilon_f}\right)^2\right]\cdot\left[1-\frac{\pi^2}{8}\left(\frac{kT}{\varepsilon_f}\right)^2\right] .$$

(7.5-20)

In writing the final form of this result, we have used the binomial theorem, writing the denominator as an inverse power, whose expansion leads to the second factor above. The expression is valid for values of $n > -3/2$. We have also shown, as equation (7.4 - 18), how the Fermi energy $\varepsilon_f(T)$ depends on temperature. Using this to write ε_f^n in the above expression, and again using the binomial theorem, we get

$$\overline{\varepsilon^n} = \varepsilon_f^n(0) \cdot \left[1 - \frac{n\pi^2}{12}\left(\frac{kT}{\varepsilon_f}\right)^2\right] \cdot \left[1 + \frac{\pi^2}{6}(n+\tfrac{1}{2})(n+\tfrac{3}{2})\left(\frac{kT}{\varepsilon_f}\right)^2\right] \cdot \left[1 - \frac{\pi^2}{8}\left(\frac{kT}{\varepsilon_f}\right)^2\right]. \qquad (7.5\text{-}21)$$

Multiplying these factors together and rejecting terms of fourth and sixth order in (kT/ε_f), we find

$$\overline{\varepsilon^n} = \varepsilon_f^n(0) \cdot \left[1 + \frac{\pi^2}{12}(n+1)(2n+1)\left(\frac{kT}{\varepsilon_f(0)}\right)^2\right]. \qquad (7.5\text{-}22)$$

So far we have been careful to preserve the distinction between $\varepsilon_f(T)$ and $\varepsilon_f(0)$. In the final expression for the above result, however, the fact that $\varepsilon_f(T)$ appears only in the denominator of what is after all a small correction term, allows us to replace it with the zero-temperature value as shown, without penalty. This result can be shown to be good to order $(kT/\varepsilon_f)^2$. The reader is asked as an exercise to verify this point.

We can now compute the Wiedemann-Franz ratio and the thermal conductivity, assuming an energy-independent mean free path which, as suggested previously, is valid for electrons scattered primarily by acoustical-mode phonons. For this case,

$$\tau(v) = \frac{\lambda}{v} = \lambda\sqrt{\frac{m}{2\varepsilon}}, \qquad (7.5\text{-}23)$$

where λ is an energy-independent mean free path. It is now clear from (7.5 - 22) that

$$\overline{\varepsilon^{3/2}} = \varepsilon_f(0)\left[1 + \frac{5\pi^2}{6}\left(\frac{kT}{\varepsilon_f(0)}\right)^2\right], \quad \overline{\varepsilon^{1/2}} = \varepsilon_f(0)\left[1 + \frac{\pi^2}{4}\left(\frac{kT}{\varepsilon_f(0)}\right)^2\right], \quad \text{and } \overline{\varepsilon^{-1/2}} = \varepsilon_f^{-1/2}(0).$$

$$(7.5\text{-}24)$$

The Wiedemann-Franz ratio (7.5 - 15), assuming a velocity-independent mean free path, can now be written as

$$\Sigma = \frac{(\overline{\varepsilon^{-1/2}})(\overline{\varepsilon^{3/2}}) - [(\overline{\varepsilon^{1/2}})]^2}{q^2 T^2 [(\overline{\varepsilon^{-1/2}})]^2} = \frac{\varepsilon_f(0)\left(1 + \frac{5\pi^2}{6}\left(\frac{kT}{\varepsilon_f(0)}\right)^2\right) - \varepsilon_f(0)\left(1 + \frac{\pi^2}{4}\left(\frac{kT}{\varepsilon_f(0)}\right)^2\right)^2}{q^2 T^2 \varepsilon_f^{-1}(0)},$$

or, $\qquad \Sigma = \frac{\varepsilon_f^2(0)}{q^2 T^2}\left(1 + \frac{5\pi^2}{6}\left(\frac{kT}{\varepsilon_f(0)}\right)^2 - 1 - \frac{2\pi^2}{4}\left(\frac{kT}{\varepsilon_f(0)}\right)^2\right) = \frac{\pi^2}{3} \cdot \frac{k^2}{q^2}. \qquad (7.5\text{-}25)$

In this calculation, a fourth-order term has been neglected in writing (7.5 - 25) in its final form. It will be observed that the "large" terms in (7.5 - 25) cancel; the result would in fact have been zero were it not for the "small" temperature dependent terms whose origins can be traced back ultimately to the temperature dependence of the Fermi energy given by (7.4 - 18). This is another important example of the usefulness of the work in the preceding section. This fortuitous cancellation, by the way, has nothing to do with the assumption of an energy-independent mean free path. It is not hard to show that it also occurs if you assume an energy-independent relaxation time, or for that matter one expressed by any other power law.

It should also be noted that the Wiedemann-Franz ratio turns out to be the pure number $\pi^2/3$ times the ratio of two fundamental constants whose value is known to a high degree of accuracy. The mean free path λ, which is not easy to determine accurately, cancels out as a consequence of how Σ is defined. This predicted value of the Wiedemann-Franz ratio is shown as the horizontal line labeled (FD) in Figure 7.3, and it is clear that though the agreement by no means perfect, it is not bad considering the difficulties involved in accurately measuring thermal conductivities. Indeed, the agreement for the "classical" free electron conductors Cu, Au, and Ag is remarkably good

The original form of the free-electron theory, as proposed by Drude, made use of Boltzmann statistics and the averaging procedure given by (7.3 - 25) and (7.3 - 26). This leads to a value $2k^2/q^2$ for Σ, which is less than 2/3 the value obtained above. The horizontal line marked (MB) in Figure 7.3 illustrates this result, which is not in very good agreement with the experimental data. For nearly 30 years this disparity cast doubt on Drude's theory, until finally the question was resolved by quantum theory and Fermi-Dirac statistics. There are other options that can also be explored, particularly regarding assumptions other than that of an energy-independent mean free path. If, for example, we assume that τ rather than λ is independent of energy, the Wiedemann-Franz ratio can be shown to be $\pi^2/4$ (FD) or 5/2 (MB); the proof is a useful exercise for the reader. It is clear, however, that of all the physically reasonable alternatives, Fermi Dirac statistics and a mean free path independent of energy agrees best with measurements for materials that best fit the concept of ideal free-electron metallic conductors.

The thermal conductivity follows from the Wiedemann-Franz ratio by multiplying by $T\sigma_t$, where σ_t is given by (7.3 - 30). The reader may show as an exercise, first that

$$\sigma_t = \frac{\pi^2 n k^2 T \lambda}{3m} \sqrt{\frac{m}{2kT_f}} \, , \tag{7.5-26}$$

and subsequently that this can be transformed to

$$\sigma = \tfrac{1}{3} \lambda \, C_v v_f \, , \tag{7.5-27}$$

where C_v is the electronic specific heat (7.4 - 24) and v_f is the "Fermi velocity", corresponding to the speed of a particle of energy $\varepsilon_f(0)$. This result has the form suggested by equation (6.9 - 14) of the preceding chapter, which was derived for the quite different case of *lattice* thermal conductivity attributable to phonon-phonon scattering. The result could possibly have been written down immediately, though its derivation in the preceding chapter assumed a different set of circumstances from those of the present calculation. In any event such an approach would have given no clue to the thermoelectric effects and other phenomena suggested by the Boltzmann equation.

All the results derived above have been obtained in the context of a sample in which no electric current flows. When the current density J_z is no longer zero, the electric field will differ from the value E_0 given by (7.5 - 12). Indeed, it is clear from (7.5 - 9) and the fact that $\sigma_e = nq^2\bar{\tau}/m$ that the current density (7.5 - 9) can be written as

$$J_z = \sigma_e(E - E_0) = \sigma_e E_e \; . \tag{7.5-28}$$

In this equation, E is the total electric field scting on a particle, while E_0 is an internal field set up by the temperature gradient. The difference between these fields is the part of the total field arising from external sources, such a battery in the circuit. This "external" field is denoted by E_e in (7.5 - 28). When there is no temperature gradient, $E = E_e$, and the current density is $\sigma_e E$; when neither external field nor temperature gradient exists, the current density is zero, as it should be in both instances.

If you solve both (7.5 - 9) and (7.5 - 11) for the quantity qE and equate the two resulting expressions, you will find that the terms containing $\partial(\varepsilon_f/T)/\partial T$ cancel, leaving after regrouping

$$\frac{1}{T}\frac{\partial T}{\partial z} \cdot \frac{\bar{\tau}(\overline{\varepsilon^2\tau}) - (\overline{\varepsilon\tau})^2}{\bar{\tau}(\overline{\varepsilon\tau})} = \frac{m}{nq}\left(\frac{J_z}{\bar{\tau}} - \frac{qK_z}{(\overline{\varepsilon\tau})}\right) . \tag{7.5-29}$$

The right side of this equation is seen to contain the thermal conductivity as given by (7.5 - 14). When the complex averages are expressed in terms of σ_t, it becomes much simpler, and can be rearranged to read

$$qK_z = J_z\frac{(\overline{\varepsilon\tau})}{\bar{\tau}} - q\sigma_t\frac{\partial T}{\partial z} \; . \tag{7.5-30}$$

From this, it is apparent that the thermal flux is no longer simply proportional to the temperature gradient, but is also partly carried by the current, which may in turn be driven largely by an external emf. Moreover, the direction of this heat flux, as given by the first term above, is reversed when the current changes sign. In contrast with ohmic heating, which is proportional to the square of the current density, and

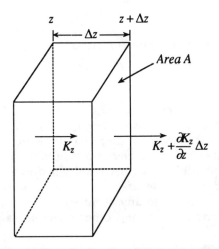

Figure 7.4 A segment of conductor in which heat and electric charge flows along the z-direction in response to an electric field and a temperature gradient in that same direction.

has the same sign irrespective of the direction of the current flow, this heat flux is *reversible*. As we shall soon see, it acts much like a reversible heat pump, in that it can cause heat to flow either with or against a temperature gradient--with the assistance, of course, of external work, in this case supplied by a battery or other external emf. This phenomenon is referred to as the *Thomson effect*.

When heat flows along a metallic conductor, there is a flux of kinetic energy given by (7.5 - 11) and also a flow of current described by (7.5 - 9) These fluxes are driven by fields and temperature gradients, but neither depends totally on one or the other, in general. If we examine how the internal thermal energy of a volume element like the one shown in Figure 7.4 can change with respect to these variables, however, it is possible to sort out their effects more clearly. In the figure, we see an element of a conductor of area A and length Δz, in which there is an electric field, a temperature gradient and charge and kinetic energy fluxes, all of which are assumed to be in the z-direction.

Let us now calculate the rate of increase of internal energy per unit volume U with time in the volume element illustrated. Charges experience electric forces that do total work $I_z \Delta \varphi = (J_z A) \Delta \varphi$ in distance Δz and time Δt, where $\Delta \varphi$ is the potential drop they experience in Δz (using φ for potential since V will represent volume). However, $\Delta \varphi = -E \Delta z$, so the amount of heat generated per unit time in the element is $J_z A E \Delta z$, the minus sign having disappeared because though the potential decreases, the work done goes into *increasing* the thermal internal energy of the element. There is also a change in internal kinetic energy due to the fact that the kinetic energy flux K_z can be a function of z. If the flux into the element at z is $K_z(z)$, and if K_z changes by the amount $dK_z = (\partial K_z / \partial z) \Delta z$ in distance Δz, the flux out of the element will be that shown in the figure. The net change of kinetic energy per unit time is the flux entering minus the flux leaving times the area A, or $-(\partial K_z / \partial z) A \Delta z$. The sum of these two contributions gives the time rate at which heat is produced within the volume element, which equals $(\partial U / \partial t) \Delta V$. Equating the sum of the two heat inputs to this quantity, and noting that $A \Delta z = \Delta V$, we can now write

$$\frac{\partial U}{\partial t} = EJ_z - \frac{\partial K_z}{\partial z} \ . \tag{7.5-31}$$

Substituting the value of E given by (7.5 - 28) and that of K_z from (7.5 - 30), this can be written

$$\frac{\partial U}{\partial t} = \frac{J_z^2}{\sigma_e} + J_z E_0 - \frac{\partial}{\partial z}\left(\frac{J_z}{q} \cdot \frac{(\overline{\varepsilon \tau})}{\overline{\tau}} - \sigma_t \frac{\partial T}{\partial z} \right) \ . \tag{7.5-32}$$

The value of E_0 follows from (7.5 - 12). In differentiating the third term above, it must be noted that the derivative of the quantity $(\overline{\varepsilon \tau})/\overline{\tau}$ with respect to z is not generally zero. Making this substitution and differentiating, the result can be written, after some algebraic maneuvering, as

$$\frac{\partial U}{\partial t} = \frac{J_z^2}{\sigma_e} - \frac{J_z}{q} \cdot T \frac{\partial}{\partial z}\left(\frac{1}{T} \frac{(\overline{\varepsilon \tau})}{\overline{\tau}} - \frac{\varepsilon_f}{T} \right) + \frac{\partial}{\partial z}\left(\sigma_t \frac{\partial T}{\partial z} \right) \ . \tag{7.5-33}$$

There are three terms in the above expression. The first is easily recognized as the rate at which heat is produced by Joule (I^2R) heating. The third, in which the

300

temperature gradient appears, but which is independent of the current density, expresses the rate at which heat would accumulate in the region in the presence of a temperature gradient if there were no current. This is evident from the fact that if you set the current density equal to zero and write dU as $C_v dT$, the expression reduces to the partial differential equation that describes the flow of heat by thermal conduction. Both of these processes are clearly irreversible thermodynamically. The second term is the rate at which Thomson heat accumulates in the region; its sign changes if the direction of current flow is reversed, so it is reversible. The Thomson heat is often written as

$$\left(\frac{\partial U}{\partial t}\right)_{\text{Thom}} = -\frac{J_z}{q} \cdot T \frac{\partial}{\partial T}\left(\frac{1}{T}\frac{(\overline{\varepsilon \tau})}{\overline{\tau}} - \frac{\varepsilon_f}{T}\right) \cdot \frac{\partial T}{\partial z} = -J_z \frac{\partial T}{\partial z} \cdot \zeta , \qquad (7.5\text{-}34)$$

where the quantity ζ, which is referred to as the *Thomson coefficient*, is given by

$$\zeta = \frac{1}{q} T \frac{\partial}{\partial T}\left(\frac{1}{T}\frac{(\overline{\varepsilon \tau})}{\overline{\tau}} - \frac{\varepsilon_f}{T}\right) . \qquad (7.5\text{-}35)$$

In most metallic substances, the Thomson coefficient is negative. This means that for a positive temperature gradient, the sign of (7.5 - 34) is positive, signifying that heat is liberated in the element dz shown on the right in Figure 7.5. In the other branch of the circuit, since the current flow is opposite in direction, the sign of the Thomson heat is negative, and heat will be absorbed in the corresponding element of thickness dz on the left. Remembering that electron flow is opposite that of conventional current, this suggests that electrons usually transport Thomson heat from hot to cold. If materials 1 and 2 in the diagram are the same, this has no effect other than to make the steady-state temperature distribution in the two branches of the circuit somewhat different. The proof of this assertion is not very difficult, and is assigned as an exercise.

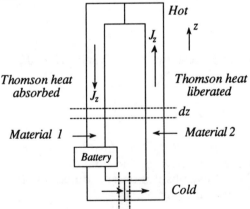

Figure 7.5 Heat fluxes and current flow in a circuit comprised of two dissimilar metals in which a battery or other emf has been inserted.

When the materials shown in the figure are different, the situation changes markedly. To see what happens, it is best to start by assuming that both junctions are at the same temperature. At the bottom, current flow is from substance 1 to substance 2. One can then obtain from (7.5 - 33) the rate at which Thomson heat is produced within an element of width Δz shown by the dashed lines on either side of the junction, as a derivative of the quantity shown in parentheses with respect to z.

Since this quantity experiences an abrupt finite change within a small distance Δz, one must write the derivative as the limit of $\Delta f / \Delta z$. The Thomson heat produced within this element is found by multiplying the rate per unit volume given by (7.5 - 33) by the volume $A \Delta z$, to obtain

$$\left(\frac{\partial U}{\partial t}\right)_{12} A \Delta z = -\frac{A \Delta z J_z}{q} \cdot T \frac{\partial}{\partial z}\left(\frac{1}{T}\frac{(\overline{\varepsilon \tau})}{\overline{\tau}} - \frac{\varepsilon_f}{T}\right) = -\frac{I_z \Delta z}{q} T\left[\left(\frac{1}{T}\frac{(\overline{\varepsilon \tau})}{\overline{\tau}} - \frac{\varepsilon_f}{T}\right)_2 - \left(\frac{1}{T}\frac{(\overline{\varepsilon \tau})}{\overline{\tau}} - \frac{\varepsilon_f}{T}\right)_1\right] \cdot \frac{1}{\Delta z},$$

or,

$$\left(\frac{\partial U}{\partial t}\right)_{12} A \Delta z = -\frac{I_z}{q}\left[\left(\frac{(\overline{\varepsilon \tau})}{\overline{\tau}}\right)_2 - \left(\frac{(\overline{\varepsilon \tau})}{\overline{\tau}}\right)_1 - (\varepsilon_{f2} - \varepsilon_{f1})\right] \quad . \tag{7.5-36}$$

If substances 1 and 2 are the same, this is zero, but if they are different, it is clear that heat is evolved or absorbed at the interface between the two materials, and that this heat is reversible, since it changes sign when the current is reversed. Moreover, at the upper junction in the figure, an equivalent amount of heat--though of opposite sign--is exchanged with the surroundings. The system will thus act as a reversible heat pump or refrigerator. This effect, which is obviously closely related to the Thomson effect, is referred to as the *Peltier effect*, and the heat evolved or absorbed at the junctions is called *Peltier heat*. The continuing action of the Peltier effect will cause the temperature of one juction to rise and the other to fall, which complicates a complete analysis of the effect, but it is clear that the circuit acts much like a reversible heat engine.

The Seebeck, Thomson and Peltier effects have been utilized in the production of sensors and temperature measuring instruments based on thermocouples. The Peltier effect has been used to produce solid-state refrigerators and heat pumps having no moving parts. Unfortunately, their cost is high and their efficiency is less than that of the best mechanical units, so they are viable only in special applications in which their advantages outweigh these shortcomings.

A more detailed understanding of of how these effects operate is possible only if the variation of the relaxation time (or mean free path) on energy can be specified. The reader should now be able to show using the semi-reasonable assumption of a velocity-independent mean free path, the following explicit relationships:

$$\frac{(\overline{\varepsilon \tau})}{\overline{\tau}} = kT_f\left(1 + \frac{\pi^2}{4}\left(\frac{T}{T_f}\right)^2\right) ; \qquad \frac{(\overline{\varepsilon^2 \tau})}{(\overline{\varepsilon \tau})} = kT_f\left(1 + \frac{\pi^2}{4}\left(\frac{T}{T_f}\right)^2\right), \tag{7.5-37}$$

$$E_0 = \frac{k}{q}\frac{\pi^2}{6}\left(\frac{T}{T_f}\right)\frac{\partial T}{\partial z} , \tag{7.5-38}$$

$$J_z = \sigma_e E - \frac{q}{kT_f}\cdot\frac{1}{2}\sigma_t\frac{\partial T}{\partial z} ; \qquad K_z = \frac{kT_f}{q}\sigma_e E - \frac{3}{2}\sigma_t\frac{\partial T}{\partial z} , \tag{7.5-39}$$

$$\zeta = \frac{k}{q} \frac{\pi^2}{3} \left(\frac{T}{T_f} \right) ; \qquad \left(\frac{\partial U}{\partial t} \right)_{12} = \frac{I_x kT}{q} \frac{\pi^2}{4} \left(\frac{T}{T_{f1}} - \frac{T}{T_{f2}} \right) . \qquad (7.5\text{-}40)$$

The frequency with which "large" temperature-independent terms cancel out of these expressions, leaving answers that depend critically on the temperature dependence of the Fermi energy and other related quantities should persuade you of the usefulness of the admittedly tedious mathematics needed to derive them.

7.6 DIFFUSION OF FREE PARTICLES

Diffusion is a phenomenon that exists everywhere in our terrestrial environment, but oddly, one that is hardly ever mentioned in elementary physics and chemistry texts. You would not be reading these words, or worrying about the subject at all if it were not for diffusion, for the oxygen in your bloodstream got there by diffusion. The oxidation of metal and semiconductor surfaces is governed by diffusion, and the impurites that govern the operation of semiconductor devices are often introduced by diffusing them into the crystal lattice. The diffusive transport of electrons and holes within these devices, moreover, is usually what makes them work. There are many other examples that could be cited, but these should suffice to convince you of its importance.

As previously noted, heat flows by thermal conduction in response to a temperature gradient, and the heat flux--heat flow per unit area per unit time--is at every point proportional to the local temperature gradient, the proportionality constant being referred to as the thermal conductivity. Diffusion is a flux of matter that arises whenever a *gradient of concentration* is present, and its mathematical description is an exact analogy of the description of heat flow. The matter flux, defined as the number of particles per unit area per unit time across a surface normal to the concentration gradient, is observed to be proportional to the concentration gradient, and the proportionality constant is called the diffusion coefficient D. The mathematical statement of this experimentally observed fact is

$$\Phi_d = -D \cdot \nabla n , \qquad (7.6\text{-}1)$$

where Φ_d is the net particle flux. This expression is sometimes referred to as *Fick's law*. In one-dimensional flow, where the flux is constrained by symmetry or other considerations to be along the z-direction, this becomes

$$\Phi_d = -D \cdot \frac{\partial n}{\partial z} . \qquad (7.6\text{-}2)$$

We shall, initially at least, confine our discussion to this case.

Diffusion is a statistical result of random processes. In a gas of free particles, equal probabilities are associated in equilibrium with positive and negative z-velocity components of any given magnitude, so the net flux of particles is zero. Since this net flux of particles is defined (in analogy with current density) as particle density times the average z-component of velocity, this statement can be expressed as

$$\Phi_d = n\bar{v}_z = 0 \qquad \text{(in equilibrium)} . \qquad (7.6-3)$$

According to (7.6 - 2), this implies that at equilibrium there can be no concentration gradient, which is in line with our intuitive expectations.

Let us now assume that a concentration gradient has been set up by some external condition, and that the concentration of particles decreases as you go along the positive z-direction, corresponding to a *negative* concentration gradient $\partial n / \partial z$. At any given value of z, say $z = z_0$, the concentration of particles to the left of the point is larger than the concentration to the right; this means that particles going to the right at z_0 originate from some point "upstream", to the left of z_0, where the concentration is greater than at the point itself. Conversely, particles that arrive at z_0 going to the left have started out at some point where the concentration is smaller than at z_0. This means that the *gross* flux to the right is greater than it is to the left at z_0, and there must be a *net* flux in the positive direction, as given by (7.6 - 2), when the concentration gradient is negative. This explains the presence of the minus sign in the first two equations above. A positive concentration gradient gives rise to a negative net flux, because particles tend by the laws of probability to diffuse from regions of high concentration to regions where concentration is low. The system thus tends in the long run toward a state where the concentration is everywhere the same, in other words, to a condition of thermodynamic equilibrium.

In connection with Figure 7.4 of the preceding section, we observed that the net increase in internal heat energy per unit time in the element illustrated is the difference between the inward flux of heat energy at the left and the outward flux at the right, times the volume $A\Delta z$, leading to the result $-(\partial K_z / \partial z)A\Delta z$. The situation with regard to diffusion fluxes and the accumulation of particles within a similar volume element is precisely analogous. The time rate at which particles accumulate within the element is given by the inward flux at left minus the outward flux on the right, times the volume $A\Delta z$, or $-(\partial \Phi_d / \partial z)A\Delta z$. If this is equated to the time rate of change of the number of particles within the volume, we find, using (7.6 - 2),

$$\frac{\partial n}{\partial t} \Delta V = -\frac{\partial \Phi_d}{\partial z} A\Delta z = -\frac{\partial}{\partial z}\left(-D\frac{\partial n}{\partial z}\right) A\Delta z ,$$

or, cancelling the volume elements, and assuming that D is constant,

$$D\frac{\partial^2 n}{\partial t^2} = \frac{\partial n}{\partial t} . \qquad (7.6-4)$$

This is the partial differential equation of diffusive transport, which is easily seen to have the same mathematical form as the heat flow equation.

A more precise description of diffusion can be obtained with the aid of the Boltzmann transport equation. It simplifies matters to assume throughout this discussion that a Maxwell-Boltzmann distribution prevails at equilibrium. There are, however, other important reasons for making this assumption. First of all, in normal metallic conductors, as a purely practical matter it is very difficult to set up significant concentration gradients over macroscopic distances, so the diffusion of free electrons in these materials is neither an easily observable nor very important effect. In *semiconductors*, however, where Maxwell-Boltzmann statistics are appropriately employed in view of the much lower density of the free-particle gas, this is no longer true, and diffusion of free electrons and holes is in many cases the dominant transport process. The reasons for this state of affairs will be discussed in more detail later. Finally, the use of Fermi-Dirac statistics can be shown--with difficulty-- to lead to results that do not differ significantly from those we shall now derive. We shall also neglect the effect of electric or magnetic fields on the particles. Strictly speaking, this isn't always justified, but the thrust at this point is simply to learn about diffusion, so we shall suppose initially that our particles are neutral.

Under these circumstances, and using the relaxation time approximation, the Boltzmann equation can be written as

$$\frac{df}{dt} = -v_z \frac{\partial f}{\partial z} - \frac{f - f_0}{\tau(v)} = 0 \ . \tag{7.6-5}$$

Substituting the derivative of the equilibrium distribution for that of the perturbed distribution function as before, and solving for f, we obtain

$$f = f_0 - v_z \tau(v) \frac{\partial f_0}{\partial z} \ , \tag{7.6-6}$$

where f_0 is the Maxwellian distribution given by (5.5 - 14) as

$$f_0(v_x, v_y, v_z, z) = n(z) \cdot \left(\frac{m}{2\pi kT} \right)^{3/2} e^{-m(v_x^2 + v_y^2 + v_z^2)/2kT} \ . \tag{7.6-7}$$

This way of writing (5.5 - 14) makes explicit recognition of the fact that the particle density n can vary as a function of z. Under the circumstances, it is apparent that its derivative can be written

$$\frac{\partial f_0}{\partial z} = \frac{\partial f_0}{\partial n} \cdot \frac{\partial n}{\partial z} = f_0 \cdot \frac{1}{n} \frac{\partial n}{\partial z} \ . \tag{7.6-8}$$

This allows us to write (7.6 - 6) as

$$f = f_0 - v_z \tau(v) \cdot \frac{1}{n} \frac{\partial n}{\partial z} f_0 \ . \tag{7.6-9}$$

The diffusion flux, as defined by (7.6 - 3) must now be averaged over this distribution function. The calculation involves exactly the same steps that were used for the case of electrical conductivity in Section 7.3, beginning with (7.3 - 12). It is clear that the integral of the diffusion flux over the equilibrium distribution itself is zero, so that (7.3 - 14) is still valid. The equation analogous to (7.3 - 16) is now written as,

$$\Phi_d = n\bar{v}_z = -n \cdot \frac{1}{n}\frac{\partial n}{\partial z}\frac{\int v^2\tau(v)f_0(v)\cdot v^2\cos^2\theta\sin\theta\ dv\,d\theta\,d\varphi}{\int f_0(v)\cdot v^2\sin\theta\ dv\,d\theta\,d\varphi} \ . \tag{7.6-10}$$

Integrating over the angular variables as before again gives a factor of $1/3$, leaving

$$\Phi_d = n\bar{v}_z = -\frac{1}{3}\frac{\partial n}{\partial z}\frac{\int_0^\infty v^2\tau(v)\cdot v^2 f_0(v)\,dv}{\int_0^\infty v^2 f_0(v)\,dv} = -\frac{1}{3}\frac{\partial n}{\partial z}\langle v^2\tau(v)\rangle \ . \tag{7.6-11}$$

Observing that $m\langle v^2\rangle = 3kT$, this can be written as

$$\Phi_d = -\frac{1}{3}\frac{\partial n}{\partial z}\frac{\langle v^2\tau(v)\rangle}{\langle v^2\rangle}\cdot\frac{3kT}{m} \ . \tag{7.6-12}$$

Finally, with the help of (7.3 - 25) and (7.6 - 2), we obtain

$$\Phi_d = -\frac{kT}{m}\bar{\tau}\cdot\frac{\partial n}{\partial z} = -D\frac{\partial n}{\partial z} \ . \tag{7.6-13}$$

In this expression the average relaxation time is defined exactly as in Section 7.3 in connection with electrical conductivity. The equation above shows that the diffusion coefficient is, like the conductivity, directly proportional to the relaxation time. We may therefore conclude that the diffusion coefficient is simply and generally related to the electrical conductivity and mobility defined by (7.3 - 27) and (7.2 - 12). This connection is most commonly expressed as a relation between the diffusion coefficient and the mobility having the form

$$D = \frac{kT}{m}\bar{\tau} = \frac{kT}{q}\cdot\frac{q\bar{\tau}}{m} = \mu\frac{kT}{q} \ . \tag{7.6-14}$$

This remarkable relationship is independent of how the relaxation time depends on velocity; moreover, though derived in the context of Maxwell-Boltzmann statistics, it is also true for Fermi-Dirac systems. It was discovered by Albert Einstein in his investigations of Brownian motion during the early years of the 20th century, and is referred to as the *Einstein relation*.

Another useful relation can be obtained from (7.6 - 12) for systems in which the mean free path is velocity-independent. Under these circumstances, $\tau(v) = \lambda/v$, where λ is independent of velocity; then, recalling (7.6 - 2), equation (7.6 - 12) can be written as

$$D\frac{\partial n}{\partial z} = \frac{1}{3}\langle v\lambda\rangle\frac{\partial n}{\partial z} = \frac{1}{3}\lambda\langle v\rangle\frac{\partial n}{\partial z} \ , \qquad \text{or} \qquad D = \frac{1}{3}\lambda\langle v\rangle \ . \tag{7.6-15}$$

Diffusion can occur in solids, liquids, or gases. The physical mechanisms of diffusion of impurity atoms into crystal lattices are quite different from those that cause diffusion of free electrons or holes in semiconductor devices. Nevertheless, they both lead to the mathematical description given above. Diffusion of a foreign atomic species into a crystal lattice is usually an extremely slow process, while diffusing free electron distributions can move very rapidly. The diffusion of gas atoms in normal gaseous mixtures exhibits an intermediate rate. This diversity of diffusion rates is expressed by the size of the diffusion coefficient D, and like the electrical conductivity it can range over a wide spectrum of values. Diffusion coefficients for the free electrons in electron gases, for example, can be more than 10^{15} times larger than those of substitutional impurity atoms in perfect crystal lattices. We shall learn more about diffusive processes in a later chapter when we study the motion of electrons and holes in semiconductor materials and devices.

7.7 HALL EFFECT AND MAGNETORESISTANCE

The motion of free electrons in metals and semiconductors can be influenced significantly by external magnetic fields. Their effect is most rigorously treated by introducing magnetic forces into the Boltzmann transport equation *via* the laws of classical electromagnetism. The procedure is in principle straightforward. It is very complex, however, and since it illustrates little that has not already been adequately demonstrated about the use of the transport equation, and is satisfactorily discussed in more advanced texts, we shall rely on simpler though less general methods to describe some of the major effects that are observed.

The most important of these is the *Hall effect*, which is most easily studied in the geometry shown in Figure 7.6. In this case, a steady current I_x flows along the longer axis of a sample in the form thin rectangular plate, and a constant external magnetic field B_z is applied normal to the surface of the plate as shown. The drift motion of the electrons in the x-direction then gives rise to a transverse magnetic force in the vertical y-direction which deflects them downward and causes them to accumulate at the lower edge of the sample, leaving a deficiency in electron concentration at the top edge. An electric field is generated by this charge distribution, which increases until it exactly counteracts the original magnetic force and restores a state in which charges and currents again move (in an average sense) horizontally.

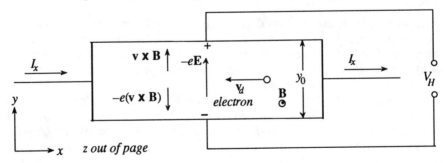

Figure 7.6 The geometry in which the Hall effect is most easily measured, showing the drift velocity of the electrons and the directions of electric and magnetic forces acting on them.

From this discussion, we see that in the final steady state there will be both magnetic and electric forces acting on electrons. The total force acting on a charged particle is described by the Lorentz force expression,

$$F = qE + q(v \times B) \tag{7.7-1}$$

The y-component of this total force, is, in the final state, zero, which allows us to write

$$F_y = qE_y - qv_x B_z = 0 , \qquad \text{or} \qquad E_y = v_x B_z . \tag{7.7-2}$$

However, the current density is given by $J_x = nqv_x$, which permits this to be stated as

$$E_y = \frac{J_x B_z}{nq} = R \cdot J_x B_z , \tag{7.7-3}$$

where

$$R = \frac{1}{nq} . \tag{7.7-4}$$

The field E_y is referred to as the *Hall field*; it is seen to be proportional to the product of the current density and the magnetic induction. The coefficient of proportionality R is called the *Hall coefficient*. The Hall field can be measured (preferably by an instrument that draws no current, such as a potentiometer) by measuring the Hall voltage V_H across the sample as shown in the diagram. This potential difference is related to the Hall field (7.7 - 3) by

$$V_H = E_y y_0 , \tag{7.7-5}$$

where y_0 is the sample width shown in the figure. Clearly the Hall coefficient R can be determined from measured values of V_H, J_x, and B_z.

The Hall effect is useful because it allows one to measure the density of the free charges in the sample. Moreover, combined with measurements of the electrical conductivity, it permits one to determine both the *density* of the free charges in the sample and their *mobility*. It is important in this regard to note that conductivity measurements alone give only the product of n and μ, as shown by (7.3 - 27) and (7.3 - 29), but provide no information about the value of either quantity separately. However, since the conductivity σ_e can be written

$$\sigma_e = nq\mu , \tag{7.7-6}$$

it is easily seen from (7.7 - 4) that the mobility is obtained as

$$R\sigma_e = \mu . \tag{7.7-7}$$

For electrons the charge is $q = -e$. The Hall coefficient is thus negative in sign for an ideal free electron gas. The fact that the measured Hall coefficients of some materials (particularly semiconductors) can have *positive* signs alerts us to the fact that the "gas" of free particles in real substances is not in all respects accurately described by the ideal free-electron model, and that the charge carriers are in some instances positively charged "quasiparticles" usually referred to as *holes*. A full discussion of this odd set of circumstances will be presented in the next chapter. Classical free-electron metals like the alkali metals, copper, silver, and gold, however, all have negative Hall coefficients as given by the simple free-electron model.

Another odd feature of the Hall effect is the inverse dependence of the Hall coefficient on electron density. This indicates that for normal metals, in which the electron gas is very dense, the Hall voltages are very small--typically of the order of a few microvolts--and are therefore difficult to measure precisely. In semiconductors, however, due to the low density of charge carriers, they are much higher, often as much as a tenth of a volt, and are easily measured with an ordinary potentiometer or its equivalent. In insulators, one might expect even larger Hall voltages, but the sample resistances soon become so large that they become difficult to detect, even with instruments that draw very little current.

The above discussion is oversimplified in many ways; it assumes that the charges all move with the average drift velocity, and ignores the distribution of velocities and relaxation times completely. Nevertheless, the important features of the effect are outlined accurately enough for many purposes. A more careful treatment introduces a factor whose magnitude depends on the velocity dependence of the relaxation time into the Hall coefficient. For the case of a velocity-independent mean free path the factor is $3\pi/8$ (= 1.18), and is often ignored in rough calculations.

In the Hall effect measurement, one can also usually detect a small decrease in the resistance of the sample when the magnetic field is applied. This effect, in which the change in resistance is found to be proportional to the square of the magnetic field, is called *magnetoresistance*. It is observed because the magnetic forces that act on the charges cause them to follow circular paths rather than straight lines in the x-direction. Such a path, of arc length equal to the mean free path λ, has a projection on the x-axis smaller than λ by the amount shown in Figure 7.7.

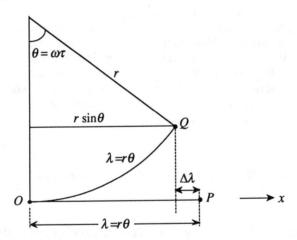

Figure 7.7 The free path of a charged particle shown as OP in the absence of a magnetic field normal to the page, and as OQ in the presence of such a field.

Consider a charged particle whose path in the absence of a magnetic field is a straight line of length λ in the x-direction, as represented above as OP. When a magnetic field **B** normal to the page is applied, the path becomes a circular arc of radius r and length λ, shown as OQ. The projection of this path OQ on the x-axis is now the effective mean free path for curent flowing along the sample, and it is less by an amount $\Delta\lambda$ than the free path in the absence of the field. The linear velocity of the particle is unaltered by the field, since the magnetic force is normal to both **v** and **B**, as shown by (7.7 - 1), and therefore has no component in the direction of motion. The angular velocity ω is obtained by equating the magnetic force qvB, which is in the radial direction, to the centripetal force mv^2/r. Then, since $v = r\omega$, we have

$$mr\omega^2 = q(r\omega)B \qquad \text{or} \qquad \omega = qB/m .\qquad (7.7\text{-}8)$$

This quantity, which we shall encounter in future work, is called the cyclotron frequency. The change in resistivity $\Delta\rho$ is clearly proportional to the amount by which the effective free path is shortened, so we may now write

$$\frac{\Delta\rho}{\rho_0} = \frac{\Delta\lambda}{\lambda} = \frac{r\theta - r\sin\theta}{r\theta} = 1 - \frac{\sin\theta}{\theta} , \qquad (7.7\text{-}9)$$

where ρ_0 is the zero-field resistivity. For normally attainable magnetic fields, the angle θ is not very large, which allows us to use the series expansion for $\sin\theta$, retaining only the first two terms. Since, additionally, $\theta = \omega\tau$, where τ is the free time λ/v, we find

$$\frac{\Delta\rho}{\rho_0} = -\frac{\theta^2}{3!} = -\frac{(\omega\tau)^2}{6} = -\frac{1}{6}\left(\frac{q\tau B}{m}\right)^2 . \qquad (7.7\text{-}10)$$

From (7.3 - 27), we see that $q\tau/m$ is the mobility μ, giving as a final result

$$\frac{\Delta\rho}{\rho_0} = -\frac{\mu^2 B^2}{6} . \qquad (7.7\text{-}11)$$

This result, neglecting as it does the distribution of free paths and velocities, is on roughly the same level of accuracy as our treatment of the Hall effect. A particle with the *average* velocity follows a straight path undeviated by the magnetic field, due to the effect of the Hall field, of course. But particles having other velocities, either larger or smaller, experience the effect described above, so magnetoresistance is observed nevertheless. The experimentally observed quadratic dependence of $\Delta\rho$ on magnetic field is seen in this equation. If we let $\mu = 0.1\text{m}^2\text{V}^{-1}\text{sec}^{-1}$ and $B = 1.0\text{T}$, which roughly describes silicon at 300K in a magnetic field as large as one can normally attain in the laboratory, (7.7 - 11) predicts a resistivity change of about 0.17%, which is of the right order of magnitude.

A more rigorous analysis based on the Boltzmann transport equation predicts a rich menu of additional electrothermomagnetic effects that can exist when electric fields, magnetic fields, and temperature gradients are all present. Most of these effects have been observed, but the complexity involved in analyzing them is such that we cannot not describe them in detail. Moreover though they are of some fundamental interest, they have found little or no practical application, so there is no need to consider them further.

7.8 SCATTERING PROCESSES

We have already mentioned some of the collision interactions that scatter electrons (and phonons), and have encountered some--like electron-electron interactions and "normal" phonon-phonon interactions--that have little or no effect in returning particles to the equilibrium distribution. We have also discussed the effect of collisions in determining the energy dependence of the relaxation time and mean free path. However, this concluding section is appropriate for examining these processes more systematically--though still qualitatively--and for summarizing all the relevant information about them in one place.

It was noted also that the effects of scattering interactions can be completely understood only from a rigorous study of the dynamics of all the possible processes, with the objective of finding the relative scattering probability for each velocity subgroup of the distribution. This is a difficult task, one that we dare not undertake, so we shall merely review some of the important aspects of the simplest cases.

We have made occasional use of the fact that the mean free path is found to be practically velocity independent when the dominant scattering mechanism is the scattering of free electrons by acoustical-mode phonons, at temperatures extending not too far below room temperature. This process is the principal interaction only in very pure and structurally perfect crystalline materials, where effects associated with impurities and lattice imperfections are negligible, and then only at temperatures high enough that there are sufficient phonons to outweigh the effects of any residual impurities or imperfections. A velocity-independent mean free path suggests that the scattering process resembles in some sense the collision of classical free particles with a random assembly of much more massive hard spheres. A particle colliding with such a sphere follows the same path as a light ray that is specularly reflected at the surface of the sphere, the equality of its angles of incidence and reflection with respect to the normal to the spherical surface at the point of contact conserving the component of momentum in the plane tangent to the sphere at that point. Whether the particle moves slowly or fast in such a collision is irrelevant; its path will be deflected through the same angle whatever the incident speed. The mean free path in such circumstances depends only on the density and geometrical arrangement of the scatterers, not on the velocity of the incident particles. Since electrons have a mass much smaller than anything (including phonons) that can scatter them, it is not surprising that the assumption of negligible incident particle mass should always be satisfied. The forces that act on a particle in the hard sphere model are strongly localized, and of very short range and duration. It is not clear that these conditions would be associated with electron-phonon scattering, but the experimental evidence suggests that they are. As noted previously, the number of available phonons increases with temperature, a fact that in normal metals results in a direct proportionality of mean free path--and thus electrical resistivity--with absolute temperature at and above the Debye temperature. Below the Debye temperature, the density of phonons falls off quite rapidly, and as in the case of the specific heat, the contribution of phonon scattering to the resistivity decreases rapidly at low temperatures.

When an impurity atom having a number of valence electrons different from those present in the pure substance occupies one of the lattice sites, its ionic charge differs from that of the ion that would otherwise be there. The excess or deficit of charge at the site generates an effective point-charge coulomb field centered on this point that can exert strong forces on electrons and can effectively scatter incident free charges. These coulomb forces can be very strong and are far less localized than those associated with the hard-sphere model. They therefore scatter electrons much more effectively than might be inferred simply from their concentration. Thus, the presence of small concentrations of impurity ions in metals, like copper, that are excellent conductors in the pure state, degrades the electrical conductivity markedly. This is the reason why copper intended for use as an electrical conductor must be refined electrolytically to exceptionally high purity. The mechanism of scattering by a point-charge coulomb force is similar to that encountered in Rutherford scattering of α-particles incident upon atomic nuclei. The classical analysis of Rutherford scattering is therefore applicable, with a few modifications, to impurity scattering in crystals. This analysis leads to a mean free path directly proportional to the impurity concentration, and also proportional to ε^2, where ε is the incident particle energy. Impurity scattering is dominant even in quite pure materials at very low temperatures, where electron-phonon scattering is weak, and as mentioned previously, at normal temperatures is often dominant in substances that are not highly purified. Electrons can also be scattered by lattice vacancies, interstitial atoms, dislocations, grain boundaries, and sample surfaces, particularly in very thin films. Radiation damage by fast neutrons and other high-energy particles can also scatter charges and cause significant changes in the electrical and thermal properties of metals.

It is apparent from this discussion that two or more scattering mechanisms can act simultaneously. When this is the case, and when the two mechanisms are independent of one another, the number of collisions caused by each of them can be summed arithmetically. This suggests that two separate collision terms of the form given by (7.3 - 4) must appear in the Boltzmann transport equation, each exhibiting a relaxation time $\tau(v)$ appropriate to its respective scattering process. For a single subgroup of velocities, this permits one to write

$$\left(\frac{\partial f}{\partial t}\right)_{coll} = -\frac{f-f_0}{\tau_1(v)} - \frac{f-f_0}{\tau_2(v)} = ---\frac{f-f_0}{\tau_{eff}(v)} \, , \tag{7.8-1}$$

where

$$\frac{1}{\tau_{eff}(v)} = \frac{1}{\tau_1(v)} + \frac{1}{\tau_2(v)} \, . \tag{7.8-2}$$

It must be observed that this additivity of reciprocal times cannot generally be extended to the averages of τ_1 and τ_2 over velocity, because of the generally different velocity dependences of the two mechanisms. For rough semiquantitative arguments, however, this fact is often ignored, and it is not uncommon to see in the literature mobilities (which depend directly on averages of the relaxation time over velocity) added reciprocally to obtain an effective mobility of the form

$$\frac{1}{\mu_{eff}} = \frac{1}{\mu_1} + \frac{1}{\mu_2} \, . \tag{7.8-3}$$

It would be satisfying to be able to say that the classical free electron theory of metals as presented in this chapter is in uniformly good agreement with experimen-

312

tal data. Unfortunately, it is not so. In some instances, particularly when calculated results do not involve the electron mass, or do not call for the exact magnitudes of the mean free path or relaxation time, or require a precise knowledge of the energy dependence of these quantities, classical free-electron theory is quite satisfactory. More frequently, however, it gives answers whose qualitative behavior (as regards order-of-magnitude, temperature dependence, concentration dependence, etc.) is pretty much on target, but which are not in good *quantitative* agreement with the measurements. Moreover, it gives no clue as to why some substances are good free-electron conductors while others are insulators or semiconductors. These problems, as we shall soon see, are largely resolved by using quantum mechanics to account for the effect of the periodic potential within the crystal caused by the regularly spaced ions of the crystal lattice. Fortunately, it turns out that this refinement can be accommodated within the conceptual framework of free-electron theory by making some simple but important alterations to its structure.

REFERENCES

F. Seitz, *Modern Theory of Solids*, McGraw-Hill, New York (1940), Chapter 4.

H. Eyring, D. Henderson, B. Stover, and E. M. Eyring, *Statistical Mechanics and Dynamics,*, J.Wiley & Sons, New York (1964), Chapter 9.

J. M. Ziman, *Principles of the Theory of Solids* (2nd Edition), Cambridge University Press, Cambridge (1972), Chapter 6.

PROBLEMS

1. Show that in a metallic ohmic conductor the heat produced per unit time by collision processes is correctly described by (7.2 - 10).

2. Show for the case of a uniform straight ohmic conductor of constant cross-sectional area A and electrical conductivity σ, that the resistance of a segment of length l is given by $R = l/\sigma A$.

3. Show explicitly that the integration over angular variables described below eq. (7.3 - 16) yields the factor 1/3 which leads to (7.3 - 17).

4. Show that the averages indicated in (7.3 - 30) lead to the final form given for the relaxation time using Maxwell-Boltzmann statistics and a time-independent mean free path.

5. How would the electrical conductivity of an ohmic metallic conductor depend on temperature if the dominant scattering mechanism were scattering by ionized impurity atoms, assuming that the mean free path for this scattering process is proportional to ϵ^2?

6. Assuming a velocity-independent mean free path, find the mean free path for a free electron in the two numerical examples (conduction in copper and silicon) given at the end of section 7.3. Use the numerical data assumed in these examples.

7. Show by simple physical arguments--without using the Boltzmann transport equation or the theory presented in section 7.4--that the specific heat of a Fermi free-electron gas must vary linearly with temperature. Derive a rough algebraic formula for it using these arguments.

8. Assuming a velocity-independent mean free path, find the magnitude of the thermoelectric field (7.5 - 12) for a free-electron metallic conductor having a Fermi temperature of 75,000K, in which there is a temperature gradient of 50K/cm. What potential difference would this field cause between the ends of a conductor 12cm long under open-circuit conditions?

9. Show that the Wiedemann-Franz ratio is $2k^2/q^2$ when Maxwell-Boltzmann statistics and a velocity-independent mean free path are assumed.

10. Show that if one assumes the relaxation time to be energy-independent, the Wiedemann-Franz ratio is $\pi^2/4$ for a Fermi-Dirac free-electron gas and 5/2 for a Maxwell-Boltzmann gas.

11. Find the Wiedemann-Franz ratio using both Fermi-Dirac and Maxwell-Boltzmann statistics and a mean free path proportion to ε^2, as in ionized impurity scattering.

12. Derive the expressions (7.5 - 26) and (7.5 - 27) for the thermal conductivity of a Fermi free-electron gas starting from (7.5 - 15). Assume a velocity-independent mean free path.

13. What is the thermal conductivity of a Maxwell-Boltzmann free-particle gas, assuming a velocity-independent mean free path?

14. Show, assuming a velocity-independent mean free path, that the electrical and thermal currents in a metallic free-electron conductor in which a temperature gradient and an external emf are present can be written as

$$J_z = \sigma_e E - \frac{1}{2} \frac{q}{kT_f} \cdot \sigma_t \frac{\partial T}{\partial z} ,$$

and

$$qK_z = \sigma_e E - \frac{3}{2} \frac{q}{kT_f} \cdot \sigma_t \frac{\partial T}{\partial z} .$$

15. Write differential equations for the steady-state temperature distribution in the left and right branches of the circuit of Figure 7.5, and show that they lead to different distributions of temperature along these two branches even when the two branches are identical in composition.

16. Derive the relationships (7.5 - 37) and (7.5 - 38). assuming that the mean free path is velocity-independent.

17. Derive the relationship (7.5 - 40), assuming a velocity-independent mean free path.

18. Find the numerical value of the Thomson coefficient for a material in which the Fermi temperature is 75,000K, assuming a velocity-independent mean free path. Discuss how the Thomson coefficient can depend on material parameters.

19. Consider the case where a steady electric current flows in an ohmic conductor in which the equilibrium state can be described as a Maxwell-Boltzmann distribution. The distribution function as perturbed by the electric field is now given by (7.3 - 11). Show that this perturbed distribution function as viewed from a frame of reference moving in the direction of current flow with the average drift velocity is essentially the Maxwell-Boltzmann equilibrium distribution if the drift velocity is small in comparison to the average thermal speed of the particles. Show also that it may depart significantly from the MB form if this condition does not hold.

20. Adopting the picture of a Fermi free-electron metal shown in Figure 4.3, show that at elevated temperatures a thermionic current may be emitted across the potential barrier into a surrounding vacuum, and that the thermionic current density can be expressed as

$$J_z = \frac{4\pi m q (kT)^2}{h^3} e^{-\varphi_o/kT} ,$$

where φ_0 is the work function described in connection with photoemission in Section 4.3. Assume that the work function is much larger than kT. Hint: this is an equilibrium situation, in which the Boltzmann transport equation isn't needed.

21 Show that for $T<<T_f$, the specific heat of a two-dimensional Fermi free electron gas can be expressed approximately as $(\pi^2/3)nk(T/T_f)$.

22. Find the diffusion coefficients of the two substances used in the sample calculations at the end of Section 7.3, at a temperature of 300K.

23. Show that the relation (7.6 - 14) is valid for a Fermi free-particle gas, assuming $T<<T_f$.

24. Consider a Hall effect sample of length 2.0cm, width 0.4cm, and thickness 0.1cm. A current of 0.05A flows along the length of the sample, and there is a magnetic field of 1.2T normal to the surface of the plate. Find the expected hall voltage for n-silicon in which there are 1.0×10^{16} electrons/cm^3, and for copper, in which the electron density is about 0.8×10^{22} electrons/cm^3. How much current would have to be passed through a copper sample to obtain a Hall voltage of 1.0 millivolt?

25. In a silicon sample of resistivity 5.0 ohm-cm and of the size described in the preceding problem, one observes a Hall voltage of 0.42 volts under the conditions of current and magnetic field described previously. Find the free electron density within the sample and also the electron mobility.

26. Find the magnetoresistance $\Delta\rho/\rho_0$ for the sample described in the preceding problem. Through what angle is the average electron deflected before being scattered?

27. Can mean free paths be added reciprocally like mean free times? Why--or why not?

28. Derive relations (7.5 - 37) and (7.5 - 38) for the case where the mean free path is proportional to ε^2.

29. Find the value of the Thomson coefficient (7.5 - 35) for the case where the mean free path is proportional to ε^2.

30. Show that the function

$$n(x,t) = \frac{n_0}{\sqrt{4\pi Dt}} \cdot e^{-x^2/4Dt}$$

is a solution of the diffusion equation (7.6 - 4). Describe how this expression behaves as a function of time, and comment on the physical behavior as t approaches infinity.

31. Describe how the solution given in the preceding problem can be used as a representation of the Dirac δ-function.

32. Find the particle flux as a function of time at any point in the diffusion process described in Problem 30. At what point does this flux attain a maximum value?

33. Calculate the average distance through which particles have diffused as a function of time in the diffusion process described in Problem 30.

34. Write the Boltzmann transport equation in the geometry of the Hall effect, taking into account all components of the electric and magnetic forces that will be present. You need not attempt to solve these equations.

CHAPTER 8

QUANTUM MECHANICS OF ELECTRONS IN CRYSTALS

8.1 INTRODUCTION

The results of classical free-electron theory are often not in good agreement with experimental data even when Fermi-Dirac statistics are used. Also, classical theory simply fails to show very clearly why some substances are free-electron conductors while others are highly insulating. Finally, it cannot account for the puzzling fact that in some substances the charges of the current carriers indicated by the Hall coefficient, seem to be positive rather than negative.

These deficiencies follow from the fact that the classical free-electron theory treats the valence electrons as being truly free, in the sense that they are influenced only by surface constraints that confine them to the interior of the crystal, to impulsive forces that act during collisions, and to forces like those associated with external electric and magnetic fields. In fact, these electrons exert strong coulomb forces on one another, and are also acted upon by strong forces associated with the regularly spaced positive ions on the lattice sites. The action of these forces on any given electron, moreover, must be described quantum mechanically. The general problem, then, concerns a very large number of particles acted upon by complex interparticle forces--a quantum many-body system. In treating these problems it is necessary to make simpifying assumptions, which are usually difficult to identify. Moreover, it is hard to know whether any such assumption is reasonable in advance; you must try it out and see whether it predicts results that agree with experimental data to know how "reasonable" it is. Only then will you have any confidence in using it in a more general context, where experimental data aren't readily available.

316

The forces exerted on a single electron by other "free" electrons are rapidly fluctuating in magnitude and direction. Is it a reasonable assumption to think of them as randomly--and rapidly--fluctuating quantities that sum to zero over any significant time interval? Maybe, maybe not, but it's an easy one to try. Fortunately, though not perfect, it usually works quite well. It leads us to think of each valence electron as being *independent* of the other valence electrons, and influenced principally by forces that can be described quantum mechanically in terms of a *periodic potential* ascribable to the positive ions on the lattice sites. This picture is referred to as the *one-electron approximation*. It leads to a description of allowed electronic energies and quantum states for the crystal--states that can be occupied subject to the now-familiar constraints of the Pauli exclusion principle and Fermi-Dirac statistics. The description, moreover, leads to physical results similar to those predicted by classical free-electron theory, but which resolve most of the troublesome experimental discrepancies and provide simple answers to many of the questions that confounded the classical theory. It is hard to challenge the suggestion that it is a foundation upon which much of modern solid-state physics has been built.

8.2 THE BLOCH THEOREM

In Chapter 3, we saw that the periodicity of the crystal lattice is responsible for a number of important differences between wave propagation in ideal homogeneous, isotropic media, and in actual crystalline materials. These differences are also encountered in the propagation of the Schrödinger "matter waves" associated with the valence electrons in crystalline substances. The periodicity of the lattice enters this description when one uses quantum mechanics in conjunction with the one-electron approximation described above. In this development, one must solve the Schrödinger equation for a single electron whose potential energy is periodic with the periodicity of the crystal lattice. The exact form of this potential is not easy to determine even when the one-electron approximation is made, but though the finer details are obtained only when it is known, the general character of the solutions can be inferred from the mere fact that the potential is periodic and has the same periodicity as the lattice. We shall now discuss the general form of Schrödinger wave functions for a one-dimensional periodic potential. We will see afterwards that the results are easily generalized to three-dimensional systems.

The one-dimensional Schrödinger equation can be expressed as

$$\frac{d^2\psi(x)}{dx^2} + f(x)\,\psi(x) = 0 , \quad \text{where} \quad f(x) = \frac{2m}{\hbar^2}[\varepsilon - V(x)] . \tag{8.2-1}$$

If the potential $V(x)$ is periodic with period a, $f(x)$ is also periodic and $f(x + a) = f(x)$. Let us assume that $\psi(x)$ is a solution of the above equation under these conditions. We may now ask whether $\psi(x + a)$ also satisfies this differential equation. Since the equation is valid for all values of x, it is certainly true that

$$\frac{d^2\psi(x+a)}{d(x+a)^2} + f(x+a)\,\psi(x+a) = 0 \ . \qquad (8.2\text{-}2)$$

However,

$$\frac{d\psi(x+a)}{dx} = \frac{d\psi(x+a)}{d(x+a)} \cdot \frac{d(x+a)}{dx} = \frac{d\psi(x+a)}{d(x+a)} \ , \qquad (8.2\text{-}3)$$

and it is clear that a similar calculation leads to a relationship of this same form for the second derivatives of the wave function at x and $x + a$. Also, because of the periodicity of the potential, $f(x + a)$ equals $f(x)$. Therefore, we can write

$$\frac{d^2\psi(x+a)}{dx^2} + f(x)\,\psi(x+a) = 0 \ , \qquad (8.2\text{-}4)$$

which tells us that $\psi(x + a)$ is also a solution of the original differential equation. This does not, however, mean that $\psi(x + a)$ and $\psi(x)$ are equal, since second-order differential equations have two independent solutions. Thus, $\sin\omega t$ and $\cos\omega t$ are both solutions of the equation for harmonic motion, but $\sin\omega t$ isn't equal to $\cos\omega t$. However, if we refer to the two solutions of (8.2 - 1) as $g(x)$ and $h(x)$, we can always write,

$$\psi(x) = Ag(x) + Bh(x) \ , \qquad (8.2\text{-}5)$$

where A and B are arbitrary constants. These constants are in general complex, because ψ itself (as well as g and h) may be complex. This same relationship must of course be satisfied at the point $x + a$. Now consider the solution $g(x)$. Since it satisfies (8.2 - 1), it follows from the above reasoning that $g(x + a)$ must also satisfy this equation. The same is true of $h(x + a)$. But any solution of this equation, at any point, can be expressed as a linear combination of $g(x)$ and $h(x)$. We can therefore write

$$g(x+a) = \alpha_1 g(x) + \alpha_2 h(x)$$

$$(8.2\text{-}6)$$

and $\quad h(x+a) = \beta_1 g(x) + \beta_2 h(x) \ ,$

where α_1, α_2, β_1, and β_2 are arbitrary complex constants. From (8.2 - 5) it now follows that

$$\psi(x+a) = Ag(x+a) + Bh(x+a)$$

or, $\quad \psi(x+a) = (\alpha_1 A + \beta_1 B)g(x) + (\alpha_2 A + \beta_2 B)h(x) \ . \qquad (8.2\text{-}7)$

Let us now define the complex parameter λ as

$$\lambda = \frac{\psi(x+a)}{\psi(x)} \ , \qquad \text{so that} \qquad \psi(x+a) = \lambda\psi(x) \ . \qquad (8.2\text{-}8)$$

Now, equation (8.2 - 7) can be written as

$$(\alpha_1 A + \beta_1 B)g(x) + (\alpha_2 A + \beta_2 B)h(x) = \lambda Ag(x) + \lambda Bh(x) \ ,$$

or, $\quad [(\alpha_1 - \lambda)A + \beta_1 B]g(x) = [(\lambda - \beta_2)B - \alpha_2 A]h(x) \ . \qquad (8.2\text{-}9)$

The functions $g(x)$ and $h(x)$ are independent solutions of the differential equation; they cannot be proportional to one another as the above equation seems to indicate. The above equation can therefore be satisfied for all values of x only when the bracketed coefficients are both zero. This requires that

$$(\alpha_1 - \lambda)A + \beta_1 B = 0$$
$$\alpha_2 A - (\beta_2 - \lambda)B = 0 \ .$$

(8.2-10)

This system of equations, regarded as linear equations for the coefficients A and B, has only the solution $A = B = 0$ unless the determinant of the coefficients vanishes, in which case we must have

$$\begin{vmatrix} \alpha_1 - \lambda & \beta_1 \\ \alpha_2 & \beta_2 - \lambda \end{vmatrix} = \lambda^2 - (\alpha_1 + \beta_2)\lambda + (\alpha_1\beta_2 - \alpha_2\beta_1) = 0 \ .$$

(8.2-11)

The two solutions of this quadratic equation in λ are,

$$\lambda = \tfrac{1}{2}\left[(\alpha_1 + \beta_2) \pm \sqrt{(\alpha_1 + \beta_2)^2 - 4(\alpha_1\beta_2 - \alpha_2\beta_1)}\right] = \lambda_+, \lambda_- \ .$$

(8.2-12)

These roots, though complex numbers, are constants. They may be written in polar form as

$$\lambda_+ = c_+ e^{ik_+ a} \quad \text{and} \quad \lambda_- = c_- e^{ik_- a} \ ,$$

(8.2-13)

the phase angle that appears in the exponents being written as ka, where k is a propagation constant. Adding and multiplying the two roots defined by (8.2 - 12), we find

$$\lambda_+ + \lambda_- = \alpha_1 + \beta_2 \quad \text{and} \quad \lambda_+ \lambda_- = \alpha_1\beta_2 - \alpha_2\beta_1 \ .$$

(8.2-14)

This leads us finally to observe that

$$\lambda_- = \frac{\alpha_1\beta_2 - \alpha_2\beta_1}{\lambda_+} = \frac{Qe^{i\theta}}{\lambda_+} \ .$$

(8.2-15)

In this expression, the numerator is merely a complex constant, which is ultimately written in the polar form $Q\exp i\theta$, where Q is real and θ is an arbitrary phase angle. It is clear that the root λ_- is, except for a constant factor, simply the reciprocal of λ_+.

For either of these roots, an iteration of the relation (8.2 - 8) over n interatomic spacings leads to

$$\psi(x + na) = \lambda^n \psi(x) = c^n e^{ikna} \psi(x) \ .$$

(8.2-16)

In this expression c is the magnitude of a complex quantity, and is therefore real. There is no mathematical restriction on the value it may have, but physically, it is apparent that whether k is positive or negative, unless $c = 1$, the wave function will have a real exponential dependence on distance ($x = na$) that will cause it in an infinite crystal to become infinite at either plus or minus infinity. Acceptable wave functions can be obtained, therefore, *only* by requiring that c have unit value. This leads us finally to see from (8.2 - 13) and (8.2 - 15) that if we allow the arbitrary phase constant θ to be zero, we can write

$$\lambda_+ = e^{ika} \quad \text{and} \quad \lambda_- = 1/\lambda_+ = e^{-ika} . \tag{8.2-17}$$

These arguments also lead to the conclusion that $\alpha_1\beta_2 - \alpha_2\beta_1 = 1$.

From (8.2 - 8) using the root λ_+, we can now write, finally

$$\psi(x+a) = e^{ika}\psi(x) . \tag{8.2-18}$$

The physical significance of this result is more clearly understood if one writes

$$\psi(x) = e^{-ika}\psi(x+a) = e^{ika} \cdot e^{ikx}e^{-ikx}\psi(x+a) = e^{ikx}[e^{-ik(x+a)}\psi(x+a)] . \tag{8.2-19}$$

Now, however, using (8.2 - 18), we see that

$$e^{-ik(x+a)}\psi(x+a) = e^{-ik(x+a)} \cdot e^{ika}\psi(x) = e^{-ikx}\psi(x) . \tag{8.2-20}$$

The expression on the left is a periodic function of x with the periodicity of the lattice. From (8.2 - 19), however, it is now clear that the wave function $\psi(x)$ associated with a periodic crystal potential can always be written as

$$\psi(x) = e^{ikx}u_k(x) , \tag{8.2-21}$$

where $u_k(x)$ is a periodic function of x whose period is that of the lattice, and which thus has the property that

$$u_k(x) = e^{-ikx}\psi(x) = u_k(x+a) . \tag{8.2-22}$$

The subscript k signifies that the function u depends on k as well as x. This result is known as the *Bloch-Floquet theorem*. It was derived by F. Bloch in 1928 in the context of wave functions in periodic crystal lattices, and is often referred to as Bloch's theorem, but it is really only a restatement of a 19th century result known to mathematicians as Floquet's theorem. Wave functions of the form (8.2 - 21) are often referred to as *Bloch functions*. In the above calculation the root λ_+ was assumed, but one obtains the same result (with $-k$ substituted for k) when λ_- is used.

The Bloch-Floquet theorem on first sight may appear a rather tenuous reward for the effort expended in deriving it, but it is the key to answering some of the unresolved questions posed by the free-electron theory, and serves as the starting point for most of the more detailed calculations of wave functions and energy levels in crystals that have been made. Physically, it can be interpreted to mean that when the usual time dependence is included, the wave functions of electrons in crystals are plane waves of the form $\exp i(kx - \omega t)$ modulated by a function $u_k(x)$ having the periodicity of the lattice. This at once suggests that the electrons may exhibit many aspects of free-particle behavior even though they experience strong forces exerted by the ions of the crystal lattice. Moreover, the probability amplitude $\psi^*\psi$ associated with these wave functions is simply

$$\psi*(x)\psi(x) = e^{-ikx}u_k*(x) \cdot e^{ikx}u_k(x) = u_k*(x)u_k(x) \ . \tag{8.2-23}$$

From this it is apparent that because of the periodic nature of u_k, the electron density must be the same in all unit cells of the crystal. This makes sense in view of the fact that all unit cells are physically equivalent, and is consistent with the requirement of translational invariance. It has the added implication, however, that the electron wave functions are not localized, but are spread out all through the crystal, another indication of free-particle behavior. It is important to observe that the Bloch theorem assumes a perfectly periodic lattice of infinite extent; external surfaces, localized impurity ions or lattice imperfections can often give rise to *localized* electronic quantum states in addition to those predicted by the Bloch theory. It is also important to see that it is $u(x)$--not $\psi(x)$--that has the periodicity of the lattice. Finally, one can show that $u(x)$ is generally complex, and except in a few special cases, is not a real quantity. The reader is asked to demonstrate this as an exercise.

The true momentum p_x of an electron in a periodic lattice is not conserved, because the particle experiences time-varying *forces* from the ions of the lattice, forces whose dynamical effect is hard to describe in detail. The quantity k that emerges from the Bloch theorem, however, is a constant of the motion, and since $\hbar k$ has the dimensions of momentum, it is tempting to regard this quantity as the momentum of the electron. However, since $\hbar k$ is not an eigenvalue of the momentum operator $(\hbar/i)\partial/\partial x$, it cannot be identified as a true dynamical momentum. Nevertheless, the quantity $\hbar k$ does behave very much like a free-particle momentum. If there are no external forces present, it is a constant of the motion, and when forces like those that stem from external electric and magnetic fields are present, it changes with time just as the free-particle momentum would change under similar circumstances. Moreover, it is frequently conserved when the electron interacts with other particles. The quasi-momentum $\hbar k$ thus acts like a free-particle momentum in many situations; it is referred to as the *crystal momentum*. In some ways, however, as we shall soon see, the crystal momentum does not behave like a true free-particle momentum.

In a one-dimensional system, for an infinite crystal lattice, one can find solutions of Schrödinger's equation for any given value of energy ε. Corresponding to each specific value of ε, there are two values of k, which as shown in (8.2 - 17) are equal in magnitude, but of opposite sign. The allowed energy values form a continuum for a system in which the number of atoms is infinite.

If the number of atoms is finite, however, the wave functions must satisfy certain boundary conditions at the surfaces, in which case the wave equation and the boundary conditions can be satisfied only for certain values of k, like the acoustic waves in a one-dimensional crystal, as discussed in Chapter 3 (Section 3.8). Since the possible energies are now associated with allowed values of k, there will also be a discrete spectrum of energies, though the eigenvalues will be very closely spaced if the number of atoms is large. Under these circumstances, it is possible, as in the previous case of acoustic waves, to consider the one-dimensional chain of atoms as having been bent into a ring, to which periodic boundary conditions are applicable. If the ring contains exactly N atoms, then if the wave function is to be single-valued, from (8.2 - 21), setting $\psi(x)$ equal to $\psi(x + Na)$ and recalling the periodicity of u_k, we must have

$$\psi(x + Na) = e^{ikx} e^{ikNa} u_k(x + Na) = e^{ikx} e^{ikNa} u_k(x) = \psi(x) = e^{ikx} u_k(x) . \qquad (8.2 - 24)$$

This equation cannot be satisfied unless

$$e^{ikNa} = 1 = e^{2\pi i} ,$$

or, $\qquad k = k_n = \dfrac{2\pi n}{Na} \qquad (n = \pm 1, \pm 2, \pm 3, \ldots \pm \dfrac{N}{2}) .$ $\qquad\qquad (8.2 - 25)$

The values of n given above are those leading to values of the propagation constant k within the range $(-\pi/a < k < \pi/a)$, corresponding to the first Brillouin zone in the reciprocal lattice space, as in Section 3.8. The reasons for this are similar to those outlined in the acoustical case, but their exact significance in this context will be more fully explored later. In any event it is clear there will be essentially N quantum states in the Brillouin zone, and when N is large, they will be spaced so closely in energy and crystal momentum that they can be regarded as a quasi-continuum.

The generalization of the Bloch-Floquet theorem to three dimensions is no more than a straightforward extension of the above calculation. One can show that the one-electron wave function (8.2 - 21) for an electron in a three-dimensional periodic potential can be written as

$$\psi(\mathbf{r}) = e^{i\mathbf{k} \cdot \mathbf{r}} u_k(\mathbf{r}) , \qquad \text{where} \qquad u_k(\mathbf{r} + \mathbf{r}_{hkl}) = u_k(\mathbf{r}) . \qquad (8.2 - 26)$$

In this expression, the crystal momentum is a propagation vector, and the function u_k has the periodicity of the lattice, as expressed by invariance under a translation by a lattice vector $\mathbf{r}_{hkl}$. The number of allowed quantum states in the Brillouin zone, as expressed by (8.2 - 25) still equals the number of atoms in the crystal.

8.3 THE KRONIG-PENNEY MODEL OF AN INFINITE ONE-DIMENSIONAL CRYSTAL LATTICE

One of the simplest possible one-dimensional periodic potentials is illustrated in Figure 8.1. This "square wave" potential, was first investigated by R. de L. Kronig and G Penney in 1931. It allows one to arrive at an exact solution for the Schrödinger equation, and to exhibit most of the features of more realistic though far less tractible periodic potential models. Though only a crude approximation of real crystal potentials, it illustrates explicitly most of the important characteristics of the quantum behavior of electrons in real crystals.

The wave functions associated with this potential model may be calculated by solving Schrödinger's equation, using the one-electron approximation, in which one assumes that the net force acting on any given electron can be regarded as derivable from a periodic potential like the one illustrated. In this case, therefore, we write Schrödinger's equation as

$$\frac{d^2\psi}{dx^2} + \frac{2m}{\hbar^2}[\varepsilon - V(x)]\psi(x) = 0 \ . \tag{8.3-1}$$

The potential $V(x)$ is zero in $(0<x<b)$ and has the constant value V_0 in $(-c<x<0)$ in the unit cell shown in the figure. The lattice constant in this periodic model is the distance a, equal to $b + c$. The results of the preceding section indicate that the wave function of an electron in such a potential must have the Bloch form

$$\psi(x) = e^{ikx}u(x) \ , \tag{8.3-2}$$

where $u(x)$ is a function having the periodicity of the lattice. If we now substitute this form of the solution into the Schrödinger equation, it is simple to show that the

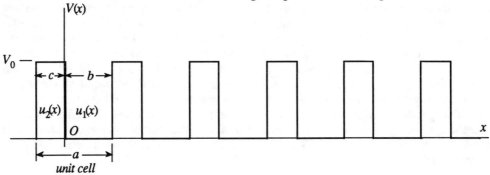

Figure 8.1 The periodic potential function assumed in the Kronig-Penney model of a one-dimensional crystal lattice.

function $u(x)$ must satisfy a differential equation of the form

$$\frac{d^2u}{dx^2} + 2ik\frac{du}{dx} - \left(k^2 - \alpha^2 + \frac{2mV(x)}{\hbar^2}\right)u(x) = 0 \ , \tag{8.3-3}$$

where

$$\alpha^2 = 2m\varepsilon/\hbar^2 \ . \tag{8.3-4}$$

For the potential shown in the figure, we must write two separate equations for the piecewise constant sections, of the form

$$\frac{d^2u_1}{dx^2} + 2ik\frac{du_1}{dx} - (k^2 - \alpha^2)u_1(x) = 0 \ , \qquad (0 < x < b) \tag{8.3-5}$$

and $\quad \dfrac{d^2u_2}{dx^2} + 2ik\dfrac{du_2}{dx} - (k^2 - \beta^2)u_2(x) = 0 \ , \qquad (-c < x < 0) \ . \tag{8.3-6}$

In these expression u_1 gives the value of $u(x)$ in the interval $(0<x<b)$, while u_2 represents its value in $(-c<x<0)$; the quantity β is defined by

$$\beta^2 = 2m(\varepsilon - V_0)/\hbar^2 \; . \tag{8.3-7}$$

Equations (8.3 - 5) and (8.3 - 6) are simple linear second order differential equations with constant coefficients. They can be solved by the usual methods to give

$$u_1(x) = Ae^{i(\alpha-k)x} + Be^{-i(\alpha+k)x} \; , \qquad (0 < x < b) \tag{8.3-8}$$

and $\quad u_2(x) = Ce^{i(\beta-k)x} + De^{-i(\beta+k)x} \; , \qquad (-c < x < 0) \; , \tag{8.3-9}$

where $A, B, C,$ and D are arbitrary constants. The requirement that wave functions be continuous and have continuous derivatives at all points requires that the function $u(x)$ in the Bloch solution (8.3 - 1) also satisfy these conditions, since the factor $exp(ikx)$ is always well-behaved. Using these boundary conditions at $x = b$ and $x = -c$, plus the requirement of periodicity for $u(x)$, one obtains equations for the four constants $A, B, C,$ and D of the form

$$A + B = C + D$$

$$i(\alpha - k)A - i(\alpha + K)B = i(\beta - k)C - i(\beta + k)D$$
$$\tag{8.3-10}$$
$$Ae^{i(\alpha-k)b} + Be^{-i(\alpha+k)b} = Ce^{-i(\beta-k)c} + De^{i(\beta+k)c}$$

$$i(\alpha - k)Ae^{i(\alpha-k)b} - i(\alpha + k)Be^{-i(\alpha+k)b} = i(\beta - k)Ce^{-i(\beta-k)c} - i(\beta + k)De^{i(\beta+k)c} \; .$$

Viewed as a set of simultaneous equations for the four arbitrary constants, this set is a homogeneous system whose only solution is $A = B = C = D = 0$ unless the determinant of the coefficients vanishes. For meaningful solutions to exist, we must therefore require that

$$\begin{vmatrix} 1 & 1 & 1 & 1 \\ \alpha - k & -(\alpha + k) & \beta - k & -(\beta + k) \\ e^{i(\alpha-k)b} & e^{-i(\alpha+k)b} & e^{-i(\beta-k)c} & e^{i(\beta+k)c} \\ (\alpha - k)e^{i(\alpha-k)b} & -(\alpha + k)e^{-i(\alpha+k)b} & (\beta - k)e^{-i(\beta-k)c} & -(\beta + k)e^{i(\beta+k)c} \end{vmatrix} = 0 \; . \tag{8.3-11}$$

Expanding the determinant, and doing some very tedious but straightforward algebra, this can be expressd finally as

$$-\frac{\alpha^2 + \beta^2}{2\alpha\beta} \sin \alpha b \sin \beta c + \cos \alpha b \cos \beta c = \cos k(b + c) = \cos ka \; , \tag{8.3-12}$$

where a is the lattice constant $b + c$, as shown in the figure. This result is useful so long as β^2 is positive, which guarantees that β will be a real quantity, a condition that according to (8.3 - 7) is satisfied for $\varepsilon > V_0$. In the range $(0 < \varepsilon < V_0)$, however, β^2 is negative, which means that β itself is a purely imaginary quantity. Under these circumstances, it is useful to express (8.3 - 12) in a slightly different form, letting

$$\beta = i\gamma \qquad (\gamma \text{ real}) \qquad (0 < \varepsilon < V_0) \ , \tag{8.3-13}$$

and recalling that $\beta^2 = -\gamma^2$, $\cos ix = \cosh x$, and $\sin ix = i \sinh x$. Equation (8.3 - 12) then becomes

$$\frac{\gamma^2 - \alpha^2}{2\alpha\gamma} \sin \alpha b \sinh \gamma c + \cos \alpha b \cosh \gamma c = \cos k(b+c) = \cos ka \ . \tag{8.3-14}$$

We must now use (8.3 - 12) when $\varepsilon > V_0$ and (8.3 - 14) when $0 < \varepsilon < V_0$. The two solutions join smoothly at the point $\varepsilon = V_0$. These equations define a relation between the energy (as expressed by α and β or γ) and the crystal momentum, which can also be regarded as a relation between $\hbar\omega$ and $\hbar k$. They therefore define the *dispersion relation* for the Bloch wave function.

These equations can be transformed to another useful form by a simple trigonometrical maneuver, based on the fact that one can always write

$$K_1 \sin \alpha b + K_2 \cos \alpha b = K_3 \cos(\alpha b - \delta) \tag{8.3-15}$$

where

$$K_3^2 = K_1^2 + K_2^2 \text{ and} \qquad \tan\delta = K_1/K_2 \ , \tag{8.3-16}$$

This result is obtained by expanding the cosine function on the right side of (8.3 - 15) and matching coefficients of $\sin \alpha b$ and $\cos \alpha b$ on both sides of the resulting expression. One then finds $K_1 = K_3 \sin\delta$, and $K_2 = K_3 \cos\delta$. Squaring these two equations and adding yields the first of the results in (8.3 - 16) and dividing one by the other gives the second. Since both (8.3 - 12) and (8.3 - 14) are of the form shown on the left side of (8.3 - 15), we can apply this maneuver to both equations, which allows us after some simplifying algebra, to write them as

$$\left[1 + \frac{V_0^2}{4\varepsilon(\varepsilon - V_0)} \sin^2 \beta c\right]^{1/2} \cos(\alpha b - \delta) = \cos ka \ , \qquad (\varepsilon > V_0) \tag{8.3-17}$$

and

$$\left[1 + \frac{V_0^2}{4\varepsilon(V_0 - \varepsilon)} \sinh^2 \gamma c\right]^{1/2} \cos(\alpha b - \delta') = \cos ka \ , \quad (0 < \varepsilon < V_0) \ , \tag{8.3-18}$$

where

$$\tan\delta = -\frac{\alpha^2 + \beta^2}{2\alpha\beta} \tan \beta c \qquad \text{and} \qquad \tan\delta' = \frac{\gamma^2 - \alpha^2}{2\alpha\gamma} \tanh \gamma c \ . \tag{8.3-19}$$

In arriving at these results, it is useful to observe that

$$\alpha^2 - \beta^2 = \alpha^2 + \gamma^2 = 2mV_0/\hbar^2 \ . \tag{8.3-20}$$

In (8.3 - 17) and (8.3 - 18), the quantities α, β, and γ are, as defined, clearly real quantities. The left sides of both equations are sinusoidally varying functions of the variable $\alpha b - \delta$, whose amplitudes, given by the coefficient of $\cos(\alpha b - \delta)$, are in both cases *greater than unity*. This means that for some values of this angular variable, the function $\cos ka$ on the right must have a value greater than 1, or, possibly, less than –1. The cosines of real quantities are always in the interval ($-1 < \cos ka < 1$), but there are *complex* arguments whose cosines are greater than unity or less than –1. These complex arguments $ka = (k_r + ik_i)a$ always have a *nonzero imaginary part*, which introduces real exponential factors into the wave function (8.3 - 2), causing it to diverge exponentially at either plus or minus infinity. Such solutions are not acceptable as wave functions, and therefore there are certain ranges of the angular variable $\alpha b - \delta$ within which quantum states of the system cannot exist. Since from (8.3 - 4) this variable is related to the total energy of the electron, there are ranges of energy wherein *no quantum states can exist*. Only energies that permit the left sides of (8.3 - 17) and (8.3 - 18) to be within the interval ($-1 < \cos ka < 1$), and thus yield real values for ka, are allowed. Other energies are *forbidden*, just as energies that differ from those of discrete atomic energy eigenvalues are forbidden.

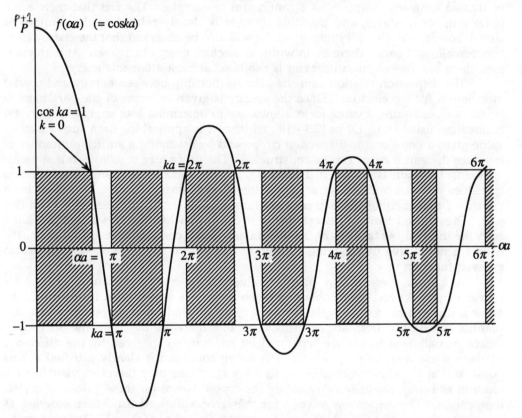

Figure 8.2 Plot of functions on the left sides of (8.3 - 17) and (8.3 - 18), showing regions where $\cos ka$ is greater than one or less than minus one. Shaded regions correspond to forbidden energy ranges in which no quantum states exist.

When one plots the left side of these two equations against the angular variable αa, using (8.3 - 17) for values of this argument corresponding to energies greater than V_0 and (8.3 - 18) for energies less than V_0, the result is a meandering curve like that shown in Figure 8.2. The regions where $\cos ka$ exceeds unity or is less than –1 are clearly visible, as are the energy ranges in which $\cos ka$ corresponds to a real value for the crystal momentum. The shaded regions show the forbidden energy intervals, while the clear areas are allowed bands in which there are quantum states of the Bloch form (8.3 - 2), that can be associated with free-electron behavior.

The picture that emerges is one of alternating allowed and forbidden regions of energy referred to as allowed and forbidden *energy bands*, as illustrated in Figure 8.2 The width in energy of the forbidden bands is sometimes called the energy gap between the allowed bands. This grouping of quantum states into energy bands is a general characteristic of periodic potentials. In a truly infinite lattice the states within any allowed band would form a continuum of allowed energies, but in a lattice in which there is a finite number of atoms N, as we have seen already, there are N discrete states--or, more realistically, $2N$ if spin degeneracy is taken into account. If the number of atoms is large, the quantum states are spaced so closely that the band can be treated for many purposes as a continuum of energies. The fact that there are a finite number of states, and that this number is closely related to the number of atoms, however, is also very important. It will also be observed that the energy gaps between allowed bands decrease in width as electron energy increases. At high energies, therefore, free electron behavior is exhibited at most attainable energies.

The dispersion relation expresses the relationship between energy and crystal momentum for the electron. Since the energy is given in terms of the parameter α by (8.3 - 4), assuming a value for α allows one to determine *both* energy and crystal momentum using (8.3 - 17) or (8.3 - 18), whichever is applicable. Each such assumed value gives a point on the dispersion curve, and by assuming a sufficient number of α-values the entire curve can be constructed. The procedure is tedious but straightforward; the result is shown in Figure 8.3, in which shaded regions correspond to forbidden energies and clear areas show the allowed energy bands. It is clear from Figure 8.2 that energies close to zero are forbidden, a fact that is seen also from this plot. The allowed band of lowest energy is obtained when the crystal momentum k is in the interval $(-\pi/a < k < \pi/a)$, as illustrated. Since $\cos ka$ is an even function, the energy is not altered by changing the sign of k; therefore, the dispersion curve is also an even function of k.

At $k = \pi/a$, there are two possible values for the energy, one an upper limit for energies in the lowest band, obtained when $k = \pi/a$ is approached from below, the other a lower limit for energies in the second allowed band, obtained when this point is approached from above. This value of k therefore describes the *band edges*, where two allowed bands are separated by an energy gap given by the difference between these two limiting values. The Bragg condition is clearly satisfied at this point, and at all other band-edge points $k = n\pi/a$. One may therefore visualize the electron as being *internally diffracted* by the crystal lattice for these values of crystal momentum. The dispersion relation for the second allowed band then emerges as one assumes α-values for which k is in intervals $(\pi/a < k < 2\pi/a)$ and $(-2\pi/a < k < -\pi/a)$. The region of the k-axis associated with the lowest allowed band is the first Brillouin zone of the lattice, the regions associated with the second-lowest allowed band is the second Brillouin zone, and so on, as shown in the diagram. The zone boundaries, moreover, are *always* points at which internal Bragg reflections occur. There are a few differences between this situation and the one encountered in Chapter 3 concerning the propagation of acoustic waves, but the many similarities are clearly evident. In the limit of high energies the Kronig-Penney dispersion curve (except near the band edges) closely approaches the parabolic relation $\varepsilon = \hbar^2 k^2 / 2m$ characteristic of a totally free particle. The somewhat different appearance of the energy bands in Figures 8.2 and 8.3 is accounted for by the fact that k is expressed as a function of αa in Figure 8.2 and as a function of ε in Figure 8.3.

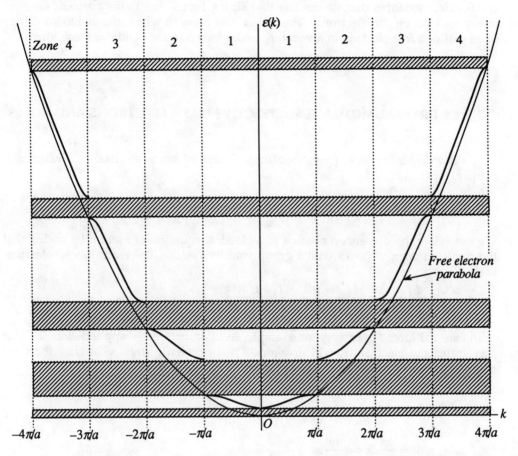

Figure 8.3 Dispersion relation for an electron in the Kronig-Penney periodic potential, showing energy plotted as a function of crystal momentum. The light parabolic curve shows the dispersion relation for a perfectly free electron, while the darker curve shows energy versus k for the Kronig-Penney model. Shaded areas show forbidden energy regions, while clear areas are allowed energy bands.

It will be noted that at the band edges, where Bragg reflection takes place, the dispersion curve has zero slope. Near the bottom of an allowed band, the electron dispersion relation is therefore practically parabolic, like that of a free particle. In this region the electron's behavior resembles that of a free particle, though since the curvature of the ε versus k curve differs from that of the free-electron parabola, the acceleration of an electron subject to a constant external force is not the same as that of a free electron in vacuum. Indeed, the electron behaves like a free particle with a mass different from the true inertial mass of the electron. For higher electron energies in the allowed band, the dispersion relation is no longer parabolic, and at the highest energies in the band, the curvature is negative, approaching that of an inverted parabola near the top of the band. The electron now behaves as a free particle with a *negative* mass, whose acceleration in an externally applied electric field is like that of a positively charged particle with a positive mass. We shall examine these effects in more detail later, but it is apparent that free-particle behavior occurs under certain circumstances despite the fact that strong forces due to the periodic array of lattice ions act on the electrons. The rather odd ways in which this behavior differs from that of a free electron in a vacuum can be traced to the action of these forces.

8.4 CRYSTAL MOMENTUM, EFFECTIVE MASS, ELECTRONS AND HOLES

The dispersion (energy-momentum) relation of a free electron in a vacuum is simply

$$\varepsilon = \hbar\omega = \frac{\hbar^2 k^2}{2m} \ . \tag{8.4-1}$$

We can relate the dispersion relation to a classical equation of motion by noting that the particle's energy moves with a group velocity $d\omega/dk$. The electron's acceleration is thus

$$\frac{dv_g}{dt} = \frac{d}{dt}\left(\frac{d\omega}{dk}\right) = \frac{d}{dk}\left(\frac{d\omega}{dk}\right)\frac{dk}{dt} = \frac{1}{\hbar^2}\frac{d^2\varepsilon}{dk^2}\frac{d(\hbar k)}{dt} \ . \tag{8.4-2}$$

If an external force F_e (arising, for example, from an externally applied electric field) accelerates the electron, it will do work dW_e in time dt, while changing the electron's energy by $d\varepsilon$ and the crystal momentum by dk; so that

$$dW_e = F_e \, dx = F_e \cdot v_g dt = F_e \frac{d\omega}{dk} dt \ ;$$

$$\tag{8.4-3}$$

$$dW_e = d\varepsilon = \frac{d\varepsilon}{dk} dk = \hbar \frac{d\omega}{dk} dk \ .$$

Equating these two expressions, we obtain

$$F_e = \frac{d(\hbar k)}{dt} \ . \tag{8.4-4}$$

Substituting this into (8.4 - 2), we arrive at an expression for the acceleration of the form

$$\frac{dv_g}{dt} = \frac{1}{\hbar^2}\frac{d^2\varepsilon}{dk^2}\cdot F_e = \frac{F_e}{m*} \ , \tag{8.4-5}$$

where

$$m* = \frac{\hbar^2}{\left(d^2\varepsilon/dk^2\right)} \ . \tag{8.4-6}$$

The parameter m^* defined above is referred to as the effective mass. For a free electron in vacuum, whose dispersion relation is (8.4 - 1), $d^2\varepsilon/dk^2 = \hbar^2/m$, and m^* reduces to the ordinary electron mass m. In the crystal lattice, however, this is no longer so, and the effective mass of the electron is different from its inertial mass. If the dispersion curve is approximately parabolic (as it is near the top and bottom of the allowed bands in the Kronig-Penney model), we have near the energy extrema,

$$\varepsilon = C(k - n\pi)^2 \qquad \text{and} \qquad \frac{d^2\varepsilon}{dk^2} = 2C , \qquad (8.4\text{-}7)$$

where C is a constant, and

$$m^* = \hbar^2/2C . \qquad (8.4\text{-}8)$$

In non-parabolic sections of the ε vs, k curve, the quantity $d^2\varepsilon/dk^2$ is no longer constant, but depends on energy. Since ordinarily the electron experiences only a small fractional energy change from external forces during the free time between collisions, however, the effective mass is still essentially constant over the particle's small free path, and the free-particle picture is still generally valid.

It is important to observe that the above arguments do not account for the action of all forces acting on the electron, but only those ascribable to macroscopic external influences like electric or magnetic fields, or (less obviously) gradients of temperature or concentration. The electron's response to such influences is that of a free particle, though one that has an effective mass different from that of an isolated electron in vacuum. Newton's law, as written above, however, includes only part of the total force on the particle. The part that has been left out--ascribable to the periodic potential of the lattice ions--does not *directly* influence free-particle transport phenomena. It does, however exert an *indirect* influence on the dynamics of "free" electrons, in that it is responsible for the appearance of the effective mass.

The above development, unfortunately, is less explicit than it could be. It is more convincing (though much more difficult) to study the motion of a localized electron wave packet, formed by Fourier superposition of wave functions having different k-values, when external forces are applied. This motion has been studied, and can be shown to obey the equation of motion developed above.

Near the top of the allowed energy regions in Figure 8.3, the curvature of the dispersion relation (as given by $d^2\varepsilon/dk^2$) is negative. The literal interpretation of this situation suggests a *negative effective mass*. Under these circumstances, an external field E in the positive x-direction acting on a negatively charged particle like an electron produces a *positive* acceleration component along the x-direction, rather than one that is negative, as it would ordinarily be. Free-particle behavior associated with these allowed energy states is therefore the same as that of positively charged free particles. The acceleration is, after all, qE/m^*, so it makes no difference whether one ascribes a reversal in sign to the mass m^* or the charge q. Since negative inertial or gravitational masses are never observed in this part of the universe, it is conventional to associate free-particle conductivity in the negative-mass region of the dispersion curve with "quasiparticles" having *positive charge and positive mass* rather than negative charge and negative mass. Such quasiparticles are referred to as *holes*, and free-particle transport involving negative-mass states is called *hole* *conduction.* In the crystal lattice, the hole--not the positron--is the antiparticle of the electron. Without the lattice, of course, holes cannot exist; that is why they are called quasiparticles. Phonons, obviously, are in the same category.

A more precise picture of hole conduction can be obtained by considering what happens when electrons occupy the states in a given allowed band. In one-dimensional systems, we have seen that when spin degeneracy is accounted for, there are exactly $2N$ states in each allowed band. Starting with an empty band, as one adds electrons, the states of lowest available energy are occupied as required by the Pauli exclusion principle. For any given number of electrons less than $2N$, the band will--at zero temperature--be partially filled, to a maximum energy that corresponds to the Fermi energy of the electron gas. If there are more than $2N$ and less than $4N$ electrons, there will be a filled lower band and a partially filled upper band, separated by an "energy gap" in which there are no allowed states. It is easy to see that a completely empty band can contribute nothing to current flow in the presence of an external field, since there are no free electrons in it. It is less obvious, though equally true, that a completely *filled* band can also carry no net current. The reasoning is as follows; the current density J associated with any band is given by

$$J = n_0 q \bar{v} \,, \qquad (8.4\text{-}9)$$

where n_0 is the number of electrons per unit volume belonging to the band, and $\bar{v}$ is the average velocity. The average velocity, however, can be written in terms of a summation over individual particle velocities v_i as

$$\bar{v} = \frac{1}{n_0 V} \sum_i v_i \,. \qquad (8.4\text{-}10)$$

The summation above includes only states occupied by electrons, since unoccupied states contribute nothing to average particle velocity or current density. With this understood, (8.4 - 9) can now be written

$$J = \frac{q}{V} \sum_i v_i \,. \qquad (8.4\text{-}11)$$

Due to the symmetry of the dispersion curve in Figure 8.3 (a symmetry that is not unique to the Kronig-Penney model), it is clear that for every state k that gives a positive group velocity $d\varepsilon/\hbar dk$, there is a state $-k$ that gives a group velocity equal in magnitude but opposite in sign, since the slope of the dispersion curve changes sign when the sign of k is reversed. Therefore, if *all* states are occupied, the sum in the above expression is zero, and the band can contribute no net current.

It is now apparent that *only a partially filled band* can contribute to free-electron transport and thus support a flow of charge. If there is a single free electron in the band, at absolute zero it will occupy a state of minimum energy at the very bottom of the band. When an external field in the x-direction is applied, it will be accelerated in a direction opposite that of the field, into states of higher and higher (though negative) group velocity in which it carries a net current in the field direction. Finally, it will undergo a scattering process that returns it (on the average) to the bottom of the band, as suggested in our earlier discussions of free-electron conductivity. This acceleration process is then repeated, as described previously. The energy the electron acquires from the field during its free path is generally much smaller than the energy from bottom to top of the allowed band, so that it never climbs far from the bottom of the band. This reasoning is very straightforward; it is merely a slight elaboration of a process that is already well understood. If a small additional number of electrons are added to the system, their behavior is similar to that of the first, and except for the fact that there are more filled states near the bottom of the band and more electrons around to be accelerated by the field the picture is not essentially altered.

In a band that is almost completely filled, at absolute zero the electrons occupy in equilibrium the states of lowest possible energy, leaving only a few unoccupied states above the Fermi energy, which is now very near the top of the allowed band. The action of the electric field is now similar to that discussed previously, in that it tends to give the entire electron population some average velocity in the negative x-direction, but the description of how this happens is complicated by the large number of particles and the large range of effective masses--negative as well as positive-- that they can have. Under such circumstances, it simplifies matters to consider only the behavior of the unfilled states, whose dynamics, it turns out, is similar to that of a small number positively charged quasiparticles called holes that reside in equilibrium near the top of the nearly filled band. The validity of such a picture can be illustrated by a slight alteration of the calculation that led to (8.4 - 11). In that equation, it was noted that the summation is over only occupied states, since empty states do not contribute to the current.

In a nearly filled band, we can write this summation in a different way, by summing over a totally occupied band and subtracting terms due to empty states. Thus, if we denote occupied states by the subscript i and empty states by the subscript j, we can write

$$J = \frac{q}{V}\left(\sum_{i=1}^{2N} v_i - \sum_{j} v_j\right).$$

(8.4 - 12)

In this expression the first sum is taken over all $2N$ quantum states--that is, over a filled band. This summation is zero, since it is identical to the sum that appears in (8.4 - 11) when all states are occupied. We are thus left with

$$J = -\frac{q}{V}\sum_{j} v_j,$$

(8.4 - 13)

where the sum is now over group velocities v_j associated with *unoccupied* quantum states--states "occupied by holes" to put it another way. This term is of opposite sign from (8.4 - 10), and is therefore of the form associated with a population of positively charged quasiparticles. The group velocities associated with the states are also those that would be attained by positive charges, since negative effective masses are associated with this part of the dispersion curve. Moreover, since the "hole population" is confined to the upper part of the allowed band, where the dispersion curve is nearly parabolic, all the quasiparticles can be considered to have the same effective mass. Holes are subject to scattering processes similar to those experienced by electrons, and the quasiparticle distribution behaves exactly like a free-particle gas of positively charged "antiparticles". It should be noted that both (8.4 - 11) and (8.4 - 13) lead to positive current densities when the field is in the positive x-direction, since q equals $-e$ and the average velocity given by the summation in (8.4 - 11) is negative, while that arising from the sum in (8.4 - 13) is positive because of the negative effective mass. Hole conduction in nearly filled bands provides an explanation for the positive values of the Hall coefficient that are observed in some metallic conductors. This is a fairly rare occurrence in metallic systems, but is often observed in semiconductors. Indeed, we could understand very little about semiconducting materials without the picture of hole conductivity. This picture will be developed more explicitly in the next chapter, in which these materials are examined in detail.

In Chapter 3, we saw that all the physical effects associated with lattice vibrations can be described within the first Brillouin zone. The problem of wave mechanics in periodic lattices is similar, though there are some differences. The assignment of k-values to the various allowed bands shown in Figure 8.2 is somewhat arbitrary since the wave equation and the boundary conditions require only that the function $\cos ka$ have the value ± 1 at the band edges, which does not uniquely determine ka; the value $k_n a = ka \pm 2n\pi$ will serve equally well. The assignment in the figure has the virtue that at large energies, for which the particle is "almost free", the dispersion curve approaches that of a free particle. It is possible nevertheless to translate higher Brillouin zones into the region of k-space occupied by the first zone by a horizontal translation through a distance $2\pi n/a$, where n is an integer. Such an operation displaces the dispersion curve horizontally by the magnitude of some lattice vector of the reciprocal lattice, divided by 2π, as discussed in Chapter 3. When a series of such translations is made in order to bring all branches of the dispersion curve within the interval $(-\pi/a < k < \pi/a)$ that defines the first zone, one obtains a diagram like that shown in Figure 8.4. This way of describing the ε versus k relation is referred to as the reduced-zone representation, while the original scheme depicted in Figure 8.3 is called the extended-zone representation. Both representations are frequently used, as convenience dictates.

Finally, it is important to note that there are no built-in scattering mechanisms in the quantum theory of electrons in periodic lattices. Indeed, the wave-mechanical treatment alone suggests that electrons in perfectly periodic potentials aren't subject to scattering at all. This is perhaps not surprising in view of the fact that Schrödinger wave mechanics deals only with forces that are described by a classical potential energy, and are therefore inherently conservative. There are no provisions in it for dissipative phenomena--mechanisms that can lead, for example, to Ohm's law. In this regard it is much like simple Newtonian mechanics, which predicts an ever-increasing drift velocity, instead of a steady current. It is therefore necessary to consider scattering interactions separately, and incorporate them into the theory in essentially the same way as in classical free-electron theory.

Scattering by phonons is important not only in the classical picture, but also in the wave mechanical treatment, and for the same reason--because in pure crystals it limits the free path of electrons and holes, leading to Ohm's law. In a vibrating lattice, the potential at any given instant of time deviates somewhat from perfect periodicity, because of the instantaneous displacements of the vibrating ions from the equilbrium lattice sites. This *deviation from periodicity* is what is ultimately responsible for phonon scattering. One can think of acoustic waves as altering the local lattice constant in a periodic fashion within the crystal. The dispersion relation of the crystal, as given, for example, by the Kronig-Penney calculation, depends on the interatomic spacing. A local variation of the lattice constant will thus cause the band edges to go up and down in energy as the interatomic spacing changes from point to point within the lattice. The bottom of the band, for example, will be at a slightly higher or lower energy than the unperturbed equilibrium value at different points within the crystal. There are now, in effect, a series of *energy barriers* in the crystal that can reflect incident electrons in somewhat the same way as the barrier treated in Chapter 4, Section 4.11. This reflection is, in the context of this description, a scattering process, and the reflection coefficient of the barriers can be related to a scattering probability per unit time whose reciprocal gives the mean free time itself. The detailed calculation is difficult, and will not be given here, but the effect, and its consequences, are easy to visualize, and are not essentially different from those that follow from the classical free-electron theory.

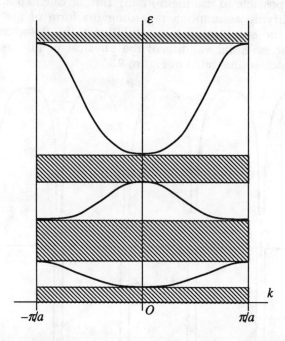

Figure 8.4   Schematic diagram of the dispersion relation shown in Figure 8.3 transformed into the reduced-zone representation.

The presence of impurity ions and structural imperfections in the lattice, such as vacant lattice sites, interstial atoms, and grain boundaries, also cause local deviations from perfect periodicity, which can scatter electrons or holes in somewhat the same way as lattice vibrations. As a result, these mechanisms also act to limit the electron mean free path, as in the classical free-electron theory. The total picture that emerges, at least with regard to transport properties of crystalline materials, is therefore similar to the classical free-electron picture, except for the introduction of the effective mass, and for certain effects such as hole conduction. These variations, however, when taken into account, bring the quantum free-electron theory into much better agreement with experiment than the classical theory, and account for effects like positive Hall coefficients that simply do not fit into the framework of classical theory.

8.5 THE SIMPLIFIED KRONIG-PENNEY MODEL; TIGHT BINDING AND FREE-ELECTRON LIMITS

The dispersion relation for the one-electron Kronig-Penney model is given by equations (8.3 - 12, 13, and 14), as relations between energy (as embodied in α, β, and γ) and the crystal momentum k. These relations are unfortunately so complex that it is frequently impossible to use them in any further calculation. Fortunately, one can make a simplifying assumption regarding the form of the potential function $V(x)$ that enables the energy-momentum relation to be stated much more simply, while retaining the essential validity of the physical picture associated with this model. The approach is illustrated in Figure 8.5.

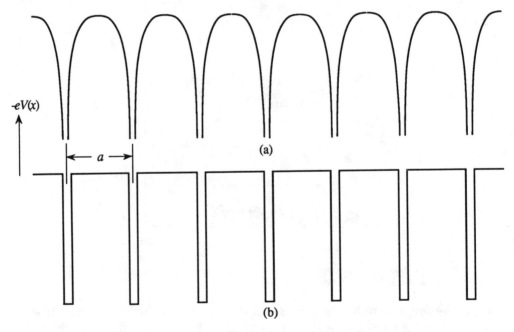

Figure 8.5 (a) Schematic representation of the potential energy of an electron in a one-dimensional lattice of positively charged ions. The negatively charged electrons experience attractive forces from the ionic charges, which means that their potential energy will be lowest close to the ions. This results in the picture of infinitely deep wells shown above. (b) The Kronig-Penney representation of the potential energy function illustrated in (a). In this representation the depth of the wells is allowed to become infinite, while their width approaches zero. The negative charge of the electron converts what would otherwise be potential spikes into potential energy wells.

At (a) in this diagram, we see schematically the potential energy of a single electron acted on by attractive coulomb forces from regularly spaced positive ions. The Kronig-Penney potential in Figure 8.1 is a crude model of this function, though the "hills" in Figure 8.1 are converted into valleys or wells when the potential V is multiplied by the negative electron charge to give the classical electron potential energy $-eV$. At (b) in the above figure, the width of the wells in the Kronig-Penney potential has been allowed to decrease while their depth increases, in such a way that the *product* of these quantities remains constant. This process can continue to a limit in which the well depth becomes infinite and the width approaches zero, the wells then resembling a set of negative δ-functions with singularities at the lattice sites. In the limit, $c \to 0$ and $V_0 \to \infty$, while the product $Q = cV_0$ is held constant. The quantities b and $b + c$ both approach the lattice spacing a in this limit. Now we can write $\sin\beta c = \beta c$ in (8.3 - 12), and obtain, with the aid of (8.3 - 4) and (8.3 - 7),

$$-\frac{\alpha^2+\beta^2}{2\alpha\beta}\sin\beta c \cong -\left(\frac{\alpha}{2}+\frac{\beta^2}{2\alpha}\right)\cdot c = -\left(\frac{\alpha}{2}+\frac{\alpha}{2}-\frac{mV_0}{\alpha\hbar^2}\right)\frac{Q}{V_0} = -\sqrt{\frac{2m\varepsilon}{\hbar^2}}\cdot\frac{Q}{V_0}+\frac{mQ}{\alpha\hbar^2} \quad . \quad (8.5\text{-}1)$$

In the above expression, the first term approaches zero as V_0 becomes infinite, and only the second survives. The dispersion relation (8.3 - 12) can now be written,

$$P\frac{\sin\alpha a}{\alpha a}+\cos\alpha a = \cos ka \quad , \qquad \text{where} \qquad P = Q\cdot\frac{ma}{\hbar^2} \quad . \qquad (8.5\text{-}2)$$

In this expression, the quantity P expresses the interaction strength or scattering power of the periodic potential due to the lattice ions. This dispersion relation is much simpler than the ones derived previously, and the potential model to which it corresponds is no less viable than the more general model of the preceding section. Indeed, it has the desirable physical property of being infinite at the lattice sites, so it is arguably more realistic than its predecessor. Unfortunately, as in the case of the earlier dispersion relations, this equation is not soluble in closed form for ε as a function of k. Nevertheless, it permits the direct calculation of many results not easily obtainable from the original model. Figures 8.2 and 8.3 have been plotted using this model. One can show, using the approach of the preceding section, that this relation can also be written as

$$\sqrt{1+\frac{P^2}{(\alpha a)^2}}\cos(\alpha a-\delta) = \cos ka \quad , \qquad \text{where} \qquad \tan\delta = \frac{P}{\alpha a} \quad . \qquad (8.5\text{-}3)$$

The details of the calculation are assigned as an exercise. It is clear from these relations that when P is very small or the energy (as expressed by αa) is very large, the free electron dispersion relation $\alpha^2 = k^2$ is obtained, as expected.

We have already suggested that the dispersion relation must have zero slope at the band edges. This can be shown in the present context quite simply. If the dispersion relation (8.5 - 2) is written as

$$f(\alpha a) = \cos ka \quad , \qquad (8.5\text{-}4)$$

where $f(\alpha a)$ is the expression on the left side of (8.5 - 2), we can differentiate with respect to energy to obtain

$$\frac{df(\alpha a)}{d\varepsilon} = \frac{df(\alpha a)}{d(\alpha a)} \cdot \frac{d(\alpha a)}{d\varepsilon} = -\sin ka \cdot a \frac{dk}{d\varepsilon} \quad . \tag{8.5-5}$$

Calculating $d(\alpha a)/d\varepsilon$ using (8.3 - 4), substituting its value in the above equation, and solving for $d\varepsilon/dk$, we find

$$\frac{d\varepsilon}{dk} = \hbar \frac{d\omega}{dk} = -\hbar \sqrt{\frac{2\varepsilon}{m}} \cdot \frac{\sin ka}{df(\alpha a)/d(\alpha a)} \quad . \tag{8.5-6}$$

It now follows that at the band edges, where $ka = \pm n\pi$, $d\varepsilon/dk$ will be zero, unless $df/d(\alpha a)$ happens to be zero. However, Figure 8.2 shows that the slope of the function $f(\alpha a)$ is never zero at any of the band edges, so $d\varepsilon/dk$ has to be zero at these points. Since $d\varepsilon/dk$ is related to the electron group velocity as shown above, the group velocity is also zero at the band edges, an effect that (as discussed in Chapter 3) is associated with Bragg reflection and the formation of standing waves. This result is of general applicability, and is not specific to the Kronig-Penney model.

Expanding the dispersion relation in a Taylor's series about the band edge points, one finds

$$\varepsilon(k) = \varepsilon_b + \frac{1}{2}\left(\frac{d^2\varepsilon}{dk^2}\right)_b (k - k_b)^2 + \ldots = \varepsilon_b + \frac{1}{2}\left(\frac{d^2\varepsilon}{dk^2}\right)_b\left(k - \frac{n\pi}{a}\right)^2 + \ldots . \tag{8.5-7}$$

In this equation, there is no linear term because the derivative $d\varepsilon/dk$ is zero at the band edge points, where $k = k_b = n\pi/a$; the subscript b will be used consistently to indicate that a quantity is to be evaluated at these points. This shows clearly that the dispersion relation is nearly parabolic, like that of a free particle, near the band edges, as suggested by the curve in Figure 8.2. The evaluation of the second derivative above is obviously important to all further work in which this "free particle" dispersion relation is needed. Moreover, the effective mass of an electron (or hole) can be obtained from this second derivative. Indeed, (8.4 - 6) allows us to write this equation as

$$\varepsilon(k) = \varepsilon_b + \frac{\hbar^2(k - k_b)^2}{2m_b*} + \ldots = \varepsilon_b + \frac{\hbar^2}{2m_b*}\left(k - \frac{n\pi}{a}\right)^2 + \ldots , \tag{8.5-8}$$

which expresses the free-electron behavior of particles near the band edge points in very explicit terminology.

It is possible to calculate the second derivative of ε with respect to k as follows, starting with (8.5 - 5);

$$\frac{d^2\varepsilon}{dk^2} = \frac{d}{dk}\left(\frac{-a\sin ka}{\left(\frac{df(\alpha a)}{d\varepsilon}\right)}\right) = -\frac{a^2\cos ka}{\frac{df(\alpha a)}{d\varepsilon}} - (a\sin ka)\frac{d}{d\varepsilon}\left(\frac{df(\alpha a)}{d\varepsilon}\right)^{-1}\frac{d\varepsilon}{dk} \quad ,$$

or,

$$\frac{d^2\varepsilon}{dk^2} = -\frac{a^2\cos ka}{\dfrac{df(\alpha a)}{d\varepsilon}} + \frac{a\sin ka}{\left(\dfrac{df(\alpha a)}{d\varepsilon}\right)^2} \cdot \frac{d(\alpha a)}{d\varepsilon} \cdot \frac{d\varepsilon}{dk} \ . \tag{8.5-9}$$

This can be evaluated by calculating the derivatives using (8.5 - 2) and substituting them into the above equation. The resulting expression is complex, and need not be written explicitly, for all that we shall need is the value of the derivative at the band edges. As in the preceding discussion, the second term in (8.5 - 7) vanishes because $\sin ka$ is zero at these points. This allows us to write

$$\left(\frac{d^2\varepsilon}{dk^2}\right)_b = -\frac{a^2\cos k_b a}{\left(\dfrac{df(\alpha a)}{d\varepsilon}\right)_b} = -\frac{\hbar^2(\alpha a)\cdot\left(\begin{array}{c}\cos n\pi\\\cos(n-1)\pi\end{array}\right)}{m\left(\dfrac{P\cos\alpha a}{\alpha a} - \dfrac{P\sin\alpha a}{(\alpha a)^2} - \sin\alpha a\right)_b} \ . \tag{8.5-10}$$

In deriving this result, we have used the relation $d(\alpha a)/d\varepsilon = ma^2/\alpha a\hbar^2$, which follows directly from differentiating (8.3 - 4). The upper expression in the numerator, $\cos n\pi$, represents the value of $\cos ka$ at the upper edge of the n-th allowed band in Figure 8.2 or 8.3, while $\cos(n - 1)\pi$ gives its value at the lower edge of this same band. Though the first derivative $d\varepsilon/dk$ is always zero at the band edges, the second derivative is never zero at these points. This is true because the numerator of the above expression is never zero, and its denominator cannot be infinite for $\alpha a > 0$.

To evaluate these expressions further, one must know the value of αa at all the band edges. At the *upper* edges of all the allowed bands this is no problem, for at the upper edge of the n-th allowed band, Figure 8.2 or 8.3 shows that $ka = \alpha a = n\pi$. This also follows from substituting $\alpha a = n\pi$. into (8.5 - 2), which then reduces to $\cos\alpha a = \cos ka = \pm 1$ (+ for n even, − for n odd), a set of points situated at the upper edges of all the allowed bands. In any event, it is clear that

$$\alpha a = ka = n\pi \qquad \text{(upper band edges)} \ . \tag{8.5-11}$$

At the *lower* edges of the allowed bands, the situation is more complex. At these points, for the n-th allowed band, ka has the value $(n - 1)\pi$, but though (8.5 - 2) is still satisfied, αa and ka are no longer equal; specifically, αa is now somewhat smaller than ka. For n even, $\cos ka = +1$ and (8.5 - 2) becomes

$$P\frac{\sin\alpha a}{\alpha a} + \cos\alpha a = 1 \ . \tag{8.5-12}$$

If we now express the angle αa as $2(\alpha a/2)$, and use trigonometric identities, we can write

$$2P\frac{\sin\frac{1}{2}\alpha a\cos\frac{1}{2}\alpha a}{\alpha a} = 1 - (\cos^2\tfrac{1}{2}\alpha a - \sin^2\tfrac{1}{2}\alpha a) = 2\sin^2\tfrac{1}{2}\alpha a \ . \tag{8.5-13}$$

Cancelling a factor $\sin(\alpha a/2)$ and rearranging, this can be put in the form

$$\cot\frac{\alpha a}{2} = \frac{\alpha a}{P} , \qquad (ka = 0, 2\pi, 4\pi, \cdots) . \qquad (8.5\text{-}14)$$

A similar calculation in which we assume $\cos ka = -1$, thus that ka is an odd multiple of π, leads to

$$-\tan\frac{\alpha a}{2} = \frac{\alpha a}{P} , \qquad (ka = \pi, 3\pi, 5\pi, \cdots) . \qquad (8.5\text{-}15)$$

Finally, at the points $ka = \pi/2, 3\pi/2, 5\pi/2 \ldots$, $\cos ka = 0$, and (8.5 - 2) can be solved for a series of intermediate values of αa which we shall refer to as "band centers", even though they are not at the exact midpoints of the bands. In this case, (8.5 - 2) reduces to

$$-\tan\alpha a = \frac{\alpha a}{P} , \qquad (ka = \tfrac{1}{2}\pi, \tfrac{3}{2}\pi, \tfrac{5}{2}\pi, \cdots) . \qquad (8.5\text{-}16)$$

The three equations above are transcendental equations, which must be solved numerically for the values of αa, and the related energies. The solutions can be shown graphically by plotting the trigonometric functions in these equations and the straight line $\alpha a/P$ against αa. The solutions are defined by intersections of this line with the appropriate set of trigonometric curves, as shown in Figure 8.6. The diagram exhibits in a different way information also given in Figures. 8.2 and 8.3.

The interval $(0 < \alpha a < \pi)$ contains the lowest band; its lowest allowed energy is defined by the intersection of the straight line marked $\alpha a/P$ with the curve $\cot(\alpha a/2)$ at the point labeled $ka = 0$. The "band center" is at the intersection marked $\pi/2$, and the highest allowed energy is at the lowest intersection marked π, corresponding to $\alpha a = \pi$. The second allowed band is in the interval $(\pi < \alpha a < 2\pi)$; the energies corresponding to the range between the two points labeled π along the inclined straight line are forbidden, the higher of them defining the lowest allowed energy in the second band. The band center is at the point labeled $3\pi/2$. Similar relationships define the third band, which is found in the interval $(2\pi < \alpha a < 3\pi)$, the energies between the two points marked 2π being forbidden, and so on. The highest allowed energy in each band is associated with the points $\alpha a = n\pi$.

In general, the transcendental character of these equations makes it difficult to proceed further, but when the quantity $\alpha a/P$ is either very large or very small compared to unity, the trigonometric functions can be replaced by approximate expressions derived from power series expansions, which allows one to work explicitly many physically significant problems. The case $\alpha a/P \gg 1$ implies that the scattering power P is very small; since P is related to the well depth V_0 in the limit described by (8.5 - 2), this case is one in which the electron behaves much like a free electron in vacuum, except possibly at the lowest allowed energies. It is referred to as the *free electron approximation*. In the limit $\alpha a/P \ll 1$, the electron is (except at very high energies) constrained to stay within--or in any event close to--the attractive potential sites representing the ions of the lattice. This case is referred to as the *tight-binding approximation*. In Figure 8.6 the lightly drawn straight line of near-zero slope illustrates the tight-binding limit, while the steeply sloped line shows the free-electron approximation. We shall now explore both of these limiting cases in the context of the Kronig-Penney potential model.

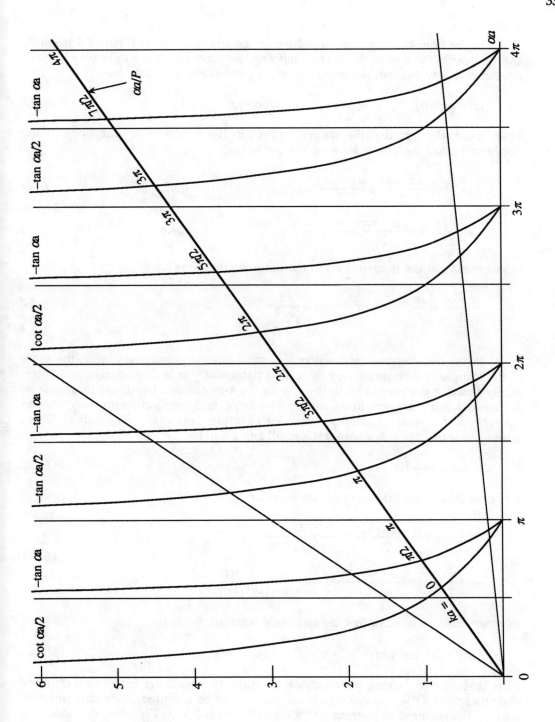

Figure 8.6 Function plots needed for illustrating graphical solutions of transcendental equations shown in text. Straight lines of very small and very steep slope illustrate (respectively) the tight binding and free-electron limits.

In the tight binding case, the slope of the straight line in Figure 8.6 is small, and its intersections with the curves defining the band edges are only very slightly smaller than $n\pi$. We can therefore introduce a small angle θ such that

$$\alpha a = n\pi - \theta, \qquad \text{where} \qquad \theta = \alpha a - n\pi \ll \pi/2 . \qquad (8.5\text{-}17)$$

Then, using the fact that the tangent curves in the figure have unit slope in the neighborhood of the points $\alpha a = n\pi$, we can write

$$\cot\frac{\theta}{2} = \cot\frac{n\pi - \alpha a}{2} \cong \frac{n\pi - \alpha a}{2} , \qquad (n = 1,3,5,\dots)$$

and

$$-\tan\frac{\theta}{2} = -\tan\frac{n\pi - \alpha a}{2} \cong \frac{n\pi - \alpha a}{2} , \qquad (n = 2,4,6,\dots) . \qquad (8.5\text{-}18)$$

In either case, at the intersections in the diagram, we must have

$$\frac{n\pi - \alpha a}{2} = \frac{\alpha a}{P} , \qquad \text{or} \qquad \alpha a = \frac{n\pi}{1+\dfrac{2}{P}} . \qquad (8.5\text{-}19)$$

In the free-electron case, where P is small and αa is relatively large, the slope of the straight line becomes very large, and particularly at higher energies, the intersections clearly get very close to $(n-1)\pi$ for the n-th allowed band. At these points, the tangent and cotangent functions are very large, and their values are very close to the *reciprocal* of the arguments--since, for example, $\cot x \cong 1/x$ for small x. Then, writing $\alpha a = (n-1)\pi + \theta$, where θ is a small angle defined by

$$\theta = \alpha a - (n-1)\pi , \qquad (8.5\text{-}20)$$

it is clear that at the intersections, we must have

$$\cot\frac{\theta}{2} = \cot\frac{\alpha a - (n-1)\pi}{2} \cong \frac{2}{\alpha a - (n-1)\pi} = \frac{\alpha a}{P} , \qquad (n = 1,3,5,\dots)$$

or,

$$-\tan\frac{\theta}{2} = -\tan\frac{\alpha a - (n-1)\pi}{2} \cong \frac{2}{\alpha a - (n-1)\pi} = \frac{\alpha a}{P} , \qquad (n = 2,4,6,\dots) . \qquad (8.5\text{-}21)$$

In either case, we observe that the quadratic equation

$$(\alpha a)^2 - (n-1)\pi \cdot (\alpha a) - 2P = 0 \qquad (8.5\text{-}22)$$

must be satiisfied. Using the quadratic formula, two roots are found, but only the one arising from the positive sign of the radical can be accepted, since only this root leads to the required answer $\alpha a = (n-1)\pi$ in the limit $P = 0$. Choosing this root, and using the result $(1 + x)^{1/2} \cong 1 + (x/2)$ suggested by the binomial theorem to simplify it in the case where $P/(\alpha a) \cong P/(n-1)\pi$ is small, as in the free-electron limit, we find

$$\frac{\alpha a}{(n-1)\pi} = \frac{1}{2} + \frac{1}{2}\sqrt{1 + \frac{8P}{(n-1)^2\pi^2}} \cong 1 + \frac{2P}{(n-1)^2\pi^2} .$$ (8.5-23)

In (8.5 - 10) it is clear that we are going to have to evaluate the quantity

$$\frac{df}{d(\alpha a)} = \frac{P}{\alpha a}\cos\alpha a - \left(\frac{P}{(\alpha a)^2} + 1\right)\sin\alpha a$$ (8.5-24)

at the band edge points. At the top edges, this presents no problem, but at the bottom edges, it is advantageous to transform this expression to a simpler form before proceeding further. To do this, it is first necessary to recall the trigonometric relations

$$\sin^2\theta = \frac{\tan^2\theta}{1 + \tan^2\theta} \quad \text{and} \quad \cos^2\theta = \frac{1}{1 + \tan^2\theta}$$ (8.5-25)

that permit us to express sine and cosine functions in terms of tangents. It is also necessary to write αa as $2(\alpha a/2)$, and express $\cos\alpha a$ and $\sin\alpha a$ as

$$\cos\alpha a = \cos^2\tfrac{1}{2}\alpha a - \sin^2\tfrac{1}{2}\alpha a = \frac{1 - \tan^2\frac{1}{2}\alpha a}{1 + \tan^2\frac{1}{2}\alpha a}$$

and (8.5-26)

$$\sin\alpha a = 2\sin\tfrac{1}{2}\alpha a\cos\tfrac{1}{2}\alpha a = \frac{2\tan\frac{1}{2}\alpha a}{1 + \tan^2\frac{1}{2}\alpha a} .$$

Substituting these relationships into (8.5 - 24), expressing $\tan(\alpha a/2)$ in terms of the quantity $(\alpha a/P)$ or its reciprocal with the help of (8.5 - 14) (n odd) or (8.5 - 15) (n even), and doing some tedious but relatively straightforward algebra, one can show that at the *lower* band edge points (8.5 - 24) can be expressed as

$$\left(\frac{df}{d(\alpha a)}\right)_b = \pm\frac{P}{\alpha a}\left[1 + \frac{2}{P}\cdot\frac{(P/\alpha a)^2}{1 + (P/\alpha a)^2}\right], \quad \begin{array}{l} + n \text{ even} \\ - n \text{ odd} \end{array} .$$ (8.5-27)

Now, $df/d\varepsilon$ follows as

$$\left(\frac{df}{d\varepsilon}\right)_b = \left(\frac{df}{d(\alpha a)}\cdot\frac{d(\alpha a)}{d\varepsilon}\right)_b = \frac{ma^2}{\hbar^2}\cdot\frac{1}{\alpha a}\left(\frac{df}{d(\alpha a)}\right)_b .$$ (8.5-28)

Substituting (8.5 - 27) into this equation and the resulting expression into (8.5 - 10) we obtain finally, for the lower band edges

$$\left(\frac{d^2\varepsilon}{dk^2}\right)_b = \frac{\hbar^2}{m}\cdot\frac{(\alpha a)^2}{P\left[1 + \frac{2}{P}\cdot\frac{(P/\alpha a)^2}{1 + (P/\alpha a)^2}\right]} .$$ (8.5-29)

The above expression is always positive, for n even or odd. It is assumed, however, in this equation, that αa is evaluated only at the lower band edges. It is important to note that no approximations were made in deriving it. It is thus true not only in the tight binding and free-electron limits, but also in the intermediate region where things are more complex. However, it contains the ratio $P/\alpha a$, which can be found only by solving a transcendental equation like (8.5 - 14) or (8.5 - 15). In this ratio, P is known and one must solve for αa. Since the transcendental equations cannot be solved algebraically, one must find *approximate* relationships between P and αa like (8.5 - 19) and (8.5 - 23) that hold for certain specific cases, before one can substitute into (8.5 - 29). The expression $(P/\alpha a)^2/[1 + (P/\alpha a)^2]$ in the denominator above approaches zero in the free-electron limit in which $P \ll \alpha a$, and unity in the tight binding case, where $P \gg \alpha a$. Moreover, its value differs from these limiting values only by the *square* of the small quantity $P/\alpha a$ (free-electron) or $\alpha a/P$ (tight binding), as the reader can easily verify as an exercise. These limits can therefore be regarded as exact in comparison with the approximations (8.5 - 19) and (8.5 - 23), which contain first-order terms in these ratios.

If we use the limiting value unity for this expression, and use (8.5 -19) to express the relationship between αa and P, we can write for the tight binding case,

$$\left(\frac{df}{d\varepsilon}\right)_b = \pm\frac{ma^2}{\hbar^2}\frac{P}{(\alpha a)^2}\left(1+\frac{2}{P}\right) = \pm\frac{ma^2}{\hbar^2}\frac{P}{(n\pi)^2}\left(1+\frac{2}{P}\right)^3 \cdot \begin{array}{l} + \; n \text{ even} \\ - \; n \text{ odd} \end{array}, \tag{8.5-30}$$

and

$$\left(\frac{d^2\varepsilon}{dk^2}\right)_b = \frac{\hbar^2(n\pi)^2}{mP\left[1+(2/P)\right]^3} . \tag{8.5-31}$$

An approximate expression for the tight binding dispersion relation is also easily obtained. It is clear from Figure 8.2 that $f(\alpha a)$ varies almost linearly with the variable αa within the first few allowed bands, where the the tight-binding approximation is satisfied. As a function of energy, $f(\varepsilon)$ would according to (8.3 - 4) vary as the square root of ε in this region. However, the square root is a slowly-varying function, which can often be approximated by a linear relationship, particularly over an interval in which the fractional change in the argument is small, as is the case for the first few allowed bands shown in the diagram. It is therefore a good approximation to write $f(\varepsilon)$ as a Taylor's expansion in powers of energy, and to retain only the first two terms--a constant plus a term linear in energy. We are therefore led to write

$$f(\varepsilon) = f(\varepsilon_b)+\left(\frac{df}{d\varepsilon}\right)_b(\varepsilon - \varepsilon_b)+\cdots = \cos ka . \tag{8.5-32}$$

In this expression, the subscript b refers to the *lower* band edge. From Figure 8.2, we see that $f(\varepsilon_b) = \pm 1$ (+ when n is odd, − when n is even), and from the above work, it is clear that if we retain only the first two terms we can write

$$f(\varepsilon) = \mp 1\pm\frac{1}{C_n}(\varepsilon - \varepsilon_b) = \cos ka , \tag{8.5-33}$$

the upper signs being used for n odd, the lower ones for n even. The constants C_n are given by

$$\frac{1}{C_n} = \frac{ma^2}{\hbar^2} \frac{P}{(n\pi)^2}\left(1 + \frac{2}{P}\right)^3 . \tag{8.5-34}$$

Solving (8.5 - 33) for $\varepsilon - \varepsilon_b$, we see, with the aid of Figure 8.2, that

$$\varepsilon - \varepsilon_b = C_n(1 - \cos ka) \qquad ((n-1)\pi < ka < n\pi) \quad (n \text{ odd})$$

and

$$\varepsilon - \varepsilon_b = C_n(1 + \cos ka) \qquad ((n-1)\pi < ka < n\pi) \quad (n \text{ even}) . \tag{8.5-35}$$

This dispersion relation is plotted for the lowest allowed bands ($n = 1$ and 2) in Figure 8.7. Since (as you can see in the diagram) $\cos ka$ is positive in the intervals encompassing bands $n = 1, 3, 5, \ldots$, and negative in those for which $n = 2, 4, 6, \ldots$, the functions $1 - \cos ka$ and $1 + \cos ka$ in (8.5 - 35) are of exactly the same graphical form in their respective domains. Indeed, if you write $ka = ka - (n - 1)\pi + (n - 1)\pi$,

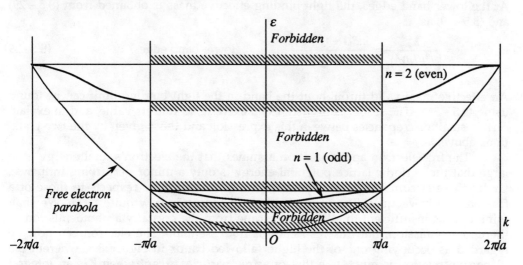

Figure 8.7 Lowest allowed bands ($n = 1$ and 2) in a system in which the tight-binding approximation is justified. Forbidden regions are broad in comparison with allowed bands, αa is quite close to $n\pi$ at all points in the allowed bands, and the dispersion relation depends on $1 \pm \cos ka$ as illustrated.

you can write the relationship given by (8.5 - 35) as a single expression of the form

$$\varepsilon - \varepsilon_b = C_n[1 - \cos(ka - (n - 1)\pi)] . \tag{8.5-36}$$

We shall find these approximate dispersion relations extremely useful in future investigations concerning electrons in two- and three-dimensional lattices.

So far, we have focused on the lower edges of allowed bands at $ka = (n - 1)\pi$. Fortunately, things are much simpler near the top edges at $ka = n\pi$. At these points

$\alpha a = ka = n\pi$, and $\sin \alpha a$ vanishes. As always, the derivative $d\varepsilon/dk$ vanishes, while the second derivative follows from (8.5 - 10) by substituting $\sin \alpha a = 0$, $\cos \alpha a = \pm 1$, as

$$\left(\frac{d^2\varepsilon}{dk^2}\right)_b = -\frac{\hbar^2(n\pi)^2}{mP} \qquad \text{(upper band edges) .} \qquad (8.5\text{-}37)$$

This relationship is a general one for the upper edges of the allowed bands, and is valid not only for the free-electron and tight binding cases, but in the complex intermediate region as well. The negative sign indicates a negative effective mass, and signifies that holes rather than electrons are to be regarded as the current carriers. The effective mass can be expressed as

$$m* = \frac{\hbar^2}{\left(d^2\varepsilon/dk^2\right)_b} = -\frac{mP}{(n\pi)^2} \qquad \text{(upper band edges) .} \qquad (8.5\text{-}38)$$

At the lower band edges, the tight binding effective mass is obtained from (8.5 - 29) and (8.5 - 19) as

$$m* = \frac{\hbar^2}{\left(d^2\varepsilon/dk^2\right)_b} = \frac{mP[1 + (2/P)]^3}{(n\pi)^2} . \qquad \text{(lower band edges) .} \qquad (8.5\text{-}39)$$

An effective mass valid throughout the band in the tight binding limit can be found using (8.5 - 35). The reader is invited, as an exercise, to find its value, and to explain certain small discrepancies between this expression and those given by the two equations above.

The free-electron approximation assumes that the electron's total energy is so large that the periodic lattice potential energy is only a minor perturbing influence. Under these circumstances, its dynamics are similar in most respects to those of a free particle in vacuum. The electron's kinetic energy is now quite large. We shall think of it as insufficient to allow it to escape from the crystal via photoemission or thermionic emission, but this restriction is not essential. The electron can now be regarded as occupying one of the higher allowed bands in Figure 8.3, wherein the dispersion relation is much like that of a free particle, except when k is an integral multiple of π/a and Bragg reflection by the atoms of the lattice occurs, which we shall assume at first is not the case. The free-electron limit in general prevails when the quantity $P/\alpha a$ is small--that is, when P is small or αa is large. In either case, the term $P \sin \alpha a/\alpha a$ in (8.5 - 2) will be small, and can ordinarily be neglected, in which case

$$\cos \alpha a = \cos ka , \qquad \text{or} \qquad \alpha = k , \qquad (8.5\text{-}40)$$

The dispersion relation then, according to (8.3 - 4), reduces essentially to that of a free particle with mass equal to the electron's inertial mass,

$$\varepsilon = \frac{\hbar^2 k^2}{2m} . \qquad (8.5\text{-}41)$$

This argument is no longer valid near the band edges, where k is an integral multiple of π/a and $\cos ka = 0$. In these regions, all three terms in (8.5 - 2) are small, and the situation is much more complex. The form of the dispersion relation, as expressed by a Taylor's series about the points $ka = n\pi$ has already been exhibited as (8.5 - 8); since $d\varepsilon/dk$ is zero at these points, the linear term in $(k - (n\pi/a))$ is absent. To obtain the dispersion relation explicitly, it is necessary only to evaluate the second derivative $d^2\varepsilon/dk^2$ at the band edge points, using (8.5 - 10). This derivative has already been found at the upper edges of the allowed bands, where $ka = \alpha a = n\pi$, and has been written as (8.5 - 38). The only additional information needed is the value of the second derivative at the lower edges of the allowed bands.

In the free-electron limit, the term in brackets in the denominator of (8.5 - 29) reduces to unity when $P/(\alpha a)$ is small, and the value of αa itself is given approximately by (8.5 - 23). Equation (8.5 - 29) then reduces to

$$\left(\frac{d^2\varepsilon}{dk^2}\right)_b = \frac{\hbar^2}{m}\cdot\frac{(\alpha a)^2}{P} = \frac{\hbar^2(n-1)^2\pi^2}{mP}\left(1+\frac{4P}{(n-1)^2\pi^2}\right) \cong \frac{\hbar^2(n-1)^2\pi^2}{mP} \quad \text{(lower band edges)} .$$

$$(8.5 - 42)$$

In writing this expression, a term involving $P^2/(n-1)^2\pi^2$ that appears when αa is squared has been neglected. The final simplified form of this equation can be used when the second term in parentheses above is so small as to be negligible, or in any event as a rough approximation. Using this final form of the result above, the effective mass at the lower band edges is

$$m* = \frac{\hbar^2}{\left(d^2\varepsilon/dk^2\right)_b} = \frac{mP}{(n-1)^2\pi^2} .$$

$$(8.5 - 43)$$

It is difficult to write a free-electron dispersion relation that will be valid over an entire allowed band as in the tight binding model, since the function $f(\varepsilon)$ is now sharply curved within the band and cannot easily be approximated by an expansion such as (8.5 - 32). The overall picture is, however, easy to describe; the dispersion relation in the immediate vicinity of the band edge points is parabolic, and has an effective mass given by (8.5 - 38) at the top and (8.5 - 43) at the bottom. These parabolic band edge regions are very narrow, however, and as one moves away from the band edge there is a quick transition to a situation in which (8.5 - 40) is valid. A dispersion relation of the form (8.5 - 41), wherein the effective mass equals the electron's inertial mass, then takes over and occupies most of the band. The picture is like that illustrated in the highest allowed band shown in Figure 8.3. When P is quite small, the electron is very "light" in the immediate vicinity of the band edges, but quickly recovers its "normal" mass as one moves away from these points.

The free-electron and tight binding cases are discussed in this book in the context of the Kronig-Penney model, but similar results follow from more general treatments based on periodic potentials of arbitrary form. In the tight binding case these treatments start with periodic potentials derived from atomic wave functions. The tight binding dispersion relations that result have the same form as (8.5 - 35), except that the constants C_n are complex integrals that involve products of wave functions of adjacent atoms with the periodic potential.

8.6 ELECTRONS IN TWO AND THREE DIMENSIONAL LATTICES; BRILLOUIN ZONES AND FERMI SURFACES

In quantum theory, three-dimensional potential functions having the property

$$V(x,y,z) = V_x(x) + V_y(y) + V_z(z) \tag{8.6-1}$$

lead to solutions of a particularly simple form. To see this more clearly, let us assume that the three functions on the right, each of which depends only on one of the three coördinates, are known to satisfy one-dimensional Schrödinger equations, as follows:

$$\left[-\frac{\hbar^2}{2m}\frac{\partial^2}{\partial x^2} + V_x(x)\right]\psi_x(x) = \varepsilon_x\,\psi_x(x)\,,$$

$$\left[-\frac{\hbar^2}{2m}\frac{\partial^2}{\partial y^2} + V_y(y)\right]\psi_y(y) = \varepsilon_y\,\psi_y(y)\,, \tag{8.6-2}$$

and $$\left[-\frac{\hbar^2}{2m}\frac{\partial^2}{\partial z^2} + V_z(z)\right]\psi_z(z) = \varepsilon_z\,\psi_z(z)\,,$$

where ε_x, ε_y, and ε_z are energy eigenvalues of the respective operators on the left. If we now multiply the the top equation by $\psi_y(y)\psi_z(z)$, the second by $\psi_x(x)\psi_z(z)$, and the third by $\psi_x(x)\psi_y(y)$, and add them up, we find (observing that $\psi_y\psi_z$ is regarded as a constant by the operator $\partial/\partial x$, etc.), that

$$\left[-\frac{\hbar^2}{2m}\left(\frac{\partial^2}{\partial x^2} + \frac{\partial^2}{\partial x^2} + \frac{\partial^2}{\partial x^2}\right) + \left(V_x(x) + V_y(y) + V_z(z)\right)\right]\psi_x\psi_y\psi_z = (\varepsilon_x + \varepsilon_y + \varepsilon_z)\,\psi_x\psi_y\psi_z\,. \tag{8.6-3}$$

From this it is easy to see that the product function $\psi_x\psi_y\psi_z$ is a solution of the three-dimensional Schrödinger equation with the potential (8.6 - 1), and that the allowed energies are simply the *sum* of the energy eigenvalues associated with the three one-dimensional problems in (8.6 - 2). We have already seen an example of how this works in Chapter 5, (Section 5.3) in connection with the eigenvalues of the three-dimensional harmonic oscillator; you may wish to review this topic if you've forgotten it. It is easy to see, in any case, that if you know the solutions to two one-dimensional potentials $V_1(x)$ and $V_2(y)$, the solution to a two-dimensional problem in which the potential is $V_1(x) + V_2(y)$ can be expressed as products of the eigenfunctions of the two one-dimensional problem, and the energy eigenvalues as the *sum* of those pertaining to the two one-dimensional problems.

This result can be used in conjunction with the Kronig-Penney potential to generate solutions of two- and three-dimensional problems involving periodic potentials derived from that used in the one-dimensional calculation. For example, if you add two one-dimensional Kronig-Penney potentials, one depending on x, the other having exactly the same functional dependence on y, you will arrive at the two-dimensional potential illustrated in Figure 8.8. Moreover, from the above work, it is clear that the allowed energies--energies that depend on k_x and k_y--will be the *sum* of those described (assuming the tight binding approximation is valid) by two separate one-dimensional dispersion relations of the form (8.5 - 35). We shall assume for simplicity in this work that the tight binding approximation can be used.

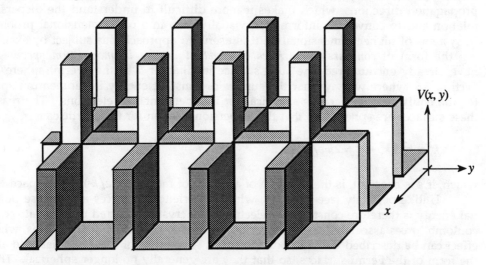

Figure 8.8 Surface illustrating the sum of two similar Kronig-Penney potential functions having arguments x and y, respectively. The spikes will invert into wells when this function is multiplied by the electron charge $q = -e$. It is clear that the result will contain an array of potential wells for electrons, located at the lattice sites, in either two or three dimensions. It can therefore be used as the basis for a reasonable physical model of a one-electron periodic crystal potential.

Using these arguments, and provided that the conditions of the tight binding model are satisfied, we can write the dispersion relation (8.5 - 35) for the lowest band ($n = 1$) in a two-dimensional simple square lattice of interatomic spacing as

$$\varepsilon(k_x, k_y) = 2\varepsilon_b + C_1(2 - \cos k_x a - \cos k_y a) , \quad (-\pi < k_x a, k_y a < \pi) \quad . \tag{8.6-4}$$

In a three-dimensional simple cubic lattice of the same interatomic spacing, defined in a similar way, the dispersion relation would clearly be given by

$$\varepsilon(k_x, k_y, k_z) = 3\varepsilon_b + C_1(3 - \cos k_x a - \cos k_y a - \cos k_z a) , \quad (-\pi < k_x a, k_y a, k_z a < \pi). \tag{8.6-5}$$

The crystal momentum is now described by a propagation vector $\mathbf{k}$ such that

$$\mathbf{k} = \mathbf{i}_x k_x + \mathbf{i}_y k_y + \mathbf{i}_z k_z , \qquad \text{with} \qquad k^2 = k_x^2 + k_y^2 + k_z^2 \quad . \tag{8,6-6}$$

The constant C_1 is defined by (8.5 - 34) as

$$\frac{1}{C_1} = \frac{ma^2 P}{\pi^2 \hbar^2}\left(1 + \frac{2}{P}\right)^3 \cong \frac{ma^2 P}{\pi^2 \hbar^2} \quad . \tag{8.6-7}$$

It is also assumed that the potentials are defined in the limit discussed in the preceding section, in which the potential wells become very deep and narrow such that the previously defined "scattering power" P remains constant. Under these circumstances, the functional dependence of energy on wave vector can be different in different propagation directions, which makes it more difficult to understand the dispersion relation and to convey its information visually than in a one-dimensional problem. In systems of higher dimensionality, it is useful to approach this subject by examining the form of *contours or surfaces of constant energy in momentum space*. We have already encountered one such surface in Chapter 5 as the "Fermi sphere" of Section 5.6, where we saw that the surface of constant energy in momentum space (or the equivalent k-space) is spherical for independent free electrons. The reason these surfaces are spherical is that the dispersion relation for free particles is

$$k^2 = k_x^2 + k_y^2 + k_z^2 = 2m\varepsilon/\hbar^2 \quad , \tag{8.6-8}$$

which, if ε is constant, is the equation of a sphere of radius $(2m\varepsilon/\hbar^2)^{1/2}$ in k-space.

Unlike perfectly free particles, which experience no forces and whose potential energy is therefore constant, the electrons in a crystal are acted upon by attractive coulomb forces associated with the periodic lattice of positively charged ions, whose effect can be described by a periodic potential. The effect of this potential is to alter the form of the Fermi surfaces, so that they are generally no longer spherical. Their form thus reflects in some hard-to-define way the form of the periodic lattice potential. The Kronig-Penney potential shown in Figure 8.8 is admittedly not a very realistic model of such a potential, but it *is* periodic with lattice periodicity, and it *does* have deep, attractive potential wells in the right places. It is these features that determine the gross features of the dispersion relation, and for this reason the KP model works better than one might expect at first sight.

We shall begin by examining the two-dimensional case described by (8.6 - 4). In this instance, the ε versus k relation along either k_x or k_y looks much like the lower curve shown in Figure 8.7, and the absolute minimum allowed energy in the band is at the point $k_x = k_y = 0$, a fact that can be established from (8.6 - 8) by observing that both $\partial e/\partial k_x$ and $\partial e/\partial k_y$ are zero at that point. At this point, the energy is $2\varepsilon_b$, where the value of ε_b, as obtained from (8.5 - 19) and (8.3 - 4) is

$$\varepsilon_b = \frac{\pi^2 \hbar^2}{2ma^2(1 + (2/P))^2} \cong \frac{\pi^2 \hbar^2}{2ma^2} \ . \tag{8.6-9}$$

As the energy rises above this minimum value, the crystal momentum also increases and the components k_x and k_y are now greater than zero; if the electron is still quite close to the bottom of the allowed band, $k_x a$ and $k_y a$ are much less than π, which allows us to approximate the cosines in (8.6 - 4) by the first two terms of their power series expansions, and write, after rearranging terms,

$$k_x^2 + k_y^2 = \frac{2}{C_1 a^2}(\varepsilon - 2\varepsilon_b) \ . \tag{8.6-10}$$

For constant values of ε, this is the equation of a circle in the k-plane whose radius is the square root of the quantity on the right side of the expression. As the energy ε increses, the radius of this circle will expand. The contours of constant energy are--for small energies--circles whose radius increases with increasing energy. These "Fermi contours" are illustrated in Figure 8.9.

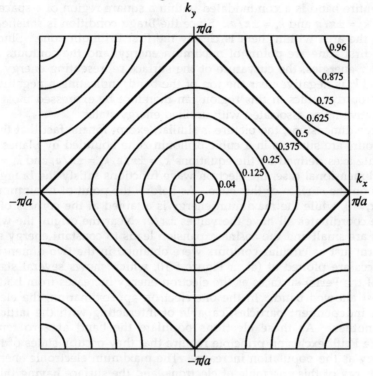

Figure 8.9 Tight binding constant-energy contours for the lowest energy band of a two-dimensional simple square lattice. The numbers indicate the energies associated with the contours expressed as fractions of the total energy width of the allowed band.

As the energy and wave vector components increase, a point is reached where it is no longer a good approximation to represent the cosine by the first two terms of its power series, and the contours are no longer circular, but become distorted as shown. One must then revert to the exact dispersion relation (8.6 - 4), assuming some constant value for ε, choosing values for k_x and solving the resulting equation for $\cos k_y a$ to obtain the coördinates of points on the contour. The procedure is tedious, but straightforward, and leads to the set of contours shown in the figure. The numbers index the energy associated with the individual contours, expressed as a fractional part of the total width (in energy) of the band, which can be seen from (8.6 - 4) to be $4C_1$. The contours of lowest energy are almost circular, but over much of the band are of a very different form, because of the electron-lattice interaction. However, near the very top of the band, the contours again become nearly circular--though in the form of four separate quarter-circles that could be assembled into a single circle by translating three of them through horizontal or vertical distances equal to $2\pi/a$--a maneuver that is quite permissible in view of the periodicity of the lattice and the cosine functions in (8.6 - 4). The reader is asked as an exercise to show that these contours are in fact circular and to find their radii. When the energy is at the midpoint of the band, the contour degenerates into the square labeled 0.5 in the figure. The reader should also be able to demonstrate this fact from the ε versus $\mathbf{k}$ relation (8.6 - 4).

The entire band is accommodated within a square region of k-space bounded by the lines $k_x = \pm\pi/a$ and $k_y = \pm\pi/a$. Since the Bragg condition is satisfied on these boundaries, the area within them is clearly the first Brillouin zone. Since the corners of this first zone are points of maximum energy, and the contours near them are at smaller energies, the curvature of the surface representing energy as a function of k_x and k_y is negative near the top of the band, indicating a negative effective mass. Electron dynamics in this region can therefore be expressed most simply in terms of positive holes associated with unfilled energy states.

In three dimensions, the picture is similar, except for the fact that the constant energy contours are surfaces in a cubic Brillouin zone bounded by planes normal to the coördinate axes defined by the equations $k_x = \pm\pi/a$, $k_y = \pm\pi/a$, and $k_z = \pm\pi/a$. As in the two-dimensional case, the electron wave functions satisfy the Bragg condition at all points on the surface of this cube. As before, the point of minimum energy is at $k_x = k_y = k_z = 0$, while the maximum energy is attained at the corners of the cube, where these coordinates all have the values $\pm\pi/a$. Near the origin, the wave vector components are small and the cosine expansion leads to constant energy surfaces of spherical form just as circular contours were obtained in the two-dimensional case. These surfaces are plotted at (a) in Figure 8.10, which shows several stages of the expansion of the Fermi surfaces as the electron energy increases from bottom to top of the lowest allowed band. In the one-electron approximation, the electrons are regarded as independent particles, capable of interacting with the lattice, but not with one another. As these electrons populate the band at zero temperature, therefore, the Pauli exclusion principle require that they occupy states of higher and higher energy as the population increases. The maximum electronic energy is then the Fermi energy of this ensemble of electrons, and the surface having this constant energy is the Fermi surface of the electron distribution.

As more electrons populate the band in such a process, the initially spherical surfaces distort in accord with the ε versus k relation (8.6 - 5), as illustrated in the figure. The drawing at (b) is typical of the situation in which the Fermi energy is less than one-third of the energy difference $6C_1$ between the maximum and minimum energies in the allowed band. When the Fermi energy is exactly $2C_1$ above the minimum the condition shown at (c) is reached. In this figure we see an octahedron with sharp points that touch the centers of the cube faces. The surfaces of the octahedron, however, are not planes, but surfaces that bulge outward slightly. As the energy difference exceeds this amount, but remains less than $4C_1$, the Fermi surfaces have the odd form shown at (d). At an energy difference of exactly $4C_1$, two-thirds of the difference between the maximum and minimum points, the condition shown at (e) is attained--a collection of eight sheets that look much like the surfaces of the octahedron at (c), except that they bulge inward, toward the center of the zone, rather than outward. Finally, near the maximum allowed energy, these eight sheets approach the form of spherical segments that can be assembled by translating them along the axes through appropriate distances into a single spherical surface that looks much like the one at (a).

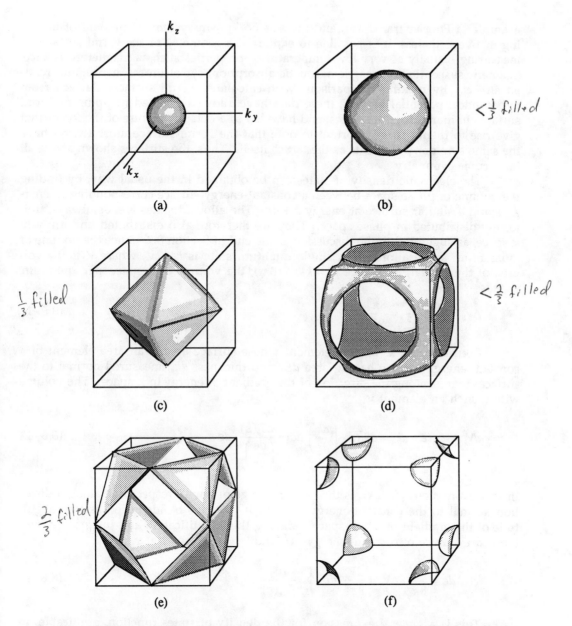

Figure 8.10 Successive stages in the growth of the Fermi surface of a simple cubic tight binding Kronig-Penney lattice, as a function of maximum electron energy. Details regarding the individual stages of its evolution are presented in the text.

The total width of the band depends on the interaction strength P *via* the constant C_1, but the geometry of the Fermi surface itself depends otherwise only on the form of the lattice potential, independent of its strength. The Fermi surface can thus be regarded as a kind of transform of the periodic potential (and therefore the forces) experienced by the valence electrons. Unfortunately it isn't as simple as (for example) a Fourier transform, and there is no known systematic method of inverting it. Nevertheless, it is possible to explore the geometry of the Fermi surface by measuring--usually at very low temperatures--properties such as magnetoresistance, magnetic susceptibility, magnetoacoustic absorption, cyclotron resonance, and related effects. By making comparisons with calculated Fermi surfaces derived from hypothetical potential models, these data have allowed detailed mapping of Fermi surfaces in many real substances, and have led to a detailed picture of the forces that give rise to them. It is important to note that the Fermi surface must always have the same symmetry elements as the lattice itself. Thus, the surfaces shown above all have cubic symmetry.

The electronic density of states can be obtained in the usual way, by finding the volume of phase space between a constant-energy surface corresponding to energy ε and a similar surface at energy $\varepsilon + d\varepsilon$. The allowed states are, as always, uniformly distributed in phase space. They are therefore also distributed uniformly in k-space, as suggested in the discussion at the end of Section 8.2. Since the volume of momentum space alloted to a single quantum state is $h^3/2V$, where V is the volume of the crystal, and since $p^3 = k^3h^3/(8\pi^3)$, the volume of k-space per quantum state is

$$\Delta V_k = \frac{h^3}{2V} \cdot \frac{8\pi^3}{h^3} = \frac{8\pi^3}{2V} \ . \tag{8.6-11}$$

Consider now a volume element whose surface area is an area element of a constant-energy surface having area dS_k, and thickness dk_n, measured normal to the surface--that is, along the direction of the gradient of energy in k-space. The volume within such an element is

$$dV_k = dS_k(\varepsilon) \cdot dk_n = dS_k(\varepsilon) \cdot \left(\frac{dk}{d\varepsilon}\right)_n d\varepsilon = \frac{dS_k(\varepsilon)}{\left(\frac{d\varepsilon}{dk}\right)_n} \cdot d\varepsilon \ . \tag{8.6-12}$$

In this expression, $(d\varepsilon/dk)_n$ is the rate of change of ε with respect to k along a direction normal to the constant-energy surface; it can thus be identified as the magnitude of the gradient of ε in k-space. Making this identification and integrating over the entire surface of constant energy, we find

$$g(\varepsilon)d\varepsilon = \frac{2V}{8\pi^3} \cdot \Delta V_k = \frac{2V}{8\pi^3} \cdot d\varepsilon \cdot \oint_{S_k} \frac{dS_k}{|\nabla_k(\varepsilon)|} \ . \tag{8.6-13}$$

This is a general expression for the density of states function, applicable, in principle, whenever the dispersion relation giving ε as a function of k is known. It is, however, except in a few very simple cases, difficult to use and must ordinarily be evaluated numerically. In the tight binding example discussed here, this is unfortunately the case. The numerical calculations lead to a density of states function of the form shown in Figure 8.11. The cusps in this curve occur at the stages of evolution shown at (c) and (e) in Figure 8.10, at energies $2C_1$ and $4C_1$ above the minimum allowed energy in the band. Density of states curves of this general form are fairly common for simple crystal structures. For the spherical Fermi surfaces shown in

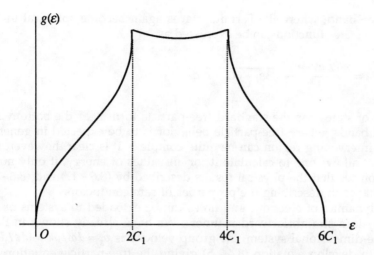

Figure 8.11 The density of states curve for the lowest allowed band in the simple cubic tight binding Kronig-Penney crystal potential model.

Figure 8.10 (a), the radius is k, independent of direction, and expanding the cosines in (8.6 - 5) yields, for small values of ka,

$$(\varepsilon - 3\varepsilon_b) = \frac{C_1 a^2}{2}(k_x^2 + k_y^2 + k_z^2) = \frac{C_1 a^2 k^2}{2} \ . \tag{8.6-14}$$

In this situation, $\nabla_k \varepsilon$ is a purely radial vector whose magnitude is $\partial \varepsilon / \partial k = C_1 a^2 k$. The surface area element dS_k, using spherical coördinates in $\mathbf{k}$-space, is $k^2 \sin\theta \, d\theta \, d\varphi$. Substituting these values into (8.5 - 13) and integrating over the angles, we find

$$g(\varepsilon)\,d\varepsilon = \frac{2V}{8\pi^3} \cdot \frac{4\pi k^2\,d\varepsilon}{C_1 a^2 k} = \frac{Vk\,d\varepsilon}{\pi^2 C_1 a^2} \ . \tag{8.6-15}$$

Expressing k in terms of ε with the help of (8.6 - 14), we obtain finally,

$$g(\varepsilon)\,d\varepsilon = \frac{\sqrt{2}\,V}{\pi^2 C_1^{3/2} a^3} \cdot \sqrt{\varepsilon - 3\varepsilon_b}\,\,d\varepsilon \ . \tag{8.6-16}$$

This looks very much like a free-electron density of states, particularly if the origin of the energy scale is taken at the band minimum $3\varepsilon_b$. Indeed, if one expresses the quantity $C_1 a^2$ in terms of the effective mass using (8.4 - 6) and (8.6 - 14), we can write

$$g(\varepsilon)\,d\varepsilon = \frac{8\sqrt{2}\,\pi V m*^{3/2}}{h^3}\sqrt{\varepsilon - 3\varepsilon_b}\,\,d\varepsilon \ , \tag{8.6-17}$$

which is the standard free-particle density of states function with an effective mass defined by (8.4 - 6). The reader is asked as an excercise, to show for the region near the top of the band, where the Fermi surfaces again become spherical in form, that the density of states function can be expressed as

$$g(\varepsilon)d\varepsilon = \frac{8\sqrt{2}\,\pi V m*^{3/2}}{h^3}\sqrt{3\varepsilon_b + 6C_1 - \varepsilon}\;d\varepsilon\;.$$

(8.6 - 18)

The density of states has the standard free-particle form near the bottom and top of the allowed bands, where free-particle behavior is to be expected in general, but its form in the intervening region can be quite complex. It is clear, however, that equation (8.6 - 13) allows one to calculate it for all values of energy, if only numerically. We shall soon see that the physical results described by (8.6 - 17) and (8.6 - 18) are of great importance in describing the properties of semiconductors.

The dynamics of electrons and holes can be extended to systems of higher dimensionality in a straightforward manner. We have already shown in Section 8.4, that in a one-dimensional system, the group velocity is $v_g = d\omega/dk = (d\varepsilon/dk)/\hbar$. This allowed us to develop equation (8.4 - 5) giving the free-particle equation of motion as

$$\frac{dv_g}{dt} = \frac{1}{\hbar}\cdot\frac{d}{dt}\left(\frac{d\varepsilon}{dk}\right) = \frac{F_e}{m*}\;.$$

(8.6 - 19)

The obvious generalization of the group velocity to three dimensions is

$$\mathbf{v}_g = \frac{1}{\hbar}\nabla_k\varepsilon\;.$$

(8.6 - 20)

This, along with (8.6 - 19) suggests that we write the equation of motion as

$$\frac{d\mathbf{v}_g}{dt} = \frac{1}{\hbar}\cdot\frac{d}{dt}(\nabla_k\varepsilon)\;,$$

(8.6 - 21)

an equation which in the above form is not very useful. Suppose, now, that $\mathbf{A}$ is a vector whose components are functions of the k-space coördinates. The time-derivative of the x-component of $\mathbf{A}$ can be expressed as

$$\frac{dA_x}{dt} = \frac{\partial A_x}{\partial k_x}\frac{dk_x}{dt} + \frac{\partial A_x}{\partial k_y}\frac{dk_y}{dt} + \frac{\partial A_x}{\partial k_z}\frac{dk_z}{dt} = (\nabla_k A_x)\cdot\frac{d\mathbf{k}}{dt}\;.$$

(8.6 - 22)

This suggests that the time derivative of the vector $\mathbf{A}$ might be expressed as the scalar product of vector $d\mathbf{k}/dt$ with the k-space gradient of the vector $\mathbf{A}$, thus,

$$\frac{d\mathbf{A}}{dt} = (\nabla_k\mathbf{A})\cdot\frac{d\mathbf{k}}{dt}\;.$$

(8.6 - 23)

There is a slight problem here, in that one usually sees the gradient operator acting on a scalar and creating a vector. In this case, it acts on a *vector*, which transforms it into a second-rank *tensor*, having nine components indexed by all possible combinations of the (x, y, z) components of $\mathbf{A}$ and the coördinates (k_x, k_y, k_z) with respect to which the derivatives in the gradient are to be taken. Such a tensor can best be regarded as a matrix whose elements transform with respect to coördinate rotations in essentially the same way as vector components. Scalar products can then be evaluated simply as *matrix products*. When the scalar product of two tensors is taken the result is another tensor. When the scalar product of a vector and a tensor is to be found, one writes the vector as a row matrix when it is the first factor in the product or a column matrix if it is second, and then performs the matrix multiplication as usual to obtain a vector. It is important to observe that *none* of these scalar products are commutative. The tensor $\nabla_k \mathbf{A}$ can thus be written in matrix form as

$$\nabla_k \mathbf{A} = \begin{bmatrix} \dfrac{\partial A_x}{\partial k_x} & \dfrac{\partial A_y}{\partial k_x} & \dfrac{\partial A_z}{\partial k_x} \\[2mm] \dfrac{\partial A_x}{\partial k_y} & \dfrac{\partial A_y}{\partial k_y} & \dfrac{\partial A_z}{\partial k_y} \\[2mm] \dfrac{\partial A_x}{\partial k_z} & \dfrac{\partial A_y}{\partial k_z} & \dfrac{\partial A_z}{\partial k_z} \end{bmatrix} . \tag{8.6-24}$$

Returning to (8.6 - 21), we may now replace the time derivative of the vector $\nabla_k \varepsilon$ with the equivalent expression given by (8.6 - 23), to obtain

$$\frac{d\mathbf{v}_g}{dt} = \frac{1}{\hbar}(\nabla_k \nabla_k \varepsilon) \cdot \frac{1}{\hbar}\frac{d(\hbar \mathbf{k})}{dt} = \frac{1}{\hbar^2}(\nabla_k \nabla_k \varepsilon) \cdot \mathbf{F}_e . \tag{8.6-25}$$

This is a Newtonian free-particle equation of motion of the form $d\mathbf{v}_g/dt = \mathbf{F}_e/m^*$; interpreted this way, it is apparent that the inverse effective mass $1/m^*$ is no longer an isotropic scalar, but is instead a tensor. Since the components of $\nabla_k \varepsilon$ are $\partial/\partial k_x$, $\partial/\partial k_y$, and $\partial/\partial k_z$, this tensor can be seen from (8.6 - 24) to have the form,

$$\frac{1}{\mathbf{m}^*} = \frac{1}{\hbar^2} \begin{bmatrix} \dfrac{\partial^2 \varepsilon}{\partial k_x^2} & \dfrac{\partial^2 \varepsilon}{\partial k_x \partial k_y} & \dfrac{\partial^2 \varepsilon}{\partial k_x \partial k_z} \\[2mm] \dfrac{\partial^2 \varepsilon}{\partial k_y \partial k_x} & \dfrac{\partial^2 \varepsilon}{\partial k_y^2} & \dfrac{\partial^2 \varepsilon}{\partial k_y \partial k_z} \\[2mm] \dfrac{\partial^2 \varepsilon}{\partial k_z \partial k_x} & \dfrac{\partial^2 \varepsilon}{\partial k_z \partial k_y} & \dfrac{\partial^2 \varepsilon}{\partial k_z^2} \end{bmatrix} . \tag{8.6-26}$$

The elements of the inverse mass tensor can also be written individually as

$$\left(\frac{1}{m^*}\right)_{\alpha\beta} = \frac{1}{\hbar^2}\left(\frac{\partial^2 \varepsilon}{\partial k_\alpha \partial k_\beta}\right) , \tag{8.6-27}$$

where the indices α and β can take on the "values" x, y, and z representing coördinate directions in k-space. The tensor representing the effective mass is usually written in the inverse form shown above, purely as a matter of convenience. The electrical conductivity and the mobility are the most conspicuous quantites that depend on effective mass, and in both cases, m^* appears in the denominator of expressions (like $\mu = e\tau/m^*$) that express them in terms of microscopic quantities. It is therefore advantageous to work with the reciprocal mass tensor from the beginning when dealing with these parameters. The tensorial nature of the effective mass is to be expected, because the effective mass is related to the curvature of the ε versus k relation, a quantity that isn't the same in all directions in anisotropic crystals.

In cubic crystals, symmetry requires that off-diagonal elements of the inverse mass tensor vanish, and that the diagonal elements be equal. Under these circumstances, the tensor is a scalar multiple of the unit tensor (whose elements are the Kronecker symbol $\delta_{\alpha\beta}$) and the effective mass is therefore isotropic. The reader is asked as an exercise to calculate all elements of the inverse mass tensor using the dispersion relation (8.6 - 5), and show that it is in fact isotropic in this instance. In non-cubic substances the anisotropy of the effective mass is responsible for the observed anisotropy of all the transport processes--in particular, electrical conductivity--that depend on particle mass. The dielectric permittivity of crystalline materials behaves similarly, being isotropic for crystals with cubic symmetry, but not for less symmetric structures. As a result, the optical properties of noncubic crystals are also anisotropic, and exhibit complex effects like double refraction.

Thus far, we have relied on intuition in defining the cubic region of k-space shown in Figure 8.10 as the first Brillouin zone, and postulating a one-to-one correspondence between allowed bands and Brillouin zones. These assignments are correct, but difficulties soon arise in finding what regions of k-space the second, third, and higher-order zones occupy. In resolving these difficulties, it is simplest to begin by considering the two-dimensional simple square lattice whose first Brillouin zone is shown in Figure 8.9. When its set of Brillouin zones is exhibited, it will be clear that the methods used to display them are easily extended to three-dimensional lattices.

Consider first an electron whose k-vector lies somewhere on the top edge of the square zone shown in Figure 8.9. The y-component of its wave vector is π/a, but the x-component may have any value k_{x0} within the range illustrated. The electron wavelength is then

$$\lambda = \frac{2\pi}{k} = \frac{2\pi}{\sqrt{k_{x0}^2 + (\pi/a)^2}} \quad , \tag{8.6-28}$$

while the sine of the glancing angle of waves incident upon crystal "planes" parallel to the x-axis is

$$\sin\theta = \frac{k_y}{\sqrt{k_x^2 + k_y^2}} = \frac{\pi/a}{\sqrt{k_{x0}^2 + (\pi/a)^2}} \quad . \tag{8.6-29}$$

It is easily seen that $2a\sin\theta = \lambda$, and that the Bragg equation (with $n = 1$) is satisfied by electrons whose k-vectors are of this form. A similar argument can be made for electrons having k-vectors that lie on the left and right sides of the zone. The electron undergoes internal Bragg reflection, therefore, whenever its k-vector touches any point on this bounding square, which clearly constitutes the first Brillouin zone, and contains the entire set of quantum states belonging to the lowest allowed band.

Points beyond this boundary in k-space are associated with states in higher allowed bands, and the number of Bragg reflections encountered in going from the origin to some given point in k-space determines *which* Brillouin zone that point belongs to. Moreover, an energy gap exists between points on opposite sides of every diffracting boundary between zones. These facts are of importance in mapping out the Brillouin zones in two- and three-dimensional structures. It is also important to note that the Brillouin zones are defined with reference to k-space, and it is therefore the reciprocal lattice, not the direct lattice of the crystal, that determines their geometry.

We have already seen in Chapter 2 (Section 2.4) that the Bragg condition can be written in terms of the wave vector of the diffracted wave and the lattice vectors of the reciprocal lattice as

$$2\mathbf{k} \cdot \mathbf{G} + G^2 = 2k_x G_x + 2k_y G_y + 2k_z G_z + G_x^2 + G_y^2 + G_z^2 = 0 \ . \tag{8.6-30}$$

This equation was originally derived in reference to X-ray scattering, but is of course applicable generally to any wave that can be Bragg reflected by the lattice. In the present context those waves are Schrödinger waves associated with the electrons; k is the wave vector--related to the crystal momentum by the de Broglie relation--that describes their propagation, and G is 2π times any lattice vector $\mathbf{r}^*_{hkl}$ of the reciprocal lattice. For a two-dimensional simple square lattice of interatomic spacing a, the reciprocal lattice is a simple square lattice of spacing $1/a$. The vectors G are then of the form

$$\mathbf{G}_{\alpha\beta} = \frac{2\pi}{a}(\alpha \mathbf{i}_x + \beta \mathbf{i}_y) \ , \tag{8.6-31}$$

where α and β are an arbitrary pair of integers. For any vector of this form (8.6 - 30) becomes

$$\alpha k_x + \beta k_y = -\frac{\pi}{a}(\alpha^2 + \beta^2) \ . \tag{8.6-32}$$

This is the equation of a family of straight lines in the k-plane, whose intercepts on the k_x and k_y axes are at

$$k_x = -\frac{\pi}{a}\frac{\alpha^2 + \beta^2}{\alpha} \quad \text{and} \quad k_y = -\frac{\pi}{a}\frac{\alpha^2 + \beta^2}{\beta} \ , \tag{8.6-33}$$

respectively. Each of these lines is a boundary along which electrons undergo Bragg reflection, and the set as a whole defines the boundaries between Brillouin zones. The question of *which* zone boundary a given segment of such a line represents can be ascertained by drawing a radius from the origin to the segment, and counting the number of crossings that take place before the segment in question is reached. If no other boundaries have been crossed, the segment separates zones 1 and 2; if one other boundary has been crossed, you are in zone 2 as you reach the segment, and it must therefore separate zones 2 and 3. If two crossings have been made, you are already in zone 3, and the segment separates zones 3 and 4, and so on. Obviously, you must draw enough boundaries initially to ensure that you have included all the lines that could possibly intervene between the origin and the zone you are mapping, but this is not a very difficult task in practice. The application of this rule can be understood more explicitly with reference to Figure 8.12, which illustrates the pattern of zones associated with the simple square two-dimensional space lattice.

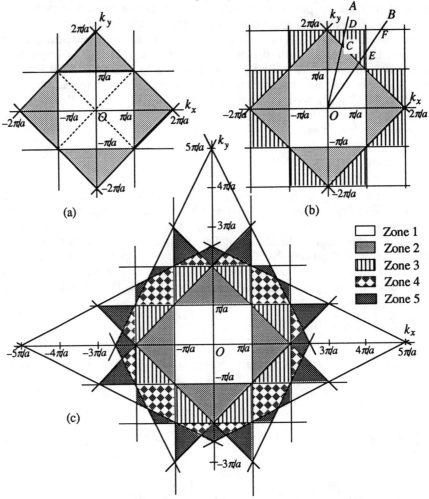

Figure 8.12 Construction of Brillouin Zones for the two-dimensional simple square lattice. (a) First and second zones (b) third zone construction (c) geometry of first five Brillouin zones.

The choices $\alpha = \pm 1$, $\beta = 0$, and $\alpha = 0$, $\beta = \pm 1$ in (8.6 - 32) or (8.6 - 33) generate the lines $k_x = \pm \pi/a$ and $k_y = \pm \pi/a$ which bound the square area already identified as the first zone, illustrated at (a) in the Figure. The choices $\alpha = \pm 2$, $\beta = 0$ and $\alpha = 0$, $\beta = \pm 2$ generate in a similar way a square whose linear dimensions are twice as large, as shown in (b) above, but there is a set of lines that stem from the choice $\alpha = \pm 1$, $\beta = \pm 1$ that come closer to the origin, and which are the first boundary one would meet on any radial path proceeding outward from the origin. These lines have equations of the form $k_x \pm k_y = \pm 2\pi/a$ according to (8.6 - 32), and are therefore lines of unit slope whose intercepts are at $\pm 2\pi/a$ along the coördinate axes, as shown at (a) and (b) above. The area outside the first zone and inside the area formed by the intersections of this second family is the second zone, since no other set of lines invades this region. One might expect superficially that the entire region between the outer boundary of the second zone and the square shown in (b) above bounded by the lines $k_x = \pm 2\pi/a$ and $k_y = \pm 2\pi/a$, arising from the choice $\alpha = \pm 2$, $\beta = 0$ and $\alpha = 0$, $\beta = \pm 2$, would be the third zone. If you observe that Bragg reflection takes place at all boundaries encountered on any outward radial path from the origin, it is clear that along the path OA shown at (b) in the figure, two reflections have taken place after point C has been passed, so that the portion of this path labeled CD must be in the third zone, as expected. However, along a path such as OB. a *third* reflection occurs at point E, and the portion EF must be in a higher zone (or zones). Therefore only the shaded portions outside the boundaries of the second zone in Figure 8.12 (b) are in the third Brillouin zone.

A systematic application of these principles for finding zone boundaries leads to the picture of the fourth and fifth zones illustrated in Figure 8.12 (c), and it is evident that higher zones can be found in the same way if desired. It will be noted from the figure that all Brillouin zones occupy the same total area in the k-plane. It will also be observed that translating the pieces of the higher zones by integral multiples of $2\pi/a$ along one or both coördinate directions will bring them into the area occupied by the first zone, and that on arrival the separate pieces fit together like pieces of a jigsaw puzzle to form an exact replica of the territory occupied by the first zone. This statement means that translating these pieces by a proper set of G-vectors of the reciprocal lattice will assemble a replica of the first zone. The idea is illustrated for the second zone by the dotted lines in Figure 8.12(a). This is how to construct what we referred to as the *reduced zone* representation in the one-dimensional discussion in Section 8.4. These remarks are equally applicable to three-dimensional structures if it is observed that the Brillouin zones are now volumes rather than plane areas, and that the k and G vectors have three components rather than two.

A quantitative justification of the reduced zone scheme is provided by the Bloch form of the electron wave functions in periodic lattices. We have seen that these wave functions can be written as

$$\psi(\mathbf{r}) = e^{i\mathbf{k}\cdot\mathbf{r}}u(\mathbf{r}) = e^{i(k_x x + k_y y + k_z z)}u(\mathbf{r}) \ , \tag{8.6-34}$$

where $u(\mathbf{r})$ is a periodic function of space coördinates whose periodicity is the same as that of the lattice. Let us now define the vector $\mathbf{k}'$ as

$$\mathbf{k}' = \mathbf{k} - \mathbf{i}_x\left(\frac{2n_x\pi}{a}\right) - \mathbf{i}_y\left(\frac{2n_y\pi}{a}\right) - \mathbf{i}_z\left(\frac{2n_z\pi}{a}\right) \ , \tag{8.6-35}$$

where a is the cubic lattice spacing and n_x, n_y, and n_z are integers. Substituting this into (8.6 - 34), this same wave function ψ can be expressed as

$$\psi(\mathbf{r}) = e^{i\mathbf{k}'\cdot\mathbf{r}}[e^{2\pi i n_x x}e^{2\pi i n_y y}e^{2\pi i n_z z}u(\mathbf{r})] = e^{i\mathbf{k}'\cdot\mathbf{r}}u'(\mathbf{r}) \ , \tag{8.6-36}$$

where $u'(\mathbf{r})$ is *also* a periodic function with the periodicity of the lattice. Clearly, then, it makes no difference whether we use the original wave vector k or the transformed wave vector k' in describing the wave function of the electron. Also, it makes no difference whether the lattice is cubic, as assumed above, or has a unit cell with three different dimensions, $a, b,$ and c. Indeed, the result can be shown to be true independent of crystal structure. It is also important to note that (8.6 - 35) can equally well be written as

$$\mathbf{k}' = \mathbf{k} - \mathbf{G} , \qquad\qquad (8.6\text{-}37)$$

where $\mathbf{G}/2\pi$ is a lattice vector of the reciprocal lattice. This transformation can always be used in two- or three-dimensional lattices to transform the bits and pieces of the dispersion relation in the unreduced zone into a single continuous function in a reduced zone occupying a region of the same form as the first Brillouin zone in the unreduced scheme.

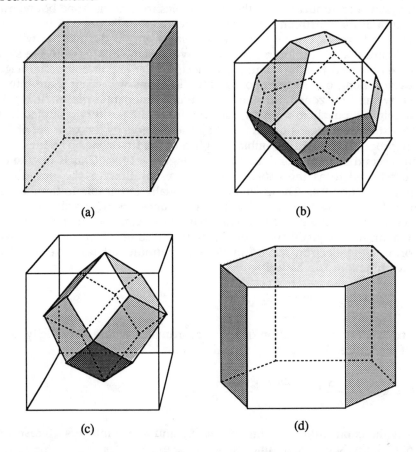

(a)   (b)

(c)   (d)

Figure 8.13 Reduced Brillouin zone for (a) simple cubic (b) face-centered cubic (c) body-centered cubic and (d) hexagonal lattices. The cubic regions shown in all cases extend from $-\pi/a$ to π/a alomg all three coördinate axes in k-space.

In three-dimensional structures, the Brillouin zones are three-dimensional polyhedra. These figures can be constructed in the same way as two-dimensional zones, the bounding lines being replaced by planes (indexed by three integers), on which Bragg reflection takes place. The defining relationship (8.6 - 30) is of the same form in either instance. The calculations, though easy enough to set up, are complex and tedious to carry out, and we shall not present them in detail. In simple cubic structures, the first zone is merely a cube, as illustrated at (a) in Figure 8.13. In the case of the body-centered and face-centered cubic structures, because there is more than one atom in the cubic unit cell, Bragg reflection can take place on sets of (100) planes more closely spaced than the faces of the cubic unit cell, as illustrated in Figure 2.10. As a result, certain planes in the *reciprocal* lattice on which the Bragg equation is satisfied *intersect* the cubical zone of the simple cubic lattice shown above. The first zones for the b.c.c. and f.c.c. structures, are therefore not cubes, but polyhedrons some of whose faces are defined by these intersecting planes. The Brillouin zone for the f.c.c. lattice is a polyhedron having 14 faces, 6 square and 8 hexagonal, as shown at (b) in the diagram. The hexagonal faces are normal to the cube diagonals. This figure is sometimes referred to as a tetrakaidecahedron. The Brillouin zone for the b.c.c. structure is illustrated at (c). It is known as a rhombic dodecahedron, a figure whose faces are all normal to the 12 (110) directions in the cubic cell. This object is an "irregular" dodecahedron, since at some of its vertices four edges intersect, while others have only three intersecting edges. Both these polyhedra possess cubic symmetry. It is interesting to note the similarity between the figure at (b) above and the Fermi surface shown in Figure 8.10(d), and the resemblance between the one at (c) above and the "bulging" octahedron in Figure 8.10(c). The Brillouin zone associated with the hexagonal lattice is shown above at (d). The form of the Fermi surface and the Brillouin zone in which it resides can significantly influence the electronic properties of crystals, as we shall soon see.

8.7 METALS, INSULATORS, AND SEMICONDUCTORS

We have already discussed the failure of classical physics to explain why some substances are electrical and thermal insulators having essentially no free valence electrons, and others are free-electron conductors in which all valence electrons can be pictured as belonging to a free-particle Fermi gas. The resolution of this difficulty is provided by quantum mechanics; the pieces of the argument are all on hand and it is now easy to assemble them into a coherent picture of the electronic properties of crystalline solids.

In Section 8.4 we learned that no current can arise from an empty band, nor one whose quantum states are entirely filled with electrons. Current can therefore flow only if there is at least one energy band that is *partially* filled. In such a band there are always unoccupied states of successively higher energy into which electrons can be promoted by an external accelerating field, like that created by a battery or other source of emf. As such states are occupied, empty states are left behind which other electrons of lower initial energy quickly occupy, the distribution of electrons becomeing somewhat skewed, in momentum as well as energy. Under these circumstances, if the field is in the x-direction, the average electron energy is raised by the small drift energy contributed by the accelerating field, and the average x-

component of momentum--or velocity--is no longer zero, but has a small finite value. A current is then observed, and if electrons are scattered so as to return to the equalibrium distribution after a very short "free time", the conditions of the classical free electron theory developed in the preceding chapter are (with one exception) satisfied, and the material behaves much like a classical free electron conductor. The one exception is that quantum theory shows that electron dynamics is charac- terized by an effective mass that may differ from the inertial electron mass not only in magnitude, but even in sign, suggesting the possibility of hole conduction and other quasiparticle phenomena as well as ordinary free-electron behavior.

It is apparent, then, that a substance in which energy bands are under normal circumstances entirely filled or entirely empty are insulators, while those with at least one partially filled band are free-electron conductors, as shown in Figure 8.14.

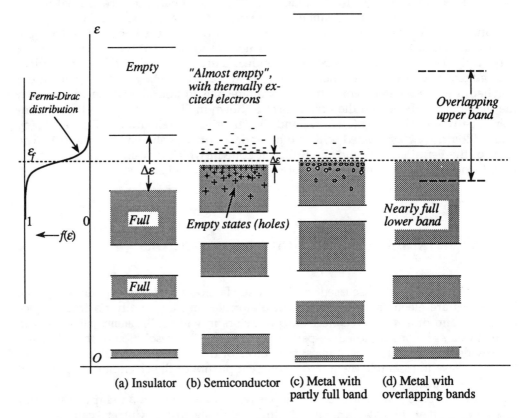

Figure 8.14 Energy band diagrams illustrating (a) insulators (b) semiconductors (c) metals having a partly filled band (d) metals having overlapping bands. Shaded regions are states fully occupied at zero temperature. The Fermi distribution at the prevailing temperature is plotted at thr left.

The band configuration for an insulator is shown at (a) in the above diagram. The filled bands of lowest energy can be shown to arise from the inner-shell atomic lev- els of the atoms in the crystal lattice, as we shall see more clearly later. The states in the highest occupied band are those that describe the valence electrons. The "ener- gy gap" $\Delta\varepsilon$ between the top of the highest filled band and the bottom of the lowest empty band is in a good insulator large enough that the probability of thermal excitation of electrons across the region in which no allowed quantum states exist is negligible. This probability depends upon the value of the Fermi-Dirac distribution function, which is plotted at the left side of the above diagram. In an ideal insulator the Fermi energy lies roughly in the center of the energy gap, as shown, so that if $\Delta\varepsilon/kT$ is large, the value of the Fermi function in the "empty" band will clearly be extremely small. The exact determination of the Fermi energy in these instances is discussed in detail in the next chapter.

In a substance having the band configuration of an insulator, but in which the energy gap is so small that the Fermi distribution is not negligibly small in the upper band, nor indistinguishable from unity in the lower band, there can be significant thermal excitation of valence electrons across the energy gap. The excitation energy for this process is provided by the vibrational energy of the crystal lattice. Such materials exhibit a small but measurable electrical conductivity, which rises steeply with increasing temperature as the Fermi function becomes less steplike. These "poor insulators" are more commonly referred to as *semiconductors*. Their band configuration is shown at (b) in Figure 8.14. It is clear from the diagram that excitation of an electron across the small energy gap leaves behind an empty quantum state in a nearly filled lower band; there is therefore free-electron conductivity in the upper band, and also conduction ascribable to *positive holes* in the lower band. The upper "almost empty" band is referred to as the *conduction band*, while the lower "almost filled" band is called the *valence band*. The terminology is misleading, since conduction takes place in both bands, but it has unfortunately become standard usage. This configuration of energy bands endows semiconductors with unique properties that allow them to be used in the fabrication of a wide variety of electronic devices. We shall examine these materials in some detail in the next two chapters.

The band scheme of a normal metallic conductor is illustrated in Figure 8.14(c). As in insulators the lower-lying filled bands are outgrowths of the inner-shell atomic levels of the atoms of the lattice. The band associated with the quantum states of the valence electrons is now only partially filled, however, and the Fermi energy therefore lies within the band. At zero temperature, the quantum states would be, in equilibrium, fully occupied up to this level and totally empty above it. Under these circumstances, there would be a sharply defined Fermi surface in the Brillouin zone, like one of the surfaces illustrated in Figure 8.10. Inside this surface the quantum states are fully occupied, and outside it are unoccupied states. The points on the surface of this figure are all at the Fermi energy. This sharp Fermi surface becomes slightly blurred at higher temperatures, because of thermal excitation of electrons to states above the Fermi energy, but its conceptual usefulness is unimpaired in view of the very large Fermi temperature in most metals. In the simplest cases the Fermi surface is almost spherical, like the one shown in Figure 8.10(a); this is a fairly good approximation for the alkali metals, somewhat less so for copper, silver, and gold. There are at elevated temperatures unoccupied states below the Fermi energy, but the concept of hole conductivity is not particularly useful, because all electrons have positive effective mass in classical metallic conductors.

The picture of the Fermi surface in the reduced Brillouin zone is useful in displaying certain effects associated with scattering of free electrons in metals. At equilibrium, the Fermi surface is symmetric about the origin of k-space, and the average value of each component of crystal momentum--and velocity--is zero. There is therefore no average drift velocity and no current under these circumstances, whatever shape the Fermi surface may have. In the simplest cases, the Fermi surface can be approximated as a sphere, as illustrated in Figure 8.10(a), and earlier in Figure 5.31. When an electric field in the $-x$-direction exists, the electrons acquire a small average drift momentum in the $+x$-direction, and the "Fermi sphere" (or other surface) moves slightly to the right along the k_x-axis, as shown in Figure 8.15. This motion is ultimately limited by scattering processes, whose net effect can be regarded as taking electrons from the "forward" part of the sphere and returning them to the opposite end. Finally a steady state is reached is which the center of the sphere is displaced a small distance along the k_x-axis, a distance corresponding to a small average drift velocity for the electron distribution, as discussed in the preceding chapter. The only difference is the appearance of an effective mass, and in some instances a nonspherical--but still symmetric--Fermi surface.

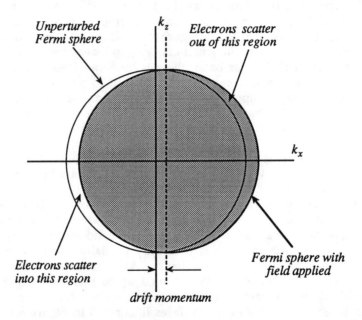

Figure 8.15 The Fermi sphere of a classical metallic conductor displaced from its equilibrium position by a constant electric field, which in this case is in the $-x$-direction. A steady state is reached in which the net effect of scattering is to remove electrons from a region on the right surface of the sphere and transfer them to unoccupied states on the left.

The scattering mechanisms responsible for this transfer of electrons in k-space are exactly the ones described in the preceding chapter. It is important to note that the drift kinetic energy acquired by the electron during its free path is normally only a small fraction of its equilibrium thermal kinetic energy, and that the average drift velocity is small in comparison with the average thermal speed, just as in classical free electron theory. The displacement of the Fermi sphere shown above within the Brillouin zone is therefore also very small on the scale of the sphere itself and the zone within which it resides.

The question of how many quantum states there are in a given energy band is difficult to answer in general. The calculation given in Section 8.2 preceding equation (8.2 - 25) shows that in one-dimensional systems the answer is N, the number of atoms, or (more correctly) $2N$ if spin degeneracy is included. In systems of higher dimensionality the problem is more difficult. It can be approached (though not solved completely) by considering the tight-binding limit, in which electrons tend to be associated with individual atoms in states that do not differ markedly from the quantum states of isolated atoms. In this limit we may observe that the Kronig-Penney dispersion relation (8.6 - 5) predicts an allowed band width of $6C_1$, as given by (8.6 - 7). Since C_1 approaches zero as the interatomic spacing a becomes large, it is clear that all the quantum states in a given band will have the same energy in this limit, and that the band itself coalesces into a single discrete "atomic" energy level. It is not hard to show that this result is true in general, and not simply an artifact of the KP model. After all, if you consider a cubic lattice of N identical atoms all in the same initial quantum state, whose spacing a is so great that the wave functions of the individual atoms do not overlap at all, then the atoms are effectively independent of one another, and the quantum states of the system are simply a collection of N identical unperturbed atomic wave functions centered on their respective lattice sites. The degeneracy of each energy level is simply what it is in the isolated atom, times the number of atoms N, since each atom contributes the same number of quantum states to the system.

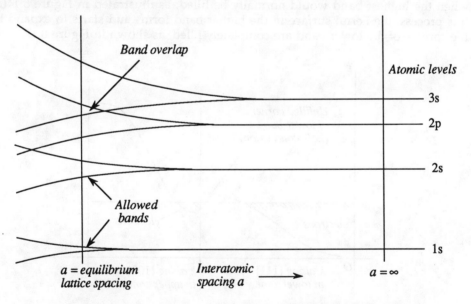

Figure 8.16 Relation of energy bands to atomic energy levels in a tight-binding cubic lattice as a function of a variable interatomic spacing a. Bands start to form when there is a significant probability for electrons to tunnel between neighboring lattice atoms.

If the lattice spacing is now decreased, at some point the wave functions of valence electrons on individual atoms begin to overlap slightly. When this happens, there begins to be a small but finite probability that the valence electrons can tunnel from one lattice site to the next, in other words, travel around like free paricles. As this happens, just as in the KP model, the discrete energy of the isolated atom starts to broaden out into a *band* of quantum states slightly perturbed from their original atomic form. This process, however, does not affect the *number* of quantum states involved. It is thus reasonable to suggest that a band based on interacting 1s, 2s, or 3s atomic states, for example, has degeneracy 2N, because atomic s-states are twofold degenerate. Likewise, if the basis states are atomic p-states, the number of states in the band is 6N, because atomic p-states are sixfold degenerate. In the same way, bands formed from interacting atomic d-states contain 10N states, because d-states are tenfold degenerate, and so on. The process is illustrated in Figure 8.16. In every case all the quantum states in the band will be accommodated within a single Brillouin zone. Thus, a valence band containing 2N states will be completely filled if the atoms of the lattice each have two valence electrons, but will be only half full if (like the alkali metals) they each have a single valence electron.

This reasoning assumes implicitly that bands formed from the interaction of atomic s, p, and d states remain *independent* of one another, and that these bands are not broadened so extensively that they themselves begin to overlap. When this happens, states of different angular momentum combine with one another and things become far more complex. The valence and conduction bands of silicon and germanium are examples of this kind of interaction between atomic s- and p-states, in which bands containing 4N states are formed. The possibility that energy bands might overlap leads to situations in which metallic conduction can take place even when the highest band would normally be filled, as illustrated in Figure 8.14(c). In this process, the Fermi surface in the higher band forms and starts to expand before the corners of the lower band are completely filled, as shown in Figure 8.17.

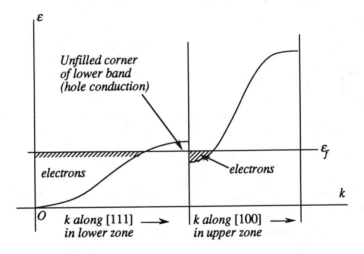

Figure 8.17 Energy bands whose allowed energies overlap. The upper band begins to fill before the corners of the lower band's zone are completely occupied. The variable k is plotted along the zone diagonal (111) for the lower band and along the x-direction in k-space for the upper band.

Overlapping bands are encountered in many common substances, and afford an explanation of why so many materials that might seem to be insulators purely on the basis of valency are in reality metallic conductors. In the diagram above, the lower band is nearly full, its behavior being that of a positive hole conductor, while the upper band exhibits normal free-electron conductivity. Materials of this kind are often referred to as *semimetals*. They can be thought of as semiconductors with negative energy gaps. The density of states function in this case is the sum of the density of states in the two bands that overlap, and it is apparent from this that the density of states function does not go to zero anywhere in the energy range covered by the overlapping bands. Indeed, in the region of overlap there is usually a peak in the density of states curve. This effect is most notable in the transition metals, in which a rather wide 3s band and a narrow 3d band accommodating 10N electrons overlap, as shown in Figure 8.18.

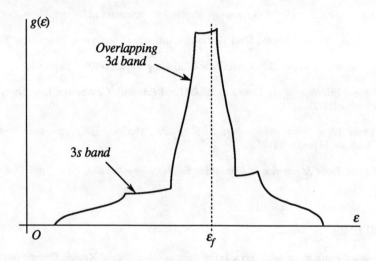

Figure 8.18 Density of states function for a typical transition element, showing wide 3s band and narrow overlapping 3d band. The position of the Fermi energy is roughly as shown for most of these elements. The height of the 3d band is reduced for convenience; actually the area under this band should be five times the area subtended by the 3s.

In this figure, the height of the 3d band is reduced for simplicity in drawing the illustration. Actually its subtended area should be five times that of the 3s, in view of the ratio of the number of states in the respective bands. Because of the large number of states in the 3d band, the Fermi energy moves only slightly from one element to the next in the transition series as the 3d band is filled. The Fermi energy and the form of the Fermi surface is therefore similar for most transition elements, which largely accounts for the fact that their chemical and physical properties are also quite similar.

It should now be apparent that the introduction of quantum mechanics has resolved most of the troubling discrepancies and unanswered questions associated with the classical free electron theory discussed in Chapter 7. We shall see many other examples of its usefulness in this and other areas as we now turn our attention, in the next two chapters, to a more detailed study of semiconductor materials and device structures.

368

REFERENCES

N. F. Mott and H. Jones, *Theory of Metals and Alloys*, Dover Publications, New York (1958).

E. T. Whittaker and G. N. Watson, *Modern Analysis* (4th Revised Ed.), Cambridge University Press, Cambridge (1948), p. 412. This mathematics text, first published in 1902, gives an excellent, though abbreviated proof of what was then known universally as Floquet's theorem.

H. Jones, *The Theory of Electronic States and Brillouin Zones in Crystals*, North Holland Publishing Co., Amsterdam (1960).

S. Raines, *Wave Mechanics of Electrons in Metals*, Interscience Publishers, New York (1961).

A. H. Wilson, *Theory of Metals*, (2nd Edition), Cambridge University Press, New York (1953).

F. Seitz, *Modern Theory of Solids*, McGraw-Hill, New York (1940), Chapter 8.

J. M. Ziman, *Principles of the Theory of Solids*, (2nd Edition), Cambridge University Press, Cambridge (1972).

L. Brillouin, *Wave Propagation in Periodic Structures*, McGraw-Hill, New York (1946); Dover Publications, New York (1953).

R. A. Smith, *Wave Mechanics of Crystalline Solids*, Wiley & Sons, New York (1961).

PROBLEMS

1. Identify the functions $\psi(x)$ and $u_k(x)$ in the one-dimensional Kronig-Penney model, and discuss their periodicity or non-periodicity, as the case may be. Do not attempt to arrive at explicit expressions for the coefficients A, B, C, and D.

2. Evaluate the determinant in (8.3 - 11) and derive the expressions shown in equations (8.3 - 12) and (8.3 - 14).

3. The dispersion relation for electrons in the lowest allowed band of a certain one-dimensional crystal is found to be of the form $\varepsilon = \varepsilon_b + C(1 - \cos ka)$, where ε_b and C are constants. Find the effective mass for any allowed energy in the band $(-\pi < ka < \pi)$.

4. Why are the effective band edge masses given by the answer to the preceding problem not exactly the same as those predicted by (8.5 - 38) and (8.5 - 39)?

5. Show that the dispersion relation (8.5 - 2) for the "simplified" Kronig-Penney potential can be written in the form (8.5 - 3).

6. Show explicitly how equation (8.5 - 27) can be obtained from (8.5 - 24).

7. Show that the dispersion relation (8.6 - 4) yields the square constant-energy contour labeled "0.5" in Figure 8.9.

8. Show that the contours near the corners of the square zone in Figure 8.9 are circular.

9. Show that the effective mass tensor for the three-dimensional Kronig-Penney tight-binding model, described by the dispersion relation (8.6 - 5) is isotropic (thus that it can be expressed as a constant times a unit matrix) for the case where the surfaces are spherical, as in Figure 8.10(a).

10. Prove that the Fermi surfaces shown in Figure 8.10(f) are essentially spherical.

11. Show that the density of states function for the three-dimensional Kronig-Penney tight binding potential has the form shown in equation (8.6 - 18) for energies near the top of the lowest allowed band.

12. Show that the group velocity of electrons vanishes at all points on the cubical boundary of the first Brillouin zone for the three-dimensional tight-binding Kronig-Penney potential discussed in Section 8.6.

13. Prove that the Bragg condition in the form $n\lambda = 2a \sin\theta$ is satisfied at all points on the outer boundaries of the second Brillouin zone of the simple two-dimensional square lattice discussed in Section 8.6.

14. Show that the Bragg condition is satisfied on the surfaces of the polyhedrons defining the first Brillouin zone of the b.c.c. and f.c.c. lattices.

15. Plot the first five Brillouin zones of a two-dimensional rectangular lattice having basis vectors $\mathbf{a} = \mathbf{i}_x a$ and $\mathbf{b} = \mathbf{i}_y b$, where $b = 3a$.

16. Plot the first five brillouin zones for a two-dimensional hexagonal lattice whose unit cell is describe by the basis vectors $\mathbf{a} = \mathbf{i}_x a$ and $\mathbf{b} = \mathbf{i}_x a/2 + \mathbf{i}_y a\sqrt{3}/2$.

17. Find the electronic density of states function $g(\varepsilon)d\varepsilon$ for a one-dimensional lattice of interatomic spacing a whose dispersion relation is the same as that given in Problem 3

18. For the one-dimensional allowed band described in Problem 3, show that the density of states function has the form

$$g(\varepsilon)d\varepsilon = \frac{2N}{\pi C} \cdot \frac{d\varepsilon}{\sqrt{\dfrac{2(\varepsilon - \varepsilon_b)}{C} - \dfrac{(\varepsilon - \varepsilon_b)^2}{C^2}}} \, .$$

19. Suppose that there are n electrons ($n < 2N$) in the allowed band described in the preceding problem. Show that the Fermi energy of the electron distrubution at absolute zero is

$$\varepsilon_f(0) = \varepsilon_b + C\left(1 - \cos\frac{\pi n}{2N}\right) .$$

20. Consider the case of a two-dimensional semiconductor having a lower allowed band, which extends from energy 0 to ε_v and is filled at absolute zero, and a higher band which extends from energy ε_c to infinity, and would be empty at zero temperature. In the range ($\varepsilon_v < \varepsilon < \varepsilon_c$) there is a forbidden energy region small enough to permit a detectable number of electrons to be excited thermally into the higher band, leaving an equal number of unfilled hole states behind. The density of states in both bands is $4\pi m A/h^2$, where A is the area, and m is the effective mass for *both* electrons and holes. Using Fermi-Dirac statistics, write expressions for the number of electrons in the upper allowed band and holes in the lower band as a function of temperature and the system's Fermi energy. Hint: The distribution function for holes must refelect the probability that a state of energy ε is unfilled, and must therefore be writter $1 - f(\varepsilon)$, where f is the usual Fermi distribution function.

21. Using the results of the preceding problem, find the Fermi energy of the system as a function of temperature, assuming that kT is much smaller than ε_v, ε_c, or ε_f. Utilize the fact that the number of electrons and holes must be equal. (Answer: $\varepsilon_f = (\varepsilon_v + \varepsilon_c)/2$, which is the midpoint of the "energy gap" between the two bands).

22. Can you work the preceding problem *without* making the simplifying assumption suggested above, and show that

$$e^{\varepsilon_f/kT} = -\tfrac{1}{2} + \sqrt{\left(\tfrac{1}{2}\right)^2 + e^{\varepsilon_c/kT}\left(e^{\varepsilon_v/kT} - 1\right)} \quad ?$$

You should now be able to show that this answer reduces to the one found previously under the right circumstances, and that in the limit of *large* temperatures, $\varepsilon_f = \varepsilon_v - kT$.

23. In Bloch wave functions of the form (8.2 - 21), both $\psi(x)$ and $u(x)$ are in general complex quantities. By writing the wave function in polar form, $\psi(x) = R(x)\exp i[kx + \varphi(x)]$, where R, k, and φ are all real quantities, show that the functions R and φ satisfy differential equations of the form

$$\frac{d^2R}{dx^2} - \left(k + \frac{d\varphi}{dx}\right)^2 R + \frac{2m}{\hbar^2}[\varepsilon - V(x)]R(x) = 0$$

and

$$R\frac{d^2\varphi}{dx^2} + 2\left(k + \frac{d\varphi}{dx}\right)\cdot\frac{dR}{dx} = 0 \ .$$

Hint: Substitute a solution of the above form into Schrödinger's equation and equate real and imaginary parts.

24. By separating variables in the second of the above equations and integrating, show that these solutions can be written as

$$vR^2 = v_0 R_0^2 = const., \quad \text{where} \quad v(x) = k + \frac{d\varphi}{dx}, \quad \text{and } v_0, R_0 \text{ are initial values,}$$

and

$$\frac{d^2R}{dx^2} - \frac{v_0^2 R_0^4}{R^3} + \frac{2m}{\hbar^2}[\varepsilon - V(x)]R(x) = 0 \ .$$

25. Show from the second of the equations given in Problem 23 that the function $u(x)$ in the Bloch wave function *cannot be a purely real quantity*, except in the trivial instance when $V(x)$ is zero and the problem reduces to that of a free electron in vacuum.

26. In an anisotropic metallic crystal, the dispersion relation has the approximate form

$$\varepsilon - \varepsilon_b = \frac{\hbar^2 k_x^2}{2m_x} + \frac{\hbar^2 k_y^2}{2m_y} + \frac{\hbar^2 k_z^2}{2m_z} \ .$$

Write the inverse effective mass tensor for this substance.

27. Find the general effective mass tensor for the three-dimensional Kronig-Penney tight binding model described by the dispersion relation (8.6 - 5). Explain why this tensor for the electron distribution as a whole is isotropic, even though the tensor that applies to a single particle isn't of the form of a constant times the unit matrix.

28. Find the volumes of the Brillouin zones associated with the b.c.c. and f.c.c. structures, expressed in terms of the edge of the cube that represents the simple cubic zone.

29 Find the fraction of the zone volume occupied by a sphere of the largest possible radius inscribed in (a) the simple cubic Brillouin zone, (b) the b.c.c. zone, and (c) the f.c.c. zone.

30. Cu, Ag, and Au are all monovalent metals whose structure in the pure state is f.c.c. When they are alloyed with divalent metals like zinc or cadmium, random solid solutions are formed in

which divalent atoms occupy f.c.c. sites at random. One effect of the alloying process is to increase the electron concentration to values increasingly larger than one electron per atom as more and more of the alloying substance is added. It is observed that as the electron-per-atom ratio reaches about 1.36, a phase change occurs in which the structure of the alloy changes from f.c.c. to b.c.c. As the electron-per-atom ratio is further increased, at a ratio of roughly 1.5 another phase change to a much more complex structure occurs. Can you explain these figures in terms of a model--obviously oversimplified--that involves a constantly expanding, roughly spherical Fermi surface in the Brillouin zone?

31. A certain one-dimensional periodic potential gives rise to a dispersion relation of the form

$$\varepsilon - \varepsilon_b = \frac{\hbar^2}{2m}\left(k_x^2 - Ck_x^4\right) \qquad (-\pi/a < k_x < \pi/a) \ .$$

Evaluate the constant C in terms of the other parameters in this expression. Find the effective mass at the bottom and top if the band.

32. Show that the effect of including the next term in the series in (8.5 - 32) is to give a dispersion relation of the form

$$\varepsilon - \varepsilon_b = \frac{D_1}{C_1} - \sqrt{\frac{D_1^2}{C_1^2} - 2D_1(1 - \cos ka)} \ , \qquad \text{where} \qquad \frac{1}{D_1} = \left(\frac{d^2 f}{d\varepsilon^2}\right)_b \ .$$

Show that this reduces to $\varepsilon - \varepsilon_b = C_1(1 - \cos ka)$ when $1/D_1$ approaches zero.

CHAPTER 9

SEMICONDUCTOR MATERIALS

9.1 INTRODUCTION

Semiconductors differ from metals in several ways. The most important of these is that in semiconductors, both positive and negative mobile charge carriers can coexist within the crystal. This permits the controlled modulation of conductivity and other material properties, which in turn permits the fabrication of all sorts of electronic devices and microcircuits. It would seem that electronic processes within semiconductors might be more complex than in metals because they involve holes as well as free electrons, but this is not necessarily so. There are two important respects in which semiconductors are simpler than metals. First of all, it is usually possible to use Maxwell-Boltzmann statistics rather than Fermi-Dirac, to describe the behavior of the electron/hole distributions in statistical terms. This makes it easy to calculate integrals, and to determine averages that would otherwise be difficult or impossible to evaluate. Moreover, the density of states functions for electrons and holes almost always has the simple form associated with a gas of free particles. It is often possible to prepare exceptionally pure and nearly perfect semiconductor single crystals, and to alter their properties by the controlled addition of minute amounts of specific impurity atoms. One can therefore observe and control experimentally effects that would be difficult to dectect, and impossible to measure accurately in metals. Semiconductors have in fact opened an entire new area of experimental investigation--an area that had been inaccessible before these substances were available as pure single crystals.

Semiconductors were used as electronic materials during the early years of the 20th century, mostly as detector diodes in the primitive radio equipment sometimes referred to as "crystal sets". The material of choice for this application was *galena*, or naturally occurring crystalline lead sulfide. A diode detector of radio waves could be made simply by placing a sharp-pointed metal filament in contact with a galena crystal whose base made a broad-area ohmic "ground contact" to a metal substrate. These point-contact diodes usually did not work very well until one found--by trial and error--a "hot spot" for the filament on the crystal. Obviously, some crystals worked better than others, and (not infrequently) some didn't work at all. These fussy and unreliable crystal detectors went out of circulation when reliable vacuum-tube detectors became commercially available. The subsequent story has already been told in the introduction to Chapter 1, which you may now find it interesting to reread. Finally, though, by about 1943, it was recognized that good solid-state amplifiers, oscillators, and other more elaborate devices could be made if a practical means of modulating or otherwise controlling the conductivity of these materials could be found. This aspiration was realized in December 1947, when a three-element point-contact *transistor* was demonstrated at Bell Laboratories by John Bardeen, Walter Brattain, and William Shockley. We shall now investigate the properties of these important electronic materials, which have formed the basis of most of the subsequent technology of solid-state electronics.

In studying semiconductors, it is important to understand that they are most accurately described as poor insulators rather than imperfect metals. A semiconductor is best characterized as an insulator having an energy gap between valence and conduction bands small enough to permit observable thermal excitation of electrons from a filled "valence" band to empty states in a higher "conduction" band, leaving behind unoccupied hole states in the lower "valence" band. A pure insulator always becomes semiconducting at a sufficiently high temperature, unless it first melts or vaporizes. Likewise, any semiconductor in the pure state will act as an insulator at temperatures sufficiently low.

9.2 INTRINSIC SEMICONDUCTORS

Semiconductors posses certain important physical properties associated with the "band gap" or forbidden energy region between the "nearly filled" valence band and the "almost empty" conduction band. Their properties are also drastically altered by the addition of miniscule amounts of certain impurities whose atoms occupy lattice sites normally filled by semiconductor atoms. Semiconductors so pure that these impurity effects are negligible--and this may mean that they must be pure to the extent of one part in a billion--are referred to as *intrinsic* semiconductors. The ideal intrinsic material is one in which the active impurity concentration is zero, though like the concept of an ideal gas, this can never be realized in actuality. Semiconductors whose properties (electrical conductivity in particular) are strongly affected by the presence of impurities are known as *impurity* semiconductors, or *extrinsic* materials. We shall first discuss the properties of intrinsic semiconductors, materials whose highest occupied energy bands have the configuration shown in Figure 9.1, and whose properties are largely determined by the band gap itself.

As suggested previously, when absolutely pure, at zero absolute temperature these materials are perfect insulators having zero conductivity. As the temperature rises, electrons are excited across a forbidden region where the density of states is zero, into the conduction band, where they give rise to free-electron conductivity.

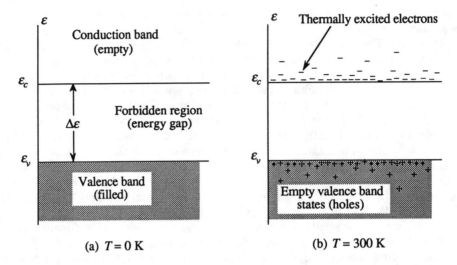

Figure 9.1 Conduction and valence bands of an intrinsic semiconductor (a) at temperature absolute zero, and (b) at room temperature, illustrating thermally excited electrons and empty valence band ststes associated with holes.

As this occurs, unoccupied states are left behind, allowing free hole conduction to take place in the valence band. This conductivity must be added to the conduction-band free-electron conductivity to arrive at the total conductivity of the material. Hole conduction, of course, is caused physically by a large-scale motion of electrons, but as we have already observed, it is advantageous to describe it as an oppositely directed motion of positive holes, equal in number to the number of vacant states.

For a semiconductor having n electrons per unit volume in the conduction band and p holes per unit volume in the valence band, the electrical conductivity can be written as the sum of the conductivities associated with the two bands. Thus,

$$\sigma = \sigma_n + \sigma_p = ne\mu_n + pe\mu_p \ . \tag{9.2-1}$$

In this expression σ_n and σ_p are the conductivities arising separately from electrons in the conduction band and holes in the valence band, respectively. The symbols n and p for conduction and valence bands, and the associated subscripts, stand for the *negative* and *positive* charges in the two bands. The mobilities in the above expression are related to the scattering mean free times and effective masses in the usual way by

$$\mu_n = e\tau_n / m_n^* \qquad \text{and} \qquad \mu_p = e\tau_p / m_p^* \ , \tag{9.2-2}$$

where τ_n and τ_p are electron and hole scattering relaxation times and m_n^* and m_p^* are electron and hole effective masses. Neither of these quantites is necessarily the same for electrons and holes. In intrinsic semiconductors n and p are equal, since the excitation of an electron across the gap creates exactly one hole in the valence band, but n and p can be very different in impurity semiconductors.

As we shall see more clearly later, in intrinsic materials the Fermi energy is roughly at the midpoint of the forbidden energy region in which the density of states is zero. Ordinarily, the energy gap $\Delta\varepsilon$ is *much larger* than kT at normal temperatures; for example, in germanium it is about 0.7eV or $28kT$ at 300K. This means that only the exponential "tail" of the Fermi distribution function extends above the energy ε_c that defines the bottom of the conduction band. Likewise, the distribution function $1 - f(\varepsilon)$ for unoccupied states or holes, is also merely an exponential tail that decreases as you go downward from the maximum energy ε_v into the valence band. Both distribution functions therefore have the Maxwellian form $A\exp(\pm\varepsilon/kT)$ shown in Figure 8.14, with exponential decay constant $1/kT$. Thus, the population of electrons in the conduction band and holes in the valence band *increase exponentially* as the temperature rises. Since the conductivity is directly related to the number of electrons and holes in the crystal, the electrical conductivity also increases exponentially with temperature.

This behavior contrasts sharply with that of free-electron conductivity in normal metals, wherein the number of free electrons is fixed and the conductivity changes with temperature only because of relatively small changes in the relaxation time or free path arising from changes in scattering probabilities. The rapid exponential change in the electrical conductivity of an intrinsic semiconductor with temperature is clearly associated with the forbidden region or energy gap. The thermal excitation process can be viewed as the annihilation of a phonon of vibrational energy greater than $\Delta\varepsilon = \varepsilon_c - \varepsilon_v$, with the production of an electron-hole pair. The inverse process, in which a thermal phonon is created when an electron makes a downward transition from the conduction band into an unoccupied valence band state, can also occur. This process can be viewed as the *recombination* or annihilation of an electron-hole pair whose excitation energy appears finally as a quantum of vibrational energy. The laws of statistical mechanics require that in thermal equilibrium, the rates at which these opposing processes occur must be equal.

Electron-hole pairs can be created optically as well as thermally, when light of photon energy equal to or greater than the gap energy impinges on a semiconductor. These photons are strongly absorbed by the material, their energy being expended in exciting valence band electrons into the conduction band, leaving unoccupied states in the valence band. The rate at which pairs are created is now (temporarily) greater than the rate at which they recombine. The population of electrons in the conduction band and holes in the valence band rises above the thermal equilibrium value, increasing with time until a new steady state is attained, in which generation and recombination rates (though now in excess of thermal equilibrium values) are again equal. This process increases the number of mobile electrons and holes in the crystal, which, according to (9.2 - 1), increases its electrical conductivity to a value that may significantly exceed the thermal equilibrium dark conductivity, the increase being directly proportional to incident light intensity. The conductivity of the crystal has thus been *optically modulated*. If the incident light is a digital laser signal reflected from the surface of a compact disc, it may be converted into an output current that can be amplified and converted into an audio or video output signal. This effect, which is intimately associated with the existence of the energy gap between valence and conduction bands, is known as *photoconductivity*. In order to excite photoconductivity, the incident photon wavelength must be equal to or less than that associated by Planck's law with the energy gap. This requires that

$$\lambda \leq hc/\Delta\varepsilon \ . \tag{9.2-3}$$

Photons of wavelength greater than this critical value will have insufficient energy to promote valence electrons into the conduction band. They therefore cannot be absorbed by the above excitation process, and are propagated through the crystal practically unattenuated. The material is thus quite transparent to light of wavelength longer than the critical value (9.2 - 3), and strongly absorbing for shorter wavelengths. The optical absorption coefficient rises sharply from a very low value to one far higher in a narrow wavelength interval about the critical photon energy. This easily observed feature, referred as the optical "absorption edge", is characteristic of all semiconducting materials, and provides a reasonably accurate method of measuring the gap energy $\Delta\varepsilon$. Nearly all of the semiconductors used as electronic materials have an absorption edge in the near infrared, but the absorption edges of GaP and $GaAs_xP_{1-x}$ are in the long-wavelength end of the visible spectrum. These materials can therefore be used as light-emitting diodes. For diamond, which has an energy gap of about 5.5eV, it is in the ultraviolet, which accounts for the fact that diamonds are transparent. One can regard photoconductivity as an internal photoelectric effect, in which electrons are excited into the conduction band rather than out of the crystal and into a surrounding vacuum.

The unique phenomena described above are characteristic of semiconductors, and are closely associated with the presence of an energy gap. They are in sharp contrast, however, with the properties of metals. For example, the simplest optical properties of metals can be understood on the basis of classical electromagnetic theory. Maxwell's equations can be used to derive wave equations for electric and magnetic fields that propagate as plane electromagnetic waves in free space at the speed of light. When such waves encounter a metal having a high ohmic conductivity, two effects can be predicted. First, the electric field of the incident light wave excites a rapid oscillatory motion of the free electrons near the surface of the metal. This ac current distribution is in effect an assembly of accelerated free charges that *reradiate* a reflected wave nearly as intense as the incident wave. These internal currents also rapidly dissipate energy within the substance as ohmic heat. The effect of ohmic conductivity is found to introduce a damping term into the wave equation, a term that gives rise to an absorption coefficient roughly proportional to the conductivity and thus to the density of free charges within the material. These effects account for the fact that metallic substances are highly reflecting, and definitely not transparent, except perhaps as very thin films. Semiconductors, of course, also have free electrons and holes, and these charges also cause some "free-carrier" absorption like that observed in metals. However, the concentration of free electrons and holes in intrinsic semiconductors is smaller by a factor of roughly 10^9 than that of electrons in metals, so that, though observable in some instances, it is a relatively small effect. We have also seen that the electrical conductivity of normal metals decreases as the temperature rises, while intrinsic semiconductors behave oppositely.

We have observed that the conductivity of semiconductors can be externally modulated quite easily. This is practically impossible in metals. The conductivity of metals varies with temperature, and also changes slightly when external magnetic fields are applied, but these effects are so small and so difficult to control that they are of little practical use. If one tries to introduce additional free electrons into a metal by charging it electrostatically, the excess free charges quickly form a surface free charge distribution, leaving the bulk conductivity unaltered. In the case of optical conductivity modulation in semiconductors, you will note that the added free charge carriers are introduced as electron-hole pairs, which modulate the conductivity *without* introducing any net charge into the sample. This kind of conductivity modulation can occur only when there are two oppositely charged species of charge carriers in the crystal, and is therefore not observed in normal metallic substances.

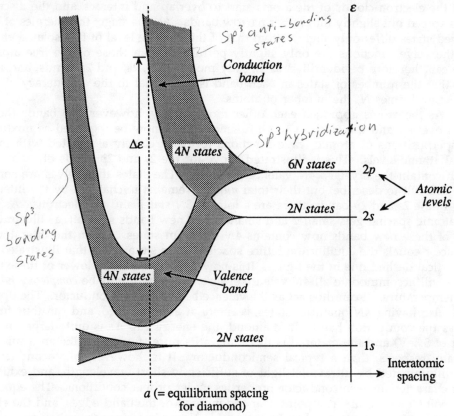

Figure 9.2 Energy bands arising from the 1s, 2s, and 2p atomic states of carbon when carbon atoms are arranged in a diamond lattice whose lattice spacing is variable. Energy levels and bands are shown as a function of this variable spacing, whose values are plotted along the horizontal axis. The shaded areas in this diagram merely indicate allowed electron energies, and are not to be interpreted as occupied states. From G. E. Kimball, *J. Chem. Phys.* **3**, 560 (1935).

The covalent semiconductors in column IV of the periodic table are most frequently used for devices and microcircuits, and most thoroughly investigated and clearly understood. Though other materials such as III-V intermetallics will also be discussed to some extent, we shall direct our attention primarily toward the column IV materials--diamond, silicon, and germanium, in view of their classic simplicity and widespread application. The energy band structure for diamond (as calculated by G.E. Kimball in 1935) is shown in Figure 9.2. Diagrams for silicon and germanium are generally similar in appearance, though in silicon and germanium, (3s, 3p) and (4s, 4p) states, respectively, are involved in forming the valence and conduction bands. This diagram is to be interpreted in the same way as Figure 8.16 in the previous chapter. One envisions a large array of carbon atoms arranged in the geometry of the diamond lattice, though with a variable interatomic spacing r. When this spacing is large compared with the extent of the electron distribution of the atom, the allowed energies are simply discrete atomic levels whose degeneracy is that of a single atomic level multiplied by the number of atoms. As r is decreased, at some point the electron clouds of the atoms start to overlap and interact, and the discrete levels spread out slightly into rather narrow bands. At this stage, the energies of the allowed states differ only slightly from that of the discrete level of the isolated atom, and the wave functions are only slightly perturbed from those of the free atoms. They can therefore be identified as slightly modified 1s, 2s, and 2p bands, and it is clear that the number of states in each band is still equal to the degeneracy of the atomic level times N, the number of atoms.

As the atoms approach each other more closely, however, the bands themselves overlap and the electron wave functions must now be regarded as mixtures or superpositions of atomic wave functions formerly closely associated with individual atomic levels. This is illustrated above for the 2s and 2p bands of diamond, which contain the crystal's $4N$ valence electrons. The states themselves are somewhat difficult to describe, but their total *number* remains unchanged by the interaction. In the 2s and 2p bands, there are a total of $8N$ states and $4N$ electrons. As the interatomic spacing gets smaller and smaller, two new bands split off, as illustrated. Each of these new bands now contains $4N$ quantum states. When the interatomic distance r equals the equilibrium lattice spacing a, the situation is that illustrated by the vertical dashed line in the figure. It is now apparent that the lower of these two bands will accommodate all $4N$ valence electrons, and will thus be *completely full* at zero temperature. It can thus act as the valence band of a semiconductor. The upper band, also having $4N$ quantum states, is *empty* at absolute zero, and can thus function as the conduction band. In diamond, the energy gap $\Delta\varepsilon$ is quite large (of the order of 5.5eV) and the material is therefore in its pure state more like an insulator, in many respects, than a typical semiconductor. It is, however, photoconducting when illuminated by ultraviolet light of sufficiently short wavelength, and exhibits other characteristic semiconductor properties under proper conditions. The equilibrium point $r = a$ occurs at a point near the minima of the band edges, and the electrons occupying the valence band are therefore *lower* in energy than they are in the widely separated atoms. This energy difference is what binds the atoms together, and it is responsible for the fact that diamond is a crystalline solid rather than a gas.

The four states per atom in the valence band are derived from a single 2s atate and three 2p states. If you construct such a state as a sum of these wave functions, of the form

$$\psi = \psi(2s) + \psi(2p, m = 0) + \psi(2p, m = +1) + \psi(2p, m = -1) \ , \tag{9.2-4}$$

using the hydrogenic wave functions listed in Section 4.14, you will find that the angular dependence of $\psi^*\psi$ consists of a single lobe whose maximum is in the (111) direction of a cubic cell. The fact that hydrogenic wave functions are used is of no consequence, since the angular dependence of all one-electron atomic wave functions is the same as those of hydrogen; it is only the radial functions that are different. Slightly different superpositions of the general form,

$$\psi = \psi(2s) + \psi(2p, m = 0) - \psi(2p, m = +1) - \psi(2p, m = -1) \ ,$$

$$\psi = \psi(2s) - \psi(2p, m = 0) + \psi(2p, m = +1) - \psi(2p, m = -1) \ ,$$

$$\psi = \psi(2s) - \psi(2p, m = 0) - \psi(2p, m = +1) + \psi(2p, m = -1) \ ,$$

(9.2-5)

give wave functions that are similar, except that the lobe describing the angular maximum of $\psi^*\psi$ is now in the direction of three other {111} cube diagonals oriented *tetrahedrally* with respect to the first. This suggests that this particular mixture of *s* and *p* wave functions fits naturally into a geometry in which atoms are tetrahedrally arranged in the diamond structure shown in Figure 1.7, and in which the electron density is greatest along the tetrahedral "covalent bonds" defined by these functions. The wave functions shown above that describe this electron density are referred to as sp^3 orbital functions. In each of these covalent bonds, one electron is contributed by each of two neighboring atoms, and are shared equally between the two. The two electrons in the bonds are of opposite spin. In the final arrangement, four valence electrons of each atom are shared equally in four tetrahedrally disposed covalent electron-pair bonds with four neighboring atoms, as illustrated in Figure 1.7. In covalent materials the electrons are strongly localized along the bond directions illustrated in the figure below. The electrons in these covalent bonds are the electrons that populate the *valence band* at zero temperature.

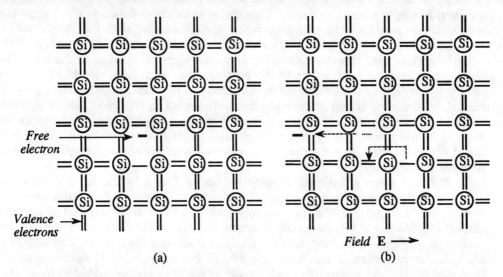

Figure 9.3 (a) A free electron formed by the removal of a valence electron from the covalent bond network, leaving a defect behind which is identified as a hole. (b) Subsequent motion of the free electron and the defect under the influence of an electric field in the direction shown above.

The situation can be illustrated by two-dimensional diagrams like those in Figure 9.3. At (a) in this figure, a regular array of silicon atoms held together by covalent electron-pair bonds is shown. Each silicon atom has four nearest neighbors, as in the three-dimensional diamond lattice. The covalent bonds that bind them together are made up of two electrons having opposite spins. Each of these electrons is represented as a line connecting neighboring silicon atoms. Each silicon atom shares its four valence electrons with neighboring atoms, and each atom is surrounded by eight electrons--four of its own and one belonging to each of four nearest neighbor atoms. In a perfect crystal at zero temperature, this bond network would be absolutely perfect throughout the crystal. At normal temperatures, however, a few electrons will be thermally excited into the conduction band. This process, as shown at (a), removes an electron from one of the covalent bonds, and allows it to move about in the crystal, independent of the valence bond network, as a mobile free electron. It also leaves behind a *defect* in the bond network in the form of a bond lacking one of its electrons. This defect can be identified as a hole, as we shall see. When a positively directed electric field is present, the free electron moves off in the direction shown at (b), and contributes to the conductivity of the material much like a free electron in a metal.

The electric field acts, of course, not only on the free electron, but also on electrons in the network of covalent bonds. Most of these electrons are restrained from going anywhere by the Pauli exclusion principle, which prevents any silicon atom from accommodating more than eight valence electrons. An electron on a site adjacent to a defect in the bond network, however, can *tunnel* from its initial valence bond site into the vacant one. In so doing, it moves in a direction opposite that of the field, thus lowering its potential energy. This process is shown at (b) by the dashed arrow at the right, which illustrates an electron tunneling in the direction opposite the field E into a defect from an adjacent valence bond site. The defect site, however, has now moved to the right, to the new location shown at (b), just as if it were a mobile *positively* charged particle. It is obvious that such a mobile defect in the bond network can be identified as our old friend, the hole. The motion of the hole to the right was actually caused by a valence electron moving to the left. This electron motion also contributes to the current flow, and gives rise to an electron current to the left, or a hole current in the direction of conventional current flow, to the right. The sign of conventional current attributed to free electrons in the conduction band and holes in the valence band is positive in both cases. It is important in using two-dimensional representations like those drawn above, to understand that the actual lattice has the three-dimensional tetrahedral bond configuration of the diamond structure.

There is some additional information to be found in the band diagram of Figure 9.2. The interatomic spacing of diamond is, in view of the differences in atomic radii, smaller than that of silicon, which is smaller still than that of germanium. If the spacing a increases, the diagram indicates that the gap energy $\Delta\varepsilon$ gets smaller. Though the band diagrams for all these materials are not precisely identical, this qualitative behavior has been confirmed by experimental observations for diamond, silicon and germanium. Moreover, if the crystal is compressed hydrostatically, the interatomic spacing decreases, and the gap energy, according to the diagram, should increase. This indication has also been confirmed experimentally for the series of Column IV covalent semiconductors. Finally, thermal expansion brings about a small increase in interatomic spacing with increasing temperature, which should cause the gap energy to exhibit a small temperature dependence, and to decrease slightly as the temperature increases. This effect has also been observed experimentally. These observations all confirm the general validity of the results illustrated in Figure 9.2.

TABLE 9.1   PROPERTIES OF COVALENT SEMICONDUCTORS

	Diamond	Si	Ge	
$\Delta\varepsilon$ (0K)	5.6	1.15	0.75	eV
$\Delta\varepsilon$ (300K)	5.48	1.11	0.67	eV
Bond length	1.54	2.35	2.43	Å
n_i (300K)	insignif-	1.5×10^{10}	2.4×10^{13}	cm^{-3}
(or)	icant.	1.5×10^{16}	2.4×10^{19}	m^{-1}
ρ_i (300K)	1×10^{8}	230,000	46	ohm-cm
(or)	1×10^{6}	2,300	0.46	ohm-m
μ_n (300K)	1,800	1,350	3,900	cm^2/volt-sec
(or)	0.18	0.135	0.39	m^2/volt-sec
μ_p (300K)	1,600	480	1,900	cm^2/volt-sec
(or)	0.16	0.048	0.19	m^2/volt-sec

Some of the more important properties of the Column IV covalent semicon-ductores are listed in the above table. The symbol n_i refers to the density of electrons (or holes) in the intrinsic substance at the given temperature, while ρ_i is the electrical resistivity of the intrinsic material at the temperature specified. Observe the high intrinsic resistivity of diamond as compared with silicon or germanium, a consequence of the large energy gap. Figures are given in cgs as well as mks/SI units since there are many situations of practical interest in which mks/SI units are awkward in magnitude and less than optimally informative. One rarely encounters in electronic applications silicon samples whose volume is conveniently expressed in m^3, for example. Indeed, cm^3 is often too large--frequently, (microns)^3 would be more realistic! In any case, these units have been legitimized by longstanding practice, and it is probably not only useless, but counterproductive to attempt to discard them.

9.3 IMPURITY SEMICONDUCTORS

We have mentioned that the properties of semiconductors can be changed drastically by the introduction of extremely small amounts of certain types of impurities. The impurities most frequently introduced in the case of the covalent semiconductors of Column IV are those in the neighboring Columns III and V of the periodic table. In Column III are the trivalent elements B, Al, Ga, and In, while the Column V elements include P, As, and Sb. All these elements can be quite easily incorporated into the diamond lattices of the covalent semiconductors as substitutional impurities, that is, impurities that occupy sites in the lattice normally occupied by covalent atoms such as C, Si or Ge. The valence electrons of these impurity atoms accommodate themselves to the extent possible to the normal covalent bond network of the Column IV semiconductor, but since they do not have exactly the right number of valence electrons, certain important effects are associated with their presence in the lattice, as illustrated in Figure 9.4. Materials in which these impurities are present to a significant extent are known as *impurity* semiconductors, or *extrinsic* semiconductors.

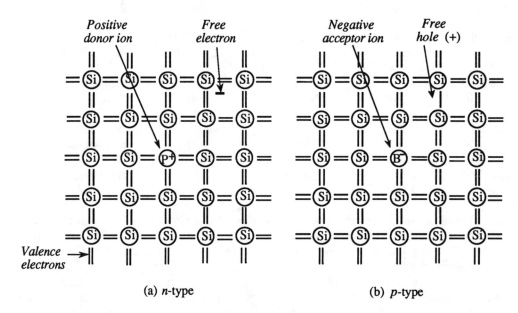

(a) *n*-type   (b) *p*-type

Figure 9.4 (a) A substitutional donor ion (phosphorus) in a covalent *n*-type semiconductor (silicon). (b) an acceptor (boron) ion in a covalent *p*-type semiconductor.

If the substitutional atom is from Column V, as shown at (a) above for a phosphorus atom in the lattice of a silicon crystal, it has five valence electrons, four of which form covalent bonds with neighboring silicon atoms--bonds that are not appreciably different from others in the valence bond network. There is an extra electron, however, for which no place exists in the covalent bond system. This electron, in the crystal, is bound far less firmly to the phosphorus atom than it would be to a normal phosphorus atom in free space. It thus requires a very small amount of energy to ionize the phosphorus atom, and to excite this extra electron into the conduction band. The energy required to do this is only a few percent of the gap energy $\Delta\varepsilon$. Indeed, the vibrational energy of the lattice at room temperature is sufficient to assure that these atoms are *completely* ionized, and that their extra electrons are in the conduction band at all times; they are in fact free electrons indistinguishable from those created by thermal excitation across the energy gap. The phosphorus atom has in effect donated its extra valence electron to the conduction band. It is referred to for this reason as a *donor* impurity atom.

In giving up its electron, of course, the donor impurity acquires a positive charge, and becomes a positive donor ion. Since the ion is bound firmly to its lattice site by strong covalent bonds, however, it is *immobile*, and plays essentially no part in free-carrier processes--except to guarantee the overall electrical neutrality of the crystal. However, there are now not only intrinsic electron-hole pairs excited thermally across the energy gap, but also *extra* electrons donated by the impurity atoms. This means that in crystals having substitutional donor impurities, there are *more electrons than holes,* and that electrical current in such crystals is carried primarily by free electrons. Such materials are referred to as *n*-type semiconductors.

You will observe from Table 9.1 that the intrinsic electron/hole concentration in silicon at 300K is only about 1.5×10^{10} carriers per cm³. You need only add donor impurities in concentrations as large as or larger than this figure to alter the equilibrium concentration of electron and holes markedly, and thus change the conductivity significantly. But the intrinsic carrier concentration given above amounts to only about *one trillionth* the number of silicon atoms in the lattice. Thus, incredibly small amounts of donor impurities can effect profound changes in the properties of the semiconductor. It is also somewhat incredible that silicon crystals of such purity as to have intrinsic conductivity at or near room temperature can be prepared, but it is possible (albeit with difficulty) to produce them. The availability of single-crystal, high purity materials such as these is what has made it possible to use the covalent semiconductors as electronic materials.

When the substitutional impurities are from Column III of the periodic table, there are only three valence electrons available to bond with neighboring semiconductor atoms There is now a defect at the impurity site that looks very much like a hole. Moreover, it is easy for electrons in adjacent covalent bonds to move into this site, and allow the defect itself to move off through the valence bond network as a free hole, as illustrated in Figure 9.4(b). This endows the acceptor site with an extra electron, which gives it a negative charge and transforms it to an immobile negative ion. The impurity atom freely accepts an additional electron; for this reason it is referred to as an *acceptor* impurity, and its lattice site is referred to as an ionized acceptor site. Very little energy is needed to introduce the electron into an acceptor site and convert it into a negative ion. As in the case of donors, the vibrational energy of the lattice is enough to keep these sites completely ionized at room temperature in most covalent semiconductors. In semiconductors to which acceptor impurities have been added there are *more holes than electrons.* Materials of this type are known as *p*-type semiconductors. As in the case of *n*-type substances, a miniscule concentration of acceptor impurity atoms can cause a radical alteration in the electrical conductivity and other properties of the material.

We have mentioned the ease with which donor and acceptor atoms are ionized. It is important to understand this subject in more detail, for it is relevant to the derivation of many of the properties of the electron/hole distribution. In the case of donor atoms, the ion itself carries a positive charge, while the donor electron is negative. The system therefore resembles a hydrogenic atom in which the donor ion plays the role of the proton or other singly charged ion, to which an electron can be bound. In the crystal, however, the environment of the electron is quite different from what prevails in a hydrogen atom, because it is surrounded by the covalent bond network. As a crude first approximation, we can consider this environment as a *uniform polarizable dielectric* with dielectric permittivity $K\varepsilon_0$, where K is the relative permittivity of the material. This problem has already been worked twice, once in connection with the Bohr atom of Section 4.5 and again using wave mechanics in Section 4.14. The results are the same in both cases, and they can be adapted to this problem by letting $Z = 1$ and replacing ε_0 by $K\varepsilon_0$ in (4.5 - 5, 6, and 7), or their equivalents in Section 4.14. These equations now show that the allowed energies are *reduced* by a factor K^2 from their values in hydrogen, while the orbital radii are *increased* by a factor K. You may recall that diamond has a very high refractive index of about 2.5, giving a relative permittivity $K = n^2 = 6.25$. The permittivities of Si ($K = 12$) and Ge ($K = 16$) are even higher. This means that the ionization energy of a donor ion in Si is 144 times less than the value 13.6eV for hydrogen, or only about 0.09eV, while the orbital radius is 12 times larger than the figure of 0.528Å characteristic of hydrogen, or 6.34Å. The experimentally measured ionization energy for phosphorus donors in Si is 0.045ev. The agreement is good considering the crude nature of the model, and it looks even better if one notes that the effective mass of electrons in silicon is roughly one-third the electron's inertial mass, which according to (4.5 - 7) lowers the calculated ionization energy to 0.03eV. Moreover, the calculated orbital radii are so large that a sphere of this size, in the case of silicon, contains over 50 atomic volumes. Under these circumstances, it isn't unreasonable to suppose that the material acts like a macroscopic polarized dielectric. You will recall that the dipole fields of the polarized atoms of any dielectric act to make the electric field within the dielectric smaller than what it would be if only the free charges were present, without the dielectric. This is physically why it takes so much less energy to ionize the atom when it is within such a medium.

When the electron belonging to a donor atom is ionized with minimum possible energy, it has been excited to a quantum state at the bottom of the conduction band. When bound to the donor atom, it is thus in a quantum ground state whose energy ε_d is a few hundredths of an electron volt *less* than this, a state which therefore lies in the forbidden region, below the conduction band by the small donor ionization energy. Such quantum states are referred to as donor states (or, less correctly, donor levels), and are shown in Figure 9.5. These donor states are *localized*, because the wave function of an electron in the donor ground state extends only a few Ångströms from the donor atom, as calculated above. Electrons associated with donor atoms can also have discrete excited states like those of the hydrogen atom, but these states play no significant part in most physical processes involving donor atoms.

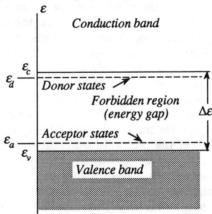

Figure 9.5 Revised band diagram showing the position of localized donor and acceptor states relative to the band edges. The spacing between the donor/acceptor states and the band edges is exaggerated for clarity; in reality it should be smaller by a factor of about 5.

In the case of a *p*-type semiconductor, a negatively charged acceptor ion repels electrons. Its energy is therefore lowest when there are as few electrons around as possible, a condition realized when a hole is at the acceptor site. This is equivalent to observing that a negatively charged acceptor ion attracts positive holes. The system is thus in equilibrium at zero temperature when holes are attached to donor atoms and there are no holes in the valence band, which is now totally occupied. In ionizing an acceptor, an electron at the top of the valence band has to move into a state of slightly *higher* energy ε_a--a state slightly *above* the top of the valence band. Such a state is referred to as an acceptor state (or acceptor level), as illustrated in Figure 9.5. Like donor states, acceptor states are localized, and can be described in terms of hole wave functions that extend outward from the site only a relatively small distance. One may think of the acceptor states as being "full of holes" in the zero-temperature equilibrium state, the effect of thermal energy then being to excite electrons into them, which amounts to creating holes in the valence band. The acceptor atom now becomes a negative ion in view of the extra electron it possesses. The ionization energy $\varepsilon_a - e_v$ is so small that at normal temperatures the acceptors are almost completely ionized, having acquired electrons from the valence band and become negative ions. It is important to note that in band diagrams like the one above, electrons seek states of the lowest possible energy, consistent with the Pauli exclusion principle and the requirement of constant total internal energy at a given temperature. Holes, on the other hand, which represent unoccupied states, tend to "gravitate upward" like bubbles in a liquid, subject to these same constraints.

9.4 STATISTICS OF ELECTRONS AND HOLES

We are now ready to discuss quantitatively the properties of the electron and hole free-particle gases in semiconductors. First of all, it is important to observe that the electron density in the conduction band is greatest at the bottom of the band, but falls off rapidly as energy increases. The decrease in electron concentration is exponential, falling off by a factor roughly $1/e$ in an energy increment kT, which at room temperature is only about 0.025eV. Thus, practically the entire electron population resides within a narrow range of energies near the bottom of the band, a range whose width is hardly greater than 0.1eV. This figure is far smaller than the entire upward extent of the band in energy, which amounts typically to several electron volts. In this region near the band edge, we have observed in Section 8.6 of the preceding chapter, that the density of states function has the form of a free-particle density of states, referred to an origin at the band edge. The only difference is that we must use an appropriately defined effective mass in place of the electron's inertial mass. Similar remarks apply to holes in the valence band, whose population for similar reasons is confined to an equally narrow range of energies near the top of the valence band. The form of the appropriate density of states functions has in fact already been found as equations (8.6 - 17) and (8.6 - 18), for regions respectively near the bottom and top of a band. We can thus write for electrons in the conduction band,

$$g_c(\varepsilon)\,d\varepsilon = \frac{8\sqrt{2\pi}}{h^3} m_n^{*3/2} \sqrt{\varepsilon - \varepsilon_c}\, d\varepsilon \qquad (9.4-1)$$

as the density of states per unit volume of crystal, and for holes near the top of the valence band,

$$g_v(\varepsilon)\,d\varepsilon = \frac{8\sqrt{2}\,\pi}{h^3}\,m_p{}^{*3/2}\sqrt{\varepsilon_v - \varepsilon}\,\,d\varepsilon\,.$$

(9.4-2)

These functions are plotted in Figure 9.6.

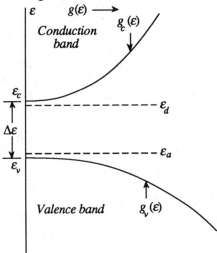

Figure 9.6 Density of states functions for the conduction and valence band of a typical covalent semiconductor. Density of states axis is horizontal. Density of states in the forbidden energy region is identically zero.

The distribution function for electrons is the standard Fermi-Dirac distribution $f(\varepsilon)$, but the distribution function for holes in the valence band, which represent unfilled electronic states, must be expressed as $1 - f(\varepsilon)$. We therefore write

$$f(\varepsilon) = \frac{1}{1 + e^{(\varepsilon - \varepsilon_f)/kT}}$$

(9.4-3)

for electrons in the conduction band, and for holes in the valence band,

$$f_p(\varepsilon) = 1 - f(\varepsilon) = \frac{e^{(\varepsilon - \varepsilon_f)/kT}}{1 + e^{(\varepsilon - \varepsilon_f)/kT}}\,.$$

(9.4-4)

The number of conduction electrons per unit volume and the number of free holes per unit volume are found by integrating the product $f(\varepsilon)g_c(\varepsilon)\,d\varepsilon$ over the conduction band or $f_p(\varepsilon)g_v(\varepsilon)$ over the valence band. These integrals are illustrated as the shaded areas in Figure 9.7, where for simplicity the effective mass of electrons and holes is assumed to be equal. In an intrinsic semiconductor, these two numbers must be the same, since thermal excitation yields one hole for every electron. In Figure 9.7(a), it is evident that the two areas representing these integrals can be equal only when the Fermi energy is at the center of the energy gap, midway between conduction and valence bands. If the two effective masses are not radically different, the Fermi energy may depart from this position somewhat, but it will still lie deep within the forbidden region, far from either band edge.

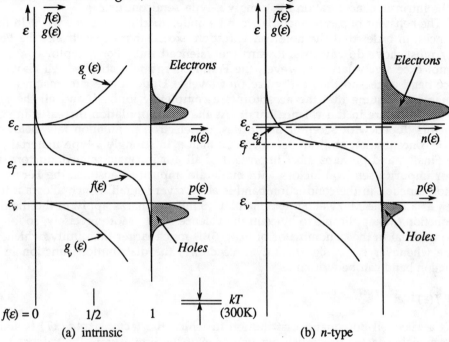

Figure 9.7 Distribution functions, Fermi energy, and electron/hole populations (shown as shaded areas) for (a) an intrinsic semiconductor, and (b) an n-type semiconductor. The spread of the Fermi distribution function is grossly exaggerated for illustrative reasons; in reality it is normally much more steplike.

It is important to observe in the diagrams above, that the spread of the Fermi distribution about the Fermi energy is *exaggerated* to facilitate drawing the figure, and at normal temperatures the Fermi function looks far more like a step function than these illustrations suggest. Note also that the region over which the Fermi function changes rapidly is only about $2kT$ in extent on either side of the Fermi energy. The size of the energy interval kT is shown in the diagram for the case of Ge.

Figure 9.7(b) illustrates the case of an impurity semiconductor, in this case an n-type substance in which the concentration of free electrons in the conduction band is much larger than the hole concentration in the valence band. To achieve this kind of asymmetry in the electron and hole populations, the Fermi energy must clearly move *upward* from the intrinsic level at the center of the gap to a position closer to the conduction band edge. If the donor impurity density is not excessively large, however, the Fermi energy will still be within the energy gap, well below the donor and acceptor levels, which, on the scale of the energy gap, are very close to the conduction and valence band edges. For such materials, the value of the Fermi distribution function will be very small at the energy ε_d. This means that the probability of an electron residing in a donor state is small, and that it is realistic to assume that donor states are completely ionized, so that all the extra electrons they contribute are in the conduction band. We shall find that this assumption is of wide (though not universal) applicability, and that it greatly simplifies the treatment of impurity semiconductors. The figure also shows that as the electron concentration increases in *n*-type materials the population of holes decreases, becoming far smaller than the intrinsic concentration in strongly *n*-type semiconductors.

The behavior of *p*-type materials can be understood in the same way. In these substances, in order that the hole concentration exceed that of electrons, the Fermi energy must move downwards, toward the valence band. For acceptor concentrations not excessively large, however, the Fermi energy will still be well above the valence band edge and the nearby acceptor levels   Under these circumstances it is reasonable to assume that the acceptors are completely ionized, and all the holes they contribute are in the valence band. As the hole population increases in semiconductors doped with acceptor impurities, the electron population falls below the intrinsic concentration and can be much less than n_i in strongly *p*-type materials.

Finally, and perhaps most important of all, for intrinsic semiconductors, and also for impurity semiconductors with moderate impurity densities, the Fermi distribution function in the conduction band is always very small, which allows it to be written as a simple Maxwellian exponential. Similar remarks apply to the distribution function $f_p(\varepsilon)$ applicable to holes in the valence band. More precisely, so long as the exponential in the denominator of (9.4 - 3) is much larger than unity, which will be true whenever $\varepsilon_c - \varepsilon_f$ significantly exceeds kT, the distribution function in the conduction band can be written as

$$f(\varepsilon) = e^{(\varepsilon_f - \varepsilon)/kT} = e^{\varepsilon_f/kT} \cdot e^{-\varepsilon/kT} \ . \tag{9.4-5}$$

This is a Maxwell-Boltzmann distribution in which the factor $\exp(\varepsilon_f/kT)$ is simply the normalizing factor previously written as $\exp(\alpha)$. Similarly, in the valence band, whenever $\varepsilon_f - \varepsilon_v$ is appreciably larger than kT, the exponential in the denominator of (9.4 - 4) will be much smaller than unity and can be neglected, leaving

$$f_p(\varepsilon) = e^{(\varepsilon - \varepsilon_f)/kT} = e^{-\varepsilon_f/kT} \cdot e^{\varepsilon/kT} \ . \tag{9.4-6}$$

This simplification, often referred to as the *Boltzmann approximation*, allows us to write the equilibrium density n_0 of electrons in the conduction band as

$$n_0 = \int_{\varepsilon_c}^{\infty} f(\varepsilon) g_c(\varepsilon) d\varepsilon = \frac{8\sqrt{2}\,\pi}{h^3} m_n^{*3/2} e^{\varepsilon_f/kT} \int_{\varepsilon_c}^{\infty} \sqrt{\varepsilon - \varepsilon_c} \cdot e^{-\varepsilon/kT} d\varepsilon \ . \tag{9.4-7}$$

The integral should extend only over the conduction band, but since the distribution function is small except near the lower band edge, little error is introduced by assuming the upper limit infinite. The integral is simplified further by the substitution

$$x_c = (\varepsilon - \varepsilon_c)/kT, \qquad dx_c = d\varepsilon/kT \ . \tag{9.4-8}$$

This allows us to write (9.4 - 7) as

$$n_0 = \frac{8\sqrt{2}\,\pi}{h^3} (m_n^* kT)^{3/2} e^{(\varepsilon_f - \varepsilon_c)/kT} \int_0^{\infty} \sqrt{x_c}\, e^{-x_c} dx_c \ . \tag{9.4-9}$$

The definite integral has been encountered previously; its value is $\sqrt{\pi}/2$. Substituting this into the above expression and simplifying, we can finally obtain,

$$n_0 = c_n e^{-(\varepsilon_c - \varepsilon_f)/kT} , \quad \text{where} \quad c_n = 2\left(\frac{2\pi m_n * kT}{h^2}\right)^{3/2} . \tag{9.4-10}$$

A similar calculation can be made for holes in the valence band; using the density of states function (9.4 - 2) and the distribution function (9.4 - 6), we find

$$p_0 = \int_{-\infty}^{\varepsilon_v} f_p(\varepsilon) g_v(\varepsilon) d\varepsilon = \frac{8\sqrt{2}\pi}{h^3} m_p *^{3/2} e^{-\varepsilon_f/kT} \int_{-\infty}^{\varepsilon_v} \sqrt{\varepsilon_v - \varepsilon} \cdot e^{\varepsilon/kT} d\varepsilon . \tag{9.4-11}$$

Now, making the substitution

$$x_v = (\varepsilon_v - \varepsilon)/kT , \quad dx_v = -d\varepsilon/kT , \tag{9.4-12}$$

we obtain

$$p_0 = \frac{8\sqrt{2}\pi}{h^3} (m_p * kT)^{3/2} e^{(\varepsilon_v - \varepsilon_f)/kT} \int_0^\infty \sqrt{x_v}\, e^{-x_v} dx_v . \tag{9.4-13}$$

Substituting the value of the integral and simplifying as above, this becomes,

$$p_0 = c_p e^{-(\varepsilon_f - \varepsilon_v)/kT} , \quad \text{where} \quad c_p = 2\left(\frac{2\pi m_p * kT}{h^2}\right)^{3/2} . \tag{9.4-14}$$

The concentrations of electrons and holes shown as shaded areas in Figure 9.7 are expressed analytically by (9.4 - 10) and (9.4 - 11). These expressions are somewhat ambiguous, since the Fermi energy is as yet unknown. It is not difficult to evaluate this quantity, but first we must observe that if one multiplies (9.4 - 10) by (9.4 - 11), the product $n_0 p_0$ so obtained is *independent* of the Fermi energy, and depends only on the temperature and the energy gap $\Delta\varepsilon$. If n_0 and p_0 are equal--that is, if the material is intrinsic--this product gives the square of the common concentration n_i of electrons and holes for the intrinsic substance. If n_0 and p_0 are *not* equal, the square root of their product equals the intrinsic electron/hole concentration n_i at any given temperature. The product of these equations thus leads to an important general result,

$$n_0 p_0 = c_n c_p e^{-(\varepsilon_c - \varepsilon_v)/kT} = c_n c_p e^{-\Delta\varepsilon/kT} = n_i^2 , \tag{9.4-15}$$

where

$$n_i = 2\left(\frac{2\pi \sqrt{m_n * m_p *} kT}{h^2}\right)^{3/2} e^{-\Delta\varepsilon/2kT} . \tag{9.4-16}$$

The constancy of the product of electron and hole concentrations expresses what is known to chemists as a *mass-action law*, similar to that which governs the dissociation of a weak electrolyte like water into two oppositely charged ions, (H^+)

and (OH$^-$). In this instance, the dissociation reaction is the thermally activated dissociation of a covalent bond into an ionized electron-hole pair. The context is different, but the form of the relationship between the concentration of the two ionized species, and the subsequent kinetics, is the same.

The Fermi level for an intrisic semiconductor can now be found by equating n_0, as expressed by (9.4 - 10) and p_0 as given by (9.4 - 14). We are then left with an equation that can be solved for $\exp(2\varepsilon_f/kT)$, Taking the logarithm, we obtain finally,

$$\varepsilon_f = \tfrac{1}{2}(\varepsilon_c + \varepsilon_v) + \tfrac{3}{4}kT \ln \frac{m_p^*}{m_n^*} \ . \tag{9.4-17}$$

In the equation above the first term can be identified as the average of the band edge energies ε_c and ε_v. It therefore defines a point at the center of the gap, midway between the band edges. The second term is zero when the hole and electron effective masses are equal. In the covalent semiconductors, the ratio of the two masses does not differ from unity so much as to make the logarithm very large, and in addition, kT is normally much smaller than the energy defined by the first term. The second term is therefore small compared with the first for covalent materials. There are other materials, however, particularly the semiconducting III-V intermetallic compounds, for which this term can be significant.

Equations (9.4 - 10) and (9.4 - 14) giving the equilibrium electron and hole concentrations can be put into another form that can sometimes be very useful. To do this, we write the factor $\exp(\varepsilon_f/kT)$ in (9.4 - 10) as $\exp[(\varepsilon_f - \varepsilon_{fi})/kT] \times \exp(\varepsilon_{fi}/kT)$, where ε_{fi} is the "intrinsic Fermi energy" defined by (9.4 - 17). Replacing the second exponential factor (but not the first) in this product with its equivalent defined by (9.4 - 17), the resulting expression can be simplified to read

$$n_0 = 2\left(\frac{2\pi\sqrt{m_p^* m_n^*}kT}{h^2}\right)^{3/2} e^{-\Delta\varepsilon/2kT} \cdot e^{(\varepsilon_f - \varepsilon_{fi})/kT} = n_i e^{(\varepsilon_f - \varepsilon_{fi})/kT} \ . \tag{9.4-18}$$

Then, from (9.4 - 15), it follows that

$$p_0 = \frac{n_i^2}{n_0} = n_i e^{-(\varepsilon_f - \varepsilon_{fi})/kT} \ . \tag{9.4-19}$$

From these expressions, it is evident that when $\varepsilon_f = \varepsilon_{fi}$, the intrinsic carrier concentration is obtained, and that otherwise the electron/hole concentrations differ from the intrinsic concentration only by Boltzmann factors involving the difference between the actual and intrinsic Fermi energies. We shall find these relations useful in dealing with impurity semiconductors, a problem we shall now address.

In intrinsic semiconductors, the equilibrium electron and hole concentrations must always be equal. Impurity semiconductors, however, need not satisfy this condition. However, in any electrically neutral crystal, the sum of all negative and positive charges within the substance must be $zero$. For an impurity semiconductor in equilibrium, assumed (for generality) to have $both$ donor and acceptor impurities, all of which are completely ionized, we can therefore write the sum of the mobile charge densities and that of the immobile impurity ions as

$$e(p_0 - n_0) + e(N_d - N_a) = 0 \; , \tag{9.4-20}$$

where N_d is the concentration of positively charged fixed donor ions, and N_a the concentration of negatively charged acceptor ions. However, according to (9.4 - 15), $p_0 = n_i^2/n_0$. Substituting this into the above equation and rearranging, a quadratic equation for n_0 of the form

$$n_0^2 - (N_d - N_a)n_0 - n_i^2 = 0 \tag{9.4-21}$$

is obtained. Its solution is

$$n_0 = \tfrac{1}{2}(N_d - N_a) + \sqrt{\tfrac{1}{4}(N_d - N_a)^2 + n_i^2} \; . \tag{9.4-22}$$

The equilibrium hole concentration may now be found with the aid of (9.4 - 15), as

$$p_0 = -\tfrac{1}{2}(N_d - N_a) + \sqrt{\tfrac{1}{4}(N_d - N_a)^2 + n_i^2} \; . \tag{9.4-23}$$

The Fermi energy can now be found from (9.4 - 20), writing n_0 and p_0 in the form given by (9.4 - 18) and (9.4 - 19). In this way, one obtains

$$-2n_i \sinh \frac{\varepsilon_f - \varepsilon_{fi}}{kT} + (N_d - N_a) = 0 \; ,$$

or, $\qquad \sinh \dfrac{\varepsilon_f - \varepsilon_{fi}}{kT} = \dfrac{N_d - N_a}{2n_i} \; . \tag{9.4-24}$

Equating the inverse hyperbolic sines of both sides of this expression and solving the resulting equation for the Fermi energy, we may finally write,

$$\varepsilon_f = \varepsilon_{fi} + kT \sinh^{-1}\left(\frac{N_d - N_a}{2n_i} \right) \; . \tag{9.4-25}$$

In intrinsic semiconductors, the electron/hole concentration is an exponentially increasing function of temperature. The presence of the quantity $\Delta\varepsilon$ in the exponential allows one use this property to determine the energy gap. The Fermi energy in *intrinsic* materials is at the center of the gap, independent of temperature, provided the electron and hole effective masses are equal. If they are different (as they actually are in Si and Ge) there is a small, temperature dependent correction term in the Fermi energy.

In *impurity* semiconductors, the electron/hole concentration depends on the net impurity concentration $|N_d - N_a|$, as well as on n_i. The relation $n_0 p_0 = n_i^2$ is still valid, however. There is therefore a *majority* carrier population and a *minority* carrier population in these materials. In *n*-type semiconductors, electrons are the majority carriers, and holes the minority carriers; these roles are reversed in *p*-type substances. The populations are given by (9.4 - 22) and (9.4 - 23). It is evident that in "heavily doped" *n*-type crystals, for which N_a and n_i are both negligible in comparison with N_d, the electron and hole concentrations can be approximated as

$$n_0 = N_d \qquad \text{and} \qquad p_0 = n_i^2 / N_d \;. \qquad\qquad (9.4\text{-}26)$$

Likewise, in heavily doped p-type materials, it is a good approximation to write

$$p_0 = N_a \qquad \text{and} \qquad n_0 = n_i^2 / N_a \;. \qquad\qquad (9.4\text{-}27)$$

Since the electrical conductivity depends critically on the electron/hole concentrations, the conductivity can be profoundly affected by the addition of small amounts of impurities. This subject will be treated in detail in the next section.

Since the intrinsic carrier density depends exponentially on temperature, it may change dramatically even though the temperature change is not very large in absolute terms. Semiconductors therefore ordinarily act as *intrinsic* substances at temperatures high enough to generate an intrinsic carrier concentration large in comparison with the net donor or acceptor concentration, and as *extrinsic* semiconductors at temperatures sufficiently low to guarantee that the intrinsic carrier density is much smaller than than the net impurity concentration. For any semiconductor there is thus an *extrinsic range* and an *intrinsic range* of temperatures, the temperature of transition between the two being determined by the net impurity concentration and the energy gap of the material. In very pure germanium, this transition temperature can be far below room temperature, while for silicon and germanium samples that are moderately impure it is ordinarily above 300K.

In impurity semiconductors whose donor and acceptor sites are completely ionized, the Femi energy differs from the intrinsic Fermi energy (9.4 - 17) as shown in (9.4 - 25). In such substances, the Fermi energy depends on the net impurity density as well as the temperature. In n-type materials, where $N_d > N_a$, it is above the intrinsic Fermi energy, ordinarily in the upper half of the energy gap, while in p-type crystals, where $N_a > N_d$, it is below this level and thus in the lower half of the gap. Our discussion of this subject depends critically on the assumption that the impurity sites are completely ionized. Fortunately, this condition is satisfied over a wide range of temperatures and impurity concentrations. There are circumstances, however, in which it can be violated. In such instances, the above calculations become much more complicated. At very low temperatures, for example, it is possible to deionize donor and acceptor sites, and thus to "freeze" electrons and holes onto the impurity atoms. Fortunately, this happens in Ge and Si only at temperatures below the boiling point of liquid nitrogen, which is 77K. It is not too difficult to see that in n-type crystals at temperatures low enough to completely deionize donor atoms, the Fermi energy must be in the small gap between the donor levels and the conduction band, since the Fermi distribution must now have unit value at the energy ε_d. Likewise, in p-type material under these conditions, the Fermi energy must be between the valence band and the acceptor levels. Also, at *normal* temperatures, the net impurity concentration $N_d - N_a$ can be so large that the Fermi energy as given by (9.4 - 25) approaches the edge of the conduction or valence band. As this happens, the condition of total ionization is also violated, because (for n-type materials) the Fermi function is no longer very small at the donor level energy ε_d. One may therefore conclude that when (9.4 - 25) suggests a Fermi energy separated from a band edge by several times kT, the condition of complete ionization is satisfied, but when this is no longer so, it is probably invalid.

Consider, for example, the case of germanium, whose energy gap at 300K is roughly 0.7eV, or about $28kT$. Suppose that the Fermi energy is only $3kT$ below the edge of the conduction band. This is about $11kT$ above the center of the gap, where the Fermi energy would be in the intrinsic state. Now, from (9.4 - 24), the net impurity density must be

$$N_d - N_a = 2n_i \sinh\frac{\varepsilon_f - \varepsilon_{fi}}{kT} = 2(2.4\times10^{13})\sinh(11) = 1.4\times10^{18}\,\mathrm{cm}^{-3} \ ,$$

using the value of the intrinsic carrier concentration at 300K from Table 9.1. This amounts to a net impurity concentration of about one atom in 40,000, or 0.002%. At first sight, this may not seem very large, but you must observe that a concentration 10^5 times smaller would have a significant effect on the electron/hole populations. So the figure shown above, in the context of semiconductor technology, is actually enormous. This figure gives a rough estimate of the maximum impurity concentration for which the assumption of complete ionization of donor impurity atoms is valid at 300K. From this, it appears that under normal circumstances, this assumption is usually very safe.

Finally, it is important to observe that all the results exhibited above for impurity semiconductors depend not on the donor and acceptor concentrations themselves, but only on the difference $N_d - N_a$. In materials that are intentionally doped n- or p-type, this quantity differs only very slightly from the concentration of the majority doping substance. Occasionally, however, one encounters crystals in which both donor and acceptor impurities are present in significant amounts; in such materials, N_d and N_a may both be as large as, or even larger than $|N_d - N_a|$. Substances such as this are said to be partially or wholly *compensated* semiconductors. The results given above suggest that wholly compensated materials, in which the net impurity density $N_d - N_a$ is zero, are similar in all respects to the pure intrinsic substance. This is not entirely true, for the presence of ionized impurity sites can itself affect the properties of the crystal, but as a first approximation it is often a reasonably good description of a wholly compensated material.

9.5 ELECTRICAL AND THERMAL CONDUCTIVITY

Uniform and homogeneous semiconductor crystals are ohmic conductors whenever the applied electric field is sufficiently small. In semiconductors, however, it is possible, because of their relatively high resistivity, to set up fields that are not "sufficiently small", in that they create drift velocities of the order of the average thermal velocity, and may even excite drift kinetic energies sufficient to create electron-hole pairs. Also, because of the high resistivity, ohmic heating can cause temperature rises that significantly increase the conductivity of intrinsic samples, an effect that leads to increased current density and a further rise in the rate at which ohmic heat is produced. This process can be unstable, and can cause thermal breakdown or "runaway" that leads to uncontrolled heating of the material in circuits where no current-limiting element is present. It is thus important in measuring the properties of semiconductors, and in using semiconductors as circuit elements, to avoid these effects unless they are of some specific interest.

Ohmic conduction in semiconductors is more complex than in metals, most obviously because there are two species of charge carriers, but also because the number of carriers is not invariant, as it is in metals. The interpretation of measurements of conductivity *versus* temperature, for example, is more difficult in semiconductors than in metallic substances. Nevertheless, the same general picture of particles--electrons and holes--being accelerated for a certain free time by an external field, and being ultimately returned to the equilibrium distribution by collisions, is still valid. The same scattering mechanisms act in both cases; electrons and holes are scattered by lattice vibrations or by ionized impurity sites. Lattice imperfections, for example, vacant lattice sites, interstitial impurity atoms, dislocations, grain boundaries, and sample surfaces, can also scatter electrons and holes, though their effects are usually not very important in relatively pure and perfect crystals.

The electrical conductivity is in general expressed by (9.2 - 1), with mobilities as defined by (9.2 - 2). Accordingly, the ohmic conductivity for a uniform crystal with net impurity density $N_d - N_a$ is

$$\sigma = e(n_0\mu_n + p_0\mu_p) \ , \tag{9.5-1}$$

with equilibrium electron and hole densities as given by (9.4 - 22) and (9.4 - 23). Making these substitutions and simplifying, we find

$$\sigma = e\left(\tfrac{1}{2}(\mu_n - \mu_p)N_0 + (\mu_n + \mu_p)\sqrt{\tfrac{1}{4}N_0^2 + n_i^2}\right) \ , \tag{9.5-2}$$

with $\quad N_0 = N_d - N_a \ .$ $\tag{9.5-3}$

At temperatures high enough that the intrinsic carriers outweigh those contributed by impurities, $n_i \gg N_0$, and (9.5 - 2) can be approximated by

$$\sigma_i = e(\mu_n + \mu_p)n_i \ . \tag{9.5-4}$$

The intrinsic-range conductivity σ_i rises rapidly with increasing temperature because of the exponential temperature dependence of intrinsic carrier concentration. This is not the whole story, however, because the mobilities vary with temperature in the same way as the electron/hole relaxation times τ_n and τ_p. This variation is not, however, as rapid as that of the intrinsic carrier density, as we shall soon see.

In the extrinsic temperature range, at temperatures low enough to assure that $n_i \ll N_0$, the limiting values of (9.5 - 2) give

and
$$\sigma_e = e\mu_n(N_d - N_a) \quad (n\text{-type})$$
$$\sigma_e = e\mu_p(N_a - N_d) \quad (p\text{-type}) \ . \tag{9.5-5}$$

In writing the second equation above, one must use the negative sign of the square root in (9.5 - 2).

At relatively high temperatures, the scattering of electrons and holes by phonons is the dominant process. In this process, as we have seen in Chapter 7, it is often reasonable to assume a velocity-independent mean free path. Under these circumstances, the relaxation time for electrons and holes is of the form

$$\bar{\tau} = \overline{\lambda / v} = \lambda / \bar{v} \ . \tag{9.5-6}$$

In semiconductors, the distributions of free electrons in the conduction band and holes in the valence band are Maxwellian. Therefore, the process of averaging over the nonequilibrium distribution applicable to this situation is that shown previously in (7.3 - 30). Since the electron and hole mobilities are related to the relaxation times as shown in (9.2 - 2), we are led to write

$$\mu_n = \frac{4e\lambda_n}{3\sqrt{2\pi m_n^* kT}} \quad \text{and} \quad \mu_p = \frac{4e\lambda_p}{3\sqrt{2\pi m_p^* kT}} \ . \tag{9.5-7}$$

This seems to predict mobilities that vary with temperature as $T^{-1/2}$. However, you must remember that the mean free path itself depends inversely on the density of scatterers, in this case phonons. At sufficiently high temperatures, as suggested in (6.9 - 6), the number of available acoustical-mode phonons is $9NT/2V\Theta$, where N/V is the number of lattice atoms per unit volume. This puts another factor of T^{-1} into the temperature variation, and suggests that, for acoustical-mode phonon scattering,

$$\mu_n \propto T^{-3/2} \quad \text{and} \quad \mu_p \propto T^{-3/2} \ . \tag{9.5-8}$$

If this argument is correct, one would expect the intrinsic conductivity (9.5 - 4) to have the form

$$\sigma_i = (const.) \cdot e^{-\Delta\varepsilon/2kT} \ , \tag{9.5-9}$$

because of the cancellation of the temperature dependences shown in (9.5 - 8) and (9.4 - 16). This suggests that the intrinsic-range conductivity is a purely exponential function, whose slope in a semilogarithmic plot would yield a precise value for the energy gap. The argument, however is less than rigorous for two reasons. First, the expression given in (6.9 - 6) for the number of acoustical phonons is valid only at temperatures significantly above the Debye temperature. The Debye Temperature of germanium is roughly 400K, and for silicon is even higher, which makes this expression only a very rough approximation. Moreover, the primitive unit cell of the diamond lattice contains two atoms, which makes it possible for optical as well as acoustical-mode lattice vibrations--and phonons--to exist. These complications do not render the arguments above completely useless, but they do lessen their quantitative validity, particularly at temperatures below 300K. Experimentally, one finds that mobilities in relatively pure samples of Ge and Si do decrease with increasing temperature, as expected, in the range 77K-300K and above. Indeed, in n-type Ge the mobility is found experimentally to be roughly proportional to $T^{1.65}$. In p-type Ge, and both n-type and p-type Si, however, the temperature dependence is steeper, corresponding to $T^{-2.3}$ or thereabouts. Still, (9.5 - 9) is usually close enough to the truth to allow rather good measurements of the energy gap to be made as suggested above.

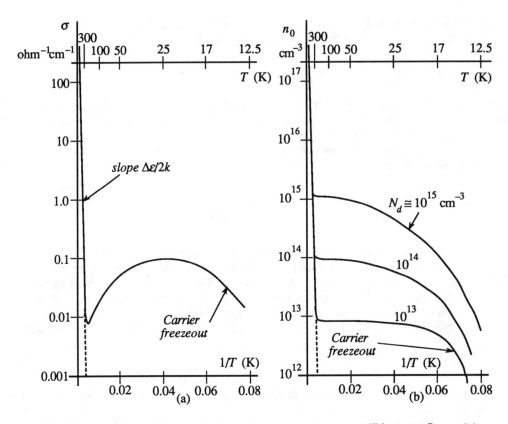

Figure 9.8 (a) Semilogarithmic plot of conductivity measurements versus $1/T$ for n-type Ge containing about 10^{13} donor impurity atoms per cm^3; (b) similar plot of free electron concentration versus $1/T$ for n-type Ge samples containing 10^{13}, 10^{14}, and 10^{15} donor atoms per cm^3. (After E. M. Conwell, Proc. IRE (IEEE) **40**, 1327 (1952).

Several experimental curves giving semilogarithmic plots of the temperature dependence of (a) the electrical conductivity and (b) the number of conduction-band electrons per unit volume are shown for n-type germanium samples in Figure 9.8. At (a) in the figure, we see the exponential behavior of conductivity *versus* $1/T$ in the intrinsic range as the straight line at the extreme left. The slope of this line gives a good estimate of the quantity $\Delta\varepsilon/2k$. In the extrinsic range on the right, the number of carriers is essentially independent of temperature, until at very low temperatures (less than about 25K in this case) the conduction electrons "freeze out" onto donor sites, which are then deionized. This behavior is shown most clearly in (b) above, in which the density of conduction electrons rather than the conductivity is plotted. The rise in conductivity with decreasing temperature in the range 25–300K is due to an increase in *mobility* associated with the decrease in the number of lattice phonons with decreasing temperature. For the relatively pure n-type material shown at (a), for which N_d is about $10^{13}cm^{-3}$, the transition between intrinsic and extrinsic behavior occurs slightly below room temperature. The resistivity of this material is about 45 ohm-cm at room temperature, and falls off (as its reciprocal, the conductivity, rises) rapidly with increasing temperature. As the temperature falls, the resistivity increases to a maximum value of somewhat over 100 ohm-cm at roughly 270K, and then, in the extrinsic range, decreases, because of rising mobility, to a minimum value of about 10 ohm-cm at 25K, after which freezeout takes over. The two more impure samples shown in (b) are extrinsic at and above room temperature. Their room temperature resistivity is therefore governed mainly by the concentration of donor impurities, and is considerably smaller than that of the purest sample. These materials do not exhibit intrinsic conductivity until their temperature is considerably higher than 300K. You are asked as an exercise to determine this transition temperature for all three of these samples.

It is evident that the theory given above describes these experimental observations quite well. The assumptions on which it is founded are, of course, violated in the freezeout range, but even so, the phenomenon of freezeout is well understood and appears in the experimental data about where it is expected to show up. In very heavily doped substances, the donor and acceptor sites may be sufficiently closely spaced in the lattice that the wave functions of electrons or holes frozen out onto adjacent sites may slightly overlap, allowing deionized carriers to tunnel with some small but perceptible probability between adjacent impurity sites. This results in a small residual conductivity at the lowest realizable temperatures, a phenomenon which has been observed and which is referred to as *impurity band conduction*. At normal doping levels, and temperatures, however, this effect is so small as to be undetectable.

The thermal conductivity of reasonably pure semiconductor crystals is almost entirely accounted for by lattice mechanisms based on phonon-phonon scattering, as described in Chapter 6 (Section 6.9). The electron/hole populations in these materials are so small that the free-carrier thermal conductivity discussed in Chapter 7 is negligible in comparison with the lattice contribution. At very low temperatures, in pure and perfect crystals, however, surface scattering can be the dominant scattering process, and measured thermal conductivity is then found to be governed largely by the size of the crystal. Other than this, there are no unexpected effects assocated with thermal conductivity in semiconductors.

9.6 THE HALL EFFECT IN SEMICONDUCTORS

The Hall effect is important in semiconductors, as in metals, because it provides a good way of measuring the charge carrier concentration, independent of the carrier mobility. It has also been utilized in devices for measuring magnetic fields and fluxes. Since the extrinsic Hall field is inversely proportional to the concentration of free charge carriers, it is much larger--and much easier to observe and measure--in semiconductors than in metals. On the other hand, its analysis in semiconductors is complicated by the appearance of two species of charge carriers. We shall assume the same sample geometry as that shown in Figure 7.6 of Section 7.7. In this geometry, a steady current flows along the long axis of a rectangular sample, taken to be in the x-direction. There is a steady magnetic field B_z out of the page, normal to the sample surface, and a Hall field is set up in the vertical y-direction, whose effect is measured as a Hall voltage between contacts placed on the top and bottom of the sample as illustrated in Figure 7.6.

Holes and electrons moving in the ±x-direction are acted upon by transverse forces due to the magnetic field, as illustrated in Figure 9.9. It is assumed, as in the previous analysis, that electrons and holes each move with a single average drift velocity (though different for the two species), the effect of the distribution of velocities being neglected. This assumption is obviously open to question, but it greatly simplifies the discussion and leads to essentially the same results obtained by using the Boltzmann transport equation as a starting point. Moreover, it provides certain physical insights into the behavior of charges and currents not easily obtained from a more rigorously mathematical approach. We may begin by observing that the magnetic forces $q(\mathbf{v} \times \mathbf{B})$ on the charges move *both* electrons and holes downwards to the lower edge of the sample, where they accumulate until a steady state is set up, in which the y-components of current and current density are zero, and in which the *total* current density vector in the sample is along the x-direction. Though the electron and hole charges that accumulate at the bottom edge of the sample tend to cancel, they do so in general only partially, so that there remains an electrostatic field E_y in the material due to a net accumulated charge at the top and bottom edges.

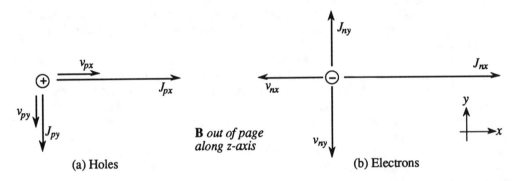

Figure 9.9 Velocity and current density components for (a) holes and (b) electrons in the geometry of the Hall effect measurement. Horizontal components are related to the steady flow of an externally excited dc current, while vertical components are ascribable to the magnetic force acting on the particles. and to electrostatic forces from accumulated charge distributions at the top and bottom of the sample. The vertical current and velocity components are ordinarily much smaller than the horizontal components, but in the drawing they have been shown much larger for clarity.

This charge distribution generates an electrostatic field $\mathbf{i}_y E_y$ in the y-direction. There are thus electrostatic force components qE_y acting on the electrons and holes, as well as the magnetic forces $q(\mathbf{v} \times \mathbf{B})$. The total y-components of force acting on the particles are the sum of these contributions, which can be written as

$$F_{py} = -qv_{px}B_z + qE_y \qquad (q = +e) \qquad \text{(holes)}$$

$$\text{and} \quad F_{ny} = -q|v_{nx}|B_z + qE_y \qquad (q = -e) \qquad \text{(electrons)} \,,$$

(9.6-1)

the subscripts p and n indicating holes and electrons, respectively. The x-components of velocity for both particles can be written in terms of a mobility times the x-component of a much larger externally applied field E_x that drives the steady current. Therefore, these equations can also be written

$$F_{py} = -q\mu_p E_x B_z + qE_y \qquad (q = +e)$$

$$F_{ny} = -q\mu_n E_x B_z + qE_y \qquad (q = -e) \; . \tag{9.6-2}$$

These forces set up ohmic current densities J_{py} and J_{ny} in the y-direction. Initially, the electrostatic field E_y is zero, and these currents cause the accumulation of charges that act as its source. After a very short time a steady state is set up, in which the accumulation of charge ceases, and in which the algebraic sum $J_{py} + J_{ny}$ is zero. If it were not so, the charges would accumulate *ad infinitum*. This condition can, in fact, be taken to define the steady state. Since the currents behave ohmically on a macroscopic level, they can be associated with a total force per unit charge F_{py}/q and F_{pn}/q in the same way that ohmic current densities are associated with electrostatic fields--that is,

$$J_{py} = p_0 q v_{py} = p_0 q \mu_p \cdot \frac{F_{py}}{q} \qquad \text{and} \qquad J_{ny} = n_0 q v_{ny} = n_0 q \cdot -\mu_n \frac{F_{ny}}{q} \; . \tag{9.6-3}$$

The minus sign in the second equation above appears because the mobilities μ_n and μ_p are conventionally regarded as *inherently positive* quantities. In the case of holes this causes no problem, but for electrons, whose velocity is opposite the direction of the field (or in this instance of F_{ny}/q), the proper sign does not occur automatically. It must therefore be supplied as above, whenever needed. Since, from the figure, J_{ny} is positive and both q and F_{ny} are negative, the minus sign has to be there.

If we now substitute the expressions for the forces F_{py} and F_{ny} from (9.6 - 2) into (9.6 - 3), using $q = +e$ for holes and $q = -e$ for electrons, we obtain

$$J_{py} = -p_0 e \mu_p^2 E_x B_z + p_0 e \mu_p E_y \qquad \text{and} \qquad J_{ny} = n_0 e \mu_n^2 E_x B_z + n_0 e \mu_n E_y \; . \tag{9.6-4}$$

The total y-component of current is the sum of these two constituents,

$$J_y = J_{py} + J_{ny} = e(n_0 \mu_n^2 - p_0 \mu_p^2) E_x B_z + e(n_0 \mu_n + p_0 \mu_p) E_y \; . \tag{9.6-5}$$

Equating this current to zero and solving for E_y, we can write the Hall field as

$$E_y = \frac{p_0 \mu_p^2 - n_0 \mu_n^2}{n_0 \mu_n + p_0 \mu_p} \cdot E_x B_z \; . \tag{9.6-6}$$

The horizontal field E_x can be expressed in terms of the current density J_x as

$$E_x = \frac{J_x}{\sigma} = \frac{J_x}{e(n_0 \mu_n + p_0 \mu_p)} \; , \tag{9.6-7}$$

from which,

$$E_y = \frac{p_0 \mu_p^2 - n_0 \mu_n^2}{e(n_0 \mu_n + p_0 \mu_p)^2} \cdot J_x B_z = R \cdot J_x B_z \; , \tag{9.6-8}$$

where R, as defined above, is the Hall coefficient. The Hall coefficient is often expressed in a slightly different form, obtained by dividing the above expression above and below by μ_p^2, and writing

$$R = \frac{p_0 - n_0 b^2}{e(n_0 b + p)^2}, \qquad \text{where} \qquad b = \frac{\mu_n}{\mu_p}. \qquad (9.6\text{-}9)$$

The quantity b is referred to as the mobility ratio. Ideally, if electrons and holes are scattered by the same mechanisms the temperature dependences of μ_n and μ_p will be the same, and the quantity b is temperature-independent and also independent of the impurity concentration. Unfortunately this ideal situation is rarely realized, and b is often somewhat temperature-dependent, though usually considerably less so than either the electron or hole mobility. At temperatures around 300K, b is about 2.1 for germanium and 3.0 for silicon. In the III-V intermatallic semiconductors, the electron mobility tends to be much larger than that of the hole, and the mobility ratio can be (in the case of InSb) as large as 80.

In strongly extrinsic n-type or p-type samples, the concentration of the minority carrier is negligible in the above expressions for the Hall coefficient, which reduce to

$$R = \frac{1}{p_0 e} \quad (p\text{-type}), \qquad \text{and} \quad R = -\frac{1}{n_0 e} \quad (n\text{-type}). \qquad (9.6\text{-}10)$$

These expressions agree with the result obtained in Section 7.7, except that the sign of the Hall coefficient is positive for p-type semiconductors. This explains the troublesome experimental finding that many substances have positive hall coefficients, which are now clearly seen to be associated with hole conduction. In the case of intrinsic material, the electron and hole densities are both equal to n_i, and the Hall coefficient then becomes

$$R = \frac{1}{e n_i} \cdot \frac{1 - b}{1 + b} \qquad (\text{intrinsic}). \qquad (9.6\text{-}11)$$

From this it is clear that intrinsic semiconductors have negative Hall coefficients provided that the mobility ratio b is greater than unity, which is ordinarily true. Also, from (9.6 - 9) it is easy to see that the hall coefficient *vanishes* when $p_0 = n_0 b^2$. When $b > 1$, this condition is satisfied for p-type materials that are fairly close to intrinsic. This condition corresponds to a reversal in the sign of the Hall coefficient, more strongly p-type substances having positive Hall coefficients, while others exhibit negative coefficients.

As suggested in Section 7.7, Hall effect and conductivity measurements can be combined to give a good estimate of the net impurity concentration and the mobility of holes or electrons. In the case of strongly extrinsic substances, the procedure is the same as that described in Section 7.7. In materials that are not strongly extrinsic, the situation is more complicated, for the product $R\sigma$ no longer gives the majority carrier mobility directly. If b is known from measurements on extrinsic samples, however, one can (with difficulty) solve equations (9.6 - 9), (9.5 - 1), and (9.4 - 15) simultaneously for n_0, p_0, and μ_p in terms of the measured quantities R, σ, and n_i.

This analysis is not particularly relevant to our ends and will be pursued no further. The functional dependence of Hall coefficient on the carrier concentration is illustrated schematically in Figure 9.10. It will be noted that the Hall coefficient has two

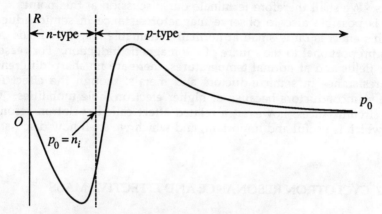

Figure 9.10 Schematic representation of the variation of the Hall coefficient with the free hole concentration p_0 (=n_i^2/n_0) in semiconductors. The drawing is not to scale and is not intended to represent accurately any particulat semiconductor material.

extremal values that are close to the intrinsic point. The reader is asked as an exercise, to show that these two values are located at the points where

$$\frac{p_0^2}{bn_i^2} = \tfrac{3}{2}(1+b) \pm \sqrt{\tfrac{9}{4}(1+b)^2 - b} \ . \tag{9.6-12}$$

In the above development the distribution of electron and hole velocities was not considered. A more rigorous calculation in which the velocity distributions are taken into account reveals that the Hall coefficient (9.6 - 8) or (9.6 - 9) should be written

$$R = \frac{\dfrac{p_0 \overline{\tau_p^2}}{(\bar{\tau}_p)^2} - \dfrac{n_0 b^2 \overline{\tau_n^2}}{(\bar{\tau}_n)^2}}{e(n_0 b + p_0)^2} \ . \tag{9.6-13}$$

The averages shown in the numerator of the above expression are easily evaluated over the Maxwellian electron/hole energy distributions. Assuming that scattering of electrons and holes by acoustical-mode phonons is the dominant scattering mechanism, these averages both give factors of $3\pi/8$, which leads to

$$R = \frac{3\pi}{8} \cdot \frac{p_0 - n_0 b^2}{e(n_0 b + p)^2} \ . \tag{9.6-14}$$

Since the value of the factor $3\pi/8$ is 1.18, which differs from unity by an amount that is barely significant on the scale of uncertainties in other measured and calculated quantities that enter into the determination of conductivity, mobility, and impurity concentrations, it is sometimes neglected altogether, unless extremely precise results are sought. There are other complications in the theory of the Hall effect, which though of some fundamental interest, are not of great importance in the determination of conductivity and Hall mobility to the degree of accuracy needed in most situations. We shall therefore terminate our discussion at this point.

It is possible also to observe magnetoresistance in semiconductors. As in metals, this effect is quite small at normally attainable magnetic fields, and its magnitude is proportional to the square of the magnetic induction. For reasonably small magnetic fields and at normal temperatures, there are no sharp differences between magnetoresistance in semiconductors and metals, though the effect is ordinarily larger in semiconductors because of higher electron/hole mobilities. Under more extreme circumstances, however, a related effect called cyclotron resonance can be excited, which is useful and important, and which we shall now discuss.

9.7 CYCLOTRON RESONANCE AND EFFECTIVE MASS

In the discussion of magnetoresistance in Section 7.7, we observed that the electrons and holes move in circular orbits under the influence of an external magnetic field normal to the surface of a thin rectangular sample. The geometry of these orbits is illustrated in Figure 7.7. In Hall effect and magnetoresistance measurements made at normal temperatures and with magnetic fields of modest intensity, the carriers are deflected only through small angles before being scattered. Indeed, the validity of the analysis of the Hall effect given in the preceding section, and in Section 7.7 depends on the fulfillment of this condition, which, according to Figure 7.7 and equation (7.7 - 8) can be stated as

$$\omega\tau \ll 1, \quad \text{where} \quad \omega = qB_z / m* . \tag{9.7-1}$$

With sufficient care in designing the experiment, it is possible to arrange conditions so that the quantity $\omega\tau$ is much larger. It is even possible to make $\omega\tau$ much greater than unity by using large magnetic fields to increase ω, and by working with very pure samples at extremely low temperatures, which minimizes both phonon scattering and impurity scattering thus increasing τ. Under these conditions, the electron or hole can make many complete revolutions before being scattered. If, now, a small oscillating radiofrequency or microwave electric field is present, whose electric vector is in the xy-plane, a resonance phenomenon can be observed when the frequency of this external field is synchronous with the orbital frequency ω of the orbiting electrons or holes. The situation is the same as that encountered in a cyclotron, in which charges absorb energy from an rf field on each half cycle, and spiral outward in orbital paths of increasing radius. The energy absorbed from the field is stored as orbital kinetic energy, and when a charge is finally scattered it transfers far more energy out of the field and into the thermal energy of the surroundings than would normally be dissipated. If the sample is enclosed in a microwave cavity, there will be a sharp peak in the energy absorbed within the cavity at the resonant frequency ω--a peak which is easily detected experimentally. This effect is referred to as *cyclotron resonance*; and if the resonance frequency and the steady magnetic field are known, it can be used to determine the electron or hole effective mass.

Let us consider first the case of free charges in a situation where the surfaces of constant energy in k-space are spherical. Under these circumstances the effective mass is isotropic. Let us assume that the magnetic field B_0 is in the z-direction and the electric vector of an rf electric field of frequency ω_0 is along the y-direction. The field components can now be written,

$$E_y = E_0 e^{i\omega_0 t} , \qquad E_x = E_z = 0$$
$$B_z = B_0 , \qquad B_x = B_y = 0 .$$

(9.7-2)

The force on the charges is the Lorentz force, which is the sum of electrostatic and magnetic $q(\mathbf{v} \times \mathbf{B})$ contributions. Since the magnetic field is in the z-direction, the vector $\mathbf{v} \times \mathbf{B}$ can have no z-component. All forces therefore lie in the xy-plane. Writing them in terms of cartesian unit vectors and performing the indicated vector product, we find

$$\mathbf{F} = q\mathbf{E} + q(\mathbf{v} \times \mathbf{B}) = q\mathbf{i}_y \cdot E_0 e^{i\omega_0 t} + q\mathbf{i}_x(v_y B_0) - q\mathbf{i}_y(v_x B_0) .$$

(9.7-3)

Equations of motion for each cartesian component of acceleration can now be written as

$$F_x = m* \frac{dv_x}{dt} = qv_y B_0 \qquad\qquad \frac{dv_x}{dt} = \omega v_y$$

$$F_y = m* \frac{dv_y}{dt} = qE_0 e^{i\omega_0 t} - qv_x B_0 \qquad \text{or} \qquad \frac{dv_y}{dt} = \frac{qE_0}{m*} e^{i\omega_0 t} - \omega v_x$$

(9.7-4)

$$F_z = m* \frac{dv_z}{dt} = 0 \qquad\qquad \frac{dv_z}{dt} = 0 ,$$

where
$$\omega = qB_0 / m* .$$

(9.7-5)

From this it is evident that the z-component of velocity is constant, and plays no essential role in any further description of the motion. The equations for the other two components are equations of motion describe an oscillatory motion driven by the rf field at the externally imposed frequency ω_0. We are therefore led to assume oscillatory solutions of this frequency, and thus to substitute

$$x = x_0 e^{i\omega_0 t} \qquad \text{and} \qquad y = y_0 e^{i\omega_0 t} ,$$

(9.7-6)

where x_0 and y_0 are oscillation amplitudes, into (9.7 - 4). Calculating the derivatives indicated in the above equations, we can show first from the top equation that

$$x = -i\omega y / \omega_0 .$$

(9.7-7)

Then, substituting this into the equation for dv_y/dt and solving first for $y(t)$, and then, with the aid of (9.7 - 6) $x(t)$, we find,

$$y = y_0 e^{i\omega_0 t} = \frac{qE_0 / m^*}{\omega^2 - \omega_0^2} \cdot e^{i\omega_0 t}, \quad \text{and} \quad x = x_0 e^{i\omega_0 t} = -\frac{i\omega(qE_0 / m^*)}{\omega_0(\omega^2 - \omega_0^2)} \cdot e^{i\omega_0 t} . \qquad (9.7\text{-}8)$$

The condition of resonance occurs at the frequency $\omega_0 = \omega$, at which the oscillation amplitudes become infinitely large. In this analysis, no mechanism for dissipating energy contributed by the rf accelerating field is included, so the calculated amplitudes are infinite. In practice, however, after a certain time, the charges are scattered by the usual mechanisms, and their energy dissipated as heat in the form of lattice vibrations. The amplitudes (so long as $\omega t \gg 1$) are therefore large but finite. A resonance will be found, therefore, when the frequency ω_0 of the rf field is

$$\omega_0 = \omega = qB_0 / m^* . \qquad (9.7\text{-}9)$$

If one measures this resonant frequency, and if the field strength B_0 is also known, one can thus infer quite accurately the effective mass m^*. For electrons, $q = -e$ and $m^* = m_n^*$, while for holes $q = +e$ and $m^* = m_p^*$. Accordingly, one should for a given substance observe two resonance peaks, one for electrons and one for holes.

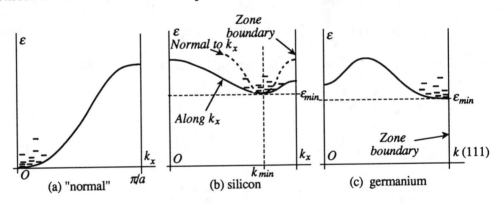

Figure 9.11 Energy *versus* crystal momentum for (a) conduction electrons in a classical free electron conductor having spherical constant-energy surfaces, (b) electrons in the conduction band of silicon, and (c) electrons in the conduction band of germanium. The horizontal axis is the k_x-direction in (a) and (b), and the (111) direction in (c). The dashed curve in (b) illustrates the variation of energy with crystal momentum in a direction normal to the k_x-axis in silicon.

When cyclotron resonance was first observed in silicon and germanium, it became obvious that things were more complicated than this, a conclusion supported by the refined band structure calculations carried out at about the same time. In both materials, far more than two resonances were observed, some of them more or less independent of sample orientation, others varying with the orientation of the crystal with respect to the magnetic field. It soon became apparent that the complexities in the electron resonances are caused by conduction band dispersion relations for which the surfaces of constant energy are *ellipsoidal* rather than spherical. This peculiarity arises from the fact that the point of minimum energy in k-space for the conduction band of silicon is not at $k = 0$, but at a set of six equivalent points in the Brillouin zone, along the cartesian $\pm k_x$–, $\pm k_y$–, and $\pm k_z$–axes, at about 4/5 the distance between the origin and the edge of the Brillouin zone, as shown in Figure 9.11(b). In the case of germanium, the energy minima are at a set of eight equivalent points along the direction of cube diagonals in the Brillouin zone at the zone boundary, as illustrated in Figures 9.11(c) and 9.12.

In the simple classical free-electron theory, and also in simpler quantum models (Kronig-Penney, for example), the energy minimum for electrons is found to be at the zone center, $k = 0$. In these cases, as we have seen, the constant-energy surfaces in the neighborhood of this minimum are spherical. However, one must remember that k is not an exact analog of the dynamical momentum p. In classical physics, a free particle of minimum possible energy must also have zero momentum. But there is nothing in the laws of quantum theory that demand the same condition be satisfied by the quasi-momentum k. The free-particle character of the motion is in part an artifact of the periodic potential, and one cannot expect that an exact replica of classical free particle motion will be obtained in all instances. We have already encountered departures from the classical free-particle model in the appearance of the effective mass, and in the distorted shape of the Fermi surfaces shown, for example, in Figure 8.10. This is simply another such peculiarity.

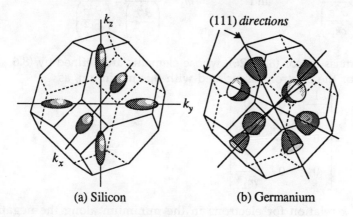

(a) Silicon (b) Germanium

Figure 9.12 Ellipsoidal cinstant-energy surfaces for electrons in the conduction band of (a) silicon, and (b) germanium within the Brillouin zone of the diamond structure. These diagrams are related to the data shown in Figure 9.11(b) and (c), respectively.

The diamond structure, as explained in Chapter 1 and illustrated in Figure 1.7 has cubic symmetry. The primitive cell of this lattice is the same as that of the f.c.c. structure, but contains two atoms, at $(0, 0, 0)$ and $(1/4, 1/4, 1/4)$ relative to the cubic cell shown at (b) in Figure 1.7. Its Brillouin zone is therefore of the same form as that shown for the f.c.c structure in Figure 8.13(b). If the edge of the cubic cell in Figure 1.7(b) is defined as a, the faces of the Brillouin zone shown in Figure 9.12 intersect the coördinate axes in k-space at distances $\pi/2a$ from the origin.

For silicon, as shown in Figure 9.12(a) the energy minima are on the axes, and the surfaces of constant energy are six ellipsoids of revolution centered on these minima. The ellipsoidal character of these surfaces stems from the fact that the curvature of the ε versus k relation measured along a direction intersecting the energy minimum but *normal* to the coördinate axis on which it lies, as shown by the dashed curve in Figure 9.11(b), is different from the curvature observed parallel to the axis. This can be explained in terms of an effective mass (as defined by (8.6 - 27)), which is not the same for an electron moving *parallel* to the axis of the ellipsoid as for an electron in motion *normal* to that axis. The effective mass thus depends on the direction of motion, and the effective mass tensor (8.6 -26) is no longer isotropic. Under these circumstances, an electron near the bottom of the conduction band can still exhibit free-particle motion along all three coördinate directions, though with different effective masses normal to and parallel to the axis of the energy minimum in which it resides. The energy relative to the band minimum can be written, for an electron near the band minimum along the positive k_x-axis at $k_x = k_{x0}$, as

$$\varepsilon - \varepsilon_c = \frac{\hbar^2(k_x^2 - k_{x0}^2)}{2m_\parallel{}^*} + \frac{\hbar^2(k_y^2 + k_z^2)}{2m_\perp{}^*} . \tag{9.7-10}$$

This equation, for a constant energy ε, will be recognized as that of an ellipsoid of revolution, in which the effective mass parameters $m_\parallel{}^*$ and $m_\perp{}^*$ are, as in (8.6 - 27), given by

$$m_\parallel{}^* = \frac{\hbar^2}{\left(\dfrac{\partial^2\varepsilon}{\partial k_x^2}\right)} , \quad \text{and} \quad m_\perp{}^* = \frac{\hbar^2}{\left(\dfrac{\partial^2\varepsilon}{\partial k_y^2}\right)} = \frac{\hbar^2}{\left(\dfrac{\partial^2\varepsilon}{\partial k_z^2}\right)} . \tag{9.7-11}$$

The inverse mass tensor (8.6 - 26), whose elements are defined by (8.6 - 27), can now be written, for the electrons associated with this minimum, as

$$\left(\frac{1}{\mathbf{m}^*}\right)_{k_x} = \begin{bmatrix} \dfrac{1}{m_\parallel{}^*} & 0 & 0 \\ 0 & \dfrac{1}{m_\perp{}^*} & 0 \\ 0 & 0 & \dfrac{1}{m_\perp{}^*} \end{bmatrix} . \tag{9.7-12}$$

The ε *versus* k relation for electrons in the minimum along the negative k_x-axis is the same as (9.7 - 10), since all the crystal momenta are squared. Thus the tensors $(1/\mathbf{m}^*)_{-k_x}$ and $(1/\mathbf{m}^*)_{k_x}$ are the same.

The ε *versus* k relations and inverse mass tensors for the other minima are easily obtained by permutation of the symbols x, y, and z. The relation for the two k_z minima, for example, must clearly have the form

$$\varepsilon - \varepsilon_c = \frac{\hbar^2(k_z^2 - k_{z0}^2)}{2m_\parallel{}^*} + \frac{\hbar^2(k_x^2 + k_y^2)}{2m_\perp{}^*} , \tag{9.7-13}$$

while the corresponding inverse effective mass tensor will be

$$\left(\frac{1}{\mathbf{m}^*}\right)_{k_z} = \begin{bmatrix} \dfrac{1}{m_\perp{}^*} & 0 & 0 \\ 0 & \dfrac{1}{m_\perp{}^*} & 0 \\ 0 & 0 & \dfrac{1}{m_\parallel{}^*} \end{bmatrix} . \tag{9.7-14}$$

Under circumstances such as these, the equations of motion for an electron differ from those derived previously assuming spherical constant-energy surfaces and an isotropic effective mass. Now, we must start with the equation of motion (8.6 - 25) and write, for the time derivative of the group velocity,

$$\frac{d\mathbf{v}}{dt} = \frac{1}{\hbar}(\nabla_k \nabla_k \varepsilon) \bullet \mathbf{F} = \left(\frac{1}{\mathbf{m}*}\right) \bullet \mathbf{F} = \left(\frac{1}{\mathbf{m}*}\right) \bullet (q\mathbf{E} + q\mathbf{v} \times \mathbf{B}) . \qquad (9.7\text{-}15)$$

This expression must be evaluated separately for electrons in each of the six ellipsoidal minima shown in Figure 9.12(a) for the case of silicon. Let us consider first the electrons in the two ellipsoidal minima along the k_z-axis, whose mass tensor is given by (9.7 - 14). Let us assume that the rf field is in the y-direction, as shown in Figure 9.13, and that there is an angle θ between the magnetic field and the z-axis.

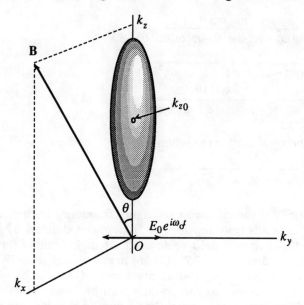

Figure 9.13 Geometry assumed in discussing cyclotron resonance for electrons in the conduction band of silicon associated with the minima oriented along the z-direction.

In this geometry, (9.7 - 15) can be written as

$$\frac{d\mathbf{v}}{dt} = \left(\frac{1}{\mathbf{m}*}\right)_{k_z} \bullet \mathbf{F} = \begin{bmatrix} \dfrac{1}{m_\perp*} & 0 & 0 \\ 0 & \dfrac{1}{m_\perp*} & 0 \\ 0 & 0 & \dfrac{1}{m_\parallel*} \end{bmatrix} \bullet \begin{bmatrix} (q\mathbf{E} + q\mathbf{v} \times \mathbf{B})_x \\ (q\mathbf{E} + q\mathbf{v} \times \mathbf{B})_y \\ (q\mathbf{E} + q\mathbf{v} \times \mathbf{B})_z \end{bmatrix} = \begin{bmatrix} \dfrac{1}{m_\perp*}(q\mathbf{E} + q\mathbf{v} \times \mathbf{B})_x \\ \dfrac{1}{m_\perp*}(q\mathbf{E} + q\mathbf{v} \times \mathbf{B})_y \\ \dfrac{1}{m_\parallel*}(q\mathbf{E} + q\mathbf{v} \times \mathbf{B})_z \end{bmatrix} . \qquad (9.7\text{-}15a)$$

Now, observing that $B_x = B\sin\theta$, $B_z = B\cos\theta$, $B_y = 0$ and evaluating the vector products in terms of field components, we arrive at a set of equations of motion of the form,

$$dv_x / dt = \omega_\perp v_y \cos\theta$$

$$dv_y / dt = \omega_\perp v_z \sin\theta - \omega_\perp v_x \cos\theta + (qE_0 / m_\perp*)e^{i\omega_0 t} \qquad (9.7-16)$$

$$dv_z / dt = -\omega_\parallel v_y \sin\theta \ ,$$

where

$$\omega_\perp = qB / m_\perp* \qquad \text{and} \qquad \omega_\parallel = qB / m_\parallel* \ . \qquad (9.7-17)$$

As in the earlier calculation, we may now assume oscillatory solutions of the form $x(t) = x_0\exp(i\omega_0 t)$, $y=y_0\exp(i\omega_0 t)$, and $z = z_0\exp(i\omega_0 t)$, substitute them into the above equations of motion and solve for the amplitudes to obtain finally

$$x_0 = \frac{qE_0}{m_\perp*} \frac{i\omega_\perp \cos\theta}{\omega_0(\omega_0^2 - \omega_\perp^2\cos^2\theta - \omega_\perp\omega_\parallel\sin^2\theta)}$$

$$y_0 = -\frac{qE_0}{m_\perp*} \frac{1}{(\omega_0^2 - \omega_\perp^2\cos^2\theta - \omega_\perp\omega_\parallel\sin^2\theta)} \qquad (9.7-18)$$

$$z_0 = -\frac{qE_0}{m_\perp*} \frac{i\omega_\parallel\sin\theta}{\omega_0(\omega_0^2 - \omega_\perp^2\cos^2\theta - \omega_\perp\omega_\parallel\sin^2\theta)} \ .$$

The amplitudes become very large when

$$\omega_0 = \sqrt{\omega_\perp^2\cos^2\theta + \omega_\perp\omega_\parallel\sin^2\theta} \ , \qquad (9.7-19)$$

a condition that defines the cyclotron resonance frequency in this situation. The resonant frequency depends only on the two frequencies defined by (9.7 - 17) and the angle θ between the magnetic field vector and the major axis of the ellipsoid. When $q = -e$ the frequencies defined in (9.7 - 17) are negative, but since (9.7 - 18 and 19) are invariant when the signs of $\omega_\perp$ and $\omega_\parallel$ are reversed, this is of no physical consequence, and the absolute values can equally well be used. For the ellipsoidal constant energy surfaces in the conduction band of silicon it is clear that the cyclotron resonance frequency varies as a function of sample orientation with respect to the magnetic field. The same conclusions can be drawn for germanium, though the mathematical analysis is more complicated.

In the case of silicon, when the magnetic field is along the z-direction, $\theta = 0$ for the two ellipsoids on the z-axis and $\theta = 90°$ for the other four. This suggests that two resonance peaks at frequencies $\omega_\perp$ and $(\omega_\perp\omega_\parallel)^{1/2}$ will be observed, the latter having twice the absorptive strength of the former because there are in equilibrium twice as many electrons in four ellipsoidal minima than in two. The observation of these two frequencies is enough to determine $\omega_\perp$ and $\omega_\parallel$. Equation (9.7 - 19) also specifies how the measured frequencies change with angle as the sample is rotated, a dependence that has been confirmed by the experimental data. Indeed, for an arbitrary angle θ in Figure 9.13, you will observe that there are in general *three* possible angles between the field and the various sets of ellipsoids, so that the two resonance peaks mentioned above will split into three as the angle θ becomes significantly larger than zero. This phenomenon has also been observed, and the models suggested in Figure 9.12 have been confirmed in all respects by the experimental data. In this description, there are, of course, two ellipsoids for which the rf electric field is parallel rather than transverse with respect to the major ellipsoid axis, and for which a separate analysis must be carried out to confirm the fact that this change does not invalidate the resonance frequency formula (9.7 - 19). This problem, whose results lead once more to (9,7 - 19) is assigned as an exercise. Measurement of the electron effective masses derived from cyclotron resonance measurements of the two frequencies defined by (9.7 - 17) yield the following results:

ELECTRON EFFECTIVE MASSES

	Germanium	Silicon
$m_\parallel^*/m$	1.64	0.98
$m_\perp^*/m$	0.082	0.19
$m_\parallel^*/m_\perp^*$	20.0	5.2 .

In germanium, the energy band minima are at the band edges, and the surfaces of constant energy near these minima therefore have the form of the half-ellipsoids shown in Figure 9.12(b). Moreover, the minima are situated at the center of the hexagonal faces of the Brillouin zone along (111) directions in k-space. The four half-ellipsoids are equivalent to four complete ellipsoids, and are usually so regarded for purposes of calculation. An effective mass tensor can be written for each of these ellipsoids, though because of the diagonal orientation of the major axes, the tensors are more complex than those written above for silicon, and unlike them have off-diagonal elements. The equations of motion for the electrons can nevertheless be written and solved in the same way as shown above to obtain a spectrum of resonance frequencies appropriate for germanium. We shall not, however, go into further detail at this point. In germanium, as well as silicon, the ellipsoidal surfaces are prolate, the axial mass $m_\parallel^*$ being considerably larger than the transverse mass $m_\perp^*$.

At first, it might appear that the anisotropy of the effective masses associated with ellipsoidal constant-energy surfaces would lead to an accompanying anisotropy of mobility $(q\tau/m^*)$ and electrical conductivity $(n_0 q^2 \tau/m^*)$. This is true if only the electrons associated with a single ellipsoid are considered, but not when all electrons in the conduction band are accounted for. In equilibrium in silicon, there are, for example, $n_0/6$ electrons per unit volume in each of the six conduction band minima. Assuming that the relaxation time τ_n is isotropic, there are six conductivity tensors, two of the form (9.7 - 12), two of form (9.7 - 14), and two of similar form in which the element $1/m_\parallel^*$ is in the center of the matrix. The conductivity associated with a single band minimum would then be a *tensor* given by $n_0 q^2 \tau_n/6$ times the inverse mass tensor associated with that minimum, and the conductivity would be anisotropic in the same way as the inverse effective mass. When all the tensors are added to obtain a total electron conductivity, however, a result of the form

$$\sigma_n = n_0 q^2 \tau_n \left(\frac{1}{\mathbf{m*}}\right) = \frac{n_0 q^2 \tau_n}{6}\left[2\left(\frac{1}{\mathbf{m*}}\right)_{k_x} + 2\left(\frac{1}{\mathbf{m*}}\right)_{k_x} + 2\left(\frac{1}{\mathbf{m*}}\right)_{k_x}\right] \qquad (9.7-20)$$

is obtained, in which the total inverse mass tensor is defined by

$$\frac{1}{\mathbf{m}^*} = \frac{1}{3}\left[\left(\frac{1}{\mathbf{m}^*}\right)_{k_x} + \left(\frac{1}{\mathbf{m}^*}\right)_{k_y} + \left(\frac{1}{\mathbf{m}^*}\right)_{k_z}\right] = \begin{bmatrix} \frac{1}{3}\left(\frac{2}{m_\perp^*} + \frac{1}{m_\parallel^*}\right) & 0 & 0 \\ 0 & \frac{1}{3}\left(\frac{2}{m_\perp^*} + \frac{1}{m_\parallel^*}\right) & 0 \\ 0 & 0 & \frac{1}{3}\left(\frac{2}{m_\perp^*} + \frac{1}{m_\parallel^*}\right) \end{bmatrix}.$$

$$(9.7\text{-}21)$$

This tensor is *isotropic*, and can be expressed as the unit tensor times a scalar multiple

$$\frac{1}{m_c^*} = \frac{1}{3}\left(\frac{2}{m_\perp^*} + \frac{1}{m_\parallel^*}\right) \qquad\qquad (9.7\text{-}22)$$

whose reciprocal is referred to as the *conductivity effective mass* for electrons in the conduction band. This example was worked out for the specific case of silicon, but the same results are obtained for germanium, or for that matter any other substance with cubic symmetry. The data in the above table can be used to show that the parameter defined above has the value $0.12m$ for germanium, and $0.26m$ for silicon, where m is the electron's inertial mass.

Despite the strongly ansiotropic effective mass tensors for the individual conduction band minima, when their effect on the the total electron population at or near equilibrium is considered, the picture is quite different, and can, as above, lead to physical properties such as conductivity that are isotropic. The optical properties of the covalent semiconductors are, for similar reasons, isotropic. This can be seen to occur because of the cubic symmetry of the array of constant energy surfaces, which is in turn related to the cubic symmetry of the lattice itself. The fact that cyclotron resonance displays the anisotropy associated with individual band minima stems from the fact that it senses effects that govern the dynamical behavior of individual charges within times short compared with the relaxation time, while effects like conductivity are averaged over times much longer than this. When silicon and germanium crystals are subjected to intense uniaxial compression, the electron populations in the individual band minima are no longer equal, and with experimental care most of the electrons can be made to occupy a single minimum. The conductivity tensor now becomes essentially that of a single ellipsoid and the conductivity is found to be highly anisotropic.]

The above analysis is based upon the assumption of a relaxation time that is isotropic, despite the anisotropy of the constant energy surfaces. There is nothing to prevent this quantity from being anisotropic also, but experimental data generally support the conclusion that any anisotropy of the relaxation time, in silicon and germanium at least, must be far smaller than that of the constant-energy surfaces and effective masses.

Cyclotron resonance spectra for holes in the valence bands of silicon and germanium show that the valence bands of these material do not exhibit the multiple band minima and ellipsoidal energy surfaces characteristic of the conduction bands.

Instead, they reveal complexities of another kind, complexities more deeply quantum mechanical and harder to present in simple terms. We shall therefore have to rely upon a more qualitative discussion. Although multiple resonance peaks are found for holes, they are either independent of crystal orientation, or display far smaller orientational effects than those observed for electrons. The valence band model that fits these (and other) data best, suggests two distinct bands having roughly parabolic energy *versus* crystal-momentum curves of different curvature, that coincide at the point $k = 0$ in the center of the Brillouin zone. There is also a parabolic "split-off band" with a maximum at $k = 0$, whose maximum energy is *below* that of the valence band edge defined by the first two bands, as shown in Figure 9.14.

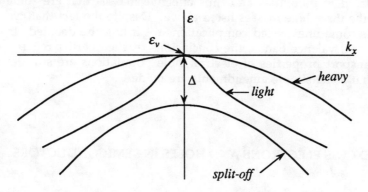

Figure 9.14 Schematic drawing of the valence band structure of the covalent semiconductors, showing light and heavy hole bands and the split-off band. The drawing is not scaled for either silicon or germanium, and is meant to suggest only the qualitative features of the band structure.

The energy difference Δ between the valence band edge and the top of the split-off band is due to the spin-orbit interaction, a coupling between the magnetic moments of the electron and orbital magnetic moments of the atoms. At the valence band maximum, the two coincident bands are known as the light and heavy hole bands, because the different curvatures of these two bands gives rise to different effective masses for the holes that populate them. The splitting energy Δ is considerably larger in germanium than in silicon, so much so that the hole population in the split-off band is usually negligible in germanium, though not in silicon except at low temperatures. The constant energy surfaces for all these bands have a spherical topology, though the surfaces of the light hole band are so severely distorted that the assumption of spherical form is only a rough approximation. The cyclotron resonance data regarding effective masses and energy splittings for these bands are given below.

HOLE EFFECTIVE MASSES

	Germanium	Silicon
Light	0.044m	0.16m
Heavy	0.28m	0.49m
Split-off	0.077m	0.25m
Energy Δ	0.28eV	0.035eV

The existence of a hole as one of the three species defined by these bands is limited to a single scattering free time, since scattering processes can easily transfer holes from one of these bands to another. It is therefore impossible for any measurement (like that of electrical conductivity), that depends only on the average behavior of holes over times large compared to the relaxation time, to distinguish between light, heavy, and split-off holes. Cyclotron resonance measurements rely on a resonance phenomenon that can be excited during a single free time between scattering interactions, and thus can investigate these three hole species separately. In this regard the situation is similar to that encountered in the conduction band with regard to free electrons. Observed hole conductivities are therefore isotropic, and are related to mobilities and thus effective masses that are some appropriate average of the three hole masses listed above. Despite the fact that cyclotron resonance reveals some unexpected complications regarding the detailed structure of the conduction and valence bands, the conclusions reached earlier regarding the statistics and transport properties of electron/hole populations are still generally valid, provided that some simple amendments are made.

9.8 EXCESS ELECTRONS AND HOLES IN SEMICONDUCTORS

We have already shown that it is easy to introduce electron-hole pairs in excess of those present in thermal equilibrium into semiconductors by external optical excitiation. We shall soon see that this can also be accomplished by passing electrical currents through rectifying point contacts or junctions between extrinsic semiconductors of opposite conductivity type. These effects lead directly to the phenomena of point-contact and *"p-n* junction" rectification, which govern the operation of many useful semiconductor devices. More generally, they permit one to modulate the electrical conductivity of semiconductors almost at will, and to control currents and process signals in many different ways. Excess electron-hole pairs can also be introduced by X-rays and γ-radiation, as well as by beams of electrons, protons, α-particles etc. The processes essential to optical conductivity modulation have already been discussed in Section 9.2, in the context of intrinsic materials, but the conclusions are also applicable to impurity semiconductors. The reader may wish to revisit this material if its imprint has faded.

As mentioned in Section 9.2, electron and hole generation and recombination processes are continually going on in any semiconductor. In any *steady-state* situation, including (though not confined to) the condition of thermal equilibrium, the rate at which conduction electrons are generated and the rate at which they disappear by recombination must be equal, a statement which applies also to holes in the valence band. Moreover, the rates at which electrons and holes are generated are always equal, as are the rates at which they disappear by recombination, because these processes always create or annihilate electron-hole pairs. In steady-state systems the generation rate of electron-hole pairs, and the recombination rate of these pairs is the same, but this is *not* true in time-dependent situations where electron and hole populations are not necessarily constant. These statements are all fairly obvious, but if they are not clearly understood, endless confusion can result, so it is important to keep them in mind at all times.

In the thermal equilibrium state, the only generation process is one in which electron-hole pairs are formed by thermal excitation across the band gap. The thermal generation rate g_0 is defined as the number of pairs produced thermally per unit volume per unit time. This quantity depends on temperature, bandgap, and other crystal parameters, but is *independent* of electron and hole concentrations. The recombination rate is related to the mean time elapsed between the generation and subsequent recombination of a given electron or hole. This quantity is referred to as the mean electron or hole *lifetime*. If there were exactly one electron or hole per unit volume of crystal there would be on the average $1/\tau$ recombination events per second per unit volume, where τ is the electron or hole lifetime. If there are n carriers per unit volume the recombination rate is increased by a factor n, and becomes n/τ. The lifetime τ is not to be confused with the mean free time between collisions, which unfortunately is represented also by the symbol τ. Indeed, electrons and holes ordinarily experience numerous scattering interactions during their lifespan as free carriers, so that the lifetime can be larger by many orders of magnitude than the mean free time between collisions. From this point forward the symbol τ will *always* refer to carrier lifetime unless otherwise specified. The notational ambiguity is regrettable, but it is firmly entrenched in the literature of semiconductor physics and technology. Using this notation, the recombination rates R_n and R_p for electrons and holes can be written

$$R_n = \frac{n}{\tau_n} \qquad \text{and} \qquad R_p = \frac{p}{\tau_p}. \qquad (9.8\text{-}1)$$

Moreover, because as indicated above these rates must always be equal, we can also write the general relation,

$$\frac{n}{\tau_n} = \frac{p}{\tau_p}. \qquad (9.8\text{-}2)$$

It is evident from this that the electron and hole lifetimes in general depend on the carrier concentrations. At equilibrium, $n = n_0$ and $p = p_0$, so (recalling that in equilibrium, generation and recombination rates must always be the same) we can express the equilibrium generation rates g_{n0} and g_{p0} for electrons and holes as

$$g_{n0} = n_0 / \tau_{n0} \qquad \text{and} \qquad g_{p0} = p_0 / \tau_{p0}. \qquad (9.8\text{-}3)$$

In general, nonequilibrium carrier populations in semiconductors are *functions of time and of position* within the material. That this is true can be seen by considering the example of a crystal, part of which is strongly illuminated and the rest in the dark, or of an intrinsic sample one end of which is at a higher temperature than the other. A further implication is that the generation and recombination rates may then also depend on space coördinates, as well as time. In such systems, currents can be caused by diffusion, which is driven by concentration gradients, as well as by drift associated with electric fields. We have already investigated these two effects separately, using the Boltzmann transport equation, in Chapter 6. At this point, therefore, we need only to combine our previously derived results concerning them.

Consider now a volume element of the crystal about the point (x, y, z), whose dimensions are dx, dy, and dz, as shown in Figure 9.15. Electrons and holes flow in and out of this region, propelled by diffusion and electric fields as suggested above. Also, electron-hole pairs can be generated and can recombine within the element. The current flow is described as always by a current density vector, as defined in the original discussion of conductivity in Chapter 6. We shall confine our discussion as far as possible to systems in which current flow is essentially one-dimensional and the current density vector J has only an x-component, as illustrated.

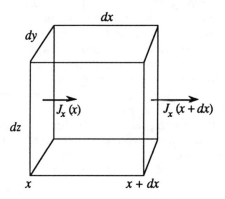

Figure 9.15 Current flow in and out of a volume element of a semiconductor crystal.

In the diagram, a current density component $J_x(x)$ flows into the sample across the leftmost face, at x, and a current density component $J_x(x + dx)$ leaves the region at the opposite face, located at $x + dx$, in the time interval dt. The *net current* into the element in this time interval is $[J_x(x) - J_x(x + dx)]dydz$. However, $J_x(x + dx)$ can be expanded in a Taylor's series about point x, of the form shown below, wherein terms of order $(dx)^2$ and higher are neglected in the limit $dx \to 0$. The net current now becomes,

$$\left[J_x(x) - J_x(x + dx)\right]dydz = \left[J_x(x) - J_x(x) - \frac{\partial J_x}{\partial x}dx\right]dydz = -\frac{\partial J_x}{\partial x}dV \; , \qquad (9.8\text{-}4)$$

where dV is the volume of the element. This net influx of current increases the amount of charge dq in the element, which can be written as $dq = \rho dV$, where ρ is the local charge density. In time interval dt, the influx of current contributes a charge increment $dq = (\partial q / \partial t)dt = $ (net current) $\times dt = -(\partial J_x / \partial x)dVdt$, according to the above equation. However, one may also write $\partial q / \partial t = \partial(\rho dV) / \partial t = (\partial\rho / \partial t)dV$. Equating the two expressions for $\partial q / \partial t$, we find,

$$\frac{\partial J_x}{\partial x} = -\frac{\partial\rho}{\partial t} \; . \qquad (9.8\text{-}5)$$

Readers familiar with electromagnetic theory will recognize this as the one-dimensional form of the equation of continuity for charge and current. If there exist y- and z-components of current density that flow across the other pairs of faces of the volume element illustrated above, their contributions to the net current influx can be similarly calculated and added to the result (9.8 - 4), which will then transform this continuity equation into the perhaps more familiar three-dimensional form,

$$\frac{\partial J_x}{\partial x} + \frac{\partial J_y}{\partial y} + \frac{\partial J_z}{\partial z} = \nabla \cdot \mathbf{J} = -\frac{\partial \rho}{\partial t} \quad , \tag{9.8-6}$$

where the expression on the left defines the scalar quantity $\nabla \cdot \mathbf{J}$ known as the *divergence* of the current density. These "continuity equations" clearly express the *conservation of total charge* entering and leaving the volume element.

In semiconductors, there are two separate species of charge, neither of which is necessarily conserved individually in every volume element and time interval; it is only the *total* charge that is conserved in general. For example, in a certain volume element there may be, temporarily, more electron-hole pairs recombining than are generated in certain time intervals. The above theory allows us to account for such effects by writing *separate* continuity equations for electrons and holes, that include terms that express--in addition to increments contributed by the flow of current as shown above--changes in the amount of charge in the element caused by the generation and recombination of electron-hole pairs. To do this, one merely adds to the charge increment per unit time $\partial J_x / \partial x$ (or $\nabla \cdot \mathbf{J}$), the previously calculated generation and recombination rates giving the number of charges per unit volume per unit time introduced or removed by generation and recombination processes. These equations will therefore have the general form,

$$-\nabla \cdot \mathbf{J} + qg - qR = \frac{\partial \rho}{\partial t} \quad , \tag{9.8-7}$$

where g is the pair generation rate, R the recombination rate, and $q = \pm e$ for holes and electrons, respectively. The situations we envision are not necessarily at thermal equilibrium, nor even in a steady state, so the generation rates are *not* necessarily those that prevail in equilibrium, shown in (9.8 - 3). They are ordinarily set, partially at least, by external parameters like the intensity of incident illumination. In this discussion, they are assumed to be *known* functions of x, y, z, and t. The recombination rates, however, are governed by *internal* processes as discussed in connection with (9.8 - 1), and are defined, in terms of the lifetimes, by those equations. Since the carrier concentrations vary with the coördinates and time, so also do the recombination rates given by (9.8 - 1). For electrons and holes, one may therefore write the continuity equations as,

$$-\nabla \cdot \mathbf{J}_n - eg_n + eR_n = \frac{\partial(-ne)}{\partial t}$$

and
$$\tag{9.8-8}$$

$$-\nabla \cdot \mathbf{J}_p + eg_p - eR_p = \frac{\partial(pe)}{\partial t} \quad ,$$

where the usual subscripts, n and p, refer to electron and holes.

The hole and electron currents are composed of diffusion currents, proportional to concentration gradients as described in Section 7.6, and also drift currents proportional to the local electric field. Equation (7.6 - 13) gives the particle flux arising from diffusion in terms of a diffusion coefficient D times the gradient of concentration of the diffusing species. This expression is applicable to electrons and holes diffusing in semiconductors, though to get the current density one must multiply the particle flux by the charge associated with the diffusing particle species, in this case $\pm e$ for holes and electrons. To the diffusion currents so defined, we must add ohmic drift currents driven by any electric field $\mathbf{E}$ that may be present. We may therefore write

$$\mathbf{J}_p = -eD_p\nabla p + e\mu_p p\mathbf{E} \qquad\text{and}\qquad \mathbf{J}_n = eD_n\nabla n + e\mu_n n\mathbf{E}\ , \qquad (9.8\text{-}9)$$

where D_p and D_n are the diffusion coefficients for holes and electrons. These diffusion coefficients are according to (7.6 - 14) related to the hole/electron mobilities μ_n and μ_p by the Einstein relations,

$$D_p = \frac{\mu_p kT}{e} \qquad\text{and}\qquad D_n = \frac{\mu_n kT}{e}\ . \qquad (9.8\text{-}10)$$

Now, substituting the current densities (9.8 - 9) into (9.8 - 8) and using (9.8 - 1), we obtain

$$D_p\nabla^2 p - \mu_p\nabla\bullet(p\mathbf{E}) + g_p - \frac{p}{\tau_p} = \frac{\partial p}{\partial t}$$

and
$$(9.8\text{-}11)$$

$$D_n\nabla^2 n + \mu_n\nabla\bullet(n\mathbf{E}) + g_n - \frac{n}{\tau_n} = \frac{\partial n}{\partial t}\ .$$

Using the vector identity $\nabla\bullet(\varphi\mathbf{A}) = \mathbf{A}\bullet\nabla\varphi + \varphi(\nabla\bullet\mathbf{A})$, where $\mathbf{A}$ and φ are arbitrary vector and scalar quantities, the second term on the right side of the equations above can be transformed to a more useful form. Also, the generation rates of electrons and holes can be written as the sum of the thermal equilibrium rates (9.8 - 3) and rates g_p' and g_n' due to external excitation, to obtain

$$g_p = g_p' + g_{p0} = g_p' + \frac{p_0}{\tau_{p0}} \qquad\text{and}\qquad g_n = g_n' + g_{n0} = g_n' + \frac{n_0}{\tau_{n0}}\ . \qquad (9.8\text{-}12)$$

These operations transform (9.8 - 11) into equations of the form

$$D_p\nabla^2 p - \mu_p\mathbf{E}\bullet\nabla p - \mu_p p(\nabla\bullet\mathbf{E}) + g_p' - \left(\frac{p}{\tau_p} - \frac{p_0}{\tau_{p0}}\right) = \frac{\partial p}{\partial t} \qquad (9.8\text{-}13)$$

and

$$D_n\nabla^2 n + \mu_n\mathbf{E}\bullet\nabla n + \mu_n n(\nabla\bullet\mathbf{E}) + g_n' - \left(\frac{n}{\tau_n} - \frac{n_0}{\tau_{n0}}\right) = \frac{\partial n}{\partial t}\ . \qquad (9.8\text{-}14)$$

It is easy to conclude that the solutions to these two seemingly independent equations give the carricer concentrations n and p as functions of space coördinates and time. Unfortunately, things are not that simple, because there are actually *three* unknowns, $n, p,$ and $\mathbf{E}$, rather than two. The reason we cannot regard the electric field as a known quantity is that the diffusing and drifting particles are charged and can therefore distribute themselves so as to generate internally coulomb fields that make up part or even all of the field written as E in the above equations. For example, since electron mobility is greater than hole mobility in germanium and silicon, electrons will normally diffuse faster than holes according to the Einstein relations (9.8 - 10). If electrons and holes could move totally independently of one another, the faster-diffusing electrons would soon outdistance the holes. As this happens, however, negative charges outrun positive ones, creating an internal coulomb field that exerts retarding forces on electrons and propulsion forces on holes until an accommodation is reached in which the effects of the disparity of diffusion rates is balanced by the action of the internal field. Even when there is no external emf, therefore, the field E in this discussion may not be zero. There are other effects as well, but in any event it is clear that this field is caused to some extent by the transport processes themselves, and that instead of being part of the known data that is fed in, it is part of the problem! Moreover, since the field appears in both of the above equations, they are no longer independent, but are coupled mathematically. Finally, since three equations are required to determine three unknowns, another equation is needed.

This third equation is simply the Maxwellian relation between the electric field and the local charge density ρ, a relation better known as Poisson's equation, which has the form

$$\nabla \cdot \mathbf{E} = \frac{\rho}{K\varepsilon_0} , \qquad (9.8\text{-}15)$$

where ε_0 is the permittivity of free space and K is the relative dielectric permittivity of the material. In this discussion, the charge density can be written as the sum of the charges of free electrons, free holes, and of the donor and acceptor centers, all of which are assumed, as usual, to be ionized. Therefore, (9.8 - 15) can be written as

$$\nabla \cdot \mathbf{E} = \frac{e(p - n + N_d - N_a)}{K\varepsilon_0} . \qquad (9.8\text{-}16)$$

In thermal equilibrium, as indicated by equation (9.4 - 20), the right side of this equation is zero. It is clear under these circumstances that in an infinite uniform crystal, a possible solution of the three coupled equations (9.8 - 13, 14, and 16) is $E = 0$, $p = p_0$, and $n = n_0$, since in thermal equilibrium, $g_p' = g_n' = 0$, and the recombination terms in parentheses also vanish. It is, in this case, the only solution.

Under more general circumstances, one must somehow solve these three equations for the unknowns E, p, and n. In general, as one might suspect, it is not possible to obtain these solutions in closed form. There are, however, simplifying assumptions of wide applicability that can be made, and which allow us to find excellent approximate solution for a large class of important problems. The coulomb forces that charges exert on each other are *very* strong. Their effect is to oppose the tendency of charges of opposite sign to drift apart and create strong charge distributions. Indeed, their effect is to *restore* as far as possible a condition of overall neutrality--a situation in which electrons and holes tend to diffuse and drift together. This accommodation cannot be attained without *some* unbalanced charge density, but it can usually be established by carrier concentration differences *small* in comparison with the total concentrations of electrons and holes. It is therefore usually reasonable to assume initially that the concentrations of electrons and holes in excess of the equilibrium concentrations n_0 and p_0 are equal, and thus that the crystal is everywhere electrically neutral. This cannot be exactly so, obviously, but if it leads to solutions wherein the net density of charged particles (as calculated from Poisson's equation) is very small, the answers will be self-consistent, and will serve as good approximate solutions to the transport equations.

This leads us to express the transport equations in terms of carrier concentrations in *excess* of the equilibrium values, and thus to write them in terms of new variables δp and δn defined by

$$p = p_0 + \delta p \quad \text{and} \quad n = n_0 + \delta n \ . \tag{9.8-17}$$

The quantities δp and δn are not necessarily so small as to be regarded as differentials, though that can sometimes occur. In general, they are excess concentrations of arbitrary magnitude, though simple solutions are usually obtainable only when they are appreciably smaller than the concentration of the majority carrier, a limitatation which is not unduly restrictive.

The initial assumption of electrical neutrality at all points can now be written as

$$e(p_0 + \delta p - n_0 - \delta n + N_d - N_a) = 0 \ , \tag{9.8-18}$$

which, with the aid of (9.4 - 20), reduces to the much simpler form

$$\delta p = p - p_0 = n - n_0 = \delta n \ . \tag{9.8-19}$$

In uniform semiconductor crystals, the equilibrium densities n_0 and p_0 are constant, which, with the above assumption, implies that $\nabla \delta p = \nabla \delta n = \nabla n = \nabla p$, and that $\partial(\delta p)/\partial t = \partial(\delta n)/\partial t = \partial n/\partial t = \partial p/\partial t$. It is clear likewise that the Laplacians $\nabla^2(\delta p)$ and $\nabla^2(\delta n)$ are equal. This allows the transport equations (9.8 - 13) and (9.8- 14) to be written, for uniform crystals, in terms of the variable δp, as

$$D_p \nabla^2 \delta p - \mu_p \mathbf{E} \cdot \nabla \delta p - \mu_p p(\nabla \cdot \mathbf{E}) + g_p' - \left(\frac{p_0 + \delta p}{\tau_p} - \frac{p_0}{\tau_{p0}} \right) = \frac{\partial(\delta p)}{\partial t} \tag{9.8-20}$$

and

$$D_n \nabla^2 \delta p + \mu_n \mathbf{E} \cdot \nabla \delta p + \mu_n n(\nabla \cdot \mathbf{E}) + g_p' - \left(\frac{p_0 + \delta p}{\tau_p} - \frac{p_0}{\tau_{p0}} \right) = \frac{\partial(\delta p)}{\partial t} \ . \tag{9.8-21}$$

In writing these equations, we have used (9.8 - 2) and (9.8 - 3) to relate the electron and hole lifetimes, and have also used the fact that the external generation rates g_n' and g_p' are equal, since excess carriers are always generated as electron-hole pairs. The divergence of the field $\mathbf{E}$, which is related to the charge density by Poisson's equation (9.8 - 16), cannot be found explicitly in any simple way, but it is possible to eliminate the terms in which it appears between the two above equations simply by multiplying (9.8 - 20) by $n\mu_n$ and (9.8 - 21) by $p\mu_p$, and adding the two resulting expressions to obtain, with the aid of the Einstein relations (9.8 - 10),

$$D*\nabla^2\delta p+\mu*(\mathbf{E}\bullet\nabla\delta p)+g_p'-\left(\frac{p_0+\delta p}{\tau_p}-\frac{p_0}{\tau_{p0}}\right)=\frac{\partial(\delta p)}{\partial t}\ ,\tag{9.8-22}$$

where

$$D*=\frac{(n+p)D_nD_p}{nD_n+pD_p}=\frac{(n_0+p_0+2\delta p)D_nD_p}{(n_0+\delta p)D_n+(p_0+\delta p)D_p}\ ,\tag{9.8-23}$$

and

$$\mu*=\frac{(p_0-n_0)\mu_n\mu_p}{n\mu_n+p\mu_p}=\frac{(p_0-n_0)\mu_n\mu_p}{(n_0+\delta p)\mu_n+(p_0+\delta p)\mu_p}\ .\tag{9.8-24}$$

The coefficients $D*$ and $\mu*$ are referred to, respectively, as *ambipolar* diffusion and drift coefficients.

The generation and recombination terms can also be simplified by the proper use of certain relations between electron/hole lifetimes and the local carrier concentrations. One such relation has already been exhibited, as equation (9.8 - 2), which is based on the fact that the recombination rates of electrons and of holes must be everywhere and at all times the same, since each recombination process reduces the carrier population simultaneously by exactly one electron and one hole. Another relation can be developed from the fact that the lifetime of a hole must be inversely proportional to the number of electrons in its immediate neighborhood, and that of an electron must likewise depend inversely on the local hole population. This leads us to observe that $\tau_n\propto 1/p$ and $\tau_p\propto 1/n$, and to enable us to write more specifically,

$$\tau_p=\tau_{p0}\cdot\frac{n_0}{n}\quad\text{and}\quad\tau_n=\tau_{n0}\cdot\frac{p_0}{p}\ .\tag{9.8-25}$$

These expressions clearly reduce to the correct values τ_{p0} and τ_{n0} in thermal equilibrium, and are consistent with the requirement $n\tau_p=p\tau_n$ imposed by (9.8 - 2). Using these results, the quantity in large brackets on the right side of (9.8 - 22) can be written

$$\frac{p_0+\delta p}{\tau_p}-\frac{p_0}{\tau_{p0}}=\frac{(p_0+\delta p)\cdot n}{n_0\tau_{p0}}-\frac{p_0}{\tau_{p0}}=\frac{1}{\tau_{p0}}\left[\frac{(p_0+\delta p)(n_0+\delta n)}{n_0}-p_0\right]\ .\tag{9.8-26}$$

We may now expand the product in the numerator above, and using $n_0p_0=n_i^2$, obtain

$$\frac{1}{\tau_{p0}}\left[\frac{(p_0+\delta p)(n_0+\delta n)}{n_0}-p_0\right]=\frac{\delta p}{\tau_{p0}}\left[1+\frac{p_0}{n_0}+\frac{\delta p}{n_0}\right]=\frac{\delta p}{\tau*}\ ,\tag{9.8-27}$$

where

$$\frac{1}{\tau*}=\frac{1}{\tau_{p0}}\left[1+\frac{p_0}{n_0}+\frac{\delta p}{n_0}\right]=\frac{1}{\tau_{n0}}\left[1+\frac{n_0}{p_0}+\frac{\delta p}{p_0}\right]\ .\tag{9.8-28}$$

The second form of this expression is found from the first using $p_0/\tau_{p0}=n_0/\tau_{n0}$, which follows from (9.8 - 2) at equilibrium. The lifetime parameter $\tau*$ is usually referred to as the *excess carrier lifetime*.

We may now write (9.8 - 22) in its final form as

$$D* \nabla^2 \delta p + \mu*(\mathbf{E} \cdot \nabla \delta p) + g'_p - \frac{\delta p}{\tau*} = \frac{\partial(\delta p)}{\partial t} \quad , \tag{9.8-29}$$

where the transport coefficients $D*$, $\mu*$, and $\tau*$ are given by (9.8 - 23, 24, and 28). The development of this transport equation expressed in terms of the excess hole density δp has been, unavoidably, long and tedious, and until now not particularly exciting. However, when we examine what it tells us, some interesting and unexpected results emerge.

First, it should be noted that all the starred transport coefficients are not strictly constant, but depend on the excess carrier level δp. This makes solving the transport equation extremely difficult in general, but when δp is small in comparison with the *larger* of the equilibrium carrier densities n_0 and p_0, this variation will be seen to be insignificant. Thus, for excess carrier levels that do not significantly modulate the conductivity of the material these parameters can be treated as constants. In a practical sense, therefore, we must limit our discussion to situations in which this condition is reasonably well satisfied. Since the excess carrier level has to be smaller than the equilibrium *majority* carrier density, however, this limitation is not very restrictive.

For a strongly extrinsic p-type substance wherein $p_0 >> n_0$, it is easily seen from (9.8 - 23, 24, and 28) that the diffusion coefficient $D*$ approaches the diffusion coefficient D_n of electrons, which are the *minority* charge carriers. Likewise, the mobility $\mu*$ reduces to the electron mobility μ_n, and the lifetime $\tau*$ reduces to the electron lifetime τ_{n0}. In the case of strongly extrinsic n-type crystals, it is exactly the opposite, all these coefficients approaching the values of the transport coefficients of holes, which are again the minority carriers. So in extrinsic substances, the transport of the excess carrier distribution is characterized, surprisingly, solely by the diffusion coefficient, the mobility, and the lifetime of the *minority carrier*. Since most semiconductor device structures utilize almost exclusively extrinsic n- and p-type materials, one need only consider *explicitly* in device analysis, the way in which minority carriers diffuse, drift, and recombine; the majority carriers are there just for the ride, so to speak. This far-reaching principle vastly simplifies the description of device structures, as we shall soon see.

In intrinsic semiconductors, $n_0 = p_0 = n_i$, and the transport coefficients become

$$D* = D_i = \frac{2D_n D_p}{D_n + D_p} \quad , \qquad \mu* = \mu_i = 0 \quad , \quad \text{and} \qquad \frac{1}{\tau*} = \frac{1}{\tau_i} = \frac{1}{\tau_{p0}}\left[2 + \frac{\delta p}{n_i}\right]. \tag{9.8-30}$$

A detailed explanation of the strange fact that the mobility $\mu*$ vanishes in this case will be assigned as a problem. At this point, it is most important to investigate the extent to which the assumption of electrical neutrality (which enables us to obtain the solution (9.8 - 29) in the first place) is justified, and to estimate the extent to which diffusion determines the field $\mathbf{E}$ in that equation.

Equation (9.28 - 29) would be very easy to solve if the second term, containing the electric field, were absent, if the excess generation rate g' were zero, and if a steady state were to prevail, making the right side zero. In a geometry whose symmetry allows the excess carrier concentration to vary with distance only along the x-direction, (9.8 - 29) under these conditions reduces to

$$\frac{d^2(\delta p)}{dx^2} - \frac{\delta p}{L^{*2}} = 0 , \qquad \text{where} \qquad L^{*2} = D^* \tau^* . \qquad (9.8\text{-}31)$$

In this expression, L^* is a parameter having dimensions of length, referred to as the *diffusion length*. The equation now has simple exponential solutions of the form

$$\delta p = e^{\pm x/L^*} , \qquad (9.8\text{-}32)$$

the general solution being a linear combination of the positive and negative exponentials multiplied by arbitrary constants determined by appropriate boundary conditions. To be specific, let us consider the situation shown in Figure 9.16.

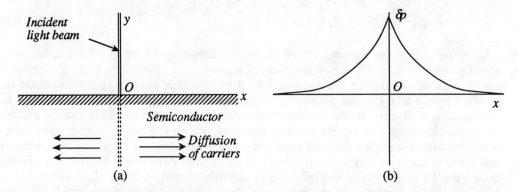

Figure 9.16 A semiconductor crystal illuminated by a narrow beam of light confined to a plane normal to the x-axis, which impinges on the surface of the crystal at O. The beam penetrates the crystal as shown at (a), generating electron-hole pairs in a thin planar region that extends relatively far into the crystal. The optically generated carrier pairs then diffuse outward in both directions into the semiconductor, their exponential concentration profile in the steady state being as illustrated at (b).

In this diagram we see the edge of a light beam which propagates downward onto the polished surface of a semiconductor crystal. The beam lies in the yz-plane, and meets the surface in a line normal to the page at O. It is assumed that the beam is monochromatic, and has a photon energy only slightly greater than the gap energy. Under these conditions the optical absorption coefficient is quite small, the crystal being relatively transparent to the incident beam, while the photon energy is still sufficient to generate electron hole pairs in a planar region illustrated by the dashed lines at (a) in the figure. It assumed that the the thickness of the layer within which the pairs are generated is so small as to be negligible. Within this layer the excess generation rate g' is large, but outside it, in the unilluminated bulk of the crystal, it is zero. The excess electrons and holes generated in the thin illuminated region diffuse outward in both directions, and eventually a steady-state profile of excess carrier concentration versus distance along the x-direction somewhat like that shown at (b) above will be achieved, the concentration falling off with distance due to electron-hole recombination in the unilluminated bulk of the crystal. These conditions can be realized in practice, which makes it possible to use this arrangement to measure the diffusion length L^*.

In this situation, it is clear that the generation rate of electron-hole pairs is zero away from the source plane, and that the time-derivative $\partial(\delta p)/\partial t$ in (9.8 - 29) is zero, as assumed in writing the easily-solved equation (9.8 - 31). It is less clear, however, when--if ever--you can neglect the term in (9.8 - 29) which contains the electric field. In the situation shown above, there is no external emf, of course, but there is an internal electric field set up by the disparity in diffusion rates between electrons and holes, which should in principle be retained, and cannot in any event be neglected without justification. We must now determine when it is important and when it can be neglected. There is also the related question, important but as yet unanswered, of when the assumption of neutrality ($\delta n = \delta p$) that allowed us to arrive at (9.8 - 29) to begin with, is justified.

The electric field **E** can be related to the current density **J** simply by adding the expressions (9.8 - 9) giving the electron and hole current densities, to obtain

$$\mathbf{J} = e(n\mu_n + p\mu_p)\mathbf{E} + e(D_n - D_p)\nabla(\delta p) \ , \tag{9.8-33}$$

if we observe that the assumption of neutrality allows us to replace the gradients of n and p with $\nabla(\delta p)$. The one-dimensional equation of continuity (9.8 - 5), though not directly applicable to the separate electron and hole current densities, must be satisfied by the *total* current density J_x. In the steady state, this requires that $\partial J_x/\partial x = 0$, or that J_x be constant. In the present situation, J_x is in fact *zero*. This can be understood by observing that far from the generation source the excess carrier concentration approaches zero, as does its gradient. There are thus no diffusion fluxes there and there is also no external emf present to drive drift currents. Far from the origin, therefore, the condition of the material is essentially that of thermal equilibrium, in which no net current can exist. But according to the continuity equation, J_x must be constant, and if it is zero far from the origin, it must be zero everywhere. The field **E** can be obtained, therefore by setting **J** equal to zero in (9.8 - 33) and solving for **E**, which yields, in this one-dimensional problem, with the aid of the Einstein relations and the notation $b = \mu_n/\mu_p$,

$$E_x = -\frac{kT}{e} \cdot \frac{b-1}{nb+p} \frac{d(\delta p)}{dx} \ . \tag{9.8-34}$$

In the absence of any electric field, the transport equation for excess carriers in the situation considered here reduces to (9.8 - 31), and its solutions are of the form (9.8 - 32). The two terms on the right side of (9.8 - 31) are not necessarily small, but *their difference is exactly zero*. When a field exists, there will be another term present, and (9.8 - 29) will now take the form

$$\frac{d^2(\delta p)}{dx^2} + \frac{\mu^* E_x}{D^*} \frac{d(\delta p)}{dx} - \frac{\delta p}{L^{*2}} = 0 \ . \tag{9.8-35}$$

This equation is more complicated than it seems at first sight, since the field E_x is itself proportional to $d(\delta p)/dx$. Nevertheless, if the field term is much smaller than either of the two other terms, in particular $\delta p/L^{*2}$, the equation will differ only slightly from (9.8 - 31), and the exponential solutions (9.8 - 32) will still be good approximations. Under these circumstances, it is still possible to assume (for the region $x > 0$) the exponential solutions

$$\delta p = Ae^{-x/L*} , \qquad \frac{d(\delta p)}{dx} = -\frac{\delta p}{L*} , \qquad \text{and} \qquad \frac{d^2(\delta p)}{dx^2} = \frac{\delta p}{L*^2} . \qquad (9.8\text{-}36)$$

The ratio $\mu*/D*$ can be evaluated using (9.8 - 23) and (9.8 - 24) as

$$\frac{\mu*}{D*} = \frac{e}{kT} \cdot \frac{p_0 - n_0}{p + n} . \qquad (9.8\text{-}37)$$

Substituting the results (9.8 - 34, 36, and 37) into (9.8 - 36) and *requiring* the second term on the left side of (9.8 - 36) to be much smaller than the third leads to the condition

$$\left| \frac{(p_0 - n_0)(b - 1)\delta p}{(p + n)(nb + p)} \right| \ll 1 . \qquad (9.8\text{-}38)$$

This condition will always be satisfied when δp is sufficiently small. Indeed, since the quantity $(p_0 - n_0)/(p + n)$ is inherently less than unity, it is always satisfied when the remaining factors are much smaller than unity. These factors can be expressed in terms of the conductivity by observing that $\sigma = e\mu_p(nb + p)$ and $\delta\sigma = e\mu_p(b + 1)\delta p$, so that

$$\frac{(b - 1)\delta p}{nb + p} = \frac{(b - 1)e\mu_p \delta p}{e\mu_p[n_0 b + p_0 + (b + 1)\delta p]} = \frac{b - 1}{b + 1} \cdot \frac{\delta\sigma}{\sigma_0 + \delta\sigma} . \qquad (9.8\text{-}39)$$

We may therefore conclude that the neglect of the second term in (9.8 - 35), and the use of the simple exponential solutions of the form (9.8 - 32) is an excellent approximation, provided that

$$\left| \frac{b - 1}{b + 1} \cdot \frac{\delta\sigma}{\sigma_0 + \delta\sigma} \right| \ll 1 . \qquad (9.8\text{-}40)$$

Physically, this condition requires that the excess carrier concentration be so small that no very large fractional change in conductivity occurs.

So far, we have assumed always that the excess carrier concentrations δn and δp are equal, which guarantees the electrical neutrality of the system. It is clear, however, that these two quantities are not precisely the same, since some disparity in their magnitudes is needed to generate the internal electric field (9.8 - 34). The magnitude of this disparity can be calculated from Poisson's equation (9.8 - 16). In this one dimensional example, the divergence $\nabla \cdot \mathbf{E}$ is simply dE_x/dx, while the total charge density is $e(\delta p - \delta n)$ as suggested by (9.4 - 20) and (9.8 - 17). Poisson's equation can therefore be written as

$$\frac{dE_x}{dx} = \frac{e(\delta p - \delta n)}{K\varepsilon_0} , \qquad (9.8\text{-}40a)$$

where the field E_x is expressed by (9.8 - 34). In evaluating the derivative it must be remembered that n and p are functions of x. Moreover, we shall continue to assume the equality of δn and δp until the very end, when the results are compared with the charge imbalance indicated by the right side of the above equation. In this way, we find

$$\frac{dE_x}{dx} = -\frac{kT}{e} \cdot \frac{b-1}{nb+p} \frac{\delta p}{L^{*2}} \left[1 - \frac{(b+1)\delta p}{nb+p}\right] = \frac{e(\delta p - \delta n)}{K\varepsilon_0} . \tag{9.8-41}$$

When condition (9.8 - 40) is satisfied, the second term in the brackets can be neglected in comparison with unity, which leads finally to

$$\left|\frac{\delta p - \delta n}{\delta p}\right| = \frac{K\varepsilon_0 kT}{e^2} \cdot \frac{b-1}{nb+p} \cdot \frac{1}{L^{*2}} . \tag{9.8-42}$$

This result can be understood most easily when expressed in terms of a parameter called the *Debye length* L_D, defined as

$$L_D = \sqrt{\frac{K\varepsilon_0 kT}{e^2} \cdot \frac{b+1}{nb+p}} , \tag{9.8-43}$$

and a related *intrinsic* Debye length L_{Di} obtained by setting $n = p = n_i$,

$$L_{Di} = \sqrt{\frac{K\varepsilon_0 kT}{e^2 n_i}} . \tag{9.8-44}$$

Using this notation, (9.8 - 42) can be written

$$\left|\frac{\delta p - \delta n}{\delta p}\right| = (b^2 - 1) \cdot \frac{L_D^2}{L^{*2}} . \tag{9.8-45}$$

The quantity $(\delta p - \delta n)/\delta p$ expresses the fractional extent to which the system must deviate from exact neutrality to produce the field suggested by an initial assumption of total neutrality. If this calculated quantity turns out to be small, the solutions determined using the charge neutrality hypothesis are in accord with such an assumption, and thus represent good self-consistent approximate solutions to the transport equations. If not, other ways of solving the equations must be sought. In the example we have just discussed, which is typical of most problems that arise in connection with semiconductor materials and devices, it is found that self-consistent solutions follow from an initial assumption of electrical neutrality whenever the diffusion length L^* is much larger than the Debye length. In silicon and germanium, the excess carrier lifetime τ^* is rarely less than 10^{-6}sec, while the diffusion coefficient D^* is about 10^{-2}m^2/sec. This implies a diffusion length greater than 10^{-4}m or 0.1mm. The intrinsic room-temperature Debye length, however, is 0.035mm for silicon and 0.00096mm for germanium. Moreover, for *extrinsic* materials, the Debye length (9.8 - 43) is significantly less than the *intrinsic* Debye length (9.8 - 44). Therefore, the electrical neutrality hypothesis is almost always valid for Si or Ge.

The preceding analysis, though lengthy and complicated, is useful, because it shows that when there is no external emf present, the explicit field dependence suggested by the second term on the right side of (9.8 - 29) and (9.8 - 35) can often be ignored. This does not mean that the effect of internal coulomb fields upon the transport processes is totally neglected; the neutrality assumption itself largely takes care of that, its effect being manifested *implicitly* in the form of the effective transport coefficients D^*, μ^*, and τ^*. When the field term can be omitted, however, the transport equation for the excess carrier concentration δp becomes much simpler than before. In the above example, it reduces to the simple form (9.8 - 31), which leads to simple exponential solutions given by (9.8 - 32). Since the excess electron-hole pairs will in time undergo mutual annihilation by recombinination, the excess carrier density must approach zero far from the generation source at the origin. This means that for $x > 0$ a negative exponential solution is required, while for $x < 0$, a positive exponential is implied. We may therefore write for this example

$$\delta p = \delta n = Ae^{-x/L^*} \quad (x > 0) , \quad \text{and} \quad \delta p = \delta n = Ae^{x/L^*} \quad (x < 0) . \tag{9.8 - 46}$$

The arbitrary constant A is clearly related to the strength of the generation source, which is in turn proportional to the intensity of the incident light.

The *total* current J_x in this example is zero, but the currents associated with electrons and holes are not zero, but are instead equal and opposite at all points. If the individual diffusion and drift currents appearing in the expressions for J_n and J_p given in (9.8 - 9) for both carrier species are calculated and added, it can be shown with the aid of (9.8 - 34) and the Einstein relations that, for hole current,

$$J_p = -eD_p \frac{d(\delta p)}{dx} + ep\mu_p E_x = -eD_p \frac{d(\delta p)}{dx} \left[1 + \frac{p(b-1)}{nb+p} \right] , \tag{9.8 - 47}$$

which, after combining terms and doing some additional algebra can be transformed to read,

$$\frac{J_p}{e} = -\frac{J_n}{e} = -D^* \frac{d(\delta p)}{dx} . \tag{9.8 - 48}$$

We can conclude, therefore, that the hole and electron currents can be represented as purely diffusive currents proportional to a diffusion coefficient times the gradient of carrier concentration. It is true, of course, physically, that some of this current is driven by internal coulomb fields, but their effects are completely accounted for in this instance by the altered form of the diffusion coefficient D^*.

If you examine the fluxes of minority and majority carriers in extrinsic materials in detail, you will find that the internal coulomb field (9.8 - 34) drives very little minority carrier current, but impels all but a small fraction of the majority carrier current. The reason is that the large density of majority carriers creates a situation in which electrical neutrality can be preserved by a small displacement of a large number of majority carriers--a situation in which minority carriers have to move by pure diffusion, while the large body of *majority* carriers are driven by a small internal coulomb field, which can easily generate the current flow needed to keep them in step with the diffusing minority carriers. The details of this calculation are instructive and are assigned as an exercise. When there is an *externally imposed* field large compared with (9.8 – 34), it must be included explicitly as the field **E** in (9.8 - 29). Since such fields are essentially independent of δp, however, relatively simple solutions to (9.8 - 29) are still easily obtained.

These results, though developed in the context of a particular example, are of general applicability to the diffusion and drift of excess carrier distributions in semiconductors. The development of this subject is, unfortunately, lengthy and not particularly simple, but some understanding of it is absolutely necessary to resolve the questions that merely go unanswered in less rigorous treatments--questions about why the diffusion and drift of majority carriers is usually ignored in the analysis of most semiconductor devices, and about why photoconductivity and carrier drift experiments are described as measuring "minority carrier lifetimes" and "minority carrier mobilities".

9.9 PHOTOCONDUCTIVITY, EXCESS CARRIER LIFETIME, AND SURFACE RECOMBINATION

We have given a basic discussion of electron-hole generation and recombination in the preceding section. We shall now examine this subject in greater detail. The mobility and diffusion coefficients of electrons and holes differ from one substance to another, but for a given material exhibit only minor variations with temperature and impurity concentration. For excess electron and hole lifetimes and generation rates, however, the situation is more complex. The processes that determine these parameters differ widely not only from one material to another, but also within different samples of the same substance. Their values depend, moreover, not only on bulk properties of the material, but also on small concentrations of certain kinds of impurities, and upon how sample *surfaces* are prepared and treated.

First of all, it is important to understand that excess carrier generation and recombination processes differ, in materials like GaAs and some other III-V intermetallics, from those in purely covalent materials like Si and Ge. In these intermetallics, the energy minimum of the conduction band and the valence band energy maximum are in the *center* of tbe Brillouin zone, at $k = 0$, while, as we have already seen, Si and Ge have conduction band minima far removed from $k = 0$. In the former group of materials, direct *vertical transitions* between conduction and valence bands at $k = 0$ can take place. This is not observed in the covalent substances because of the large energy difference between conduction and valence band states and the negligible electron population near $k = 0$ in the conduction band, as shown in Figure 9.17. The former materials are referred to as "direct-gap" semiconductors, the latter as "indirect-gap" substances. Generation-recombination processes in direct-gap materials are usually vertical or nearly vertical transitions as shown at (a) in the figure, and can be accompanied by absorption of radiation in upward transitions and emission of light of frequency corresponding to the energy gap in the downward transition. The requirement of momentum and energy conservation is easily satisfied in these transitions, which means that they occur with high probability. The generation and recombination rates, are therefore high, and the excess carrier lifetimes correspondingly short--usually of the order of 10^{-7} or 10^{-8} sec--in these substances.

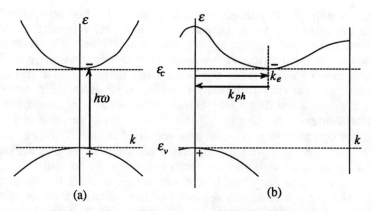

Figure 9.17 (a) Vertical generation/recombination transitions in a direct-gap semiconductor. (b) The situation in an indirect-gap material, showing the phonon vector needed for momentum conservation in the generation of the electron-hole pair of lowest possible energy.

In indirect gap materials, in order to conserve momentum in across-the-gap absorption or radiative recombination, the generation or absorption of a phonon having a large k-vector must take place, as shown at (b) in the figure. This restriction causes across-the-gap generation or recombination to occur much less frequently in indirect gap materials, and causes excess carrier lifetimes to be longer by a factor of about 10^5 than in the direct-gap substances. Moreover, the optical absorption edge in indirect-gap materials is not as sharply defined as in direct-gap semiconductors, the absorption coefficient rising far less steeply in the range of photon energies near $\Delta\varepsilon$ than it does in the direct-gap materials. A rigorous treatment of these effects is somewhat beyond the scope of this text, so we shall confine ourselves to a primarily qualitative description.

In most indirect-gap semiconductors, across-the-gap processes like that illustrated at (b) above are so rare as to play only a minor role in actual carrier generation and recombination in these materials. Instead, in substances like Si and Ge, certain types of impurities and lattice defects act as localized *recombination centers* where electron-hole recombination occurs such that the energy of the electron-hole pair is dissipated as heat, without the emission of a photon. Such centers always posess a localized quantum state much like that of an ordinary donor or acceptor center, except that its energy level lies *deep within the forbidden gap*. These centers can capture an electron, holding it until a hole comes along and annihilates it. Since the center is tightly coupled to the lattice, it can dissipate the energy of the electron and the hole as lattice vibrational energy, which is ultimately perceived as heat. There is thus no light quantum emitted or absorbed in these processes. Recombination centers can also act in an inverse mode to convert lattice energy into thermally generated electron-hole pairs. In Si and Ge, the presence of these centers causes the observed lifetime of excess electrons and holes to be somewhat shorter than the very long predicted radiative lifetime, and in addition, to be sensitive to extremely small concentrations of lattice defects and certain impurity atoms. Excess carrier lifetimes in Si and Ge can therefore range over a wide spectrum of values, from about 10^{-2} to 10^{-7} sec, depending on the kind and amount of defects or impurities that are present.

A recombination center is usually a substitutional atom or some other structure similarly coupled to the crystal lattice, which posesses a localized quantum state deep within the gap, which can accommodate an electron or hole. Ordinary donor and acceptor impurities do not usually act as recombination centers, because they are always ionized and cannot (except at very low temperatures) effectively capture electrons and holes. To be an effective recombination center the energy of the quantum state must be much further from the band edge than that of a normal donor or acceptor atom. Certain substitutional impurities, such as those in columns II or VI of the periodic table have deep-lying donor or acceptor levels, and can thus act as recombination centers. A column VI atom easily gives up one of its two excess electrons to the conduction band, like an ordinary Column V donor. The site then becomes positively charged, and the attractive coulomb forces that act on the second electron make it necessary to supply much more energy to ionize it. As a result, there is a quantum state deep within the gap corresponding to this ionization process, and the site can act as a recombination center. Similar considerations apply to divalent acceptor impurities, and also to certain types of interstitial impurity atoms.

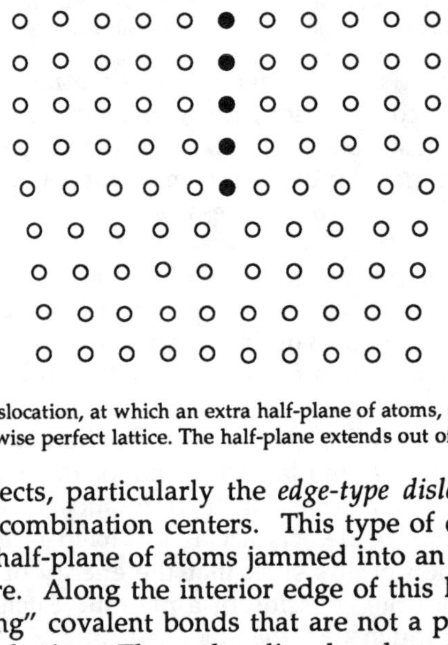

Figure 9.18 An edge-type dislocation, at which an extra half-plane of atoms, shown by black circles, is introduced into an otherwise perfect lattice. The half-plane extends out of the page, normal to the paper.

Certain lattice defects, particularly the *edge-type dislocation* shown in Figure 9.18, are also effective recombination centers. This type of dislocation is formed by the presence of an extra half-plane of atoms jammed into an otherwise perfect lattice as illustrated in the figure. Along the interior edge of this half-plane there is a line of atoms having "dangling" covalent bonds that are not a part of the bond network of the otherwise regular lattice. These dangling bonds act as deep-lying acceptor sites, and since their atoms are strongly coupled to the lattice, the dislocation site can act as a recombination center. To acheive long excess carrier lifetimes, one must generally obtain very pure and structurally perfect crystals. When active impurities and lattice imperfections are present, the excess carrier lifetime will be shorter than it might otherwise be. Long excess carrier lifetimes are needed for the fabrication of good bipolar transistors and photovoltaic cells, but is some instances, particularly in devices that operate at very high frequency, excessively long lifetimes are undesireable. The excess carrier lifetime is clearly a very important parameter for characterizing semiconductor materials.

It is apparent that the presence of lattice imperfections and impurity atoms gives rise to localized quantum states with energies in the forbidden energy region between the conduction and valence bands. The appearance of these quantum states in the energy gap is associated with the interruption of an otherwise perfectly periodic lattice potential by these inclusions. In general *any* interruption of this perfect periodicity tends to create such localized states. The exterior surface of the crystal can be viewed as such an interruption, and it can be shown that quantum states in the gap arise whenever a periodic lattice is terminated by a high surface potential barrier that confines the electrons and holes to the interior of the crystal. Such states are referred to as *Tamm states*, after the Russian physicist Igor Tamm who first discovered them in 1932. Tamm demonstrated the reality of these surface states using a one-dimensional Kronig-Penney potential terminated at some point by a high square barrier that models the effect of the surface and restricts electrons to the interior of the crystal. His calculation shows that there are quantum states localized near the surface of the crystal, whose wave function decays exponentially with distance from the surface barrier in either direction. The energy eigenvalues associated with these states are in the forbidden energy regions, and there is one such state in each forbidden band. Tamm's calculations involve merely the matching of exterior and interior solutions of Schrödinger's equation and their derivatives at the surface; the algebra is complex, however, and for this reason we shall not present the details. Though Tamm's original work was framed in the context of the KP model, later studies showed that the same results follow for a general periodic potential terminated with a surface barrier. It also follows from this more general analysis that there is one surface state in each forbidden band for every surface atom.

It is apparent from this that we might expect surface states to act as recombination centers, and to cause electron-hole pairs to recombine at crystal surfaces by mechanisms similar to (but separate from) those associated with recombination centers within the crystal itself. Experimental studies have shown that this hypothesis is a valid one, and that excess electron-hole recombination has two separate components, one associated with bulk recombination centers distributed (uniformly, one frequently assumes) in the interior of the crystal, the other with a separate set of recombination centers at the surfaces. Crystal boundaries in polycrystalline materials also interrupt the periodicity of the lattice, and thus give rise to interfacial states that can act as recombination centers, which accounts for the fact that these materials usually exhibit excess carrier lifetimes significantly lower than those found for good single crystals of the same substance.

It is sometimes useful to view generation-recombination processes as chemical dissociation reactions in a weakly ionized "electrolyte". From this point of view the electrolyte is the covalent bond network, and generation of an electron-hole pair resembles the "dissociation" of a covalent bond into a pair of oppositely charged particles, like the dissociation of a water molecule into H^+ and OH^- ions. Recombination is simply the "reverse reaction" in which the two charged particles recombine to form an undissociated covalent bond. In this context, it is easy to see that recombination centers--both in the bulk and at the surface--behave like *catalysts*, which increase reaction rates without undergoing any permanent chemical change themselves. It is also easily seen that any such "reaction" and its inverse must proceed at the same rate at thermal equilibrium. Thus, any recombination center--bulk or surface--must *also* function as a center where electron-hole pairs are generated, and the generation rate and the recombination rate for each type of center must be equal at thermal equilibrium. Indeed, since from the chemical point of view *any* reaction and its inverse must proceed at the same rate in equilibrium, it is clear that the same is true of other processes subject to similar kinetics, even though they are not conventionally classified as chemical reactions. The general assertion of the equality of forward and inverse equilibrium rates for all processes needed to describe the kinetics of a physical system is referred to as the principle of *microscopic reversibility*, or sometimes as the principle of *detailed balance*. It is important not only in chemical problems, but also, as we shall soon see, in the analysis of semiconductor devices.

Measurements of excess carrier lifetime are most easily obtained from experimental studies of photoconductivity. One such experiment, illustrated in Figure 9.16 in the preceding section, has already been suggested. It is simpler, however, to use the somewhat different configuration shown below, to make these studies.

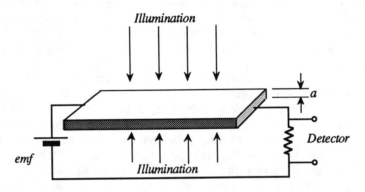

Figure 9.19 Sample geometry and circuit configuration used in dc photoconductivity studies.

In this experiment, a thin uniform sample of thickness a in the form of a rectangular plate is used. The thickness is chosen to be much smaller than either of the lateral dimensions of the plate. This allows us to regard the plate as a one-dimensional planar system of essentially infinite extent in these lateral directions. The plate is uniformly illuminated on both sides, as shown, with light that we shall assume penetrates the sample with only slight absorption, so that excess electron-hole pairs are generated *uniformly* throughout the sample. The light wavelength must be *slightly* less than the critical value $hc/\Delta\varepsilon$ associated with the gap energy in order to excite electron-hole pairs, but not so much so as to be strongly absorbed within a distance equal to the thickness of the sample. In practice, it is not too difficult to satisfy this condition, particularly in Si and Ge, whose absorption edge is not as abrupt as in direct-gap semiconductors. The increase in conductivity due to excess electrons and holes in the sample can be detected by passing a small dc current through the sample and observing the increase in dc voltage across the resistor when the sample is illuminated. In the figure, this current is excited by the emf of an external battery. This experiment measures what is referred to as dc photoconductivity. The excess carrier lifetime follows from the observed photoresponse.

It is also possible to observe the transient effects that occur when the illumination is abruptly turned on and off. In this case, one must use a pulsed light source, or in any event one which produces a sharp step of light intensity *versus* time when turned on and off. A xenon flashtube or a pulsed laser is suitable for this application. Under these circumstances a fast oscilloscope is used as a detector rather than a dc instrument such as a potentiometer. The observed transients show directly the rise and decay of the excess carrier distribution; their time constant leads directly to the lifetime. The observed waveform is illustrated in Figure 9.20. This ac photoconductivity experiment is more difficult to perform, but is easier to interpret, than the dc measurement. We shall discuss first the dc case, then the ac experiment.

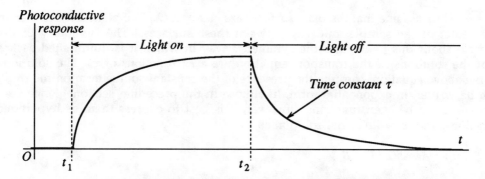

Figure 9.20 Transient (ac) photoconductivity signal, showing time constant observed when light is turned on and off. Excess carrier lifetimes are directly related to this time constant.

In the dc case, a time-independent excess carrier concentration is present for times larger than t_2 in the above figure. The dc photocurrent due to the conductivity modulation is easily measured. This photocurrent is directly proportional to the total number of excess carriers in the sample, a quantity we can calculate if we know the light intensity, sample dimensions, excess carrier mobility, and lifetime. If all but one of these quantities is known, the unknown parameter can be found in terms of the observed photocurrent. In order to determine this photoresponse, we must solve the transport equation for the excess carrier concentration, as in the example shown in Figure 9.16 in Section 9.8. We shall assume that the sample is *extrinsic*, and that the excess carrier density is small compared to the equilibrium majority carrier density. The thin-plate geometry assures that carrier diffusion takes place primarily along the x-direction normal to the plate, and allows us to write a one-dimensional transport equation. Under these circumstances, the starred ambipolar transport coefficients in (9.8 - 29) reduce to the transport coefficients of the minority carrier. In this experiment, there is a small electric field along the sample, in the direction of current flow. However, since this field is normal to the x-axis, and since any gradient of carrier concentration can have only an x-component in this geometry, the term containing $\mathbf{E} \cdot \nabla(\delta p)$ vanishes. It is necessary, however, to include the term g' in (9.8 - 29), which gives the rate at which excess minority carriers are photoexcited within the sample. If the sample is uniformly illuminated as described above this quantity will be constant. Under these circumstances, the minority carrier transport equation (9.8 - 29) can be written

$$D\frac{d^2(\delta p)}{dx^2} - \frac{\delta p}{\tau} = -g' \, , \qquad (9.9\text{-}1)$$

where δp is the excess minority carrier density, D and τ are the minority carrier diffusion coefficient and lifetime, and g' is the constant number of minority carriers photoexcited per unit volume per unit time. Since it is assumed that a steady state has been reached, the quantity $\partial(\delta p)/\partial t$ is zero. Dividing by D, this becomes

$$\frac{d^2(\delta p)}{dx^2} - \frac{\delta p}{L^2} = -\frac{g'}{D} \quad , \qquad \text{where} \qquad L^2 = D\tau \quad . \tag{9.9-2}$$

Let us assume that the plate surfaces are at $x = \pm a/2$. The plane $x = 0$ is then in the center of the sample, midway between these surfaces. The symmetry of the sample about this plane, and the symmetric way in which it is illuminated assure that the solutions of the transport equation are *even* functions of x. The solutions of the above equations, despite the presence of the constant source term on the right, can be written in exponential form, like those in the preceding section. Since they are known to be even functions, however, it is best to express them as hyperbolic functions, and to write a trial solution as

$$\delta p = A\cosh(x/L) + B \quad , \tag{9.9-3}$$

where A and B are constants. Substituting this solution into (9.9 - 2), it is apparent that $B = g'\tau$, and that

$$\delta p = A\cosh(x/L) + g'\tau \quad . \tag{9.9-4}$$

The remaining constant A must be determined by surface boundary conditions at $x = \pm a/2$. As discussed previously, excess electron-hole pairs can recombine not only in the bulk material, but also at the surfaces, where there are recombination centers independent of those within the crystal. Recombination within the crystal is accounted for by the lifetime τ in the transport equation, which in this calculation is incorporated in the diffusion length L. The effect of surface recombination, however, must be accounted for by the surface boundary condition.

If there were no surface recombination at all, the surfaces would simply "reflect" excess carriers back into the sample by elastic collisions. In this situation, there can be no net flux of minority carriers into the surface. Since the diffusion flux is given in terms of the concentration gradient, by $-D[d(\delta p)/dx]$, this means that the derivative $d(dp)/dx$ must be *zero* at $x = \pm a/2$. Applying this requirement to (9.9 - 4) leads at once to the result $A = 0$, in which case (9.9 - 4) reduces to

$$\delta p = g'\tau = \text{const.} \tag{9.9-5}$$

One obtains in this case an excess carrier density constant throughout the bulk, and proportional to the photogeneration rate and the minority carrier lifetime--a reasonable, if somewhat trivial, result.

At the other extreme, every excess minority carrier that collides with the surface recombines *via* surface recombination centers, with *unit probability*. In this case, the excess carrier density is reduced essentially to zero at the surface, so that for $x = \pm a/2$, we may set $\delta p = 0$. Applying this boundary condition to (9.9 - 4), we obtain $A = -g'\tau/[\cosh(a/2L)]$, and (9.9 - 3) now becomes,

$$\delta p = g'\tau\left[1 - \frac{\cosh(x/L)}{\cosh(a/2L)}\right] \quad . \tag{9.9-6}$$

In reality, neither of these extreme conditions is ever quite realized; excess carriers recombine at surfaces, though not with unit probability; frequently they simply "bounce off" the surface barrier and return to the bulk distribution. They may then wander about in the bulk, and finally recombine there. Alternatively, their random diffusive motion may return them to the surface before that happens, and they may have another try at colliding with the surface. Indeed, they may have several tries (or even several thousand) before recombining either at the surface or in the bulk. In this complicated situation, there is some diffusive flux toward a partially absorbing surface, but not as much as their could be if it were a totally efficient absorber of excess carriers, and the excess carrier concentration is reduced at the surface, but not necessarily to an amount negligible in comparison to its value in the bulk. Thus, neither δp nor the flux $-D[d(\delta p)/dx]$ is zero at $x = \pm a/2$, and we must seek a more general boundary condition involving both these quantities.

Under these circumstances the *ratio* of diffusion flux to concentration at the surface turns out to be crucial to the formulation of a realistic surface boundary condition. This ratio, which we shall denote as s, is defined by

$$s = -\frac{D[d(\delta p)/dx]_{a/2}}{\delta p(a/2)} .$$
(9.9-7)

The quantity s has the dimensions of velocity. It is referred to as the *surface recombination velocity*, and its magnitude is related to the probability that a single collision of a minority carrier with the surface will result in its recombination.

Using (9.9 - 4), we can evaluate the quantities in the numerator and denominator of this expression at $x = a/2$ and obtain

$$-\frac{D[d(\delta p)/dx]_{a/2}}{\delta p(a/2)} = s = \frac{-A(D/L)\sinh(a/2L)}{A\cosh(a/2L) + g'\tau} .$$
(9.9-8)

You will observe that the constant A in (9.9 - 4) can now be evaluated in terms of s, simply by solving the above equation for A to obtain

$$A = \frac{-sg'\tau}{s\cosh(a/2L) + (D/L)\sinh(a/2L)} .$$
(9.9-9)

and

$$\delta p = g'\tau\left[1 - \frac{s\cosh(x/L)}{s\cosh(a/2L) + (D/L)\sinh(a/2L)}\right].$$
(9.9-10)

By setting s equal to zero and infinity, the limiting expressions (9.9 - 5) and (9.9 - 6) can be obtained. In the intermediate range a sequence of functions like those shown in Figure 9.21 is obtained.

It is not quite clear in (9.9 - 7) that the numerator of the fraction on the right varies proportionally to the denominator, and thus that s is a constant, independent of the quantity δp. More detailed kinetic studies of the interchange of excess carriers between bulk and surface show that this is the case, and that s is, in fact, a constant. These studies also show that if R is the probability that a minority carrier *escapes* recombination in a single collision with the surface barrier (a probability often referred to as the "reflection coefficient") then s can be stated in terms of this quantity as

$$s = \frac{\langle v \rangle}{2} \cdot \frac{1-R}{1+R} \quad , \tag{9.9-11}$$

where $\langle v \rangle$ is the Maxwellian average minority carrier speed, equal to $(8kT/\pi m^*)^{1/2}$. It is clear from this that the recombination velocity cannot really be infinite, but has a maximum value $\langle v \rangle/2$ corresponding to $R = 0$. Since $\langle v \rangle$ is about 10^7cm/sec at 300K, which is much larger than s under all normal circumstances, it makes hardly any difference whether one assumes $s = \langle v \rangle/2$ or $s = \infty$. Observed values of $1 - R$ are often of the order of 10^{-4} (corresponding to s of the order of 1000), which suggests a reflectivity only very slightly less than unity. The carrier under these conditions has to make about 10,000 "tries at the surface" before recombining. This small recombination probability may nevertheless profoundly influence the behavior of excess carrier distributions.

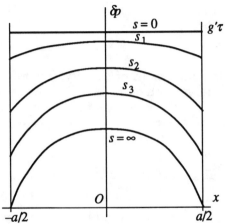

Figure 9.21 Excess carrier concentration profiles within photoconducting samples like those illustrated in Figure 9.19, showing profiles for the cases $s = 0$ and $s = \infty$, as well as several intermediate cases, in which increasing subscript values indicate successively higher surface recombination velocities.

The actual photocurrent is proportional not to the excess carrier density, but to the total *number* of excess carriers δP in the sample, where δP is the *integral* of the carrier density over the sample volume, from $x = -a/2$ to $+a/2$. This integral can be written

$$\delta P = A \int_{-a/2}^{a/2} \delta p(x) \cdot dx \quad , \tag{9.9-12}$$

where A is the area of the plate. The reader is asked to show, as an exercise, that in the situation described above, the quantity δP can be expressed as

$$\delta P = Ag'\tau \left[a - \frac{L}{\coth(a/2L) + (D/sL)} \right] . \tag{9.9-13}$$

The measurement of dc photoconductivity is complicated by the fact that photoresponse depends on incident light intensity and the optical absorption coefficient and reflectivity of the crystal for the light wavelength (or wavelength band) of the source. These quantities are hard to measure precisely, and as a result dc photoresponse measurements are not usually very useful for accurately determining lifetimes or surface recombination velocities. The direct observation of the transients shown in Figure 9.20 allow more accurate measurements of these parameters.

For the ac case, the excess carrier concentration is time-dependent, and we can no longer set the time derivative on the right side of (9.8 - 29) equal to zero. On the other hand, for times immediately following t_2 in Figure 9.20, the generation rate g' is zero, since the sample is then in the dark, and only a previously generated set of carriers is present--a set whose number decays with the time elapsed after turnoff. Under these circumstances, and retaining all the other assumptions that were made for the dc case, we must solve a time-dependent transport equation of the form

$$D\frac{\partial^2(\delta p)}{\partial x^2} - \frac{\delta p}{\tau} = \frac{\partial(\delta p)}{\partial t} .$$ (9.9-14)

This equation can be simplified to some degree by assuming a solution of the form

$$\delta p(x,t) = e^{-t/\tau} u(x,t) .$$ (9.9-15)

Substituting this into (9.9 - 14) and simplifying, one obtains an equation for $u(x, t)$ of the form

$$D\frac{\partial^2 u}{\partial x^2} = \frac{\partial u}{\partial t} .$$ (9.9-16)

This partial differential equation can be solved using the technique of separation of variables, which we have already used in some of the quantum mechanical examples--notably that of the hydrogen atom--that were considered in Chapter 4. We therefore begin by assuming solutions of the product form

$$u(x,t) = X(x) \cdot T(t) .$$ (9.9-17)

Substituting this solution into (9.9 - 16) and dividing both sides of the resulting equation by $DX(x)T(t)$, we find

$$\frac{1}{X(x)} \frac{d^2 X}{dx^2} = \frac{1}{DT(t)} \frac{dT}{dt} = -\alpha^2 ,$$ (9.9-18)

The first two expressions above are functions, respectively, of the variables x and t alone; they must therefore be separately equal to a constant, which is written as $-\alpha^2$ to guarantee that the solutions decay with time as negative exponentials. Solving the two ordinary differential equations expressed above for $X(x)$ and $T(t)$, we obtain

$$X(x) = A\cos\alpha x + B\sin\alpha x \qquad \text{and} \qquad T(t) = e^{-\alpha^2 Dt} .$$ (9.9-19)

The sample geometry and illumination are assumed to be symmetric about the plane $x = 0$, as in the dc case; we may therefore restrict ourselves to solutions that are even functions of the variable x. Under these circumstances B is zero, and the basic set of solutions, according to (9.9 - 17) are functions of the form

$$u(x,t) = A \cos \alpha x \cdot e^{-\alpha^2 Dt} \ . \tag{9.9-20}$$

This appears to require that the spatial variation of the solution must be a cosine function, but it must be recalled that a more general solution can be written as a sum of solutions having different "wavelengths", as described by the constant α. Such solutions have the form

$$u(x,t) = \sum_n u_n(x,t) = \sum_n a_n \cos \alpha_n x \cdot e^{-\alpha_n^2 Dt} \ . \tag{9.9-21}$$

The functions $u_n(x, t)$ are the *eigenfunctions* of the diffusion equation (9.9 - 16). Unlike Schrödinger wave functions, their time dependence is exponential rather than sinusoidal, but though this alters the time-variation of the solution, it doesn't alter the mathematics of obtaining it. At time $t = 0$, all exponential factors in the above expression are zero, and the series reduces to a Fourier expansion, which by proper choice of the coeffients a_n, can be made to represent an arbitrary function of x. In this way, the solution can be made to reduce to any prescribed initial concentration profile $u(x, 0)$. Also, it must satisfy a boundary condition of the form (9.9 - 7) at $x = \pm a/2$. We shall in fact require *each term* in the above series to satisfy such a boundary condition, and insist that

$$-D \left(\frac{\partial u_n(x,t)}{\partial x} \right)_{\pm a/2} = s \cdot u_n(\pm a/2, t) \ . \tag{9.9-22}$$

Actually, this boundary condition should be applied to $(\delta p)_n = u_n(x, t)\exp(-t/\tau)$, but multiplying (9.9 - 21) on both sides by $\exp(-t/\tau)$ it is easy to see that if $(\delta p)_n$ obeys such a condition, so must u_n. Substituting the explicit form of $u_n(x, t)$ from (9.9 - 21) into (9.9 - 22), we obtain after rearranging, an expression of the form

$$\cot \frac{\alpha_n a}{2} = \frac{\alpha_n D}{s} = \frac{\alpha_n a}{2} \cdot \frac{2D}{sa} \ . \tag{9.9-23}$$

This transcendental equation defines a set of eigenvalues $\{\alpha_n\}$ ($n = 0, 1, 2, 3, \ldots$) that specify the arguments of the cosine functions in (9.9 - 21). When these arguments reduce to $\alpha_n = 2n\pi/a$, the series is a conventional Fourier cosine expansion. This occurs, however, only when s is infinite. Otherwise, the periods of the Fourier components are *not* integral multiples of $2\pi/a$, but are defined by the solutions of the above transcendental equation. This does not alter the possibility of expanding arbitrary functions as a series of the cosine functions thus obtained, though it does affect the mathematical details of doing so. The set α_n can be viewed graphically as the intersection of the branches of the function $\cot(\alpha a/2)$ with the straight line that represents the right side of (9.9 - 23) plotted as a function of $\alpha a/2$, as shown in Figure 9.22.

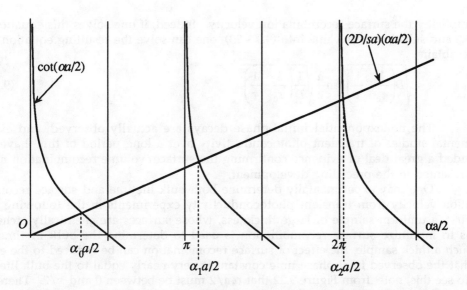

Figure 9.22 Graphical solution of the transcendental equation (9.9 - 23) showing the first three eigenvalues.

One can show that this set of functions is orthogonal, and an expression for the coefficients a_n for any desired initial concentration profile $u(x, 0)$ can be found in the usual way. These details, though interesting, are not of tremendous importance, and are assigned as a series of exercises. What is of greater importance is the observation that *any* solution of this form, which expressed in terms of δp becomes

$$\delta p(x,t) = \sum_n (\delta p)_n(x,t) = \sum_n a_n \cos \alpha_n x \cdot e^{-\alpha_n^2 Dt - (t/\tau)} , \qquad (9.9\text{-}24)$$

is in general not a simple exponential with a single time constant, but a *sum* of exponential functions of time each term of which has a different time constant. The time-decay of photocurrent, therefore is not a simple exponential, but a more complex superposition of exponentials with different time constants. However, as illustrated in Figure 9.22, the first eigenvalue α_0 is significantly *smaller* than any of the others, and moreover, our experience with Fourier expansions shows that if we are dealing with well-behaved profile functions, the amplitude coefficients a_n also fall off rapidly as n increases. As a result, the higher terms in the series die out much more rapidly than the first, and affect primarily only the initial phase of the time decay. If you wait until this initial phase is over, and measure only the final "tail" of the decay of photoresponse, you will observe a simple exponential time decay having a single time constant τ_0 given by

$$\frac{1}{\tau_0} = \frac{1}{\tau} + \alpha_0^2 D . \qquad (9.9\text{-}25)$$

It is clear from this that even the time constant of this final exponential decay mode is not simply the bulk lifetime of the material, but is affected to some degree by surface recombination, since the second term in the above expression contains implicitly the surface recombination velocity. Indeed, if one solves this equation for α_0, and substitutes its value into (9.9 - 23), one can solve the resulting equation for s to obtain

$$s = \sqrt{D\left(\frac{1}{\tau_0} - \frac{1}{\tau}\right)} \, \tan \frac{a}{2} \sqrt{\frac{1}{D}\left(\frac{1}{\tau_0} - \frac{1}{\tau}\right)} \ . \tag{9.9-26}$$

The nonexponential initial-phase decays are actually observed, and experimental studies of transient photoconductivity over a long period of time have provided a great deal of evidence confirming the surface/volume recombination model presented in the preceding development.

One may experimentally determine both bulk lifetime and surface recombination velocity from transient photoconductivity experiments in the following way. First, a uniform sample of large thickness, whose surfaces are chemically etched so as to minimize surface recombination is used to determine the bulk lifetime. In such a thick sample, the effect of surface recombination can be reduced to the extent that the observed final-phase time constant is very nearly equal to the bulk lifetime. To see this, note from Figure 9.22 that $\alpha_0 a/2$ must be between 0 and $\pi/2$. Therefore, if a is large, α_0 must be very small. According to (9.9 - 25), however, under these conditions, the observed lifetime τ_0 and the true bulk lifetime τ must be nearly the same. Having determined τ in this way, the thick sample can now be sliced into much thinner ones, whose surfaces are treated in any desired way to determine (for example) the effect of surface preparation on surface recombination velocity. The transient decay constant τ_0 is now measured again using these thin samples, and the surface recombination velocity for each of them determined from (9.9 - 26), using known values of thickness, diffusion coefficient, and bulk lifetime.

Measurements of bulk lifetime in Si and Ge have provided much experimental justification for the picture of recombination centers and deep-lying impurity levels discussed previously. Surface recombination measurements have shown that the surface recombination velocity is quite sensitive to the way in which sample surfaces are prepared. Surface recombination velocities associated with rough-cut, ground, or lapped surfaces are quite large, of the order of 100,000 cm/sec or more. This is understandable in view of the large amount of lattice damage at the surfaces caused by such treatments. This damage can be "healed" by chemically etching the surface to remove the damaged region. Depending on the exact nature of the etching process, the surface recombination velocity in Ge can be reduced to less than 100cm/sec, with somewhat higher values being obtained for Si. The surface recombination velocity is also affected by the gaseous environment of the surface, any protective coating that may be applied, or the presence of an oxide layer. The picture of Tamm states associated with surface atoms is undoubtedly correct in principle, but it is so difficult to achieve ideally clean and otherwise perfect vacuum-semiconductor interfaces that it is hardly possible to study them experimentally. One can definitely observe surface states in the forbidden gap that act as recombination centers, but in practice these are usually localized interfacial states associated with oxide layers, surface imperfections, chemical contamination, adsorbed gaseous atoms, and other such "garbage".

REFERENCES

W. Shockley, *Electrons and Holes in Semiconductors*, D.van Nostrand Co., New York (1950).

R. A. Smith, *Semiconductors*, Cambridge University Press, Cambridge (1961).

E. Spenke, *Electronic Semiconductors*, McGraw-Hill, New York (1958).

K. Seeger, *Semiconductor Physics*, Springer Verlag, New York/Vienna (1973).

PROBLEMS

1. Calculate the wavelength corresponding to the optical absorption edge in (a) Ge, $\Delta\varepsilon = 0.7eV$, (b) Si, $\Delta\varepsilon = 1.15eV$, (c) Diamond, $\Delta\varepsilon = 5.5eV$, (d) GaAs, $\Delta\varepsilon = 1.35eV$, (e) InSb, $\Delta\varepsilon = 0.25eV$.

2. Find an expression for the smallest concentration of donor impurities that permits intrinsic conductivity to be exhibited at 300K in a semiconductor. Assume Maxwell-Boltzmann statistics. Find the numerical vakue of this concentration for each of the substances listed in the preceding problem, assuming effective masses equal to the inertial electron mass.

3. Using Maxwell's electomagnetic theory, calculate the optical absorption coefficient caused by free majority carrier ohmic conduction in an extrinsic semiconductor, for light wavelengths *longer* than that corresponding to the bandgap energy. Find the distance over which the light intensity drops by a factor $1/e$.

4. Find the total number of quantum states below an energy 0.1eV above the bottom of the conduction band of silicon. Only a rough calculation is required; use the picture of spherical constant-energy surfaces and an effective mass equal to the inertial mass of the electron.

5. What fraction of the total band population occupies the set of states defined in the preceding problem, assuming Maxwell-Boltzmann statistics and a temperature of 300K? At what temperature, approximately, does this become significantly less than the total number of conduction electrons?

6. At what temperature, roughly, does the approximation of Boltzmann statistics for the conduction and valence bands of intrinsic Ge begin to break down?

7. Assuming a temperature of 300K. find the Fermi energy (relative to its value in an intrinsic crystal) in germanium crystals having net donor impurity concentration of 10^{10}, 10^{11}, 10^{12}, 10^{13}, 10^{14}, 10^{15}, 10^{16}, and 10^{17} atoms per cm^3.

8. What would the answers to the preceding problem be for the case of silicon?

9. What concentration of phosphorus impurity atoms is needed to produce a silicon crystal with resistivity 10ohm-cm at room temperature (300K)? What would the resistivity of this material be at temperatures 200K and 400K?

10. For what values of equilbrium carrier concentrations n_0 and p_0 does the conductivity of a semiconductor have the smallest possible value? What value does this imply for the net impurity content $N_d - N_a$?

11. Calculate the mean free path of a conduction electron in *n*-type Ge, whose mobility at 300K is 3900cm^2/volt–sec. Assume a velocity-independent mean free path, and an effective mass equal to that of a free electron in vacuum. Assuming acoustic-mode phonon scattering, what would the mean free path be at 77K?

12. Determine approximately the temperature of transition between extrinsic and intrinsic conductivity for the three n-type Ge samples illustrated in Figure 9.8(b).

13. Show using the simplified analysis described in Section 7.7 (Chapter 7) that the Hall coefficient of a substance with a single species of positive charge carriers (charge $+e$) is $+1/p_0 e$.

14. Find the electrical conductivity of a semiconductor whose Hall coefficient vanishes. Express your result as a fraction of the intrinsic conductivity.

15. Show that the carrier concentration p_0 satisfies the relation (9.6 - 12) at the points where the Hall coefficient reaches its maximum and minimum values.

16. Cyclotron resonance is observed for electrons in a certain semiconductor using a magnetic field of 0.8T at a frequency of 67,000MHz. Assuming spherical constant-energy surfaces, what is the electron effective mass?

17. In the preceding problem, what is (approximately) the smallest value of the relaxation time that will permit cyclotron resonance to be observed?

18. Show from the cyclotron resonance data on page 409 that the conductivity effective mass for electrons in Ge is $0.12m$ and for electrons in Si is $0.26m$, where m is the free electron inertial mass.

19. Find the conductivity tensor for a single ellipsoidal constant energy surface in Ge (as shown in Figure 9.12 (b)), and show that the total conductivity tensor reduces to the form given by (9.7 - 20) and (9.7 - 21) when summed over all ellipsoids.

20. Describe the cyclotron resonances observed for electrons in the conduction band of Si when the steady magnetic field is in the [110] direction. What would the resonance spectrum look like if the magnmetic field is in the [111] direction?

21. Show that the density of states associated with a single k-space ellipsoid like those illustrated in Figure 9.12 can be wrtten as

$$g(\varepsilon)\, d\varepsilon = \frac{8\sqrt{2}\pi}{h^3} (m_{ds}^*)^{3/2} \sqrt{\varepsilon - \varepsilon_c}\, d\varepsilon \,,$$

where m_{ds}^* is a "density-of-states average" effective mass defined by

$$(m_{ds}^*)^{3/2} = \sqrt{m_\perp^{*2} m_\parallel^*} \,.$$

Hint: start by transforming the ellipsoid into a sphere by an appropriate coördinate transformation.

22. Compare the numerical values of the density-of-states effective mass obtained in the preceding problem and the conductivity effective mass defined by (9.7 - 22) for conduction band electrons in Si and Ge.

23. In a sample of n-type silicon containing 10^{16} acceptor impurities per cm^3, the lifetime of minority holes is observed to be 200 microseconds. (a) What is the lifetime of the majority electrons? (b) Find the equilibrium generation rate of electrons and of holes in this sample. (c) What is the recombination rate at equilibrium for electrons and for holes in this sample?

24. A one-watt laser beam of wavelength 6300Å is incident on the surface of a sample of silicon whose relative permittivity is 12.5. (a) What is the optical reflectivity of the sample? (b) Assuming that the effect of multiple internal reflections is negligible, and that every photon not reflected is absorbed internally creating a single electron-hole pair, how many excess electron-hole pairs per unit time are generated within the sample?

25. From the data given in Table 9.1 at the end of Section 9.2, find the diffusion coefficients for electrons and holes in silicon and in germanium.

26. Prove the vector identity quoted directly below equation (9.8 - 11).

27. A sample of n-type Ge is known to have a uniform net donor concentation of 2.0×10^{13} per cm³. Find the room-temperature equilibrium electron and hole concentrations in the conduction and valence bands. What is the equilibrium conductivity at 300K and at 250K? Use the data in Table 9.1, p. 382.

28. The lifetime of excess carriers in the sample described in the preceding problem is observed to be 240 microseconds for very low excess carrier densities. Find the ambipolar diffusion coefficient and the the ambipolar drift mobility exhibited by excess carriers in this sample. Find also the electron and hole lifetimes in the sample, assuming in all cases a temperature of 300K.

29, 30. Work problems 27 and 28 assuming a uniform net donor concentration of 2.0×10^{15} per cm³, an observed excess carrier lifetime of 240 microseconds, and a temperature of 300K.

31. Show that the ambipolar transport equation (9.8 - 29) assumes the form

$$D \frac{\partial^2 (\delta u)}{\partial x^2} \pm \mu E \frac{\partial (\delta u)}{\partial x} + g' - \frac{\delta u}{\tau} = \frac{\partial (\delta u)}{\partial t}$$

in *extrinsic* materials, where δu is the excess minority carrier density, D, μ, and τ are minority carrier transport coefficients and lifetime, and where the plus sign is to be used in p-type substances, and the minus sign in n-type, and where the field E assumed to be constant.

32. Consider the situation shown in Figure 9.16(a). Assume that the material is n-ype and extrinsic, and that there is a constant externally applied field E along the x-direction. Show that in the steady state, the excess minority carrier density is $\delta p = A\exp(\gamma_+ x / L)$ for $x > 0$ and $\delta p = A\exp(\gamma_- x / L)$ for $x < 0$, where

$$\gamma_\pm = \gamma \pm \sqrt{1 + \gamma^2} \qquad \text{with} \qquad \gamma = \mu EL / 2D \ ,$$

and $L^2 = D\tau$. Make a plot of this concentration profile.

33. (a) What is the excess *majority* carrier concentration profile $\delta n(x)$ in the sample described in the preceding problem? (b) Make rough plots showing the *total* concentration of holes and electrons in the sample as functions of x.

34. Consider the function $f(x, t) = (4\pi Dt)\exp(-x^2/4Dt)$. (a) Show that the area under this curve between $x = \infty$ and $x = -\infty$ is unity for all values of t, and that as t approaches zero its "width" approaches zero while its height becomes infinite, so that in this limit it behaves like a δ-function. Show also that this function is a solution of the diffusion equation $D(\partial^2 f / \partial x^2) = \partial f / \partial t$. Describe the physical significance of this function as the solution of a diffusion problem.

35. Derive equation (9.9 - 13) by integrating (9.9 - 12) over the interval $(-a/2 < x < a.2)$.

36. How many electron-hole pairs per unit volume per unit time are generated by the uniform absorption of 1 watt of light of frequency 6300Å and photon energy sufficient for pair excitation in a sample 1.0 cm square and 0.1cm thick? What steady-state excess minority carrier concentration is produced if the excess carrier lifetime is 100 microseconds?

37. Show that the eigenfunctions $\cos(\alpha_n a/2)$ (n - 0, 1, 2, 3, . . .) form an orthogonal set on the interval $(-a/2 < x < a/2)$ when α_n satisfies the transcendental equation (9.9 - 23).

38. Calculate the value of the normalization intergral that arises when two functions of the set of eigenfunctions described in the preceding problem having the same index n are multiplied and integrated over the interval $(-a/2 < x < a/2)$.

39. Consider the case in which the initial excess carrier distribution $u(x, 0)$ in the transient photoconductivity experiment is constant throughout the sample. Calculate the "Fourier" coefficients a_n for this case, and show that they decrease as n increases. Assume a surface recombination velocity s.

40. Using the results of the preceding problem find the function δP that expresses the total number of excess carriers in the sample, and thus the observed photocurrent, under the conditions described in the preceding problem.

41. Make rough plots of the excess minority carrier density profiles at several different times, for the cases $s = 0$, $s = \infty$ and intermediate values of s for the situation described in Problem 39.

42. A thick sample of n-type germanium ($D_p = 45\text{cm}^2/\text{sec}$, $\mu_p = 1800\text{cm}^2/\text{volt-sec}$) exhibits a transient photoconductivity decay time of 500 microseconds when its surfaces are are prepared in such a way as to minimize surface recombination. This sample is then cut into thinner samples in the form of plates of thickness 1.0mm. One of these thin samples is then etched chemically, and its transient photoconductvity decay again observed. The decay constant is now found to be 300 microseconds. What is the surface recombination velocity associated with the surfaces of the thin sample?

43. In the situation described in the preceding problem, what is the probability that a single excess hole will recombine in colliding with the surface?

44. In the situation described in Problem 32, suppose that the excess carrier concentration is known at two points $x = a$ and $x = b$, both along the positive x-axis. Show that the diffusion length can be calculated from the ratio $K = \delta p(a)/\delta p(b)$ and the distance $d = b - a$, as

$$L = \frac{d}{\sqrt{\ln K \left(\ln K + \dfrac{eEd}{kT} \right)}} \; .$$

45. Explain physically the significance of the fact that tha ambipolar mobility μ^* is zero in an intrinsic semiconductor. *Hint*: Begin by observing that this mobility gives the velocity with which a "hump" or "pulse" of excess carrier concentration drifts under the influence of a constant externally applied electric field $\mathbf{E}$.

46. Show that the ratio of the Debye length L_D and the intrinsic Debye length L_{Di} can be written as $L_D^2/L_{Di}^2 = \sigma_i/\sigma$, where σ and σ_i are the actual and intrinsic conductivities of the semiconductor.

CHAPTER 10

$p - n$ JUNCTIONS AND SOLID STATE DEVICES

10.1 INTRODUCTION

This book is primarily about basic solid-state physics, not solid-state devices. Nevertheless, since most of those who study solid-state physics are involved, or intend to be involved, in the development, production, or technology of solid-state devices, it is appropriate to give an introductory account of device structures of primary importance in current applications. It is useless to try to describe all the numerous solid-state devices now being used. There are hundreds of them, and a complete account of even the most important ones would require a book by itself, a book which at the present rate of development would be out-of-date in a few years. There are in any event several such works already available. We shall be content with the more modest goal of describing structures common to many different devices of continuing usefulness over time in the history of solid-state technology.

Solid-state device technology is generally regarded as having been a product of the years since the invention of the transistor in 1947. However, circuit elements in the form of conductors, insulators, resistors, capacitors, and inductors are solid-state devices that have been around since the birth of electrotechnology. Thermionic cathodes and lamp filaments are in the broadest sense solid-state elements, though their use has always been more closely related to vacuum electronics. Selenium rectifiers and photocells, moreover, have been in use since before 1900. Clearly, solid-state devices have been around longer than is generally supposed. We have already learned some of the physics that governs the behavior of several of these older circuit elements, and have also assimilated the basic principles of thermoelectricity, photoconductivity and semiconductor physics, all of which is basic to many device applications. It is now time, however, to take a look at p–n junctions, field effect phenomena, photovoltaic effects, and other subjects that have dominated the more recent growth of microelectronics and solid-state device technology.

10.2 POINT–CONTACT RECTIFICATION

The behavior of semiconductors as rectifiers, or unidirectional conductors of electricity, was well-known long before any physical explanation was proposed. The rectifying properties of amorphous selenium were utilized to make solid-state diodes over 100 years ago, and selenium rectifiers were used occasionally in electronic circuits throughout the era of vacuum-tube electronics. Selenium rectifiers, however. exhibit high leakage currents in the "reverse" or nonconducting polarity state, and thus tend generate excessive heat, which leads, too often, to catastrophic failure. For this reason, they were not widely employed in commercial products. Selenium, particularly in the amorphous state, is a poorly characterized material, difficult to prepare in pure form. Its semiconducting properties are for this and other reasons not very attractive. The advent of pure crystalline silicon and germanium has relegated the selenium rectifier to the status of a historical curiosity.

Silicon and germanium rectifiers were first produced about 50 years ago in the form of point-contact diodes, useful as detectors of radio waves and microwave radiation. These devices were no more than a refined version of the old "cat whisker" detector, in which a fine metal point makes contact with the crystal. The difference is that the semiconductor has now become a relatively pure and uniform crystal of Ge or Si, whose rectifying properties are predictably excellent. The rectifying properties of such a point contact device can be understood in a crudely qualitative sense by observing that for an n-type crystal, the device is practically nonconducting when the metal point contact is biased negatively with respect to the crystal substrate, and conducts current freely when the point contact is positive with respect to the crystal, as illustrated in Figure 10.1.

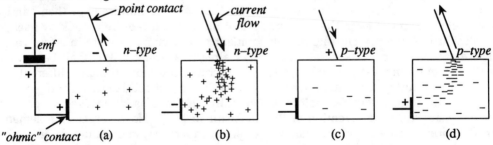

Figure 10.1 Diagrams illustrating point-contact rectification effect in covalent semiconductors. (a) n-type crystal, reverse bias, (b) n-type crystal, forward bias; (c) p-type crystal, reverse bias, (d) p-type crystal, forward bias. The phenomenon of minority carrier injection is shown at (b) and (d).

At (a) in the figure, we see an n-type crystal and a point contact biased negatively with respect to the semiconductor. The negatively biased point tends to repel the negative majority electrons of the semiconductor, and to attract only positive holes, which, as minority carriers in the n-type crystal, are relatively scarce. Under these circumstances the point contact collects all the holes in its immediate vicinity. This causes the concentration of minority holes near the point to become even smaller than the already small equilibrium concentration prevailing in the bulk regions of the crystal far from the point. The concentration gradient generated in this way causes holes in the distant bulk to *diffuse* to the point contact, generating, in the steady state, a very small, though observable, minority carrier current that is relatively independent of the bias voltage between point and substrate. This situation is referred to as the *reverse-bias* case, and the small, almost voltage-independent current that flows due to the minority carrier diffusion is called a *saturation current*. The circuit is completed by a broad-area soldered or evaporated metal contact. Such contacts are ohmic in nature and exhibit little or no rectification, for reasons we shall explore more fully later. In addition to the minority carrier current, there is also a small *majority* carrier current that flows because of the tendency to preserve the condition of electrical neutrality in the crystal at all times. The total saturation current is the sum of these two small currents.

When the bias polarity is reversed, the metal point becomes positive with respect to the crystal. Now majority conduction-band electrons are attracted to the positive point contact, and enter the external circuit in large numbers. However, electrons in the *valence* band are also impelled by coulomb forces to leave the semiconductor and enter the metal point contact. In the semiconductor, we perceive this extraction of carriers from the valence band as an *injection of minority holes* from the metal into the *n*-type semiconductor. These positively charged injected holes exactly compensate the loss of majority electrons that leave the crystal and enter the metal, so that electrical neutrality is again preserved at all times. In this *forward bias* case, large currents can flow even though the positive potential of the metal point with respect to the crystal may be quite small. The semiconductor thus offers little resistance to current flow when forward-biased, while permitting only a small saturation current to pass in the reverse-bias case. The device acts as a very efficient rectifier, and works well as a diode detector and in other rectifier applications.

If the semiconductor crystal is *p*-type, the roles of minority and majority carriers are reversed, as shown at (c) and (d) in the figure. Now, when the point is biased positively with respect to the crystal, it acts only to collect minority electrons in its vicinity, and only a small saturation current can flow. When biased negatively, however, holes flow readily into the metallic contact, a situation that can also be described as electrons leaving the metal and filling defects in the valence band of the semiconductor. Electrons from the metal also enter the conduction band of the crystal as injected minority carriers, so that the number of positive holes lost to the metal is balanced by the number of "injected" electrons, preserving the neutrality of the semiconductor. The recognition of two species of carriers in the semiconductor is crucial to any understanding of how rectification takes place at a point contact, and particularly to the explanation of minortiy carrier injection, an effect that was not clearly understood until Shockley's analysis of this effect in 1947.

The "ohmic" contacts in the circuits illustrated above are interfaces whose contact area exceeds that of the extremely small area of the contact between the fine metal point and the crystal by a factor of a million or more. They are prepared in such a way as to be either non-rectifying or very poorly rectifying junctions. Since their area is so large, and since the saturation current of a rectifier is proportional to the area of the contact, such contacts, even if rectifying, exhibit saturation currents much larger than that of the point contact. They are therefore, even if rectifying, poor rectifiers that allow large reverse currents to flow and produce little minority carrier injection in the forward direction, thus behaving much like ohmic contacts at the low current levels that the point contacts can safely sustain.

There is an apparent paradox that afflicts this intuitive discussion of point-contact rectification, and whose resolution illuminates a very important point about rectifying junctions. It is this; how can there be a difference of potential between two conducting materials that are after all in contact? The answer is simply that no such difference can exist unless there is a thin *barrier layer* between the two materials, a layer of high enough electrical resistivity to allow such a potential difference to arise, and through which charges can pass easily enough to permit substantial currents to flow. We shall postpone a more detailed description of such layers until we discuss *p-n* junction rectification, when we shall explore their properties more thoroughly. Point-contact rectification has been utilized in diode detectors and other devices, and opened the way to the fabrication of the original point-contact transistor invented in 1947. The limited ability of these devices to carry current, their poor overload tolerance, and their lack of uniformity, however, led to their demise in the marketplace when *p-n* junction rectifiers and transistors were perfected.

10.3 *p-n* JUNCTIONS IN SEMICONDUCTORS

The deficiencies of point contact devices were largely surmounted when *p-n* junction devices were introduced, about 1951. A *p-n* junction is merely the boundary region between an *n*-type section and a contiguous *p*-type section in a single crystal of a semiconductor. To form such a junction, it is not enough simply to put an *n*-type crystal in contact with a separate crystal of opposite conductivity type; surface effects, adsorbed gases, oxide layers, and lattice mismatch make such an approach unworkable. The junction has to be somehow incorporated into a single crystal whose lattice structure is essentially perfect throughout. This can be accomplished by addding impurities to the melt as the crystal is grown, or by diffusing a substitutional impurity from a gas or vapor phase into a heated crystal substrate doped with impurities of the opposite conductivity type. Junctions can also be formed by the technique of *ion implantation*, in which impurity ions are accelerated externally by a large external electric field and allowed to collide with the surface of an oppositely doped semiconductor crystal. The energetic ions penetrate some distance into the crystal, and can be incorporated substitutionally into the lattice by a final high-temperature annealing step. Other techniques are also possible, but in any event the final product is a crystal in which there is a *p*-type layer and a contiguous *n*-type region, separated (ideally) by a *planar* junction. We shall concern ourselves mostly with the electronic properties of the junction itself rather than the numerous metallurgical processes used to prepare it, though these technologies are in themselves of great importance to practical device fabrication.

We shall begin by considering the *abrupt junction* model illustrated in Figure 10.2. In this model it is assumed that the net donor concentration N_d in the *n*-region is constant throughout this region up to the junction itself, and is *zero* in the *p*-region. Similarly, the net acceptor concentration is assumed to have the constant value N_a everywhere in the p-region, and zero in the n-region. The junction itself is assumed to be planar and infinite in extent. The x-axis is normal to the junction, which is assumed to lie in the yz-plane, intersecting the x-axis at the origin.

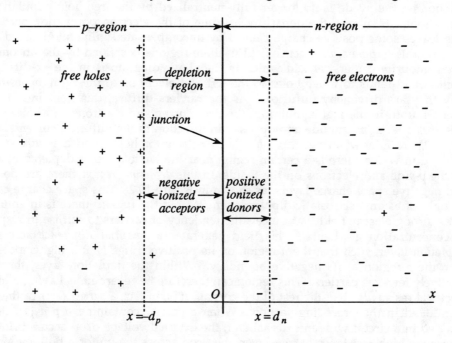

Figure 10.2 Schematic diagram illustrating a planar abrupt p–n junction. Acceptor concentration in the p-region and donor concentration in the n-region are uniform throughout the two halves of the device.

A crystal containing a p-n junction is an example, perhaps the simplest example, of an *inhomogeneous* material. It is inhomogeneous because the impurity concentration is not uniform, but is a function of position within the crystal. As a result of this inhomogeneity, such a crystal posesses a number of properties that differ sharply from those of homogeneous samples. Most of these properties can be traced to the fact that there are now two different subspaces, each containing its own electron-hole free particle gas. These two gases differ in respect to particle concentrations, but if (as we shall assume) there is no temperature gradient, the two gases must nevertheless be in thermal equilibrium with each other.

The fact that there is a junction juxtaposes a p-region where holes are the majority carrier, with an n-type realm in which electrons predominate. Consider a case--a thought experiment--in which two such initially separate regions are suddenly joined into a single perfect crystal at time $t = 0$. Initially there is a constant high concentration of holes up to the junction on the p-side juxtaposed with an n-section in which only a few holes are present as minority carriers. The situation is just the reverse with regard to electrons; a constant high initial concentration on the n-side, but only the very small minority electron density in the p-region. There are thus steep *gradients* of both electron and hole concentrations at the junction. The presence of these concentration gradients generates diffusion fluxes--a flux of holes to the right and of electrons to the left in the above diagram.

These fluxes tend to reduce the concentration of holes in the p-region in the vicinity of the junction and of electrons in the n-region close to the junction. This means that the negative charge associated with immobile acceptor ions near the junction on the p-side is no longer fully neutralized by the free hole population in that region. Similarly, the departure of some of the electron population on the n-side leaves some positive charge caused by uncompensated immobile ionized donors. As this happens, an electric field in these regions is created by the uncompensated impurity centers, a field which in the above diagram is in the $-x$-direction. Such a field tends to move holes to the left and electrons to the right, *opposite* the way they are driven by diffusion. As the carriers diffuse, this field increases in strength until in thermal equilibrium the drift currents of electrons and holes it creates are equal in magnitude and opposite in direction to the diffusion currents.

There is now no net flux of either electrons or holes, and a steady state is attained in which there is a certain region near the juction that is depleted of holes on the p-side and electrons on the n-side. In this *depletion region* there are positive and negative space charge layers, as shown in Figure 10.2. This space charge can be thought of as an electrostatic dipolar layer. Within the region, there is in equilibrium a strong electric field that cancels the tendency of carriers to diffuse in response to concentration gradients. This field generates a *potential difference* across the depletion layer, such that the n-region on its positive fringe is at a higher potential than the p-region at its negative boundary. Within the depletion layer, there are relatively few free carriers. This region can therefore be regarded as having a higher electrical resistivity than the rest of the crystal. It is, in fact, a *barrier layer* of the kind mentioned in the preceding section. When a crystal containing a p-n junction is inserted in a circuit with an external emf, the external voltage drop occurs primarily across the high resistance barrier layer, the drop across the uniform bulk regions on either side being frequently so small as to be negligible. Indeed, the main physical effect of such an external emf is to increase or decrease the "height" of the potential barrier, as expressed by the potential difference across the depletion region.

The situation can be represented by the energy band diagram shown in Figure 10.3. It should be recalled that diagrams such as these show the potential energy of an electron, $-eV(x)$, whose sign is *opposite* that of the electrostatic potential. Deep in the p-type and n-type bulk regions, far from the abrupt junction, conditions at equilibrium must clearly be similar to those that prevail in a homogeneous crystal of the same conductivity type. This suggests that the Fermi energy must be near the top of the valence band on the p-side far from the junction and close to the bottom of the conduction band far on the n-side. The fact that the potential energy of an electron "at rest" at the bottom of the conduction band, or that of a hole at the top of the valence band, differs on either side of the depletion region because of the junction's dipolar charge layer, suggests that *the band edges themselves* must form a potential barrier across this region, as shown in the figure. At the same time, the fact that the two free carrier gases on either side of the junction are in thermal equilibrium with one another implies that the crystal as a whole must be viewed, in the sense of thermodynamics or statistical mechanics, as one system with a *single constant Fermi energy*, as shown. In this system, the band edges, and even the "intrinsic Fermi level" ε_{fi} are functions of position, while the Fermi energy itself is everywhere the same. The equilibrium potential difference across the junction can be viewed as an *internal contact potential*. This potential difference cannot act in equilibrium as an emf, for then, if the junction were short-circuited externally, a steady current would flow in the external circuit, and could be made to perform external work, in contradiction to the laws of thermodynamics. It is more apprpriate to regard it as a purely electrostatic potential, similar to the voltage across a capacitor. There is, in fact, a capacitance associated with charge "stored" in the depletion region, and the junction can also act as a capacitor in certain other ways, as we shall soon see.

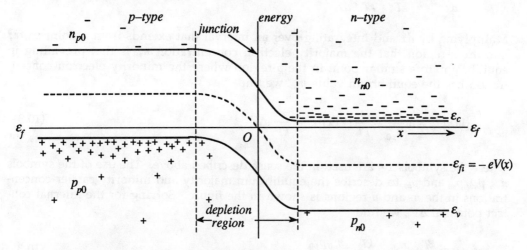

Figure 10.3 Schematic representation of energy bands, electrostatic potential, and the Fermi energy in the neighborhood of an abrupt p–n junction in thermal equilibrium.

In the diagram, since the Fermi energy is constant throughout the system, the minority carrier electron gas on the p-side has the same energy distribution as the subset of the majority carrier electron gas on the n-side having particle energies higher than the potential barrier presented by the conduction band edge in the depletion region. Similar remarks can be made with regard to the hole gases on either side of the junction. We shall find these facts helpful in formulating boundary conditions for the transport equations for electrons and holes near the junction, boundary conditions that can be useful even when the system is not in equilibrium.

We can now calculate the internal potential difference. The above figure is drawn so that the Fermi energy passes through the origin, as does the planar junction. With this choice of coördinates, the Fermi energy is everywhere zero, and the junction is at $x = 0$. We also assume that the electrostatic potential $V(x)$ is zero at the junction. Since this potential determines the band edges, the "bending" of the bands in the depletion region is illustrated by curves having the same form as $V(x)$ except for a vertical displacement. The position of the level ε_{fi} near midgap, defining an intrinsic equilibrium condition, also has this form. In thermal equilibrium, there is no *net* flux of either holes or electrons at any point in the system, which permits us to equate the sum of drift and diffusion current to zero for either species, as follows;

$$J_n = ne\mu_n E_x + eD_n \frac{dn}{dx} = 0 \qquad (10.3\text{-}1)$$

and

$$J_p = pe\mu_p E_x - eD_p \frac{dp}{dx} = 0 \quad . \tag{10.3-2}$$

For electrons, (10.3 - 1) can be expressed with the aid of the Einstein relation (9.8 - 10) as

$$\frac{d(\ln n)}{dx} = -\frac{eE_x}{kT} = \frac{e}{kT} \cdot \frac{dV}{dx} \quad . \tag{10.3-3}$$

Multiplying by dx and integrating over an interval that extends from a point so far into the n-region that the majority electron concentration n_{no} is that prevailing in equilibrium, to a similar point in the p-region where the minority electron concentration has the equilibrium value n_{po}, we find

$$[\ln n]_{-\infty}^{+\infty} = \ln \frac{n_{n0}}{n_{p0}} = \frac{e}{kT} [V(x)]_{-\infty}^{+\infty} = \frac{e}{kT} \cdot \Delta V_i \quad , \tag{10.3-4}$$

where the symbols $\pm\infty$ are used in the sense described above. The use of the symbols n_{no}, p_{no}, p_{no} and p_{po} to describe the equilibrium majority and minority carrier concentrations in the n- and p-regions is shown in the figure. Solving for the internal contact potential ΔV_i, we find

$$\Delta V_i = \frac{kT}{e} \ln \frac{n_{n0}}{n_{p0}} = \frac{kT}{e} \ln \frac{n_{n0} p_{p0}}{n_{p0} p_{p0}} \quad . \tag{10.3-5}$$

In the argument of the logarithm, the product $n_{po}p_{po}$ is the product of equilibrium majority and minority carrier concentrations in the *same* region, and can therefore be replaced by n_i^2. Moreover, the product $n_{no}p_{po}$ in the numerator refers to majority carrier concentrations on *opposite* sides of the junction. If the material on both sides of the junction is highly extrinsic, this product can be approximated as $N_d N_a$, where N_d is the donor concentration on the n-side and N_a the acceptor concentration on the p-side. We can therefore write,

$$\Delta V_i = \frac{kT}{e} \ln \frac{n_{n0} p_{p0}}{n_i^2} \cong \frac{kT}{e} \ln \frac{N_d N_a}{n_i^2} \quad . \tag{10.3-6}$$

The reader should have no difficulty showing, as an exercise, that the same result can be obtained starting with (10.3 - 2).

It is also possible, setting $N_a = 0$ in (9.4 - 22) and $N_d = 0$ in (9.4 - 23) to use these equations to to express the equilibrium concentrations n_{no} and p_{po} in (10.3 - 6) in terms of N_d and N_a, and thus to derive an exact form of this result in which the assumption that both p- and n-sides are highly extrinsic is not required. The result is

$$\Delta V_i = \frac{kT}{e} \left(\sinh^{-1} \frac{N_d}{2n_i} + \sinh^{-1} \frac{N_a}{2n_i} \right) \quad . \tag{10.3-7}$$

The algebraic details in arriving at this result involve the use of (9.4 - 18), (9.4 - 19) and (9.4 - 25), and the recognition that in the latter equation ε_f is zero. The derivation itself is assigned as an exercise. In Figure 10.3, it will be noted that the intrinsic Fermi energy is shown passing through the origin, so that $\varepsilon_{fi} = -eV(x)$. A detailed explanation of this feature will be given later.

One can use the equilibrium distribution functions in connection with Poisson's equation to write a differential equation describing the precise form of the potential $V(x)$, and therefore the "bending" of the energy bands in the depletion region. This equation can be written

$$\frac{d^2V}{dx^2} = \frac{e}{K\varepsilon_0}\left(2\sinh\frac{eV}{kT} - \frac{N_d}{n_i} + \frac{N_a}{n_i}\right) , \qquad (10.3-8)$$

where K is the relative permittivity. The derivation is assigned as an exercise. This equation is valid even for junctions that are not "abrupt", and in which the donor and acceptor concentrations may themselves be functions of x. Despite its generality, it is less useful than it appears, for even when N_d and N_a are constant, it cannot be solved in closed form. It is, however, possible to obtain a useful solution in the abrupt-junction case by using an approximation of quite general applicability, as we shall now demonstrate.

It is clear from the form of the equilibrium Maxwell-Boltzmann distribution that the electron density decreases exponentially with increasing energy within the conduction band. Indeed, nearly all the electrons reside at energies less than about $3kT$ greater than ε_c. A similar situation prevails for holes, most of which are to be found within a few kT from the valence band energy maximum. Moreover, kT is only about 0.025eV at 300K. In Figure 10.3, the height of the potential barrier is a substantial fraction--more than half, as drawn--of the energy gap, which for Ge is about 0.7eV and for Si 1.15eV. One does not under these conditions have to proceed very far into the depletion region from either the p- or n-side before the majority carrier population has been drastically reduced by the change in the band edge energy. Indeed, in the figure, the exponential decrease of the carrier populations is considerably understated to facilitate drawing the diagram. Under these circumstances, it is reasonable to *neglect* the small incursion of carriers into the edges of the depletion region, and to assume that the carrier populations everywhere within it are negligible in comparison with the concentrations of uncompensated impurity ions N_d and N_a. This approximation is obviously quite good when the n- and p-regions are decidedly extrinsic, but is less so in cases where one or both regions approach the intrinsic state. Fortunately, it is optimal in most junction devices to employ materials of the former type, for which the approximation is a good one. We shall now use this approximation in our further study of p-n junctions. It is at its best in wide-gap materials like Si or GaAs, where n_i is small, but is often useful for Ge as well.

Making this approximation, we can write the charge density in the depletion region as

$$\rho(x) = -eN_a \quad (-d_p < x < 0) , \quad \text{and} \quad \rho(x) = eN_d \quad (0 < x < d_n) , \qquad (10.3-9)$$

where d_n and $-d_p$ are the x-coördinates of the two boundaries of the depletion region, as shown in Figure 10.4. According to Poisson's equation (9.8 - 15), these charge

452

densities must be equal to $-K\varepsilon_0[d^2V(x)/dx^2]$. Since N_d and N_a are constant for an abrupt junction, this suggests that the second derivative of the potential is constant

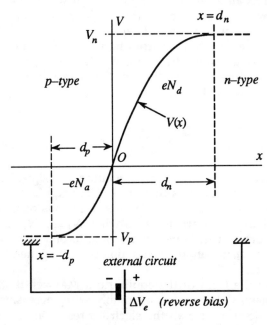

Figure 10.4 The form of the potential in the depletion region of an abrupt junction, using the approximation explained in the text. The two solutions in the n- and p-regions are parabolic segments that are joined smoothly at the origin. An external emf that reverse-biases the junction is also shown.

on both the n-side and p-side of the depletion region, but different in each region. Integrating the charge densities given in (10.3 - 9) over the depletion region from $-d_p$ to zero and from zero to d_n must therefore lead to a result of the form

$$V(x) = \frac{eN_a}{2K\varepsilon_0}(x+d_p)^2 + V_p \qquad (-d_p < x < 0)$$

and $\qquad\qquad\qquad\qquad\qquad\qquad\qquad\qquad\qquad\qquad$ (10.3 - 10)

$$V(x) = -\frac{eN_d}{2K\varepsilon_0}(d_n-x)^2 + V_n \qquad (0 < x < d_n) \ .$$

In these expressions, V_p and V_n represent the potentials at the outer boundaries of the depletion region, where x assumes the values $-d_p$ and d_n, respectively. It is important to note that the distances d_p and d_n are both taken to be positive, while V_n is positive and V_p is negative. The potential must be continuous at all points, and, as assumed earlier in connection with Figure 10.3, it is zero at the junction. Therefore, the two solutions given above must both be zero at $x = 0$, which allows us to write

$$V(0) = \frac{eN_a d_p^2}{2K\varepsilon_0} + V_p = -\frac{eN_d d_n^2}{2K\varepsilon_0} + V_n = 0 \ .$$
$\qquad\qquad\qquad\qquad\qquad\qquad\qquad\qquad\qquad\qquad$ (10.3 - 11)

In the figure, an external bias emf ΔV_e is illustrated. In its absence, the total potential difference $V_n + (-V_p)$ is simply the equilibrium internal contact potential given by (10.3 - 7). Otherwise, this total potential difference will be the *sum* of the internal contact potential and the external emf. The inclusion of this external potential difference allows us to see what happens when the junction is placed in an external circuit and is no longer at equilibrium. The polarity of the emf shown in the diagram is such as to make the negative side of the space charge layer still more negative, and the positive side more positive, thus increasing the height of the junction potential barrier. We shall see later that the effect of this is to apply reverse bias to a rectifying device. From (10.3 - 11), it is now clear that this total potential difference across the junction region is

$$V_n - V_p = \frac{e}{2K\varepsilon_0}(N_a d_p^2 + N_d d_n^2) = \Delta V_i + \Delta V_e \quad , \tag{10.3-12}$$

where ΔV_i is given by (10.3 - 7). It also follows from (10.3 - 11) that

$$V_n = \frac{eN_d d_n^2}{2K\varepsilon_0} \qquad \text{and} \qquad V_p = -\frac{eN_a d_p^2}{2K\varepsilon_0} \quad . \tag{10.3-13}$$

The solutions shown above clearly satisfy Poisson's equation (9.8 - 15) in the n- and p-regions. and are both zero at $x = 0$, so that $V(x)$ passes through the origin, as shown in Figure 10.3. Also, it is easy to see from (10.3 - 10) that their slopes are zero at the points d_n and $-d_p$, which allows the interior parabolic potential sections to join smoothly with constant *exterior* potentials $V(x) = V_p$ and $V(x) = V_n$ outside the depletion region where the charge density is zero. The entire potential function thus has much the same appearance as that shown in Figure 10.3.

The electric field follows from (10.3 - 10) as the negative derivative of the potential, so

$$E_x = -\frac{eN_a}{K\varepsilon_0}(x + d_p) \qquad (-d_p < x < 0)$$

and

$$E_x = -\frac{eN_d}{K\varepsilon_0}(d_n - x) \qquad (o < x < d_n) \quad . \tag{10.3-14}$$

The field is seen to be zero at the outer boundaries of the depletion region at $x = d_n$ and $-d_p$. At the junction, the electrostatic boundary conditions require the normal component of the dispacement $D_x (= K\varepsilon_0 E_x)$ to be continuous across the boundary. Letting $x = 0$ in both expressions and equating them, the field at the origin now becomes

$$E_x(0) = -\frac{eN_d d_n}{K\varepsilon_0} = -\frac{eN_a d_p}{K\varepsilon_0} \quad , \tag{10.3-15}$$

which can only be satisfied if

$$N_a d_p = N_d d_n \quad . \tag{10.3-16}$$

Using the above relation to express $d_p{}^2$ and $d_n{}^2$ in terms of $d_n d_p$ in (10.3 - 12), it follows that this product can be written in terms of the voltage difference $\Delta V_i + \Delta V_e$ as

$$d_n d_p = \frac{2K\varepsilon_0}{e} \cdot \frac{\Delta V_i + \Delta V_e}{N_d + N_a} \ . \tag{10.3-17}$$

From this it is clear that the distances d_n and d_p, and thus the width of the depletion region that surrounds the junction depends not only on the internal potential ΔV_i which is related to N_d and N_a through (10.3 - 7), but also on the *external* voltage ΔV_e. It is apparent, in fact, that the depletion region expands when the external voltage is positive, and contracts when it is negative. When it is zero, (10.3 - 17) gives the equilibrium value of $d_n d_p$ in terms of the impurity concentrations, and from (10.3 - 7) it follows that

$$(d_n d_p)_0 = L_{Di}^2 \cdot \frac{2n_i}{N_d + N_a} \left(\sinh^{-1}\frac{N_d}{2n_i} + \sinh^{-1}\frac{N_a}{2n_i} \right) , \tag{10.3-18}$$

where the zero subscript refers to the equilibrium state and L_{Di} is the intrinsic Debye length defined by (9.8 - 44). The distances d_n and d_p themselves can be found from (10.3 - 17) by using (10.3 - 16) once more, as

$$d_n = \sqrt{\frac{2K\varepsilon_0}{e} \cdot \frac{N_a}{N_d} \cdot \frac{\Delta V_i + \Delta V_e}{N_d + N_a}} \tag{10.3-19}$$

and

$$d_p = \sqrt{\frac{2K\varepsilon_0}{e} \cdot \frac{N_d}{N_a} \cdot \frac{\Delta V_i + \Delta V_e}{N_d + N_a}} \ . \tag{10.3-20}$$

The total width of the depletion region is the sum of these quantities, which can be written as

$$d = d_n + d_p = \sqrt{\frac{2K\varepsilon_0}{e} \left(\frac{1}{N_d} + \frac{1}{N_a} \right) \cdot (\Delta V_i + \Delta V_e)} \ . \tag{10.3-21}$$

The maximum field E_0 now follows from (10.3 - 15) as

$$-E_0 = \sqrt{\frac{2e}{K\varepsilon_0} \cdot \frac{N_d N_a}{N_d + N_a} (\Delta V_i + \Delta V_e)} = \frac{2(\Delta V_i + \Delta V_e)}{d} \ . \tag{10.3-22}$$

From (10.3 - 13), (10.3 - 19) and (10.3 - 20), one can also show that the potentials V_n and V_p can be expressed as

$$V_n = \frac{N_a}{N_d + N_a} \cdot (\Delta V_i + \Delta V_e) \quad \text{and} \quad V_p = -\frac{N_d}{N_d + N_a} \cdot (\Delta V_i + \Delta V_e) \ . \tag{10.3-23}$$

The charge densities in the depletion region are $-eN_a$ on the p-side and $+eN_d$ on the n-side. The total charge associated with an area A of the junction region is therefore,

$$Q = eAN_d d_n = -eAN_a d_p = \pm eA\sqrt{\frac{2K\varepsilon_0}{e} \cdot \frac{N_d N_a}{N_d + N_a}(\Delta V_i + \Delta V_e)} \; . \qquad (10.3\text{-}24)$$

It is obvious from this that the n- and p-sides of the depletion region, on either side of the junction, bear charges that are equal but opposite in sign, much like an ordinary capacitor. This charge resides not on a pair of discrete conducting plates, as in a normal capacitor, however, but as a *space charge* distribution within the depletion region. The capacitance can be found by dividing the above expression by the external voltage ΔV_e; it is clear, however, that the capacitance so obtained is not constant, but will be voltage-dependent. It is simpler in this situation to describe the behavior of the junction in terms of a differential capacitance defined as dQ/dV_e, the incremental charge associated with an incremental voltage change about some arbitrary voltage V_e. This differential capacitance is found merely by differentiating (10.3 - 24) with respect to V_e. The result, expressed as a capacitance per unit area is

$$\left(\frac{C}{A}\right)^2 = \left(\frac{1}{A} \cdot \frac{dQ}{d(\Delta V_e)}\right)^2 = \frac{K\varepsilon_0}{2} \cdot \frac{eN_d N_a}{N_d + N_a} \cdot \frac{1}{\Delta V_i + \Delta V_e} = \left(\frac{K\varepsilon_0}{d}\right)^2 \; . \qquad (10.3\text{-}25)$$

The final form of this result looks very simple; indeed, it is merely the expression for the capacitance of an ideal parallel-plate capacitor of plate spacing d. This simplicity is deceptive, however, for it must be observed that the width d of the depletion region is voltage-dependent, as shown in (10.3 - 21). The more detailed form given above indicates that the differential capacitance is inversely proportional to the square root of the total potential difference $\Delta V_i + \Delta V_e$. Differential capacitance is easily measured, and this square root dependence is observed for many junction structures. If the junction is not abrupt, as assumed above, but is "graded" in the sense that the net impurity concentration in the material varies gradually from strongly n-type to strongly p-type across the junction region, this capacitance-voltage relationship will be different. For example, a junction about which there is a linearly varying net impurity density exhibits an inverse cube root voltage dependence. Capacitance measurements can also be used to determine experimentally the internal contact potential ΔV_i. This is most easily accomplished by plotting a series of measurements of the quantity $(C/A)^{-2}$ versus ΔV_e for an abrupt junction to obtain a straight line whose intercept on the horizontal voltage axis yields a voltage ΔV_e for which $\Delta V_e + \Delta V_i = 0$, and for which ΔV_e equals $-\Delta V_i$.

The results derived above give a great deal of useful information about the behavior of p-n junctions, not only at equilibrium, but also when external voltages are applied. A number of features are to be observed. At first, it is best to examine a *symmetric* junction in which N_d and N_a have the common value N_0. For such a junction in thermal equilibrium at 300K, the internal contact potential and total depletion region width d vary with the impurity content as shown in the table below. The values listed are calculated with the aid of (10.3 - 7) and (10.3 - 18–20). The internal contact potential is significant only when the impurity density greatly exceeds the intrinsic carrier density n_i. The approximations used in the above calculations begin to break down when this internal potential approaches the band-gap energy, which occurs, however, only at impurity concentrations very high on the scale of semiconductor technology. In calculating these quantities, it is helpful to recall that the intrinsic Debye length is about 36 microns for Si and 0.96 microns for Ge at 300K.

TABLE 10.1

SYMMETRIC p–n JUNCTIONS IN EQUILIBRIUM AT 300K

N_0 (cm^{-3})	ΔV_i (volts)		d (microns)	
	Si	Ge	Si	Ge
10^{10}	0.016		71.	
10^{11}	0.096		55.	
10^{12}	0.210	0.0010	25.5	1.92
10^{13}	0.325	0.0103	10.0	1.91
10^{14}	0.440	0.074	3.70	1.62
10^{15}	0.555	0.187	1.31	0.81
10^{16}	0.671	0.302	0.457	0.327
10^{17}	0.786	0.417	0.156	0.121
10^{18}	0.901	0.532	0.053	0.0434
10^{19}	1.016	0.647	0.0178	0.0151

The equilibrium internal potentials are a fraction of a volt, always less than the bandgap energy. They increase with increasing impurity content. The depletion region width is larger for silicon than for germanium, substantially so for small impurity densities. The width decreases with increasing impurity content; it ranges from a small fraction of a micron to more than 70 microns in the cases listed above. The mean free path of electrons and holes can be inferred from the measured values of carrier mobility and effective mass and from the calculated average Maxwellian thermal velocity $<v>$. The reader is asked to show as an exercise that it is around 0.1 micron at room temperature in Si and Ge. From the table, it is apparent that the depletion region width can be either larger or smaller than the mean free path in the equilibrium state.

In the equilibrium condition, the external voltage ΔV_e is zero. When a positive external voltage is present, however, the barrier height increases, and (10.3 - 19) and (10.3 - 20) reveal that the distances d_n and d_p whose sum defines the depletion region's total width become larger than the equilibrium values--much larger if the external voltage is large compared with the equilibrium internal potential. Indeed, since it is ordinarily possible to apply positive external potentials more than 100 times larger than the internal potential, the equations indicate that it is quite possible for the depletion region width to be larger by a factor of 10 or more than the equilibrium width. It is also possible to apply *negative* external voltages, in which case the depletion region width is somewhat lessened. However, in this case the barrier height is decreased, and (as we shall see more clearly in the next section) the device becomes a forward-biased rectifier which carries large currents under these circumstances. The amount by which the potential can be changed in this mode of operation is limited by the current-carrying capacity of the semiconductor to a fairly small amount, in most cases *less* than the internal potential.

The electric field within the depletion region can easily reach surprisingly high values, even in the equilibrium state when there is no external voltage at all.

This can be appreciated by observing from the table that an internal potential drop of about 0.5 volt occurs in a distance of less than half a micron. This suggests a field of at least one volt per micron, which is 10,000volts/cm. A more exact determination is given by (10.3 - 22), which expresses the maximum value of the field within the depletion region. From (10.3 - 14), it is clear that this field is zero at the outer boundaries of the depletion region, and increases *linearly* in magnitude on either side to this maximum value at the junction. It is obvious also, that if there is an external voltage that increases the barrier height, the maximum internal field can be much larger than the equilibrium field; one can easily see from the above equations that fields of several hundred thousand volts per centimeter can occur near the junction.

As we shall soon see, it is of some importance to know how long it takes an electron or hole to cross the depletion region. A carrier of mobility 1000cm²/volt-sec in an average field of 1000volt/cm moves with average velocity 10⁶cm/sec. It will therefore traverse a depletion region one micron or 10⁻⁶m wide in 10⁻¹²sec. This time interval is far shorter than the lifetime of excess carriers in Si and Ge, which is usually larger than 10⁻⁷sec. This admittedly crude calculation indicates that it is ordinarily possible to *neglect* electron-hole recombination that takes place *within* the depletion layer of *p-n* junction semiconductor devices, an assumption that vastly simplifies the analysis of *p-n* junction rectifiers, transistors, and other devices. We shall use this assumption frequently in our future work.

The capacitance associated with *p-n* junctions can be quite large. For $d = 1.0$ micron and $K = 12$, which is about right for Si, the quantity $K\varepsilon_0/d$ in (10.3 - 25) equals roughly 0.01farad/m² or 1.0μf/cm². Of course, the area of many junction devices is far smaller than 1cm², but even a junction of area 10⁻⁶cm², corresponding to a device whose dimensions are of the order of 0.01mm, can have a capacitance of a picofarad. The capacitance of *p-n* junctions may thus form an important part of circuit capacitance, and must be accounted for in circuit analysis. By the same token, reverse-biased *p-n* junctions are frequently used in circuits as dedicated capacitors, whose capacitance can be varied by changing an external bias voltage.

In asymmetric junctions, the situation is more complicated in detail, but not essentially different in substance, from what has been observed in reference to symmetric junctions. The equations indicate, however, that the part of the depletion layer in the less heavily-doped region is *wider* than the part in the more strongly-doped region, and that these two widths can differ greatly if the doping asymmetry is pronounced. A full discussion of all the possible cases embodied in the equations is time-consuming, and at this level unnecessary, but the reader is encouraged to study in more detail the effect of material parameters, dimensions, and external influences that appear in them, on the size and properties of the depletion region.

In the equilibrium state, no current flows across the junction. When there is a bias voltage applied externally as in Figure 10.4, the system is no longer in thermal equilibrium and current will flow through the junction and the surrounding depletion region, and in the external circuit as well. The determination of this current and the relationship between it and the external voltage is the next subject to be considered.

10.4 *p–n* JUNCTIONS AS RECTIFIERS AND PHOTOVOLTAIC CELLS

The potentials, fields, and depletion regions that exist near *p-n* junctions, and their response to external voltages have now been explored in some detail. When external voltages are present, currents also flow, across the junction and in the external circuit. This current is driven externally by an emf as shown by the battery in Figure 10.4. Within the device, however, due to the action of the depletion region as a barrier layer of high resistance, the internal potential drop occurs primarily across the depletion region of the junction, and only to a negligible extent within the bulk semiconductor outside this region. In the bulk *n*- and *p*-type material on either side of the depletion region, therefore, currents flow almost exclusively by *diffusion*, and are driven by concentration gradients rather than electric fields. In this discussion, the effect of electric fields in the bulk regions is neglected.

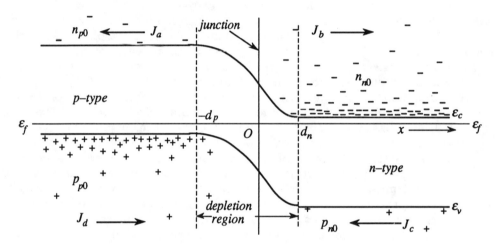

Figure 10.5 Potentials, fields, and current flows in the neighborhood of a *p-n* junction in equilibrium.

In the equilibrium state, when no external voltage is present, the situation is as shown in Figure 10.5. There is no total current, but there are nevertheless internal processes that can be thought of as driving four *partial* currents whose sum is zero at equilibrium. These four processes can be described as follows: (a) electron-hole pairs are generated thermally in the *p*-region; the electrons diffuse as minority carriers to the junction, where they cross unobstructed into the *n*-region and join the majority carrier distribution there. Because of the negative charge of the electrons this process generates a negative current density J_a as illiustrated above. (b) Majority electrons in the *n*-region having sufficient energy to surmount the junction potential barrier diffuse to the junction, cross to the *p*-region, where, as minority carriers they eventually recombine with holes; this process gives rise to the positive current J_b. (c) Electron-hole pairs are thermally generated in the *n*-region; the holes diffuse as minority carriers to the junction where they cross unobstructed to the *p*-region and join the majority carrier distribution; current J_c is associated with this process. (d) Majority holes in the *p*-region having enough energy to surmount the junction potential barrier cross to the *n*-side, where as minority carriers they eventually recombine with electrons. This process gives rise to current J_d. These same four partial currents will persist even when an external voltage is applied, but the relationships between them will not be as simple as in the equilibrium state. Let us now write these currents using a zero subscript at equilibrium, and omitting the subscript when there is an external voltage present.

It is clear from the above description that process (b) is the inverse of process (a), and that process (d) is the inverse of process (c). At equilibrium, therefore, each process and its inverse must proceed at equal rates, so that

$$J_{a0} + J_{b0} = 0 \qquad \text{and} \qquad J_{c0} + J_{d0} = 0 \ . \tag{10.4-1}$$

Processes (a) and (c) are thermally activated. Their rate is governed *only* by thermal generation in the bulk, and is thus *independent* of the barrier height, and hence of any external voltage. Therefore it will always be true that

$$J_a = J_{a0} = -J_{b0} \qquad \text{and} \qquad J_c = J_{c0} = -J_{d0} \ . \tag{10.4-2}$$

Processes (c) and (d), on the other hand, are governed by the fraction of the majority carrier population that can surmount a barrier of height $\Delta V_i + \Delta V_e$ which depends on the external voltage. This fraction is expressed by a Maxwellian factor of the form $\exp(-e\Delta V_e / kT)$. Therefore,

$$J_b = J_{b0} e^{-e\Delta V_e / kT} = -J_{a0} e^{-e\Delta V_e / kT} \qquad \text{and} \qquad J_{d0} e^{-e\Delta V_e / kT} = -J_{c0} e^{-e\Delta V_e / kT} \ . \tag{10.4-3}$$

The total current can now be written as

$$J = J_a + J_b + J_c + J_d = (J_{a0} + J_{c0})(1 - e^{-e\Delta V_e / kT}) \ . \tag{10.4-4}$$

In this equation, it is evident from the figure that the two currents J_{a0} and J_{c0} are negative. There is therefore a small negative "saturation current" equal to the sum of these two currents when the external voltage is positive to the extent of many times kT/e, while if the external voltage is negative, a condition which *reduces* the barrier height, a very large positive current flow is predicted. The device thus acts as a "one-way" conductor, or in more formal language, a rectifier.

The situation can be appreciated physically by observing the current flows discussed above when the barrier height is larger and smaller than the equilibrium height, as illustrated in Figure 10.6. At (a) in the figure, the case of reverse bias, in which ΔV_e is positive is illustrated. In this case, the total barrier height $\Delta V_i + \Delta V_e$ is increased. Under these circumstances, the thermally activated currents J_a and J_c are unchanged, but the currents that arise from majority electrons and holes surmounting the barrier are much smaller than in the equilibrium state shown in Figure 10.5, since there are fewer such carriers in the majority distributions that have enough energy to surmount the barrier. In this case only a small current composed mostly of the thermally generated currents J_a and J_c flows, and the direction of the total current is negative, along the $-x$-direction. At (b), we see the forward bias case, in which ΔV_e is negative, which decreases the total barrier height with respect to the equilibrium value. Again, the currents J_a and J_c controlled by thermal generation are unchanged, but now a much larger fraction of the majority holes and electrons in the p- and n-regions can surmount the lowered barrier, and holes stream across the barrier from the p-region into the n-region, while a large number of electrons likewise enter the *p*-region from the *n*-side. In this condition, it is clear that minority carrier injection is taking place, holes being injected into the *n*-region and electrons into the *p*-region, much as in the forward-biased point contact rectifier. The total current is now mostly due to these injected carriers, and its direction is now positive, along the +*x*-axis as illustrated. This description is consistent with our previous discussion, and with the current-voltage relation (10.4 - 4).

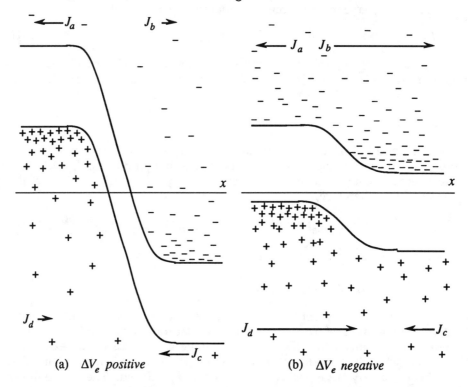

Figure 10.6 Energy bands and current flows in a *p–n* junction rectifier (a) with a reverse bias which increases barrier height, and (b) with a forward bias voltage which decreases barrier height. It is important to observe that electrons flow in a direction opposite to that shown by the arrows, which are in the direction of conventional current (and hole current) flow.

The explanation given above unfortunately provides no fundamental expression for the saturation current. This can be arrived at by actually calculating the flow of electrons and holes across the junction from the minority carrier transport equations developed in the preceding chapter. It is worth going through this exercise, for, though it affords little additional physical insight into the behavior of *p-n* junctions, it demonstrates a method of analysis that is applicable to other more complicated semiconductor devices, such as transistors and photovoltaic cells.

We shall begin by assuming that both *p*- and *n*-regions are not only uniform, but also extrinsic. This assumption isn't really necessary, but it avoids unnecessary algebraic complexity. We shall also assume a planar geometry in which diffusion and current flow can be treated as one-dimensional effects that involve only an *x*-coördinate normal to the junction. Finally, we shall assume that the uniform *p*- and *n*- regions on either side of the depletion regions are several times wider in extent than the diffusion length of the minority carrier in those regions. This permits us to write steady-state *minority carrier* diffusion equations of the form

$$\frac{d^2(n_p - n_{p0})}{dx^2} - \frac{n_p - n_{p0}}{L_n^2} = 0 \quad \text{for electrons in the } p-\text{region} \tag{10.4-5}$$

and

$$\frac{d^2(p_n - p_{n0})}{dx^2} - \frac{p_n - p_{n0}}{L_p^2} = 0 \quad \text{for holes in the } n-\text{region.} \tag{10.4-6}$$

In these equations, the former usage δp and δn has been replaced by the more explicit notation $p_n - p_{n0}$ and $n_p - n_{p0}$, purely as a matter of convenience. The solutions in this case can be written as

$$n_p - n_{p0} = Ae^{x/L_n} \tag{10.4-7}$$

and

$$p_n - p_{n0} = Be^{-x/L_p} . \tag{10.4-8}$$

The possible "growing" exponential solutions $C\exp(-x/L_n)$ and $D\exp(x/L_p)$ must vanish if the bulk regions are of infinite width. If the widths of the n- and p-regions are not truly infinite, but nevertheless large compared to the diffusion length, the assumption $C = D = 0$, which we shall adopt, is still an excellent approximation.

We have seen that at equilibrium, the energy distribution of the minority electrons in the p-region is the same as that part of the majority electron distribution in the n-region whose particle energies are in excess of the barrier height, in view of the fact that these two "gases" are in thermal equilibrium at the same temperature. If the barrier height is changed, the distributions are no longer of exactly Maxwellian form, but as previous experience in metals indicates, the form of the distribution function is not heavily perturbed unless very large current levels are attained. Moreover, a collision of an electron or hole with a lattice phonon is known to restore the equilibrium form of the distribution, and such collisions are very frequent. It is therefore reasonable to suggest that this relationship between the electron distribution functions on opposite sides of the junction is approximately correct even when the system is not strictly in equilibrium, and that a similar relationship can be postulated for holes. This leads us to write boundary conditions for carriers on opposite boundaries of the depletion region of the form

$$n_p(-d_p) = n_{n0}e^{-e(\Delta V_e + \Delta V_i)/kT} = n_{p0}e^{-e\Delta V_e/kT} \tag{10.4-9}$$

and

$$p_n(d_n) = p_{p0}e^{-e(\Delta V_e + \Delta V_i)/kT} = p_{n0}e^{-e\Delta V_e/kT} . \tag{10.4-10}$$

The final form of these equations is obtained with the aid of (10.3-6) and the relation $n_{n0}p_{n0} = n_{p0}p_{p0} = n_i^2$.

Let us consider first the flux of electrons that cross the junction. If we evaluate (10.4-7) at the left edge of the depletion region, where $x = -d_p$, and then apply the boundary condition (10.4-9), we can solve the resulting expression for the arbitrary constant A to obtain $A = n_{p0}[\exp(-e\Delta V_e/kT) - 1]\exp(d_p/L_n)$. Substituting this value into (10.4-7), we may write the electron concentration in the p-region as

$$n_p(x) = n_{p0} + n_{p0}(e^{-e\Delta V_e/kT} - 1)e^{d_p/L_n} \cdot e^{x/L_n} \quad . \tag{10.4-11}$$

The current arising from electrons crossing the junction is expressed as a diffusive current of minority carriers in the p-region of the device of the form $eD_n(dn_p/dx)$, evaluated at $x = -d_p$, the boundary of the depletion region. It might seem more reasonable to evaluate this current at the junction itself ($x = 0$) rather than at $x = -d_p$; the reasons for the procedure we use are those of simplicity, and will be fully justified in due course. In any event, evaluating the diffusive current as suggested leads to

$$J_n = eD_n\left(\frac{dn_p}{dx}\right)_{-d_p} = \frac{en_{p0}D_n}{L_n}(e^{-e\Delta V_e/kT} - 1) \quad . \tag{10.4-12}$$

The current due to holes crossing the junction can be obtained from a precisely similar calculation starting with (10.4 - 8) and (10.4 - 10), to obtain

$$J_p = -eD_p\left(\frac{dp_n}{dx}\right)_{d_n} = \frac{ep_{n0}D_p}{L_p}(e^{-e\Delta V_e/kT} - 1) \quad . \tag{10.4-13}$$

The total current crossing the junction, which because of continuity of current is the same as the current anywhere else in the circuit, is the sum of these two contributions, or

$$J = J_n + J_p = \left(\frac{en_{p0}D_n}{L_n} + \frac{ep_{n0}D_p}{L_p}\right) \cdot (e^{-e\Delta V_e/kT} - 1) \quad . \tag{10.4-14}$$

This is the current-voltage relation of a p-n junction rectifier. It has the same form as (10.4 - 4), except that the saturation current is now obtained explicitly in terms of material parameters. It should be observed that diffusion theory yields a total current rather than the individual currents associated with the four fundamental processes identified at the beginning of this development. However, since we know that the electron and hole currents J_a and J_c are independent of the barrier height, while J_b and J_d depend exponentially on this height, it isn't difficult to see that

$$J_a = J_{a0} = -\frac{en_{p0}D_n}{L_n} \qquad \text{and} \qquad J_c = J_{c0} = -\frac{ep_{n0}D_p}{L_p} \quad , \tag{10.4-15}$$

while J_b and J_d are given by

$$J_b = \frac{en_{p0}D_n}{L_n} \cdot e^{-e\Delta V_e/kT} \qquad \text{and} \qquad J_d = \frac{ep_{n0}D_p}{L_p} \cdot e^{-e\Delta V_e/kT} \quad . \tag{10.4-16}$$

When ΔV_e is positive, the barrier height is larger than it is in equilibrium. Under these circumstances very few electrons from the n-region can surmount the barrier, but minority electrons thermally generated in the p-region can still diffuse to the barrier and "fall over" into the n-region. This tends to reduce the concentration of minority electrons to values *less* than the equilibrium value n_{p0} in the p-

region near the boundary of the depletion region at $x = -d_p$. This effect is expressed by the second term in (10.4 - 11), wherein it is clear that at $x = -d_p$ the concentration is reduced to $n_{p0}\exp(-e\Delta V_e/kT)$. A similar reduction of the minority hole concentration in the n-region close to the opposite boundary of the depletion region also occurs, for similar reasons. Under these circumstances, which correspond to the "reverse bias" case, the junction tends to "collect" thermally generated minority carriers from the neighborhood of the junction in both n-region and p-region, and deliver them to the opposite side, where they become majority carriers. The effect has been observed earlier in connection with our discussion of point-contact rectifiers.

When ΔV_e is negative, the barrier height is reduced, allowing majority carriers to spill over the top of the barrier in large numbers, and enter regions of opposite conductivity type, where they become minority carriers. Under these circumstances, the junction is "forward biased" and carrier injection takes place, electrons being injected into the p-region and holes into the n-region. The exponential term in equation (10.4 - 11) is now much larger than unity, and the concentration of minority carriers in regions adjacent to the junctions is increased. These concentrations can become much larger than the equilibrium majority carrier density in forward-biased rectifiers.

We must now address the question of why the above calculation evaluates carrier diffusion fluxes at the outer boundaries of the depletion region rather than at the junction itself. The reason is basically that carrier transport in the depletion region is difficult to analyze, partially because of the fact that there are high fields there, fields that depend on the height of the barrier itself. Moreover, if the width of the depletion layer is comparable to the mean free path, a situation that we have already observed to be quite possible, conventional diffusive transport theory is no longer valid. In the extreme limit of a very narrow depletion region, in which very high fields prevail, there are few collisions within the region, and transport is a ballistic process rather than one that is diffusive. Finally, even if diffusion theory is valid, the carrier mobilities and diffusion coefficients can become field-dependent at the high fields that exist in the depletion region. These difficulties can all be avoided by the approach we have adopted. There is one point to be noted, however. Our approach calculates the minority carrier currents delivered to the depletion region, and assumes that *all* these minority carriers cross the junction and emerge on the other side. This amounts to assuming that there is no recombination of carriers within the depletion region. We have observed in the preceding section that fields within the region are so large that the transit time of carriers is ordinarily far smaller than the smallest minority carrier lifetime ordinarily encountered, at least in Si and Ge. The neglect of recombination in the depletion region is therefore justified except under unusual circumstances.

The notation we have used so far assumes that the external bias voltage ΔV_e is positive when it increases the height of the internal potential barrier at the junction, and negative when it causes the barrier height to decrease. This is a natural assumption to make from an internal point of view concerned with the influence of the barrier on currents within the device. If you are concerned only with how the device operates from the point of view of the *external* circuit, however, it is advantageous to regard the externally applied voltage as being positive in the "easy" direction of current flow corresponding to forward bias and negative for reverse bias, when the junction is in the "nonconducting" state. To orient yourself to this more conventional point of view, you need only write the external voltage as $V_0 = -\Delta V_e$, and express (10.4 - 14) as

$$J = J_0(e^{eV_0/kT} - 1) \; , \tag{10.4-15}$$

where

$$J_0 = \frac{en_{p0}D_n}{L_n} + \frac{ep_{n0}D_p}{L_p} \qquad \text{and} \qquad V_0 = -\Delta V_e \; . \tag{10.4-16}$$

Using the relation $n_i^2 = p_{p0}n_{p0} = n_{n0}p_{n0}$ and recalling that the majority carrier density is nearly equal to the donor or acceptor impurity concentration in extrinsic materials, the saturation current density (10.4 - 6) can be written as

$$J_0 = en_i^2 \left(\frac{D_n}{N_a L_n} + \frac{D_p}{N_d L_p} \right) \; , \tag{10.4-17}$$

a form in which the dependence of saturation current on material parameters is more directly apparent.

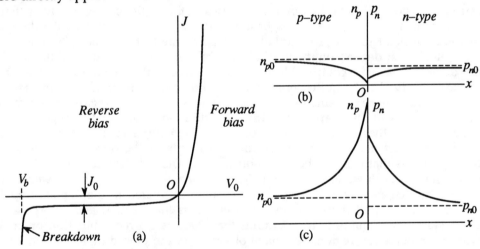

Figure 10.7 (a) Current density-voltage relation for a p–n junction rectifier, showing reverse breakdown. (b) Minority carrier concentrations as a function of distance x from the junction depletion region for a reverse-biased p-n junction rectifier; (c) minority carrier concentrations as a function of distance from the junction depletion region for a forward-biased p-n junction rectifiier. The depletion region is so narrow on the scale of the horizontal axis in (b) and (c) as to be imperceptible in the diagram.

A plot of the current density-voltage relation (10.4 - 15) is shown at (a) in Figure 10.7. For positive values of the voltage V_0 (negative ΔV_e) large currents can flow even at small forward voltages. In the reverse direction the current density for reverse biases appreciably larger than kT/e is restricted to the small saturation current density given by (10.4 - 16 or 17). The reverse current is then practically constant with increasing reverse bias voltage, until at a relatively high reverse bias, a phenomenon known as *reverse breakdown* begins to occur, at a fairly sharply defined breakdown voltage V_b. As the reverse bias nears this voltage, the reverse current begins to increase and suddenly becomes large compared to the saturation current as the breakdown voltage is approached. In this condition, since both current and voltage across the junction are large, a great deal of power is dissipated in the junction region, accompanied by the generation of an amount of heat so large that the device will self-destruct in a very short time if the current is not interrupted. There are two different physical mechanisms for breakdown. The breakdown voltage depends on which mechanism is operative, and also, in a complex way, on the material parameters of the device. In good silicon p-n junction rectifiers, breakdown voltages can exceed 1000 volts. The physical mechanisms of breakdown will be explained more fully in a later section.

At (b) and (c) in Figure 10.7 are plotted the minority carrier concentrations in the bulk p- and n-regions on either side of the depletion region. The depletion region itself is so narrow on the scale of the total thickness of the device and the diffusion lengths L_n and L_p as to be insignificant in the figure. At (b) we see the reverse biased junction, which merely collects minority carriers that diffuse to the junction from its immediate neighborhood. The effect of this diffusion is to decrease the minority carrier density near the junction to a value less than the equilibrium concentration far in the interior, but within a few diffusion lengths from the junction the concentration closely approaches the equilibrium value. At (c) the forward bias case is illustrated. Now, large concentrations of minority carriers are *injected* into the p- and n-type bulk regions from the majority populations on the opposite side of the junction. Under these circumstances the minority carrier density near the junction can be quite large--indeed, large enough to profoundly modulate the conductivity of the bulk regions and in extreme circumstances make them quasi-intrinsic. Under these conditions, the assumptions of extrinsic behavior that the above analysis relies upon are violated, and for this reason as well as others, the quantitative validity of (10.4 - 15) does not extend to values of forward bias that are greatly in excess of kT/e.

Light energy, in particular solar energy, can be converted into electrical energy by solid-state *photovoltaic cells*, whose structure is topologically the same as the p-n junction rectifier. Photovoltaic cells are large-area rectifiers in which the p-n junction is parallel to and a small distance beneath the illuminated surface of the device, as shown in Figure 10.8. We have already seen that in semiconductors the optical absorption coefficient depends on wavelength. A crystal of Si is practically transparent to light of wavelength longer than the critical value corresponding to the energy gap. This light cannot excite electron-hole pairs within the material, and therefore cannot contribute to the photovoltaic effect. Light having sufficient energy to create excess electron-hole pairs is absorbed within the crystal; wavelengths whose photon energy hardly exceeds the bandgap energy may penetrate fairly far into the crystal before being absorbed, while light of larger photon energy will be absorbed very near the surface. Excess electron hole pairs are therefore created throughout the crystal, on both sides of the junction. If the light is intense, the concentration of electron-hole pairs may far exceed the minority carrier density on both sides of the junction.

In the dark, excess minority electrons in the p-region are in equilibrium with majority electrons in the n-region so that no current flows. When there is a large population of excess photogenerated electrons and holes, however, this equilibrium is disrupted. Minority electrons in the p-region can now descend the potential slope at the junction and enter the n-region in large numbers to become majority carriers, while minority holes in the *n*-region "gravitate upward" into the *p*-region. Now, if the external terminals of the cell are shorted, as illustrated in the figure, a current caused by this excess electron/hole transport across the junction will flow in the external circuit. The current so obtained depends obviously on the illumination level, but also on the geometry and material parameters of the rectifier structure. The current obtained under these conditions is known as the *short-circuit current*.

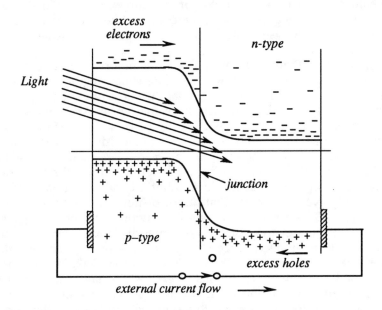

Figure 10.8 A *p–n* photovoltaic cell, illuminated by light incident on the left surface of the crystal. As shown, the terminals of the rectifier are shorted, allowing current to flow in the external circuit. If the switch is opened, the flow of charge persists for a time, until the potential barrier is lowered sufficiently to restore equilibrium between the electron and hole population on either side of the junction. As this happens, the excess charges that build up within the device generate a voltage between its external terminals.

In this situation, there can be no change in the potential drop across the sample, since its terminals are shorted. The height of the internal barrier is thus the same as the equilibrium height, and the external voltage is ideally zero. Actually, of course, due to the small finite resistance of the bulk semiconductor and the external circuit this ideal situation in which current flows though the emf is essentially zero is never quite realized. Suppose, now, the switch in the above diagram is suddenly opened. The current in the external circuit is now zero, but the electron and hole flows shown above persist for a very short time, there being nothing (initially at least) to stop them. As a result. the *p*-region acquires a positive charge and the *n*-region becomes somewhat more negative. A field builds up because of this, a field to the right, along the +*x*-direction. Its direction is *opposite* that of the field associated with uncompensated impurity sites in the depletion region, and which is responsible for the formation of the equilibrium internal potential barrier. The effect is to *lower* the internal barrier, which allows more majority carriers in the *n*-and *p*-bulk regions to surmount the barrier and *counteract* the photoactivated minority carrier fluxes. After a very short time, a steady state is again established, in which there is no net current, either within the device or in the external circuit. Now, however, the contact to the positively charged p-region is at a higher electrostatic potential than the one on the negatively charged n-side, and a *voltage* in the external circuit is created, a voltage that is analogous in every sense to the terminal emf of a battery. Indeed, it is a photovoltaic emf, referred to as the *open-circuit voltage*, or the open circuit emf of the cell. This voltage also depends on the illumination level and on the geometry and material parameters of the system.

There is also a wide range of intermediate situations in which currents in the circuit are restricted by external circuit impedance to values greater than zero but less than the short-circuit current. There is no power consumed in the external circuit in either the open-circuit or short-circuit limits, but power is dissipated in the external resistance otherwise. The situation is not essentially different in this respect from that of a battery emf and an external current-carrying circuit with resistance. In both cases, maximum external power is obtained when external and internal impedances are equal.

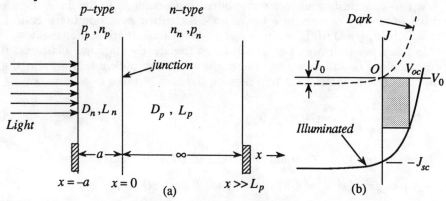

Figure 10.9 (a) Geometry of *p–n* junction photovoltaic cell. A planar one-dimensional system in which light is assumed to be absorbed very close to the surface is considered. (b) The current-voltage relation associated with the device illustrated in (a) for dark and illuminated cells.

We shall now examine in more detail the one-dimensional planar photovoltaic structure illustrated in Figure 10.9 (a). The device has an illuminated *p*-region of thickness a and a much thicker *n*-region, of "infinite" width, in the sense that it is very thick on the scale of the minority carrier diffusion length L_p. We shall assume that the light is totally absorbed near the surface, so that all photogenerated excess carriers can be viewed as being generated *at the illuminated front surface* of the cell. Both *p*- and *n*-regions are assumed to be highly extrinsic. Under these conditions the width of the depletion region is so small as to be negligible, allowing boundary conditions to be applied at the assumed location of the junction itself, at $x = 0$. Front (positive) and rear (negative) terminals are illustrated schematically in the diagram. In practice, the front terminal is connected to an open grid of fine metallic conductors applied to the front surface of the cell to collect internal currents at that surface, and the rear terminal covers the entire area of the device. Under these conditions, the vertical currents that might seem to conflict with the one-dimensional analysis we shall undertake are not a serious problem. For such a structure, the steady-state minority carrier transport equations have the form,

$$n_p - n_{p0} = Ae^{x/L_n} + Be^{-x/L_n} \quad , \qquad (-a < x < 0) \tag{10.4-18}$$

and

$$p_n - p_{n0} = Ce^{-x/L_p} \quad , \qquad\qquad (x > 0) \; . \tag{10.4-19}$$

It is assumed that the n-region's thickness is so large that excess minority holes will all have recombined before reaching the back surface of the cell. This implies that the excess concentration $p_n - p_{n0}$ is zero at $x = \infty$, and accounts for the absence of a term of the form $D\exp(x/L_p)$ in (10.4 - 19). At the junction, the boundary conditions are the same as (9.4 - 9) and (9.4 -10), used in our study of the p-n rectifier, except that the depletion region is of negligible width compared to other relevant distances, so that

$$n_p(0) = n_{p0} e^{-e\Delta V_e/kT} \quad \text{and} \qquad p_n(0) = p_{n0} e^{-e\Delta V_e/kT} . \tag{10.4-20}$$

At $x = -a$, there is a surface recombination velocity s. In the dark, there would be a flux of minority carriers *into* the surface described by a boundary condition of the form $D_n[d(n_p - n_{p0})/dx]_{-a} = s(n_p - n_{p0})_{-a}$. With illumination that creates G electron-hole pairs per unit area per unit time in the steady state, an *additional* flux of minority carriers G will flow *from* the surface into the bulk p-region, and the total diffusion flux out of the surface will then be the sum of these two terms, or

$$-D_n\left(\frac{d(n_p - n_{p0})}{dx}\right)_{-a} = G - s(n_p - n_{p0})_{-a} \; . \tag{10.4-21}$$

Substituting (10.4 - 21) into (10.4 - 18) and (10.4 -19), we can now write

$$n_p(0) - n_{p0} = n_{p0}\varphi(V_e) = A + B, \qquad \text{or} \qquad B = n_{p0}\varphi(V_e) - A \tag{10.4-22}$$

and

$$p_n(0) - p_{n0} = C = p_{n0}\varphi(V_e) \; , \tag{10.4-23}$$

where

$$\varphi(V_e) = e^{-e\Delta V_e/kT} - 1 \; . \tag{10.4-24}$$

Substituting (10.4 - 18) into the boundary condition (10.4 - 21), expressing B in terms of A with the aid of (10.4 - 22), and solving for A, we find

$$A = \frac{n_{p0}\varphi(V_e)(s + (D_n/L_n))e^{a/L_n} - G}{2\left(\dfrac{D_n}{L_n}\cosh\dfrac{a}{L_n} + s\sinh\dfrac{a}{L_n}\right)} \; , \tag{10.4-25}$$

and

$$B = \frac{\dfrac{D_n}{L_n}\sinh\dfrac{a}{L_n} + s\cosh\dfrac{a}{L_n}}{\dfrac{D_n}{L_n}\cosh\dfrac{a}{L_n} + s\sinh\dfrac{a}{L_n}} - \frac{G}{2\left(\dfrac{D_n}{L_n}\cosh\dfrac{a}{L_n} + s\sinh\dfrac{a}{L_n}\right)} \; . \tag{10.4-26}$$

In writing (10.4 - 26) we have used the identity $\exp(x) = \sinh x + \cosh x$. As in the case of the p-n rectifier, the minority currents into the junction region can be written as

$$J_p = -eD_p\left(\frac{d(p_n - p_{n0})}{dx}\right)_0 \quad \text{and} \quad J_n = eD_n\left(\frac{d(n_p - n_{p0})}{dx}\right)_0 . \tag{10.4-27}$$

Substituting (10.4 - 18) and (10.4 - 19) into these relations, and using (10.4 - 22), we obtain

$$J_p = \frac{eD_p C}{L_p} = \frac{ep_{n0}D_p}{L_p}\varphi(V_e) \quad \text{and} \quad J_n = \frac{eD_n}{L_n}(A - B) = \frac{eD_n}{L_n}\left(2A - n_{p0}\varphi(V_e)\right). \tag{10.4-28}$$

Finally, with the aid of (10.4 - 25) and (10.4 - 23), we find after some algebra,

$$J = J_n + J_p = \left[\frac{ep_{n0}D_p}{L_p} + \frac{en_{p0}D_n}{L_n}\left(\frac{\dfrac{D_n}{L_n}\sinh\dfrac{a}{L_n} + s\cosh\dfrac{a}{L_n}}{\dfrac{D_n}{L_n}\cosh\dfrac{a}{L_n} + s\sinh\dfrac{a}{L_n}}\right)\right]\cdot\varphi(V_e) - \frac{eD_n G / L_n}{\dfrac{D_n}{L_n}\cosh\dfrac{a}{L_n} + s\sinh\dfrac{a}{L_n}} . \tag{10.4-29}$$

In this expression, the first term is independent of the illumination level, as expressed by G. The second term, on the other hand, is independent of the barrier potential difference V_e but is directly proportional to the light intensity. Indeed, the first term in brackets has the form of a rectifier saturation current, which leads us to write this equation with the aid of (10.4 - 24) as

$$J = J_0(e^{eV_0/kT} - 1) - J_g , \tag{10.4-30}$$

where

$$J_0 = \frac{ep_{n0}D_p}{L_p} + \frac{en_{p0}D_n}{L_n}\left(\frac{\dfrac{D_n}{L_n}\tanh\dfrac{a}{L_n} + s}{\dfrac{D_n}{L_n} + s\tanh\dfrac{a}{L_n}}\right) \quad \text{and} \quad J_g = \frac{eD_n G / L_n}{\dfrac{D_n}{L_n}\cosh\dfrac{a}{L_n} + s\sinh\dfrac{a}{L_n}}. \tag{10.4-31}$$

When the surface recombination velocity is zero, these expressions reduce to

$$J_0 = \frac{ep_{n0}D_p}{L_p} + \frac{en_{p0}D_n}{L_n}\tanh\frac{a}{L_n} \quad \text{and} \quad J_g = eG\,\mathrm{sech}\frac{a}{L_n} . \tag{10.4-32}$$

The current-voltage relation (10.4 - 30) is plotted in Figure 10.9(b). The voltage V_0, as before, is equal to $-\Delta V_e$. If the cell is in the dark, G is zero and the equation reduces to that of an ordinary p-n rectifier, as illustrated by the dashed curve passing through the origin. Under illumination, there is a constant generation current J_g, and the current-voltage curve is shifted downward, as shown by the bold curve in the figure. The short-circuit current and the open-circuit voltage correspond to the intercepts of the current-voltage curve with the axes, as shown in the diagram. The actual operating point is determined by the impedance of the external circuit. In the diagram, a typical situation in which there is an external load is illustrated by the shaded rectangle, a corner of which intersects the curve at the operating current and voltage. The area of the rectangle represents the product of output current and terminal voltage, and thus shows the power delivered to the external circuit. The power output can be maximized by choosing a circuit impedance that maximizes the area of this "power rectangle". It is clearly advantageous that the generation current J_g be as large as possible, a condition realized when the diffusion length L_n is very large, according to (10.4 - 31) and (10.4 - 32). It is also desirable to have as low a surface recombination velocity as possible. Physically these criteria are explained by the fact that minority carriers that recombine before reaching the junction do not contribute to the generation current nor to the output current.

The open circuit voltage and short-circuit current can be calculated by setting V_0 and J_0 respectively equal to zero in (10.4 - 30). One obtains in this way,

$$V_{oc} = \frac{kT}{e} \ln\left(1 + \frac{J_g}{J_0}\right) \qquad \text{and} \qquad J_{sc} = -J_g \qquad (10.4\text{-}33)$$

The open-circuit terminal voltage of a photovoltaic cell depends on the difference between the equilibrium barrier height and that which prevails under strong illumination. It is therefore limited by the bandgap energy, which suggests a maximum open-circuit voltage of around 0.7 volts for Ge, 1.1 volts for silicon, and 1.3 volts for GaAs. Naturally, higher voltages can be obtained by connecting many cells in series. The short circuit current is limited primarily by the number of pairs generated, and the fraction that survive internal recombination and arrive at the junction. Solar radiation delivers energy at normal incidence to an absorbing surface at the rate of 1390W/m² at the outer fringe of the earth's atmosphere, and at about half that rate at sea level. The power generated by a photocell is limited to this amount, but since not all solar energy is converted to electrical energy, the output power is reduced by an efficiency factor.

Actual photovoltaic devices are of two general types; high-efficiency, single-crystal cells with the best possible conversion efficiency and relatively high cost, and low-cost amorphous silicon thin-film devices designed to cover large areas, and provide large power output at lowest possible cost. The first type is used largely for satellite power systems, the second for low-cost terrestrial solar conversion applications. The geometry we have chosen is a good representation of the high-efficiency single-crystal cell, but does not give a very accurate picture of thin-film cells, wherein "ballistic" rather than diffusive transport is important. The actual calculation of conversion efficiency is complex, and involves several factors not considered explicitly in our model. Single-crystal silicon absorbs incident radiation of wavelength less than about 1.2 microns (1200nm), which accounts for most of the solar energy incident on a cell at the earth's surface or in a satellite orbit. The short-circuit voltage of silicon cells can be relatively high because of the wide bandgap; moreover high lifetimes and long diffusion lengths are readily obtained. Silicon is also very stable and works well even at high operating temperatures. It is at present the optimal material for photovoltaic devices, though GaAs is potentially very promising. Single crystal silicon cells should in theory be able to convert roughly 30% of solar energy into electrical energy, but in practice the best currently available cells are only about 20% efficient. Thin film cells are much less expensive though also somewhat less efficient and far less durable.

10.5 BREAKDOWN PHENOMENA

The reverse breakdown effect in *p-n* rectifiers has been described in the preceding section. The immediate cause of breakdown is a very high electric field in the neighborhood of the junction; for this reason the effect is most often encountered in the depletion region of *p-n* junctions, though it can sometimes be observed in uniform bulk semiconductors and insulators. There are two distinct and independent effects that lead to breakdown in *p-n* junctions; they are referred to as Zener tunneling and the avalanche mechanism. The phenomenon of thermal runaway discussed in Chapter 9 is also a form of breakdown. Though it can appear in the final stages of catastrophic device failure, it is seldom involved in initiating breakdown in reverse biased junctions, and will not be further considered in this discussion.

Zener breakdown is named after its discoverer, C. Zener, who described it in the context of the catastrophic failure of bulk crystalline dielectrics subjected to high external electric fields in 1933. We shall describe its action in *p-n* junctions, though it is essentially the same in bulk materials. Zener breakdown is a tunneling phenomenon, in which valence band electrons tunnel into empty conduction band states of the same energy under the influence of high fields. We have already seen that high electric fields perturb the energy of the band edges in the neighborhood of a *p-n* junction. This "band bending" is simply a reflection of the fact that an electric field causes the potential energy of a charged particle to be different at points having different electrostatic potentials. The band sloping or bending is most evident in the neighborhood of junctions, as explained in Section 10.3, but it also exists in uniform bulk semiconductors and insulators when external fields are present. If the field is uniform, as it usually is in homogeneous materials, the band edges simply become parallel straight lines which are no longer horizontal, but have a *slope* proportional to the potential gradient, in other words, the field. At a junction, the fields are not only very high, but are definitely *not* uniform within the material, which causes the band edges to assume the form of the now-familiar junction potential barrier.

When a reverse bias is applied to a *p-n* junction, the barrier height increases, drastically so for high reverse bias voltages. The effect of this is to distort the bands in the neighborhood of the junction as illustrated in Figure 10.10. Beyond a certain voltage, not large on the scale of the bandgap, filled states in the valence band of the *p*-region can have the same energy as unoccupied states in the *n*-region on the opposite side of the junction, some distance away. These states are physically separated by a potential barrier of roughly triangular form, whose "height" in energy is equal to the band gap, and whose thickness AB at small reverse voltages is so large that the probability of tunneling between states of equal energy is negligible. Under these conditions the junction withstands the reverse bias voltage, and the only observable current that flows is the small reverse saturation current discussed in the preceding section. At larger reverse voltages, however, the fields within the depletion region as expressed by (10.3 - 22) become much larger. Now the slope of the triangular barrier becomes far steeper, and as it does, states of equal energy in the valence and conduction bands on opposite sides are separated by a barrier much thinner than before. Finally, it becomes so thin that the tunneling probability is significant, and tunneling current begins to increase the reverse current. At some well-defined reverse voltage the tunneling current becomes larger than the saturation current, causing a

472

noticeable increase in reverse current. The tunneling probability increases exponentially as the barrier becomes thinner, so that when this critical voltage is exceeded, the tunneling current rises dramatically, and the device will self-destruct unless an external current limiter is provided. If provision is made to limit the current, it can be used as a voltage reference diode in view of the sharply defined voltage at which breakdown occurs. Such dedicated reference diodes are referred to as *Zener diodes*.

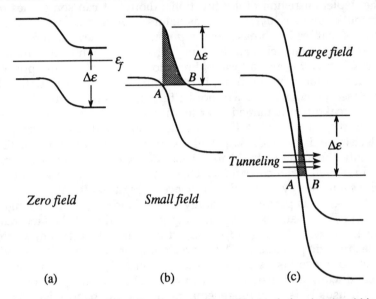

Figure 10.10 Energy bands and tunneling barriers in the neighborhood of *p-n* junctions (a) in the absence of external fields (b) in the presence of a small field, and (c) in the presence of a field so large that tunneling can occur through a barrier of significantly reduced width *AB*. The shaded areas exhibit the form of the tunneling barrier "seen" by a valence-band electron in the *p*-region.

The avalanche process is similar to one which initiates an electrical discharge in mercury-vapor and sodium-vapor lamps, neon tubes, and similar devices. In this process, when the electric field becomes so large that an electron can acquire enough energy to ionize a gas atom in the mean free time between electron-atom collisions, breakdown occurs, the gas becoming ionized and highly conducting. In a semiconductor, a free electron or hole may similarly acquire enough energy from an electric field during the collision mean free time to generate an electron-hole pair in a collision with a lattice phonon. When this happens, the new electron-hole pair can generate yet another pair in a subsequent collision, giving rise to a chain reaction or avalanche in which the electron-hole gas becomes much more dense, and much more highly conducting than it is in its normal equilibrium state.

It is possible in this case to obtain an approximate expression for the breakdown voltage fairly easily. The condition for avalanche formation requires that the energy acquired in a mean free path be equal to the bandgap energy. If we equate the bandgap energy to the work done by the field in accelerating a free electron or hole, we can write

$$eE_b\lambda = \Delta\varepsilon , \qquad \text{or} \qquad E_b = \Delta\varepsilon / e\lambda , \qquad (10.5\text{-}1)$$

where E_b is the critical breakdown field and λ the mean free path. In a device in which there is a p-n junction, the voltage drop occurs primarily at the junction, and due to the high fields within the depletion region, that is where avalanche breakdown will occur. In this region, if abrupt-junction theory is applicable, the maximum field within the depletion region is given in terms of the external potential by (10.3 - 22). Equating this field to the critical field E_b, as given by (10.5 - 1), writing the external voltage ΔV_e as the breakdown voltage V_b, and making the further assumption that the internal contact potential is small in comparison with the breakdown voltage, we may solve the resulting expression for V_b to obtain

$$V_b = \frac{K\varepsilon_0 (\Delta\varepsilon)^2}{2e^3 \lambda^2} \left(\frac{1}{N_d} + \frac{1}{N_a} \right) . \tag{10.5-2}$$

From this expression it is easily seen that low breakdown voltages are associated with high doping densities and that the best reverse breakdown behavior is obtained when the p- and n-region, though extrinsic, are moderately doped. It is also apparent that wide-bandgap materials are also useful from this point of view.

A quantitative treatment of Zener breakdown is more difficult, because the tunneling behavior of the triangular barrier is hard to describe in detail. It is apparent, however, from (10.3 - 22), that high internal fields and thin barriers follow from high doping densities. Therefore, moderate doping levels must also improve the breakdown voltages associated with Zener tunneling. Zener tunneling depends only on the character of the tunneling barrier, and is independent of the mean free path. The breakdown field associated with this mechanism is thus practically independent of temperature, while avalanche breakdown occurs at lower voltages as the temperature decreases, due to an increased mean free path at low temperatures. Junction devices can therefore exhibit Zener breakdown at high temperatures and avalanche breakdown at lower values of temperature. Indeed, the two mechanisms can act simultaneously. Which specific breakdown mechanism occurs in any particular situation is determined by which process leads to a *lower* breakdown voltage in the given device under the prevailing conditions. Good silicon p-n junction power rectifiers can exhibit breakdown voltages in excess of 1000 volts at normal temperatures.

10.6 JUNCTION TRANSISTORS; THE HAYNES–SHOCKLEY EXPERIMENT

A classic demonstration of minority carrier injection and transport in a homogeneous semiconductor crystal was made in 1951 by J. R. Haynes and William Shockley. In the Haynes-Shockley experiment a long thin bar of single crystal germanium or silicon of uniform cross-section is arranged as shown in Figure 10.11. In the figure, the sample is an n-type crystal, in which two p-n junctions have been incorporated as shown. One of these junctions, shown in the figure as the *emitter*, is used as a forward-biased rectifier to inject holes into the long n-type "filament". The other junction, referred to as the *collector*, is reverse-biased in order to collect the holes after they have moved some known distance down the bar under the influence of a small dc "sweep field" created by a battery connected between the ends of the sample. In the original experiment, these electrodes were point contacts of the kind discussed in Section 10.2. In the diagram below, a more modern arrangement is shown, in which a shallow p-n junction has been produced by diffusing an acceptor impurity like boron into the top surface of the sample. then etching most of of it away, except for two small "mesas" where the surface was shielded from the action of the chemical etch by two dots of an insoluble coating, later removed, leaving tiny emitter and collecter junctions as shown below.

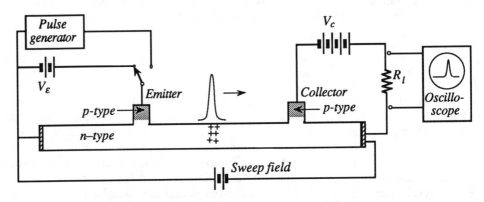

Figure 10.11 A filamentary transistor, illustrating both the Haynes-Shockley experiment for measuring the drift of a pulse of injected carriers between an emitter and a collector electrode some distance away, and the action of a filamentary transistor in which a steady dc current of injected minority carriers is emitted and subsequently collected. In the first application the pulse generator is switched into the circuit and the oscilloscope used as a detector, while for the second the emitter battery is selected so that a steady current flows through the emitter junction.

The Haynes-Shockley experiment was originally designed to determine the "drift mobility" of excess carriers by measuring the time interval between injection of carriers at an emitter and their detection at the collector, a known distance d away. In this application, a pulse generator is switched into the circuit to inject a narrow pulse of carriers from an emitter, which is later collected and detected by an oscilloscope (whose sweep circuit is triggered by the injection pulse) after a time interval Δt which can be measured accurately on the cathode-ray tube. The measured drift velocity $v = d/\Delta t$ can be written as the product of a minority carrier drift mobility and the known field created by the sweep battery, allowing the drift mobility to be determined from the measurements. The experiment can be seen, in fact, to measure the *ambipolar* mobility (9.8 - 24), which is equal to the minority carrier mobility in extrinsic materials. The drift mobility in extrinsic crystals differs somewhat from the Hall mobility, because different average relaxation times and effective masses are displayed by the two experiments. It is clear, however, that the drift mobility is more directly related to the conductivity mobility $e\tau/m_c^*$ shown in (9.7 - 20) and (9.7 - 22) than the Hall mobility. Unfortunately, however, the Haynes-Shockley measurement can be made only on materials with minority carrier lifetimes long enough to allow a sizeable fraction of the initial injected distribution to survive a drift time of the order of 10 to 100 microseconds, a requirement that excludes many substances.

The Haynes-Shockley experiment is of interest not only because of its usefulness as a way of measuring drift mobility, but also because it contains all the elements of a p-n-p *junction transistor* neatly separated so that their operation is clearly visible and independently displayed. In the filamentary transistor shown above, minority carriers are emitted from a forward-biased rectifying *p-n emitter* junction into a *base* region of opposite conductivity type, where they subsequently drift (or more commonly diffuse) to a *collector* junction biased in the reverse direction so as to collect incident minority carriers. Such a structure can achieve not only voltage gain but also power gain, and can therefore *amplify* signals that are applied either to the emitter or base leads. It can also be employed as an oscillator, cathode follower, switching circuit, storage device, or in any other electronic application that could be assigned to earlier circuit elements like vacuum tubes. The truth of this assertion can be seen more clearly if the pulsed emitter of the Haynes-Shockley experiment is replaced by a steady emitter voltage V_ε that injects a constant emitter current I_ε whose minority carriers traverse the base region to be collected at the collector junction, where they augment the current I_c in the collector circuit at the right in the figure. The subscript ε is used in the emitter region to avoid confusion with the symbol V_e used previously to express external voltages in another context.

Using the results already obtained for abrupt junction *p-n* rectifiers, we can write, for the emitter current-voltage relation,

$$I_\varepsilon = I_{\varepsilon 0}(e^{eV_\varepsilon/kT} - 1) \qquad \text{or} \qquad V_\varepsilon = \frac{kT}{e}\ln\left(1 + \frac{I_\varepsilon}{I_{\varepsilon 0}}\right). \tag{10.6-1}$$

In the collector circuit, we assume that the collector junction is sufficiently reverse-biased that the collector current is simply equal to the saturation current I_{c0} in the absence of any emitter current. When emitter current flows, excess minority carriers are injected, and a certain number of them will survive recombination in the base region to be picked up at the collector, where they contribute to an *increase* in the reverse current that flows through the collector junction and into the collector circuit. This increase in the collector reverse current is clearly proportional to the emitter current, which allows us to write for the collector circuit,

$$I_c = I_{c0} + \alpha I_\varepsilon , \tag{10.6-2}$$

where α is the *fraction* of emitter current carried by minority carriers that survive to be collected by the collector junction. From the above expression it is apparent that this quantity can also be defined in terms of external circuit parameters as

$$\alpha = \left(\frac{\partial I_c}{\partial I_\varepsilon}\right)_{V_c} . \tag{10.6-3}$$

The power dissipated in the emitter circuit is $I_\varepsilon V_\varepsilon$, from which,

$$\frac{dP_\varepsilon}{dI_\varepsilon} = I_\varepsilon \frac{dV_\varepsilon}{dI_\varepsilon} + V_\varepsilon = \frac{kT}{e}\left[\ln\left(1 + \frac{I_\varepsilon}{I_{\varepsilon 0}}\right) + \frac{I_\varepsilon/I_{\varepsilon 0}}{1 + (I_\varepsilon/I_{\varepsilon 0})}\right]. \tag{10.6-4}$$

The incremental power dP_c or $d(I_c^2 R)$ associated with the collector circuit can be related to an increment dP_ε in the emitter circuit, using (10.6 - 2), as

$$\frac{dP_c}{dP_\varepsilon} = \frac{dP_c}{dI_\varepsilon} \cdot \frac{dI_\varepsilon}{dP_\varepsilon} = \frac{2(I_{c0} + \alpha I_\varepsilon)\alpha R_l}{dP_\varepsilon / dI_\varepsilon} \, , \tag{10.6-5}$$

where R_l is the load resistance shown in the collector circuit. We shall assume that the emitter junction is forward-biased to the degree that the exponential term in (10.5 - 1) is far greater than unity, which implies that the ratio $I_\varepsilon / I_{\varepsilon 0}$ is much larger than unity. Making these assumptions, and substituting from (10.6 - 4) into (10.6 - 5), we obtain an approximate expression for the incremental power gain of the form

$$\frac{dP_c}{dP_\varepsilon} = \frac{2(I_{c0} + \alpha I_\varepsilon)\alpha R_l}{\dfrac{kT}{e}\left(1 + \ln \dfrac{I_\varepsilon}{I_{\varepsilon 0}}\right)} \cong \frac{2\alpha^2 I_\varepsilon R_l}{\dfrac{kT}{e}\left(1 + \ln \dfrac{I_\varepsilon}{I_{\varepsilon 0}}\right)} \, . \tag{10.6-6}$$

The final form of this expression involves the added assumption that αI_ε is much larger than the saturation current I_{c0}, which is reasonable if α is not too small, in view of the fact that the foward biased emitter current will normally far exceed the small saturation current drawn by the collector.

Let us now consider the case of a germanium p-n-p transistor, with N_a in the emitter region equal to 10^{18}cm^{-3} and N_d in the base region equal to 10^{15}cm^{-3}; the doping level in the collector region is not important except insofar as it permits the junction to withstand a large reverse bias without breakdown. For Ge, according to Table 9.1 at the end of Section 9.2, $n_i = 2.4 \times 10^{13} \text{cm}^{-3}$, and the diffusion coefficients follow from the listed mobilities, using the Einstein relations, as $D_n = 98 \text{cm}^2/\text{sec}$ and $D_p = 48 \text{cm}^2/\text{sec}$. Let us assume a minority carrier lifetime of 10^{-5}sec in the n-region and 10^{-6}sec in the heavily doped emitter. Then, L_n follows as $(D_n \tau_n)^{1/2}$, or 0.0099cm, and similarly one finds $L_p = 0.0219 \text{cm}$. From (10.4 - 17), the saturation current density of the emitter junction now follows as $2.0 \times 10^{-4} \text{amp}/\text{cm}^2$. For a junction area of 1mm^2, this yields a saturation current $I_{\varepsilon 0}$ of $2.0 \times 10^{-6} \text{amp}$. If we now assume $\alpha = 0.9$, $I_\varepsilon = 10^{-2} \text{amp}$ and $R_l = 200$ ohms, we find from (10.6 - 6) a power gain of about 13.6. The factor α is referred to as the *current gain*, and is by definition less than unity, though it is desirable that it be as large as possible. Since there is power gain, however, it is clear that the circuit possesses voltage gain. This gain can be written, using (10.6 - 1), (10.6 - 2) and the approximations already described, as

$$\frac{dV_l}{dV_\varepsilon} = \frac{d(I_c R_l)}{dV_\varepsilon} \cong \alpha R_l \frac{dI_\varepsilon}{dV_\varepsilon} = \alpha R_l I_{\varepsilon 0} \cdot \frac{e}{kT}\left(1 + \frac{I_\varepsilon}{I_{\varepsilon 0}}\right). \tag{10.6-7}$$

The numerical data assumed in this example, used in connection with this expression indicate a voltage gain of about 72.

The Haynes-Shockley geometry, while excellent for measuring drift mobility, as well as for displaying the concepts of transistor action, is essentially *useless* for a circuit element. The reason is that the long distance between emitter and collector practically guarantees that recombination in the base region will lead to a small current gain, rather than one close to unity, as needed for a good transistor. The value 0.9 assumed in the calculation above is typical of a good planar p-n-p transistor; you would be lucky to acheive a tenth of that in a Haynes-Shockley filamentary device. In a real junction transistor, in order to achieve the desired value of α, the planar emitter and collector junctions must be parallel and closely spaced, as illustrated in Figure 10.12. Under these circumstances, the battery generating the sweep field that propels minority carriers down the sample is no longer needed, and diffusion in the now narrow base region can be relied upon to accomplish this task. The forward-biased emitter now injects carriers into its side of the base region, which creates a high concentration of minority carriers there, while the strongly reverse-biased collector *lowers* the concentration of carriers in its vicinity to a very small value. This creates a steep minority carrier concentration gradient in the narrow base region, and allows diffusion currents to do the job that the sweep field was needed for in the Haynes-Shockley arrangement. The calculation given above suggests that the width of the central base region should ideally be much less than the diffusion length of minority carriers in that region, which with the *n*-type base material assumed in the example, indicates a desirable base width no more than about 0.1mm. This discussion has assumed a *p-n-p* emitter-base-collector configuration, but is obviously valid for *n-p-n* transistors as well. Transistors of both types are commonly used.

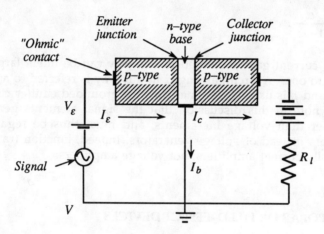

Figure 10.12 The emitter, base, and collector configurations in a typical *p-n-p* junction transistor. Ideally, the width of the base region should be very small, indeed, smaller than indicated in the schematic diagram above.

The preceding discussion assumes an input "signal" in the form of an incremental change in emitter current and a "figure of merit" α defined as the ratio of incremental collector current to incremental emitter current as given by (10.6 - 3). In Figure 10.12, such a signal element is shown in the emitter circuit, as suggested by this discussion. Naturally such an input signal could also have the form of a small ac signal or a stream of digitally encoded information in the form of discrete current pulses. In any event, in this "grounded base" circuit configuration, the current gain α is by definition always less than unity.

Current gains greater than unity can be achieved simply by moving the signal element from the emitter circuit and inserting it into the central base lead in the above diagram. If the current gain were exactly unity, the emitter and collector currents would be the same and no current would flow in the base lead. In practice, this is never possible, since recombination attenuates the excess minority carrier current injected at the emitter junction. This makes the collector current smaller than the emitter current. However, continuity of current flow requires that all currents into and out of the base region sum to zero, thus that

$$I_\varepsilon = I_c + I_b \; , \tag{10.6-8}$$

where I_b is the base current shown in the figure. Then,

$$\frac{dI_c}{dI_b} = \frac{d}{dI_b}(I_\varepsilon - I_b) = \frac{dI_\varepsilon}{dI_c} \cdot \frac{dI_c}{dI_b} - 1 = \frac{1}{\alpha} \cdot \frac{dI_c}{dI_b} - 1 \; . \tag{10.6-9}$$

The quantity dI_c/dI_b expresses the ratio of an incremental change in collector current ascribable to a current "signal" dI_b in the base lead; this can be regarded as a current amplification factor defined in the same way that α is defined in (10.6 - 3). Solving for this factor, which we shall write as β, we find

$$\beta = \frac{dI_c}{dI_b} = \frac{\alpha}{1-\alpha} \; . \tag{10.6-10}$$

The base-circuit current gain β defined in this way can be much larger than unity when α is close to one. A circuit arranged in this way is referred to as a "grounded emitter" circuit and β is usually designated as the grounded emitter current gain. It is important to note in this discussion that the signal elements generate current increments rather than voltage increments, and must thus be regarded as ideal current generators instead of voltage generators. Indeed, junction transistors themselves are basically current amplifiers, not voltage amplifiers.

10.7 UNIPOLAR OR FIELD–EFFECT DEVICES

The operation of transistors like those discussed in the preceding section depends on the injection of minority carriers into a narrow base layer and their subsequent collection by a reverse-biased collector junction. Such devices are known as bipolar transistors, because two carrier species are involved in their action, and they can exist in the two complementary forms p-n-p and n-p-n.

Transistors can also be made from structures in which the effective width, and thus the conductance, of a narrow channel through which current flows, is modulated by an external voltage. Such devices are referred to as field-effect transistors, or FETs. They are said to be *unipolar* transistors because there is no carrier injection required for their action, which depends on current carried only by the majority carriers. The simplest form of this device is one in which one boundary of the conducting channel is the depletion region of a p-n junction, whose extent can be controlled externally in such a way as to modulate the channel current. This type of device is referred to as a junction field-effect transistor or JFET. Its form is illustrated schematically in Figure 10.13.

The device shown in the diagram consists of an n-type bar into which acceptor impurities have been introduced by diffusion or other means, so as to form a p-n junction parallel to the top surface. If the p-region is heavily doped, while the n-type substrate is doped to a lesser degree, equations (10.3 - 16, 19, and 20) indicate that the depletion region will extend much further into the n-type substrate than into the heavily doped p-region. The equations of Section 10.3 show also that if the junction is reverse-biased (ΔV_e positive), the depletion region width can be much larger than it is in equilibrium. Under these circumstances, the depletion region in which there are very few carriers can be made to extend into the n-region to a significant fraction of its total thickness, as illustrated.

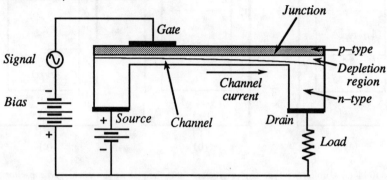

Figure 10.13 Schematic diagram illustrating a junction field-effect transistor and its associated circuitry.

There are three ohmic contacts to the device, referred to as source, drain and gate electrodes, which correspond, respectively, to the cathode, plate, and grid of a triode vacuum tube. A "channel current" is made to flow between source and drain, as illustrated, and a dc reverse bias is established across the p-n junction as shown in the diagram. When this bias voltage increases, as it might when a negative signal voltage is introduced in the gate circuit, the extent of the depletion region associated with the junction *increases* in the n-region, decreasing the channel width and thus the channel current. A positive signal voltage, on the other hand, increases the width, and the conductance, of the conducting channel, increasing the channel current. The device thus functions much like a vacuum triode amplifier, and allows an amplified version of the input signal voltage to appear across the load resistor. The circuit can also function as an oscillator, switching circuit, or memory element, and can do anything that a vacuum triode or bipolar transistor can do. For purposes of illustration an n-type substrate has been assumed, but the device works equally well with a p-type substrate and a heavily doped n-region adjacent to the gate contact.

Another type of unipolar transistor relies on the properties of surface states on silicon crystals to create a conducting channel and dispenses with the need for a specifically prepared p-n junction like the one incorporated into the sample in Figure 10.13. The ultimate device structure that stems from this operating principle is the metal-oxide-semiconductor field effect transistor, more frequently referred to by the acronym MOSFET.

If there were no surface states, the MOSFET would be a simpler device than it is in reality. For simplicity, let us consider such a device in this "ideal" situation. Consider a uniformly doped n-type crystal, which is situated between the plates of a parallel-plate capacitor that allows external electric fields to be applied, as shown in Figure 10.14. If no external field is present, as shown at (a) in the diagram, and if there are no surface states, the conduction and valence band edges have the same energy at the surface as they do deep in the interior of the crystal.

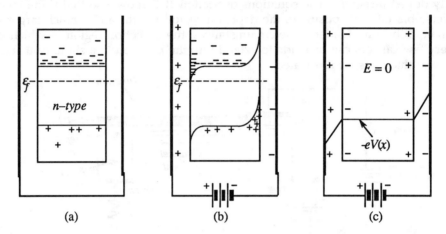

Figure 10.14 (a) A uniform n-type semiconductor within the plates of an uncharged capacitor. (b) Situation when the capacitor is charged to a constant voltage (c) A metallic conductor within a charged capacitor like the one shown at (b).

When there is an external field applied, as shown at (b) above, conventional electrostatics suggests that a distribution of induced surface charge will form so that positive charges are on the surface nearest the negatively charged capacitor plate and negative ones on the opposite surface. In a metallic conductor, this distribution adjusts itself so that the sum of the field due to the surface charges and that of the external charges on the capacitor plates is zero *everywhere* within the conductor. This situation is illustrated at (c) in the figure.

Inside a semiconductor, as we have seen in reference to p–n junctions, it is possible to have charge distributions and fields whose magnitudes are significant over distances of the order of the Debye length, as indicated by (10.3 - 18). Within the crystal, electrons are attracted toward the positive capacitor plate, and free holes toward the negative electrode. The electrons and holes are eventually stopped by the surface potential barrier of the crystal. Excess negative charges pile up near the left surface of the sample, while positive charge accumulates at the surface on the right. This accumulation of charge continues until a steady state is reached in which the coulomb forces from the external field and those ascribable to the excess charge distribution (which are in opposite directions) reduce the field practically to zero deep in the interior of the sample, and prevent any further charge buildup near the surfaces. An equilibrium is finally reached, in which there are excess electrons and very few holes at the left end and many holes and a deficiency of electrons at the right. The potential that arises from these charge distributions, internal and external, is reflected in the curvature of the edges of the conduction and valence bands shown in Figure 10.14(b). The extent of the regions near the surface in which the potential varies significantly is related to the Debye length, which in intrinsic silicon is about 36 microns. The reader is invited as an exercise to show that the Debye length in metallic conductors is of the order of one Ångström, a result relevant in explaining the differences between the diagrams at (b) and (c) in the above figure.

One of these differences has to do with the fact that in an ideal metallic conductor, the opposite surfaces of the substance are at precisely the same potential, while in the case of the semiconductor there can be an appreciable *difference* in potential between the two surfaces. This is also true for an ideal insulating dielectric, of course, but the fact that an insulator can carry no current rules out any device application. Near the left-hand surface in (b) there is an excess concentration of electrons, which in this instance are majority carriers. The material in this region is effectively more heavily *n*-type than in the bulk interior. Such a site is referred to as an *accumulation region*. As one proceeds to the right, the potential flattens out and becomes practically constant after a few Debye lengths, and remains so until the opposite surface is approached. The potential then rises, the conduction band edge now forming a barrier for the majority electrons, which become scarcer; at the same time, since holes tend to be upwardly mobile in this diagram, due to their positive charge, the equilibrium hole concentration tends to increase. The material is effectively less *n*-type in character. If the external voltage is sufficiently large, the valence band edge near the surface can be closer to the Fermi energy than the lower edge of the conduction band. Under these circumstances, as the surface is approached, the material becomes intrinsic and finally effectively *p*-type in character. In this situation, there is a high-resistance region, where carriers of both species are in short supply, and a markedly *p*-type layer immediately adjacent to the surface. This structure is referred to as a *depletion region*, followed by an *inversion layer*. It is, in effect, a shallow *p-n* junction.

Since the internal surface potential distibutions depend on the external voltage, the width of the junction depletion region, and also the width of the narrow surface *p*-type channel--as well as the number of holes it contains--are responsive to changes in this externally applied voltage. In principle, such a structure can act as the narrow conducting channel of a surface field-effect transistor.

All this has been understood as long as basic *p-n* junction theory. Indeed, experimental attempts were made to utilize surface inversion channels as transistors in the very early stages of transistor development. These attempts were successful inasmuch as it was possible to observe channel conductivity changes, but the changes were an order of magnitude less than expected on the basis of the above theory. This problem, among others, led to more careful investigations of semiconductor surfaces, investigations which incorporated the effect of localized surface states into the picture of internal potentials and charge distributions.

We have already noted that the termination of a one-dimensional periodic potential gives rise to surface states, referred to as *Tamm states*, in the bandgap. Simple one-dimensional quantum theory predicts that there is exactly one such quantum state per surface atom, located at a single discrete energy within the gap. Although much experimental evidence confirms the existence of surface states, neither of these specific predictions is upheld by experimental studies pertaining to actual semiconductor materials. Frequently the observed density of surface states is less than one per surface atom, and usually, rather than being at a single dicrete energy, they are somewhat smeared out in energy. In the case of silicon, there is almost always an adherent crystalline film of SiO_2 on real crystal surfaces, and the structure of interfacial states is complicated by its presence.

The simple picture of "Tamm states" is therefore only a rough guide to the properties of the surface state distribution on real crystals. The presence of actual surface states in materials like silicon creates a situation in which there can be a depletion layer at the surface of the crystal, or an actual inversion layer, *even if no external voltage is present*. These effects can be understood with reference to Figure 10.15.

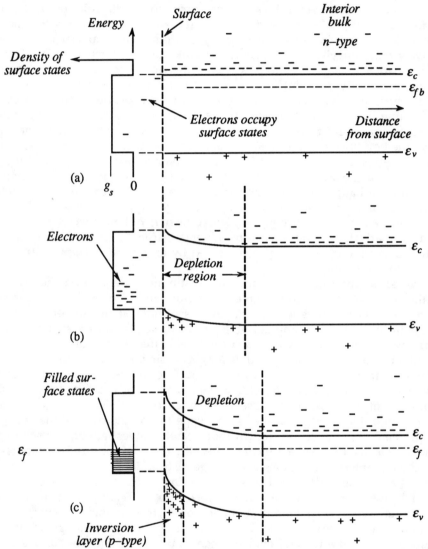

Figure 10.15 Schematic diagram illustrating how the occupation of surface states by electrons can lead to band bending and the formation of surface depletion layers or even surface inversion layers of conductivity type opposite that of the bulk interior.

At (a) in the figure we see the conduction and valence band edges of a sample of n-type silicon deep in the interior of the substance extrapolated unaltered all the way to the surface. This now does *not* accurately represent the equilibrium state of the crystal, because there is an electron/hole gas in the interior and a distribution of electrons in surface states, which must be in equilibrium with each other in order that the crystal as a whole be at equilibrium. If, as depicted at (a) there are initially no electrons in the surface states, whose assumed density as a function of energy is shown at the left, then electrons in the conduction band near the surface can fill these states of lower energy. As this happens, the surface acquires a negative charge, while in the interior adjacent to the surface, the density of the electron gas is reduced, leaving uncompensated donor centers which create a positive charge density in this region. The density of surface states is assumed for purposes of illustration to be uniform within the bandgap in this discussion and in the figure, though in reality it is more complicated than this, and may vary as a function of surface preparation and environment.

As electrons occupy the surface states, a dipolar charge distribution is formed with negative charges on the surface, and a thin layer of compensating positive charge density in the interior adjacent to it. The situation is similar to that found in the neighborhood of a *p-n* junction in bulk material, and as in the case of the *p-n* junction, electrostatic forces associated with this charge distribution exert coulomb forces to the right on an electron near the surface, forces which oppose its tendency to leave the interior electron gas and go to the surface. The forces are described by an electrostatic potential which bends the band edges just as they are bent in a *p-n* junction, forming a *depletion region* in which few electrons or holes reside, as illustrated at (b) in the figure. The electron transfer to the surface states continues until the dipole potential becomes strong enough to reduce the electron flux into the surface to zero. The surface is then in equilibrium with the interior, but in the equilibrium state the band edges are bent upward in the surface region as shown above at (c), so strongly in some cases that there may be more holes than electrons present in a thin *inversion layer* immediately adjacent to the surface. Such a layer is, in effect, *p*-type. This frequently happens in *n*-type silicon, which because of a distribution of surface states that may be somewhat like that shown above, can exhibit a *p*-type free surface. The inversion layer is separated from the bulk interior (as in a *p-n* junction) by a depletion region relatively devoid of carriers, which therefore has a high electrical resistivity. It is important to note in these processes that the surface state energies are *fixed with respect to the band edges at the surface*, and they will therefore move up or down in response to potential variations in the same way as the bands at the point where they meet the surface.

The electrons in the surface states are *immobile*, and do not contribute to current flow in response to electric fields. The carriers in the inversion layer adjacent to the surface, however, are free carriers essentially no different from those deep inside the sample. The majority carriers, holes in this case, are naturally constrained to remain in a potential well near the surface, a well separated from the interior by a high-resistance depletion region. They can move *parallel* to the surface, however, in response to transverse electric fields. Their situation is the same as that of carriers in the channel of a junction field-effect transistor. The picture is not really very different from that drawn in the previous discussion in which surface states were neglected, except for the fact that the inversion and depletion regions are present even when there is no external voltage. Clearly, when the density of surface states is very low, their effect on the system will be negligible, and the picture then reduces to that of the previous discussion, except for the formation of a very weak surface depletion layer. If there is a very large density of surface states, the effect of external charges induced by a relatively large change in the external voltage can be compensated by a comparatively *small* change in the surface state populations, a change that can be brought about about by a small shift in the surface potential with respect to the Fermi energy. The presence of a large density of surface states thus tends to lessen the response of the holes in the surface channel to external signals, in agreement with the fact that this response is observed to be less than predicted by a theory in which surface states are not considered. Despite this reduction of sensitivity, it is possible to utilize the modulation of surface channel conductivity by external voltages to fabricate excellent surface field-effect transistors.

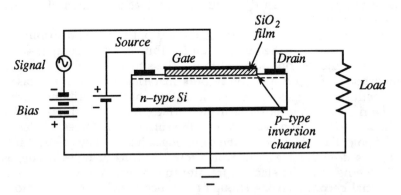

Figure 10.16 Schematic diagram illustrating operating principles and circuitry associated with the silicon MOSFET. Channel current flows to the right through the narrow channel formed by the surface inversion layer. The dielectric in the "capacitor" on the surface of the silicon is an adherent oxide film that can be grown to any desired thickness and is a good insulator.

The discussion given above has been set in the context of a sample subjected to external fields set up within a parallel-plate capacitor. This somewhat artificial model was chosen in order to eliminate effects arising from metal-semiconductor contacts, and to display physical effects associated with semiconductor surfaces and surface states in the simplest possible way. It is evident that the results obtained would be generally similar if the free space between the external electrodes and sample surfaces were replaced with a uniform linear dielectric. In actual MOSFET units this dielectric is an oxide film of controlled thickness grown directly on the surface of the n-type silicon, as illustrated in Figure 10.16. An ohmic base contact has also been made between the semiconductor and the positive capacitor plate shown in Figure 10.14(b). Even so, this diagram, though showing the essential features of the MOSFET, is schematic in character, and may differ in certain details from the structure of actual operating units.

Our treatment of semiconductor surfaces has been purely qualitative. As in the case of the p-n junction, it is possible to carry out a quantitative calculation of interior charge densities, fields, and potentials, starting with Poisson's equation and the condition that all the charges in the semiconductor--including that of electrons in the surface states--sum to zero. The calculations are not irrelevant to a more complete understanding of surface field-effect devices, but simple closed-form solutions are not possible, and a full treatment of the subject somewhat beyond the scope of this text.

10.8 LIGHT–EMITTING DIODES AND SEMICONDUCTOR LASERS

Light-emitting diodes are merely forward-biased *p-n* junction rectifiers made from direct-gap materials in which electron-hole recombination generates light. Also, in order for this light to be visible, the energy gap of the semiconductor must correspond to a photon wavelength somewhere in the visible spectrum. Silicon and germanium are not useful, since they satisfy neither of these criteria. Gallium arsenide is a direct-gap material having a bandgap energy of about 1.35eV, which corresponds to a wavelength of about 9000Å, barely beyond the visible in the near infra-red. Gallium phosphide is a transparent substance with an orange color. It has a bandgap of around 2.2eV, corresponding to a wavelength of about 5700Å, in the yellow region of the spectrum, but it is unfortunately an indirect-gap semiconductor. It is not difficult to prepare alloys of these two materials having the composition $GaAs_xP_{1-x}$, where $0 < x < 1$, which are direct-gap materials, and whose bandgaps lie between those of pure GaP and GaAs. It is possible to form light emitting *p-n* junctions in some of these substances which exhibit visible electroluminescence at wave-lengths intermediate between those associated with GaAs and GaP. Red light-emitting diodes made from these materials are in common use. The application is a simple one, but the diodes are efficient light emitters which can be very tiny, and generate very little heat. Morever, their useful lifetime is essentially infinite, which is an important advantage in many applications.

Laser diodes can also be fabricated from these materials, provided that they are made and operated so as to maximize *stimulated* photon emission. Stimulated photon emission is emission of radiation from filled conduction band states to empty valence band states that is triggered by the presence of photons whose frequency is $\Delta\varepsilon/\hbar$, where $\Delta\varepsilon$ is the energy difference between the two states. Stimulated photons are emitted in the same direction and phase as the stimulating radiation, and can add intensity to a coherent photon distribution, while spontaneous photon emission, which occurs randomly, independent of this triggering mechanism, generates photons of the same frequency, but with random direction and phase. In thermal equilibrium, both stimulated and spontaneous emission are present, but under normal circumstances the probability associated with stimulated emission is so small that it is difficult to detect. It is clear from the above discussion, however, that laser action stems from situations in which stimulated emission is enhanced to the point where stimulated processes are self-sustaining, and give rise to emission of light coherent in phase and with a single propagation vector.

The number of stimulated transitions depends on the number of electrons in excited states, ready to recombine, and also on the number of photons available to stimulate transitions. To promote laser action, these numbers must be made as large as possible. One can show, that population *inversion* is needed if laser emission is to be obtained; this means that there must be, locally at least, more electrons in conduction band states than in valence band states. Also, to attain the needed density of radiation, optical transitions must take place within an optical cavity resonator with highly reflecting surfaces. These surfaces, though highly reflecting, must be slightly transparent to let the coherent output beam escape. The population inversion can be attained in *p-n* junctions rather heavily doped in both regions, when large forward currents flow. Under these circumstances both *p*- and *n*-regions in the vicinity of the junction are flooded with minority carriers to the extent needed for laser action. Plane end surfaces can be attained in a properly cleaved or polished diode crystals, and evaporated dielectric coatings can also be used to maximize reflectivity, though this is frequently unnecessary. The resulting laser diode structure is shown schematically in Figure 10.17.

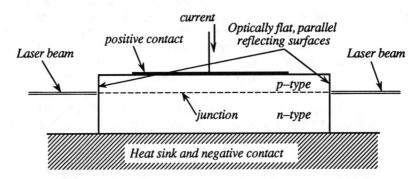

Figure 10.17 Schematic cross-sectional view of a laser diode. Opticaly flat, parallel faces form a resonant cavity for trapped coherent light inside the device, some of which leaks through surfaces, which are not quite totally reflecting. The emergent laser light is a narrow parallel beam in the plane of the junction.

At low forward currents, there is not enough minority current injection to attain population inversion, and the device operates as an ordinary light-emitting diode. Beyond a certain threshold current, however, population inversion occurs and the device acts as a solid-state laser. Laser diodes are used commercially in optical-fiber communication systems, and also in consumer and data processing applications like digital compact disc players and optical data storage/retrieval systems.

10.9 QUANTUM WELLS AND SUPERLATTICES

We have already observed some examples of quantum potential wells in our study of quantum mechanics; in particular we have observed the discrete energy states associated with wells of finite and infinite depth as well as the oscillator levels of the parabolic well in Chapter 4. We have also studied the quantum behavior of the one-dimensional Kronig-Penney lattice, a series of interacting square well potentials, in considerable detail in Chapter 8. In the broadest sense, of course, any crystal lattice is an array of atomic potential wells. In this section, we shall briefly examine how potentials of square well form can be produced in semiconducting materials, and suggest some of the possibilities they display as semiconductor devices.

Potential wells of approximately "square-well" form can be fabricated by juxtaposing layers of different semiconducting materials having the same (or nearly the same) lattice structure and interatomic spacing, so that a good "atomic fit" between atoms in adjacent regions of different composition is obtained. These structures can be as simple as closely spaced p- and n-type regions in substances of the same composition, Si or Ge, for example, or adjacent layers of dissimilar materials having different bandgaps. In the first case the junctions are ordinary p-n junctions, sometimes referred to as homojunctions, in the second, the junctions, referred to as heterojunctions, have more complex structural features, though generally similar properties. Such structures can be prepared by controlled chemical vapor deposition and molecular beam deposition. The successive controlled growth of thin layers by methods such as these is referred to as *epitaxial* growth, and regular *p-n*, *p-n-p*, and other devices can also be fabricated this way.

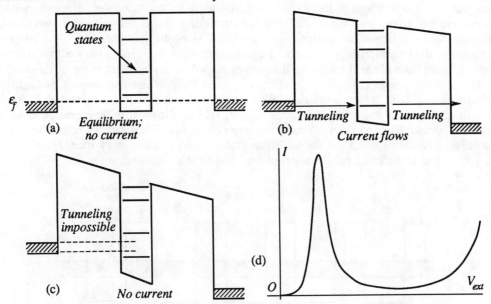

Figure 10.18 (a) Potential well showing quantim states corresponding to electrons bound to the well, in the case where the external field is zero. Shaded areas show electron distribution in external electrodes. (b) With a small external field present, electrons can tunnel through the barriers into and out of the lowest quantum state, allowing current to flow. (c) With a larger field, tunneling through the barrier into interior quantum states of equal energy cannot occur, and little or no current flows. (d) Current-voltage curve for this device, measured at $T = 4K$.

The simplest quantum well device is the double barrier illustrated in Figure 10.18. These devices have been fabricated by depositing a sandwich having outer layers about 100Å thick composed of $Ga_{0.6}Al_{0.4}As$, and an inner potential well of pure GaAs around 40Å in thickness. External contacts essentially metallic in behavior are then fabricated. The diagrams above illustrate the position of the conduction band edge, which represents the minimum energy a free electron can have. At (a) in the diagram, we see the situation when no external voltage is present. The central layer is so thin that instead of the quasi-continuum of conduction band states that would normally be present, there are only a few discrete states corresponding to those of the potential well of finite depth discussed in Chapter 4. The outer layers present a potential barrier to electrons, but their thickness is small enough to allow an appreciable probability of tunneling, provided there is an interior quantum state of equal energy to tunnel into. At (a) there is no such state available, so that tunneling cannot take place and there can be no current. In any event, when there is no external field no current can flow--even if tunneling were possible, equal and opposite tunneling currents would be set up under these conditions.

When a small external voltage is applied, as at (b), the potential energy of an electron is lower at the right contact than at the left. This causes the band edges in the intermediate regions to slope downwards to the right, as shown, and lowers the energies of the quantum well states with respect to those of the electrons in the contact on the left. Electrons can now tunnel through the potential barrier on the left into the lowest quantum state of the well, and subsequently out of this state into the contact on the right. Under these circumstances an appreciable current is observed. As the external voltage is increased, as illustrated at (c), however, a region where there are no quantum states available for tunneling coincides with the energies of the incident electron distribution, and tunneling is no longer possible. The current, therefore, drops practically to zero. Further increases in voltage may allow tunneling to again take place through well states of higher energy. Tunneling of this sort is referred to as *resonant tunneling*, since it occurs only when the energy of incident electrons and well states coincide. The current-voltage relation, illustrated at (d) in the diagram has a negative resistance region, which allows the device to be used as an oscillator, switching device or data storage element. Since tunneling is a very fast process, devices of this kind switch from one state to another very quickly, allowing a very rapid transfer of information in and out of the element.

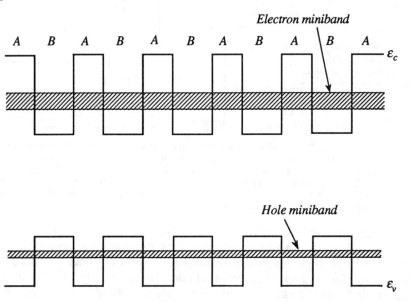

Figure 10.19 Structure of Ga As–GaAlAs superlattice showing electron and hole minibands. Layers marked A are GaAlAs, while layers labeled B are pure GaAs.

Another very interesting quantum well structure, referred to as a superlattice, can be made by growing alternate layers of different semiconuctors adjacent to one another, in such a way that an extensive periodic array of layers is formed, as illustrated in Figure 10.19. This drawing indicates the position of conduction and valence band edges in a superlattice composed of alternating layers of $Ga_xAl_{1-x}As$ (marked A) and pure GaAs (labeled B). Since the bandgaps of the two materials differ markedly, both conduction and valence band edges are converted to square well potentials as illustrated. The minimum vertical distance between well boundaries in the diagram corresponds to the bandgap of pure B material, while the maximum vertical distance represents the bandgap of pure A material. If the wells in the conduction and valence bands were narrow but widely separated, they would exhibit discrete sets of quantum levels like those associated with the interior of the double barrier shown in Figure 10.18. If the separation between wells is decreased to the point where electrons in adjacent wells have an appreciable probability of tunneling, these levels will broaden into a series of narrow bands, referred to as *minibands*. This broadening begins to occur when the wave functions of electrons associated with adjacent potential minima begin to overlap to a significant extent. The lowest electron miniband associated with the conduction band square wells and the highest hole miniband in the valence band are shown in the diagram. Electrons of lowest energy in the conduction band and holes of higest energy in the valence band will populate these bands at reasonably low temperatures. When an external potential is applied, electrons and holes will travel in the partially filled minibands with an effective mass and mobility determined by the ε versus k relation associated with these minibands, and a current will be observed In this example the hole mobility is much smaller than that of electrons.

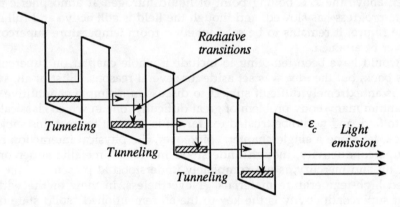

Figure 10.20 Schematic diagram showing sequential tunneling between minibands in adjacent wells of a superlattice.

At low external voltages the material behaves like an ordinary ohmic conductor. However, at larger external potentials, a situation somewhat like that shown in Figure 10.18(b) begins to occur, and the phenomenon of *sequential tunneling* can take place. For simplicity, only the lowest minibands are illustrated in Figure 10.19, but there can also be a second electron miniband at higher energy within the conduction band wells, and in some cases even higher bands, corresponding to excited electronic levels of the individual wells. Sequential tunneling begins when states in the lowest miniband are at the same energy as states in the next highest miniband in an adjacent well. Tunneling then takes place sequentially from one well to the next, as illustrated. Light is emitted in radiative transitions as electrons in the higher band subsequently decay to states in the lower one. The tunneling process clearly tends to depopulate the lower bands and to increase the electron population in the next higher ones. Under proper conditions, the tunneling current can be increased to the point where population inversion takes place, and there are more electrons in the higher band than the lower. Laser action then can take place, and the superlattice now functions as an infrared solid-state laser.

There are many other interesting applications of quantum-well structures and superlattices. The ones described are perhaps the simplest and most important, and will give the reader a good idea of further applications. It may be too much to suggest that quantum wells are the solid state devices of the future, but their potential to form an important part of solid state device development in the near term seems promising.

10.10 SUPERCONDUCTING MATERIALS AND DEVICES

The discovery of "high-temperature" superconductivity by G. Bednorz and K. Müller in 1986 opened a new era of investigation in the field of superconductivity. In a year or so after their initial discovery, it was possible to make oxide superconductors that retained their superconducting properties to temperatures of 100K or more, well above the 77K boiling point of liquid nitrogen at atmospheric pressure. Since then, progress has slowed, and though the field is still active and full of promise for the future, it remains to be seen whether room-temperature superconductivity will ever be attained.

It would have been tempting to include a whole chapter on superconductivity in this book, but the idea was set aside for several reasons. First of all, superconductivity is an extremely difficult subject to discuss in a simple or intuitive manner. It is a quantum many-body problem of great difficulty, one in which classical analogs are hard to find, and not to be trusted too far. It is difficult to treat this subject in an entire book, let alone a single chapter. Moreover, the physical interaction responsible for superconductivity, though understood in "ideal" metallic superconductors like lead, tin and mercury, is not completely understood at present for the recently discovered high-temperature materials. Nevertheless, in view of the widespread belief that superconductivity is the key to the aforementioned "solid state device of the future", a brief description of the phenomenon and its applications is in order.

Superconductivity is a phenomenon associated with the electron gas in metals and other substances, in which below a certain transition temperature, electrical resistance disappears entirely, and the material displays the *Meissner effect*, in which magnetic fields are completely expelled from its interior. It is this Meissner effect, in fact, that most accurately characterizes superconductivity, and the phenomenological relationship $\mathbf{B} = 0$ that stems from it is a more reliable guide to its presence than the mere fact of infinite electrical conductivity. Indeed, the equation $B = 0$ is a constitutive relation for a superconductor that plays much the same role as does the relation $E = 0$ for metallic conductors in electrostatic equilibrium. Superconductivity was first discovered in mercury by H. Kammerlingh Onnes in 1911, but the Meissner effect, though some of its consequences were well known, was not fully explained until 1933.

Superconductivity is basically a *phase transition* exhibited by the electron gas in metals and semimetals. In the absence of a magnetic field, there is in certain materials a transition temperature T_c below which superconductivity is observed. For most metallic superconductors, this transition temperature is below 10K; for lead it is 7.2K, for tin, 3.7K, for mercury, 4.1K, for indium, 3.4K, and for niobium, which has the highest transition temperature of all pure metals, it is 9.25K. When a superconductor is placed in an external magnetic field that is not too strong, it expels the field from its interior. Within the material B is zero, except in a very thin surface region into which the field penetrates, dying off exponentially in the direction of the inward normal to the surface. This expulsion of the internal field is accomplished by a distribution of supercurrents that are essentially *surface currents*, or at least currents that flow only in the thin surface field penetration region. These surface currents distribute themselves over the surface of the sample in such a way as to guarantee that the field B is zero everywhere inside, just as the surface charges on a metallic conductor in an external electrostatic field do, to make the internal electrostatic field zero. The field penetration depth is a function of temperature; it is very small, only a few hundred Ångströms or so near absolute zero, but it increases as the temperature is increased, and becomes infinite when the temperature reaches the transition temperature.

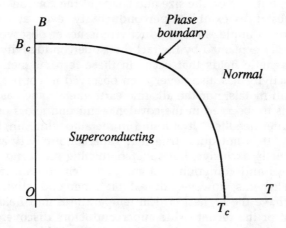

Figure 10.21 Phase diagram for superconductivity in ideal metals showing superconducting and "normal" regions,

When an external magnetic field is applied, the penetration depth increases as the surface current distribution strengthens, so as to keep the interior field zero. This *lowers* the temperature at which the transition from superconducting to normal behavior is observed. With increasing external fields, the transition temperature decreases continually until at some critical field value B_c it is reduced to zero. Above this critical field superconductivity *cannot exist*. This behavior can be illustrated as a phase diagram like that shown in Figure 10.21, in which the curve that gives the critical field needed to quench superconductivity is shown as a function of temperature. This curve can be regarded as a phase boundary that separates a region where superconductivity is observed from one where normal ohmic conductivity takes place. The critical field B_c is different for different substances. For Pb it is 0.080Tesla, for tin, 0.031T, for mercury 0.041T, for indium, 0.028T, and for niobium 0.198T. It appears that in a superconductor, superconducting electrons and normal electrons can coexist. At absolute zero, all electrons are in the superconducting state. As the temperature is raised, some of the electrons "go normal", and the proportion of superconducting electrons decreases with increasing temperature, reaching zero at the transition temperature. Superconductivity can thus be regarded as a "two-fluid" system in which there is an equilibrium concentration of each species at any given temperature. Superconductivity is, like ferromagnetism, a coöperative phenomenon, involving long-range interactions between many particles, and for this reason it is quite difficult to treat theoretically. Superconductivity resembles ferromagnetim in this and many other respects, but it is even more subtle and complex.

Supercurrents can, as far as we now know, persist indefinitely. Supercurrents induced in a lead ring, for example, will flow for months or years with no detectable diminuition, so long as the temperature is kept below the transition temperature. However, the current-carrying capacity of a superconducting wire or other conductor is limited to a current less than the critical value that creates a magnetic field at the surface of the material in excess of the critical field B_c. The substance "goes normal" and conducts ohmically whenever this current is exceeded. This maximum current is referred to as the *critical current*. The critical current depends not only on the material itself, but also on the size and shape of the conductor.

Not all substances exhibit superconductivity, even at the lowest attainable temperatures. For example, superconductivity is never observed in iron, nickel or cobalt. This is easily explained by the fact that superconductivity is quenched by the large internal magnetic fields that occur in these ferromagnetic substances. However, superconductivity has also never been observed in copper, silver or gold, nor in any of the alkali metals, nor the alkaline earth metals such as calcium, strontium or barium. Nor is it observed in the covalent semiconductors or the most common semiconducting intermetallics. It is found in metallic white tin, but not in semiconducting gray tin. It is not quite true that superconductivity and semiconducting behavior are mutually exclusive, but superconducting semiconductors are very rare. Intermetallic alloys and compounds, some of which contain large proportions of semiconducting elements, however, do exhibit superconductivity. Indeed, some of these substances have the highest critical temperatures and fields that were known before the advent of the recent oxide superconductors discovered by Bednorz and Müller. For example, the compound V_3Si has a zero-field transition temperature of 16.3K and a critical field of 20T, while for Nb_3Ge, T_c is 23.2K and B_c is 38T. The superconducting *elements* are often soft materials with low melting points, like tin, lead, indium and mercury. On the other hand, the alkali metals share these properties, but are not superconductors. What makes a material superconducting, anyway?

This question has puzzled physicists since the discovery of superconductivity, and has not yet been totally resolved, particularly where the high temperature oxide superconductors are concerned. However, in 1957, Bardeen, Cooper and Schrieffer proposed a theory which answered this (and other) questions about the fundamental nature of superconductivity, at least in regard to the metallic and intermetallic compound superconductors. Their theory involves a complex many-body quantum calculation that even today many good physicists are not familiar with in all detail. It succeded, however, in explaining all the experimental data about superconductors then in existence, and satisfactorily predicted many results that were then unknown, but which were subsequently verified. The BCS theory, as it has come to be known, proceeded from the hypothesis that a net *attractive coupling* between conducting electrons can be set up by lattice phonons. This somewhat counterintuitive coupling is created as follows; a fast-moving electron instantaneously polarizes the lattice by attracting surrounding positive lattice ions, and repelling their electron clouds. The electron races on--it travels much faster than the speed of sound in the lattice, after all--leaving in its wake a trail of polarization charge that now exerts an attractive force on some other electron, just as it did a very short time ago on the first one. The polarized lattice ions moving in the wake of the first electron can be represented as phonons, moving with sound velocity, and they can effectively provide an attractive coupling between two normally repulsive electrons--a coupling that binds the electrons into what is referred to as a Cooper pair, and correlates their subsequent motion. The Cooper pairs can move through the lattice unaffected by processes that scatter normal electrons, They are in fact, the superconducting electrons. The coupling persists indefinitely at very low temperatures, but can be broken by thermal agitation of the lattice, and cannot be sustained above the transition temperature.

This admittedly sketchy description is solidified by quantum mechanics into quite a satisfactory description of superconducting phenomena, and even provides some excellent guidance as to what materials will and will not be superconducting; obviously materials which facilitate this type of electron-phonon-electron coupling are good superconductors while those inimical to it aren't. There is, however, one prediction it makes that was until recently treated as revealed truth: it is this: BCS phonon-electron-phonon coupling cannot be sustained in any realistic physical system above about 40K, which is thus--according to the original BCS model--the absolute top transition temperature attainable

The author once--over 20 years ago--asked Bernd T. Matthias, then one of the world's leading authorities on superconductivity, about when, if ever, superconductivity at 77K or even 300K might be attained. Answer: "Never; the BCS limit of 40K is it for any conceivable substance." Well, there are substances now available with T_c higher than 100K, whose critical fields are also very high. It seems clear that electrons are still attractively coupled, because most predictions of the BCS theory are fulfilled by the new materials, but the simple phonon coupling that seems to work for the metallic/intermetallic substances seems to have been replaced by another mechanism, one which has been the subject of much speculation, but which has not yet been identified.

These new substances are non-stoichiometric materials which invariably contain copper and oxygen. The most easily prepared and frequently investigated of these materials is a yttrium barium copper oxide of the composition $YBa_2Cu_3O_7$ with a slight deficiency of oxygen with respect to the amount indicated by the formula. Because of the proportions of the metallic constituents, this material is often referred to as the "123-compound". It has a very complex unit cell and a transition temperature of about 95K. It is difficult to prepare in single-crystal form, but has been made in the form of thin films, and has been used to make certain device structures. It is thought that superconductivity follows from the interaction of copper and oxygen valence state wave functions in this substance, and that the function of the yttrium and barium atoms is hardly more than to hold the copper and oxygen atoms in positions that will optimize the interaction.

The highest transition temperature on record jumped discontinuously from 23.5K to about 100K during the year 1986. Since then its upward progress has been slow, commensurate with the rate that prevailed before the discovery of the new copper/oxygen-based materials. The lack of understanding regarding the basic coupling interaction, however, has inhibited progress and made the problem of how to proceed in search of newer and better superconducting materials difficult.

There are many possible uses for superconducting materials, and a considerable number of superconducting devices have been demonstrated. Superconductivity offers most obviously the possibility of transmitting and distributing power with no ohmic loss, and prototypes of superconducting power lines have been built. Superconducting intermetallic compounds like Nb_3Sn and Nb_3Ge have very high critical fields, which allows the production of solenoid magnets which can generate steady homogeneous magnetic fields in excess of 100 Tesla over substantial volumes. These magnets have many commercial uses, the most important of which is as a vital component of NMR imaging systems, and are manufactured in fairly large numbers. Their future use in magnetic levitation applications is also envisioned. They have been used as beam line magnets for particle accelerators, and are an essential part of the SSC design. Superconducting generators, motors, and transformers have also been demonstrated, and the use of solenoids as inductive power storage units has even been discussed.

The superconducting transition can be used as the basis for a number of useful devices. The simplest of these is the *cryotron*, a device in which the magnetic field of a small current is used to switch a superconductor near the transition temperature between the normal and superconducting states. Devices of this kind can be used as data storage and processing units as well as for other purposes.

Magnetic flux in superconducting circuits can be shown to be *quantized* in units of $h/2e$, and superconducting devices in which individual flux quanta can be detected have been designed. These devices are in effect sensitive magnetometers and fluxmeters. Tunneling phenomena involving superconducting electrons and Cooper pairs are also observed, and these phenomena can be utilized to make fast data storage elements and switching devices, as well as microwave/infrared generators and detectors. There is thus a rich variety of applications that stem from the unique properties of superconductors.

The problem is, of course, the need to cool these materials to cryogenic temperatures in order to realize their potential uses. The new oxide superconductors like the 123 compound are a step in the right direction, since liquid nitrogen is far less expensive and much easier to handle than the liquid helium needed to refrigerate the older materials. However, though limited applications are now being realized, and in time new ones will surely materialize, the problem of refrigeration is still there. Why do we need computers the size of this book that need cryogenic auxiliary equipment 100 times that size to keep them running? There is no good answer, other than new materials that are superconducting at room temperature. Will they ever be availible? We shall see; time will tell.

REFERENCES

W. Shockley, *Electrons and Holes in Semiconductors*, D. van Nostrand, New York (1950).

R. A. Smith, *Semiconductors*, Cambridge University Press, London (1961 and subsequent eds.).

E. Spenke, *Electronic Semiconductors*, McGraw-Hill, New York (1958).

J. K. Jonscher, *Principles of Semiconductor Device Operation*, G. Bell & Sons, London (1960).

A. Nussbaum, *Semiconductor Device Physics*, Prentice-Hall, Englewood Cliffs, NJ (1957).

D. R. Frankl, *Electrical Properties of Semiconductor Surfaces*, Pergamon Press, London (1966).

K. Seeger, *Semiconductor Physics*, Springer Verlag, New York/Vienna (1973).

S. M. Sze, *Physics of Semiconductor Devices*, J. Wiley & Sons, New York (1969).

J. L. Pankove, *Optical Processes in Semiconductors*, Dover Publications, New York (1975).

L. L. Chang and L. Esaki, *Semiconductor Quantum Heterostructures*, in *Physics Today* **45**, 36 (October 1992).

V. L. Newhouse, *Applied Superconductivity*, J. Wiley & Sons, New York (1964).

R. D. Parks (editor), *Superconductivity* (2 vols), J. Wiley & Sons, New York (1965).

PROBLEMS

1. Starting with (9.4 - 18) and (9.4 - 19) write an equation for the charge density at any point within a semiconductor crystal that may be inhomogeneous. (b) Using this result show that Poisson's equation can be written in the form shown in (10.3 - 8). Hint: Recall that $\varepsilon_{fi} = -eV(x)$.

2. When one tries to measure the internal contact potential by connecting a high-resistance voltmeter to opposite terminals of a p-n junction rectifier, the meter reads zero. A potentiometer is then substituted for the voltmeter, but the reading is still zero. Why do these methods fail to detect the presence of this potential difference?

3. Discuss the limiting form of the current-voltage relation for an ideal p-n junction rectifier in the limit of zero absolute temperature. What factors determine the maximum temperature at which such a device will operate?

4. An abrupt p-n junction is formed between p-type germanium in which the constant acceptor concentration is $10^{18} cm^{-3}$ and n-type material having a uniform donor concentration of $10^{14} cm^{-3}$. (a) Find the equilibrium internal contact potential, the widths of the depletion region on both sides of this junction, and the maximum internal field when no external voltage is present. (b)What are the depletion region widths and the maximum internal fields when a reverse voltage of 400 volts is applied across this junction? (c) What are the answers to part (b) when there is a *forward* bias of 0.20 volts?

5. (a) Find the differential capacitance per unit area exhibited by the p-n junction in the preceding problem when there is no external voltage. (b, c) What is the differential capacitance of such a junction when a 400-volt reverse bias, or a 0.20-volt forward bias is applied?

6. (a) Assuming that the minority carrier lifetime on the n-side of the device described in the two preceding problems is 50 microseconds and on the p-side 0.5 microseconds, find the relevant minority carrier diffusion lengths in both regions (b) What is the saturation current density predicted for this junction by conventional junction theory? (c) What is the current through a junction of area $1.0 mm^2$ when a reverse bias of 0.2 volts is applied? What is the current when a reverse bias of 20 volts is imposed? What is the current when a forward bias of 0.2 volts is applied? (c) What is the voltage drop across the junction when a forward current of 1.5amp flows?

7. A silicon abrupt p-n rectifier of $1.0 mm^2$ junction area exhibits a differential capacitance of 1.0×10^{-10} farad under an external reverse bias voltage of 25 volts. The junction is symmetric, that is, the donor concentration on the n-side and the acceptor concentration on the p-side are equal. What is the value of this common impurity concentration?

8. Find an expression for the fraction of the total junction current carried by electrons and by holes for an ideal abrupt p-n junction rectifier. Under what circumstances will these two fractions have the common value $1/2$?

9. Find the room-temperature intrinsic Debye length for the following substances:
   (a) InSb: ($K = 12.6$, $n_i = 2.0 \times 10^{16}$ cm^{-3})
   (b) GaAs ($K = 12.9$, $n_i = 1.0 \times 10^5$ cm^{-3})

10. Show that the intrinsic Debye length can be written in the form

$$L_D^2 = \frac{K\varepsilon_0}{2e} \cdot \frac{h^3}{(2\pi)^{3/2}(m_p{}^* m_n{}^*)^{3/4}} \cdot \frac{e^{\Delta\varepsilon/kT}}{\sqrt{kT}} \; .$$

11. The intensity of bright summer sunlight incident on the earth's surface in temperate latitudes is about 700W/m^2. Find the area of a solar photovoltaic array 15% efficient needed to generate 10 watts of dc power. How much area would be needed to generate a megawatt?

12. Find an expression that describes the voltage for which the power output of a p-n junction photovoltaic cell is a maximum, in terms of the generation current and saturation current of the device. (Result is a transcendental equation that must be solved numerically).

13. Calculate the mean free path for electrons in germanium at 300K using the conductivity effective mass, measured values of the mobility, and the assumption that the mean free path is independent of velocity.

14. Using the result of the preceding problem, estimate the breakdown voltage attributable to the electron avalanche mechanism in Ge at 300K, for an abrupt junction in which $N_d = N_a = 10^{15}$cm^{-3}. Note that the relative permittivity for germanium is $K = 16$.

15. The two preceding problems were concerned with electron impact ionization. Holes can also cause impact ionization and avalanche breakdown. Work the preceding problem to find the reverse breakdown voltage associated with hole impact ionization. What would be the breakdown voltage observed in an actual device?

16. A lens is used to concentrate solar radiation on a p-n junction solar cell   If this concentrator doubles the pair generation rate, find the factors by which the short-circuit output current and open-circuit output voltage increase.

17. The way in which an instantaneous δ-function pulse of excess carriers injected at an origin at $x = 0$ at time $t = 0$ in a one-dimensional sample in which the electric field is zero, spreads out by diffusion, is described by the solution

$$u(x,t) = \frac{N}{\sqrt{4\pi Dt}} \exp\left(\frac{-x^2}{4Dt}\right) \; ,$$

where $u(x, t)$ is the excess carrier concentration and D the excess carrier diffusion coefficient. Show, assuming *infinite* excess carrier lifetime, that this solution satisfies the zero-field transport equations for excess carriers derived in Chapter 9, and assumes the form of a δ-function at $t = 0$. Plot the subsequent time evolution of this function and show that at any time t, its integral over the interval $(-\infty < x < \infty)$ equals N.

18. In the preceding problem, show that if the excess carrier lifetime is τ, the solution of the excess carrier transport equation becomes

$$u(x,t) = \frac{N}{\sqrt{4\pi Dt}} \exp\left(-\frac{x^2}{4Dt} - \frac{t}{\tau}\right) \; ,$$

and that its integral now becomes $N\exp(t/\tau)$.

19. Show that the relevant one-dimensional diffusion equation for excess carriers that stems from the transport equations of Chapter 9, in the case where there is a constant externally applied electric field is

$$D\frac{\partial^2 u}{\partial x^2} - \mu E_0 \frac{\partial u}{\partial x} - \frac{u}{\tau} = \frac{\partial u}{\partial t} \quad ,$$

where μ is the excess carrier mobility and E_0 the electric field. Show that the function

$$u(x,t) = \frac{N}{\sqrt{4\pi Dt}}\exp\left(-\frac{(x - \mu E_0 t)^2}{4Dt} - \frac{t}{\tau}\right)$$

is a solution of this equation that reduces to the solution shown in the preceding problem when the electric field is zero.

20. Plot the time-evolution of the solution shown in the preceding problem and find the "drift velocity" with which the point of maximum concentration moves.

21 Consider a case in which the base lead of the transistor in Figure 10.12 is disconnected, and the load resistance is short-circuited. Show that the collector current I_{c0} under these circumstances is self-amplified to the extent that the total collector current is now $I_{c0}/(1 - \alpha)$.

22. (a) What is the form of the time-dependent transport equation for excess minority holes in the base region of the p-n-p junction transistor discussed in Section 10.5 when there is an ac signal voltage present? (b) Assuming that the ac signal frequency is ω, and that the solution of this time-dependent transport equation is of the form $p_n(x, t) = u(x)\exp(i\omega t)$, show that the function $u(x)$ satisfies a differential equation of the form

$$\frac{d^2 u}{dx^2} - \frac{1}{L_p^2}(1 + i\omega\tau_p)u(x) = 0 \quad .$$

23. Show that the general solution to the equation derived in the preceding problem is

$$u(x) = A\exp\left(\frac{(\beta + i\gamma)x}{L_p}\right) + B\exp\left(-\frac{(\beta + i\gamma)x}{L_p}\right),$$

where

$$\beta^2 = \tfrac{1}{2}\left(1 + \sqrt{1 + \omega^2\tau_p^2}\right) \quad \text{and} \quad \gamma^2 = \tfrac{1}{2}\left(-1 + \sqrt{1 + \omega^2\tau_p^2}\right).$$

24. Show that the solution to the two preceding problems can be written in the form

$$u(x) = A\exp\frac{x}{L_p'}\cdot\exp\frac{i\gamma x}{L_p} + B\exp-\frac{x}{L_p'}\cdot\exp\frac{i\gamma x}{L_p} \quad ,$$

where

$$\frac{1}{L_p'} = \frac{\beta}{L_p} = \frac{1}{L_p\sqrt{2}}\cdot\sqrt{1 + \sqrt{1 + \omega^2\tau_p^2}} \quad .$$

25. Investigate the solution written in Problem 24, and show that for low frequencies the effective diffusion length L_p' is approximately the same as the steady state vaue L_p, while at high frequencies it is approximately equal to $(2D_p/\omega)^{1/2}$. Make a plot of L_p' as a function of frequency and comment on the physical consequences of this variation on transistor gain.

26. Using "square barrier" tunneling theory, estimate roughly the required thickness of the outer barrier layers shown in Figure 10.18 needed to achieve a signifcant probability for resonant tunneling.

27. A certain superconducting material has a critical field value B_c. Consider a conductor made of this material in the form of a circular tube having very thin walls of outer radius a. How much current can this conductor carry without "going normal"?

28. Show that for very small applied voltages, an ideal p-n junction rectifier exhibits an ohmic differential resistance equal to kT/eI_0.

29. The saturation current of a p-n junction diode can be obtained by measuring the forward current I_+ at some given psitive voltage V_0, and then reversing the polarity of the applied voltage and measuring the current I_- corresponding to this voltage of opposite sign. Show that the saturation current follows as $I_0 = (I_+ + I_-)/2\sinh(eV_0/kT)$.

INDEX

502